ADVANCED CHEMICAL CALCULATIONS

By the same author

TEXTBOOK OF PHYSICAL CHEMISTRY

ELEMENTARY INORGANIC CHEMISTRY

PRINCIPLES OF ORGANIC CHEMISTRY

INTRODUCTORY CHEMICAL CALCULATIONS

INTERMEDIATE PRACTICAL CHEMISTRY
(*in the Press*)

ADVANCED CHEMICAL CALCULATIONS

By the same author

TEXTBOOK OF PHYSICAL CHEMISTRY

ELEMENTARY INORGANIC CHEMISTRY

PRINCIPLES OF ORGANIC CHEMISTRY

INTRODUCTORY CHEMICAL CALCULATIONS

INTERMEDIATE PRACTICAL CHEMISTRY
(*in the Press*)

ADVANCED CHEMICAL CALCULATIONS

BY

SYLVANUS J. SMITH, M.A.

LATE SENIOR SCHOLAR OF TRINITY COLLEGE, CAMBRIDGE
CHEMISTRY MASTER, THE HIGH SCHOOL, NEWCASTLE, STAFFS

MACMILLAN AND CO., LIMITED
ST. MARTIN'S STREET, LONDON
1950

PRINTED IN GREAT BRITAIN

ADVANCED CHEMICAL CALCULATIONS

BY

SYLVANUS J. SMITH, M.A.

LATE SENIOR SCHOLAR OF TRINITY COLLEGE, CAMBRIDGE
CHEMISTRY MASTER, THE HIGH SCHOOL, NEWCASTLE, STAFFS

MACMILLAN AND CO., LIMITED
ST. MARTIN'S STREET, LONDON
1950

PRINTED IN GREAT BRITAIN

PREFACE

Any book in which the largely relative term "advanced" appears in the title must have its aims and scope sharply defined; particularly is this so when the book has for its subject-matter a rapidly expanding field such as that of chemical calculations. The objective of the present volume is to furnish practice in numerical problems up to, and including, questions of Honours Degree standard and, at the same time, to continue the sequence of my *Introductory Chemical Calculations*; the two books, taken together, may be considered, I hope, to provide a reasonably "complete" course in numerical chemistry.

In order to preserve continuity with my smaller book, I have included a considerable proportion of intermediate work; where such work proceeds to an advanced stage (insufficient to justify a separate chapter) I have indicated the appropriate paragraphs and questions so that they may well be deferred to a second reading. All matter marked with an asterisk may be so treated.

It is clear that the major difficulty in the construction of a book of chemical calculations is that of deciding the standard to which it shall be written. There are many interesting and important aspects of the subject which do not lend themselves, unfortunately, to a comparatively easy mathematical treatment; these I have omitted. To have included them would have presented the option of a formal development, which would have increased the size of the book unduly, or of simply stating the formulae to be used, in which case the "problems" might well reduce to mere substitution.

The inclusion of a large number of questions set at examinations of Intermediate and Degree standard has been made possible by the courtesy of University and other authorities to whom I wish to record my thanks; in many instances, this courtesy has been extended to active help and advice. The scope of this book has been largely determined by an analysis of these questions.

It is, perhaps, too much to hope that the numerous examples and questions have been worked entirely without error although I have taken every care in checking them, wherever possible, by alternative methods. I shall, of course, be grateful to any student who will bring to my notice any error or ambiguity.

I would like to thank the publishers and their printers for the excellent manner in which the book has been produced.

S. J. Smith

February, 1949

CONTENTS

ABBREVIATIONS

The examination papers from which questions have been taken are indicated as follows :

Degree standard. The letters F.R.I.C. and A.R.I.C. indicate examinations for the Fellowship and Associateship respectively of the Royal Institute of Chemistry. In other questions, the University is specifically stated.

Intermediate standard.

O. and C. : Oxford and Cambridge Joint Board Higher School Certificate.

N.U.J.B. : Northern Universities Joint Board Higher School Certificate.

1st M.B. London : First Examination for Bachelor of Medicine, London University.

1st M.B. Manchester : First Examination for Bachelor of Medicine, Manchester University.

H.S.C., London : Higher School Certificate, London.

Inter. B.Sc., London : Intermediate Examination, Bachelor of Science, London University.

C.U.O.S. : Cambridge University Open Scholarship.

O.U.O.S. : Oxford University Open Scholarship.

C.H.L. : Cambridge Higher Local Examination.

N.U.J.B. Schol. : Northern Universities Joint Board Scholarship.

Durham Ent. Schol. : Examination for Entrance Scholarship, Durham University.

Temperatures throughout are on the Centigrade scale unless otherwise stated.

CHAPTER I

EQUIVALENTS AND ATOMIC WEIGHTS

1. The oxygen standard

The chemical equivalent of an element is now usually referred to oxygen = 8·0000 as the *standard equivalent*, the equivalent of hydrogen then being 1·0078. When the equivalent of an element is determined by the analysis of its compounds with elements other than oxygen, it is assumed that the equivalents of these elements are on the oxygen standard; for example, if it is stated that the equivalent of silver is 107·9, then 107·9 units of weight of silver are assumed to combine with, or to be indirectly equivalent to, 8·0000 of the same units of weight of oxygen.

Example 1. 0·5302 gm. of a metal was placed in an excess of silver nitrate solution and the precipitated silver, when collected and dried, weighed 2·0500 gm. Calculate the equivalent of the metal, given that the equivalent of silver is 107·9.

In this question it is assumed that the equivalent of silver is on the oxygen standard and is equivalent to 8·0000 units of weight of oxygen.

∴ Chemical equivalent of the metal

$$=\frac{0{\cdot}5302}{2{\cdot}0500}\times 107{\cdot}9 = 27{\cdot}92\ (O = 16{\cdot}0000\ ;\ O/2 = 8{\cdot}0000).$$

The equivalent of the metal referred to H = 1·0000 is calculated by means of the law of reciprocal proportions and is 27·92/1·0078 = 27·70.

Example 2. 0·3501 gm. of the chloride of an element was dissolved in water and treated with an excess of silver nitrate solution. The precipitated silver chloride, when collected and dried, was found to weigh 0·8586 gm. Calculate the equivalent of the metal. [Ag = 107·9 ; Cl = 35·46.]

Weight of chlorine in 0·8586 gm. of silver chloride

$$=\frac{35{\cdot}46}{(107{\cdot}9+35{\cdot}46)}\times 0{\cdot}8586 \text{ gm.}=0{\cdot}2123 \text{ gm.}$$

∴ Weight of chlorine in 0·3501 gm. of the chloride of the element = 0·2123 gm.

∴ Weight of the element in 0·3501 gm. of the chloride of the element = (0·3501 − 0·2123) gm. = 0·1378 gm.

∴ Chemical equivalent of the element

$$=\frac{0{\cdot}1378}{0{\cdot}2123}\times 35{\cdot}46=\mathbf{23{\cdot}01}.$$

2. Equivalents or reacting weights of compounds

The equivalent or reacting weight of a compound can be obtained, in many instances, merely by adding the equivalents of the electropositive and electronegative radicals of which the compound is composed. The general application of the method can be proved as follows.

Assume that a compound (C) is formed as a result of the combination of an element (E) with a compound radical, one of which is denoted by R. Let the element have valency n and denote one atom of the element by A. Then, if the valency of the compound radical is n_1, the formula of the compound will be $A_{n_1}R_n$. Assuming that the atoms A_{n_1} can be replaced by hydrogen, we have the equation :

$$A_{n_1}R_n+n_1n\text{H}=\text{H}_{nn_1}R_n+n_1A,$$

since nH would be required to displace 1 atom of A of valency n. It is immaterial whether or not this equation represents an action which can occur in practice or is merely theoretical.

If, now, the molecular weight of the compound $A_{n_1}R_n$ is denoted by M, then :

$$\text{chemical equivalent of } C=\frac{M}{nn_1},$$

that is, the number of units of weight of C which are equivalent to the unit weight of hydrogen is M/nn_1.

Then, if X denote the atomic weight of A, and Y denote the "molecular weight" of the radical R :

$$\text{chemical equivalent of } C=\frac{M}{nn_1}=\frac{n_1X+nR}{nn_1}=\frac{X}{n}+\frac{R}{n_1}.$$

But $\frac{X}{n}$ = chemical equivalent of the element, E,

and $\frac{R}{n_1}$ = " chemical equivalent " of the radical, R.

∴ Chemical equivalent of C = chemical equivalent of E + " chemical equivalent " of R.

In the foregoing proof, the unit of atomic weight has, for convenience, been taken as H = 1·0000; the proof clearly holds if the unit of atomic weight is taken as $\frac{1}{16}$ of the atomic weight of oxygen with H = 1·0078.

Example 3. 1·538 gm. of the oxide of an element was converted completely into the chloride of the element which then weighed 3·634 gm. The equivalent of chlorine is 35·46. Calculate the equivalent of the element.

If X denote the equivalent of the element, then X gm. of the element will unite with exactly 8 gm. of oxygen to form $(X+8)$ gm. of the oxide of the element. Similarly, X gm. of the element must give $(X+35{\cdot}46)$ gm. of the chloride of the element.

∴ $(X+8)$ gm. of the oxide would give $(X+35{\cdot}46)$ gm. of the chloride.

∴ 1·538 gm. of the oxide would give

$$\frac{(X+35{\cdot}46)}{(X+8)} \times 1{\cdot}538 \text{ gm. of the chloride.}$$

$$\therefore \frac{(X+35{\cdot}46)}{(X+8)} \times 1{\cdot}538 = 3{\cdot}634.$$

$$\therefore X = 12{\cdot}16.$$

The same method can be applied to Example 2. If E = the equivalent of the metal, then $(E+35{\cdot}46)$ = the equivalent of the chloride. The equivalent of silver chloride = the equivalent of silver + the equivalent of chlorine = 107·9 + 35·46 = 143·36.

$$\therefore \frac{(E+35{\cdot}46)}{143{\cdot}36} = \frac{0{\cdot}3501}{0{\cdot}8586}.$$

$$\therefore E = 23{\cdot}01.$$

Example 4. 0·3806 gm. of the carbonate of a metal was treated with an excess of dilute sulphuric acid and gave 0·5176 gm. of the anhydrous metallic sulphate. Calculate the equivalent of the metal.

Since the carbonate radical is divalent, its equivalent

$$=\frac{CO_3}{2}=\frac{12\cdot00+(3\times16\cdot00)}{2}=30\cdot00.$$

Similarly, the equivalent of the divalent sulphate radical

$$=\frac{SO_4}{2}=\frac{32\cdot06+(4\times16\cdot00)}{2}=48\cdot03.$$

Then, as in Example 3,

$$\frac{(X+30\cdot00)}{(X+48\cdot03)}=\frac{0\cdot3806}{0\cdot5176},$$

where X = the chemical equivalent of the element.

$$\therefore X=20\cdot04.$$

Example 5. 0·862 gm. of the anhydrous carbonate of a metal was allowed to react with an excess of dilute hydrochloric acid and gave 193 c.c. of carbon dioxide, measured at *N.T.P.* What is the equivalent of the metal?

Let E = the equivalent of the metal. Then equivalent of the metallic carbonate = $(E+30\cdot00)$.

In general, it can be proved that the reaction of one gm.-equivalent of a metallic carbonate with an excess of dilute acid evolves $\frac{1}{2}$ gm.-molecule of carbon dioxide. The following equations show that the reaction of 1 gm.-equivalent of a metallic carbonate with 1 gm. of acidic hydrogen involves the formation of 22 gm. ($=\frac{1}{2}$ gm.-molecule) of carbon dioxide :

$$CaCO_3 + 2HCl = CaCl_2 + H_2O + CO_2$$
$$Na_2CO_3 + 2HCl = 2NaCl + H_2O + CO_2.$$

Taking the gm.-molecular volumes of all gases as 22·4 litres at *N.T.P.*, 22 gm. of carbon dioxide occupy 11·2 litres at *N.T.P.*

∴ The reaction of one gm.-equivalent of any metallic carbonate with an excess of dilute acid liberates 11·2 litres of carbon dioxide at *N.T.P.*

$$\therefore (E+30\cdot00)=\frac{0\cdot862\times11\cdot200}{193}=50\cdot0.$$

$$\therefore E=20\cdot0.$$

3. Limitation of the method of equivalents

It should be noted carefully that, in using the methods given in the foregoing examples, it is assumed that the element does not undergo a change of valency during the reaction. Thus, the method could not be used in its simplest form in a reaction of the type $PbO_2 \rightarrow PbCl_2$ since this reaction involves a change of valency from 4 to 2; the equivalent of Pb is, therefore, twice as large in $PbCl_2$ as in PbO_2. In using the method, therefore, it is assumed (unless otherwise stated in the question) that one compound is converted into another *corresponding* compound, that is, the reaction takes place without change of valency.

4. Calculation of atomic weights (Dulong and Petit's law)

Dulong and Petit's law is usually stated as follows:

$$\text{The specific heat of an element} \times \text{the atomic weight of the element} \doteqdot 6{\cdot}4$$

It is assumed that the student is acquainted with the method of using this law for the calculation of accurate atomic weights when the accurate chemical equivalent is given. It should be noted carefully, however, that the law is restricted to elements which are solid at ordinary temperature and that the law breaks down for a number of elements of exceptionally low atomic weight, for example, carbon, beryllium.

The law should be used, therefore, only for solid elements whose equivalents are such that they would not give a very low value for the atomic weight. Since these "abnormal" elements conform more closely to the law at high temperatures, the specific heat at high temperature, if given in the question, should be used.

Example 6. The specific heat of an element is 0·43 at 15° and 0·62 at 400°. 0·200 gm. of the anhydrous chloride of the element gave, on treatment with sulphuric acid, 0·263 gm. of the anhydrous sulphate. What is the most probable value for the atomic weight of the element?

If E = the equivalent of the element, then:

$$\frac{E+35{\cdot}5}{E+48} = \frac{0{\cdot}200}{0{\cdot}263}. \quad \therefore E = 4{\cdot}50.$$

Since the equivalent is low, the atomic weight, whatever the valency of the element, must also be small. It would be expected, therefore, that Dulong and Petit's law might not apply at ordinary temperature. We take, therefore, the value 0·62 which gives :

$$\text{Rough atomic weight} = \frac{6{\cdot}4}{0{\cdot}62} = 10{\cdot}3.$$

From the increase of specific heat with temperature, we are justified in assuming 10·3 to be high.

$\therefore$ Probable atomic weight $= 4{\cdot}50 \times 2 = \mathbf{9{\cdot}00}$.

5. Calculation of atomic weight (Mitscherlich's law of isomorphism)

Mitscherlich's law can be stated as follows :

Compounds which are isomorphous are similar in chemical structure ; compounds are said to be isomorphous when

(1) they are identical (or nearly identical) in crystal habit ;

(2) they will continue to crystallise, one on the other (overgrowths) ;

(3) they form " mixed " crystals.

Example 7. The equivalent of an element is 13·16. The element forms an acidic oxide which, with potassium hydroxide, forms a salt isomorphous with potassium sulphate. Deduce the atomic weight of the metal.

Potassium sulphate has the formula K_2SO_4. Therefore, by the law of isomorphism, the salt formed from the acidic oxide and potassium hydroxide will have the formula K_2XO_4, where X denotes one atom of the element.

But the acidic oxide which reacts with potassium hydroxide to form potassium sulphate is sulphur trioxide, SO_3.

$\therefore$ The formula of the acidic oxide is XO_3.

$\therefore$ The valency of the element in the acidic oxide is 6 and the atomic weight of the element $= 13{\cdot}16 \times 6 = \mathbf{78{\cdot}96}$.

Example 8. Assuming that the atomic weight of calcium is 40·1, find the atomic weight of magnesium, using the following data of percentage composition :

Calcium carbonate : Ca = 40·06 ; C = 11·99 ; O = 47·95.
Magnesium carbonate : Mg = 28·91 ; C = 14·22 ; O = 56·87.
(N.U.J.B.)

The two substances are isomorphous and, therefore, have similar chemical formulae.

∴ 1 gm.-atom of calcium and 1 gm.-atom of magnesium must unite respectively with the same weight of the carbonate radical.

But 40·06 gm. of calcium unites with (11·99 + 47·95) gm. = 59·94 gm. of the carbonate radical.

∴ 40·10 gm. (1 gm.-atom) of calcium unites with

$$\frac{59{\cdot}94}{40{\cdot}06} \times 40{\cdot}10 \text{ gm.} = 59{\cdot}99 \text{ gm.}$$

of the carbonate radical.

We have, now, to calculate the weight of magnesium which will combine with 59·99 gm. of the carbonate radical.

But 71·09 gm. of the carbonate radical unites with 28·91 gm. of magnesium.

∴ 59·99 gm. of the carbonate radical will unite with

$$\frac{28{\cdot}91}{71{\cdot}09} \times 59{\cdot}91 \text{ gm. of magnesium} = 24{\cdot}40 \text{ gm.}$$

∴ Atomic weight of magnesium = 24·40.

QUESTIONS ON CHAPTER I

[Where necessary use the accurate atomic weights given on p. 430.]

1. 1·038 gm. of the chloride of a metal was dissolved in water and an excess of silver nitrate solution was added. The precipitated silver chloride was collected and found to weigh 1·995 gm. Calculate the equivalent of the metal. [Ag = 107·9 ; Cl = 35·46.]

2. 1 gm. of zinc bromide when added to a slight excess of silver nitrate yielded 1·667 gm. of silver bromide. Calculate the equivalent weight of zinc, taking the atomic weights of silver and bromine as 107·9 and 79·9. (Inter. B.Sc., London.)

3. 5·601 gm. of a metallic chlorate was heated and gave 3·834 gm. of the metallic chloride. What is the equivalent of the metal? [Cl = 35·46.]

4. 1 gm. of copper sulphate crystals, $CuSO_4 \cdot 5H_2O$, was dissolved in water and treated with an excess of barium chloride solution.

The precipitated barium sulphate was found to weigh 0·9330 gm. Assuming the formula for barium sulphate, calculate the equivalent of copper in copper sulphate. [H = 1·008 ; Ba = 137·4 ; S = 32·06.]

5. 5·006 gm. of the oxide of a metal was completely reduced by heating in a stream of dry hydrogen. The water formed was collected and weighed 1·133 gm. Given that the equivalent of the metal is 31·78, calculate the equivalent of hydrogen.

6. 5·000 gm. of the chloride of an element whose equivalent is 10·35 is converted quantitatively into the corresponding oxide. Calculate the weight of the oxide.

7. The chloride of an element was converted quantitatively into the corresponding oxide and the following figures were obtained : 0·1827 gm. of the chloride gave 0·1507 gm. of the oxide. Calculate the chemical equivalent of the element. (C.U.O.S.)

8. Carbon monoxide was passed over heated copper oxide and the resulting loss of weight of the copper oxide was 0·5318 gm. The carbon dioxide formed was collected in potash bulbs and found to weigh 1·4600 gm. Assuming the formulae of carbon monoxide and carbon dioxide, calculate the atomic weight of carbon.

9. Calculate the weight of the anhydrous sulphate of a metal which could be obtained theoretically by the action of an excess of sulphuric acid upon 2·008 gm. of the corresponding bromide, the equivalent of the metal being 20·04.

10. 2·000 gm. of a metallic nitrate gave on strong heating 1·347 gm. of the corresponding oxide. What is the equivalent of the metal? [N = 14·01.]

11. 1·861 gm. of a metallic carbonate was strongly heated to a constant weight and gave 0·890 gm. of the corresponding metallic oxide. Deduce the equivalent of the metal. [C = 12·00.]

12. What is the smallest volume of barium chloride solution, containing 5 gm. of barium chloride crystals, $BaCl_2 . 2H_2O$, per litre, which would completely precipitate the sulphate radical from 100 c.c. of a solution containing 10 gm. per litre of the anhydrous sulphate of a metal of equivalent 31·75?

13. Compare the percentages of (*a*) nitrogen, (*b*) oxygen in the nitrate and the nitrite of a metal whose equivalent is 23·01[N = 14·01].

14. The specific heat of a metal is 0·152. 0·0564 gm. of the metallic oxide yielded 0·2040 gm. of the anhydrous bromide. Calculate the atomic weight of the metal. (1st M.B., London.)

15. 1·632 gm. of a metallic carbonate was heated to a constant weight and gave 1·062 gm. of the corresponding oxide. The oxide dissolved in dilute sulphuric acid and evaporation of the resulting solution gave a crystalline salt isomorphous with ferrous sulphate, $FeSO_4 . 7H_2O$. What is the atomic weight of the metal?

16. The gaseous product of combustion from 0·3660 gm. of a metallic sulphide was passed into bromine water. This solution, after boiling, gave 0·8754 gm. of barium sulphate. Calculate the equivalent of the metal in the sulphide. (1st M.B., London.)

17. Assuming the formula for potassium chlorate, calculate the equivalents of potassium, chlorine and silver from the following data:

(*a*) 86·50 gm. of potassium chlorate gave 52·61 gm. of potassium chloride;

(*b*) 10·78 gm. of silver dissolved in nitric acid required for complete precipitation 7·450 gm. of potassium chloride;

(*c*) 91·46 gm. of silver gave 121·5 gm. of silver chloride.

18. 3·174 gm. of the sulphate of a metal was dissolved in water and treated with an excess of barium chloride solution, the resulting barium sulphate weighing 5·559 gm. Calculate the equivalent of the metal. If the specific heat of the metal is 0·119, what is its accurate atomic weight?

19. 4·823 gm. of the anhydrous chloride of a metal, treated with an excess of sulphuric acid, gave 5·631 gm. of the anhydrous sulphate. The specific heat of the metal is 0·173. What is its accurate atomic weight?

20. 0·5183 gm. of the sulphite of a metal was oxidised to the sulphate and treated with an excess of barium chloride solution. The barium sulphate formed weighed 1·171 gm. What is the equivalent of the metal?

21. 1·034 gm. of a metallic carbonate was placed in 50 c.c. of 0·982 normal sulphuric acid; after the carbonate had dissolved, the residual solution was heated to expel carbon dioxide and then required 32·71 c.c. of 0·870 normal sodium hydroxide for neutralisation. Calculate the equivalent of the metal.

22. A mixture of 2 gm. each of the sulphates of two metals whose equivalents are 12·20 and 32·72 respectively was dissolved in water. What weight of barium sulphate should theoretically be formed by the addition to this solution of an excess of barium chloride?

23. What conclusions can be drawn from the following data? 0·500 gm. of the chloride of a metal gave, with an excess of silver nitrate, 1·793 gm. of silver chloride. The specific heat of the metal is 0·44. [Ag = 107·9; Cl = 35·46.]

24. When 0·2000 gm. of a metallic oxide was allowed to react with an excess of sulphuric acid it gave 0·7049 gm. of a hydrated metallic sulphate isomorphous with magnesium sulphate, $MgSO_4 . 7H_2O$. What is the probable atomic weight of the metal? [Mg = 24·32; S = 32·06; H = 1·008.]

25. The oxide of an element, *X*, reacts with caustic potash to form a salt isomorphous with potassium permanganate, $KMnO_4$. The oxide contains 61·2 per cent of oxygen. What are (*a*) the formula of the oxide, (*b*) the atomic weight of the element, *X*?

26. Calculate (*a*) the weight of water, (*b*) the weight of carbon dioxide, and (*c*) the volume of carbon dioxide, measured at *N.T.P.*, which would theoretically be obtained from the strong heating of 10 gm. of a metallic bicarbonate, assuming that a residue of the metallic oxide is formed and that the equivalent of the metal is 68·5.

27. The chloride of an element is completely hydrolysed by a large excess of water into an insoluble oxide and hydrochloric acid. The acid liberated in this way from 1·635 gm. of the chloride requires 23·1 c.c. of 1·12 normal sodium hydroxide for neutralisation. Calculate the equivalent of the element.

28. 100 c.c. of a solution of a chloride of a metal containing 0·25 gm. of the anhydrous chloride required 24·05 c.c. of *N*/10 sulphuric acid for the exact precipitation of the metal as the metallic sulphate. What is the equivalent of the metal?

29. The carbonate of a metal is isomorphous with magnesium carbonate and contains 6·091 per cent of carbon. What is the atomic weight of the metal? [C = 12·00.]

30. Two chlorides, *A* and *B*, of a metal were converted quantitatively into their corresponding sulphates, the following results being obtained:

(*a*) 0·8047 gm. of *A* gave 0·9642 gm. of the metallic sulphate.

(*b*) 0·7605 gm. of *B* gave 0·9369 gm. of the metallic sulphate.

The sulphate obtained from *B* combined with ammonium sulphate to form an alum. Deduce the two equivalents of the element and its accurate atomic weight. If *M* denote one atom of the metal, write the formulae for the two chlorides. [Cl = 35·46; S = 32·06. Note that the general formula for an alum is

$$X_2SO_4 . Y_2(SO_4)_3 . 24H_2O,$$

where *X* denotes one atom of a monovalent element or the monovalent radical (NH_4) and *Y* denotes one atom of a trivalent metal. All alums are isomorphous and crystallise in regular octahedra.]

31. What conclusions regarding the atomic weight of an element can be drawn from the following data? The element forms three oxides containing 72·72 per cent, 57·14 per cent and 47·06 per cent of oxygen respectively. The specific heat of the element is 0·12 at 15° and 0·35 at 400°.

32. Silver sulphide, Ag_2S, and cuprous sulphide are isomorphous; they contain 12·90 per cent and 20·20 per cent respectively of sulphur. Deduce the atomic weight of copper. [Ag = 107·9.]

33. The cyanide of a metal, *X*, forms a complex cyanide with potassium cyanide isomorphous with potassium ferricyanide, $K_3FeC_6N_6$. The percentage compositions of the complex cyanide of *X* and of potassium ferricyanide are respectively:

K = 36·71; *X* = 16·29; C = 22·54; N = 24·46, and

K = 35·57; Fe = 16·97; C = 21·89; N = 25·57.

Deduce the atomic weight of *X*. [Fe = 55·84.]

34. An element, X, forms a sulphate which combines with ammonium sulphate to give a double salt isomorphous with potash alum ; on strong ignition the double sulphate of X and ammonium left only a residue of the corresponding oxide of X and it was found that 0·8253 gm. of the double salt gave 0·2292 gm. of the oxide. What is the atomic weight of X? [N = 14·01 ; S = 32·06 ; H = 1·008.]

35. An element of metallic appearance and properties is found to yield (*a*) an oxide with 23·12 per cent of oxygen, (*b*) a chloride with 43·25 per cent of chlorine, and (*c*) two sulphides having respectively 37·55 per cent and 25·58 per cent of sulphur. The specific heat of the element is 0·0346. Show clearly and fully what inferences can be drawn from these data. (O.U.O.S.)

36. The nitrate of a metal is heated and decomposed into oxygen, nitrogen peroxide and the corresponding metallic oxide. The equivalent of the metal is 31·70. Calculate (*a*) the weight of the oxide, (*b*) the volume of oxygen, measured over water at 14° and 736 mm., which would be obtained in this way from 10·00 gm. of the metallic nitrate. [Vapour pressure of water at 14° = 12 mm. ; 32·00 gm. of oxygen occupy 22,400 c.c. at *N.T.P.*]

37. The double sulphate of thallium and magnesium is isomorphous with potassium magnesium sulphate, $K_2SO_4 \cdot MgSO_4 \cdot 6H_2O$. Using the following percentage compositions of the two double salts, calculate the atomic weight of thallium.

Thallium magnesium sulphate : Tl = 55·66 ; Mg = 3·32 ; S = 8·76 ; O = 17·49 ; H_2O = 14·77. Potassium magnesium sulphate : K = 19·42 ; Mg = 6·04 ; S = 15·92 ; O = 31·78 ; H_2O = 26·84. [K = 39·10].

38. An element, X, forms three oxides containing 89·71 per cent, 86·74 per cent and 83·95 per cent respectively of the element. 1·380 gm. of the chloride of the element gave, on complete hydrolysis, 1·138 gm. of the corresponding hydroxide. The specific heat of the element is 0·03. Calculate the accurate atomic weight of the element and write the formulae of its oxides, chloride and hydroxide. [H = 1·008 ; Cl = 35·46].

39. 10 gm. of a mixture of the anhydrous nitrates of two metals, A and B, were heated to a constant weight and gave 5·531 gm. of a mixture of the corresponding oxides. The equivalents of A and B are 103·6 and 31·8 respectively. What was the percentage of the nitrate of A in the mixture? [Hint : Let x = weight of nitrate of A and $(10 - x)$ = weight of nitrate of B. Hence obtain an equation in x].

40. 1 gm. of the carbonate of a metal was acted upon by an excess of dilute hydrochloric acid and gave 235 c.c. of carbon dioxide, measured at 18° and 742 mm. What is the chemical equivalent of the metallic carbonate? If 10 gm. of this carbonate were converted into the corresponding anhydrous sulphate, what weight of the metallic sulphate should theoretically be obtained?

41. When 1·500 gm. of the anhydrous cupric salt of an organic acid is decomposed by heat it leaves 0·392 gm. of cupric oxide. What is the equivalent of the organic acid? [Cu = 63·57.]

42. 10 gm. of the chloride of a metal was converted into the corresponding sulphate by the action of concentrated sulphuric acid. The hydrogen chloride liberated occupied 1·610 litres at *N.T.P.* What is the equivalent of the metal?

43. 1·307 gm. of the hydrated chloride of a metal, X, was heated to a constant weight, the final weight of the anhydrous chloride being 1·114 gm. Treated with an excess of sulphuric acid, 1·582 gm. of the anhydrous chloride gave 1·774 gm. of the anhydrous sulphate. The specific heat of the metal is 0·047. Calculate the accurate atomic weight of the metal and write the formula for its hydrated chloride. [Cl = 35·46 ; S = 32·06 ; H = 1·008.]

44. When 1 gm. of a metallic carbonate was strongly heated it gave 154 c.c. of carbon dioxide measured at *N.T.P.* and left a residue of the metallic oxide. What is the equivalent of the metal?

45. 5 gm. of the sodium salt of an organic acid was heated to a constant weight and gave a residue of 3·955 gm. of sodium carbonate. What is the equivalent of the acid?

46. The cupric salt of an acid contains 3 molecules of water of crystallisation per atom of copper. Calculate the equivalent of the acid given that 1·381 gm. of the hydrated salt on strong heating left a quantity of cupric oxide weighing 0·4565 gm.

47. The action of an excess of dilute hydrochloric acid upon 1 gm. of a metallic sulphide gave 230·5 c.c. of hydrogen sulphide measured at *N.T.P.* What is the equivalent of the metal?

48. A certain element in its highest state of valency gives rise to a monobasic acid and also to an oxychloride which on hydrolysis gives the same acid. This oxychloride contains 64·1 per cent of chlorine. A molecule both of the acid and the oxychloride contain one atom only of the element. When the acid is reduced in sulphuric acid solution containing ammonium sulphate an ammonium alum containing the element is formed. Find the most probable atomic weight of the element. [Cl = 35·46.] (C.U.O.S.)

49. The oxide of a certain element contains 85·2 per cent of the element. This oxide combines directly with chlorine to give an oxychloride containing 24·7 per cent of chlorine. The oxychloride treated with potash gives a potassium salt isomorphous with potassium manganate and boiled with hydrochloric acid and ethyl alcohol gives acetaldehyde, water and a chloride of the element which treated with alkalis regenerated the original oxide. Find the atomic weight of the element and write equations for the various reactions. [Cl = 35·46.] (C.U.O.S.)

CHAPTER II

MOLECULAR THEORY

1. Molecular weight and vapour density

Molecular weights of volatile substances are obtained from gas densities by means of one of the following relationships :

(1) Molecular weight $= 2 \times$ vapour density.

(2) The gm.-molecular weight, that is, a quantity equal to the molecular weight in gm., of any substance in the form of a vapour occupies 22·4 litres at *N.T.P.*

The two relationships give slightly different results. Using (1), the molecular weight is referred to hydrogen as unit of vapour density, and all molecular weights obtained in this way will be on the standard of atomic weights in which $H = 1{\cdot}0000$. The gm.-molecular-volume is then the volume occupied by 2 gm. of hydrogen at *N.T.P.*

When the value 22·4 litres is taken as the gm.-molecular-volume it refers to the volume occupied by 2·0174 ($2 \times 1{\cdot}0087$) gm. of hydrogen at *N.T.P.*, and molecular weights deduced from this value are on the standard of atomic weights in which $O = 16{\cdot}0000$ (see p. 17 for method of limiting densities).

The following are the main uses to which the values obtained for molecular weights by vapour density determinations are applied :

(1) To give the true or molecular formulae of a compound whose empirical formula is known.

(2) The determination of the atomic weight of an element by method of least weight, the equivalent of the element being accurately known.

(3) For the determination of the *accurate* atomic weights of the inert gases. Since these gases do not enter into chemical combination, the accuracy with which their atomic weights are known will depend solely upon the accuracy with which their vapour densities can be determined. Accurate values for

the atomic weights of other elements, for example, nitrogen, have been obtained by vapour density methods (see p. 17).

(4) For studying "abnormality" due to thermal dissociation (see p. 119).

For purposes (1) and (2) it is immaterial whether $H = 1{\cdot}0000$ or $O = 16{\cdot}0000$ is taken as standard, since accurate values for the molecular weight are not required. It will be seen that in the following examples only rough values for the vapour density and molecular weight are required.

Example 9. Determine the formula of a compound which contains 2·1 per cent of hydrogen, 12·8 per cent of carbon and 85·1 per cent of bromine, and of which, at 140° and 765 mm., one gm. of the vapour occupies 179 c.c. (1st M.B., London.)

Obtaining the empirical formula by dividing the percentage of each element by its respective atomic weight, we have :

$$C = 12{\cdot}8/12 = 1{\cdot}06,$$
$$H = 2{\cdot}1/1 = 2{\cdot}1,$$
$$Br = 85{\cdot}1/80 = 1{\cdot}06.$$

$\therefore$ Empirical formula $= CH_2Br$.

The approximate molecular weight can be obtained as follows :

179 c.c. of hydrogen at 140° and 765 mm. weigh :

$$179 \times \frac{273}{413} \times \frac{765}{760} \times 0{\cdot}00009 \text{ gm.} = 0{\cdot}01071 \text{ gm.}$$

$$\therefore \text{ Vapour density of the compound} = \frac{1}{0{\cdot}01071}.$$

$$\therefore \text{ Molecular weight} = \frac{1}{0{\cdot}01071} \times 2 = 187.$$

But the molecular weight corresponding with the formula $CH_2Br = 12 + 2 + 80 = 94$.

$\therefore$ Molecular formula $= \mathbf{C_2H_4Br_2}$.

2. Determination of atomic weight by method of "least weight" (Cannizzaro's method)

The principle of the method is most easily appreciated by considering a number of compounds of one element such as carbon. Let m = the molecular weight of a compound of carbon of molecular formula C_xA, that is, the molecule con-

tains x atoms of carbon, the remainder of the molecule being denoted by A. Then since the atomic weight of carbon is 12 :

$$\frac{12x}{m}=p,$$

where $p=$the fraction of the molecular weight due to the presence of the carbon atoms.

$$\therefore\ 12x=p\times m.$$

If, then, we determine the molecular weights of a large number of compounds of carbon and multiply these molecular weights by the corresponding fractions by weight of carbon (obtained by analysis), we shall have a number of values for $12x$ where x will be some simple whole number. The least value for $12x$ will be obtained when $x=1$, and the value of $p\times m$ is then 12, which is the atomic weight of carbon. This is the principle of Cannizzaro's method, the least weight of an element found in the molecular weights of its compounds being taken as its atomic weight.

Example 10. Four compounds of an element contain respectively 90·3 per cent, 16·5 per cent, 26·4 per cent and 22·8 per cent of the element. The corresponding vapour densities of these compounds are 31, 85·5, 53 and 184. Deduce the probable atomic weight of the element.

The molecular weights of the compounds are 62, 171, 106 and 368 respectively. To find how much of these molecular weights are due to the presence of the element, each must be multiplied by a fraction corresponding with the percentage given.

$$62\times 0{\cdot}903=56, \quad\text{.......................(1)}$$

$$171\times 0{\cdot}165=28, \quad\text{.......................(2)}$$

$$106\times 0{\cdot}264=28, \quad\text{.......................(3)}$$

$$368\times 0{\cdot}228=84. \quad\text{.......................(4)}$$

The "least weight" of the element found in the molecular weights of these four compounds is, therefore, 28, and since it probably corresponds with one atom of the element, the atomic weight of the element is also 28. The molecules of the compounds to which the figures of (1) and (4) refer obviously contain 2 and 3 atoms of the element respectively.

The value, 28, for the atomic weight is clearly only approximate, since the vapour densities may be assumed to be rough values; the method, however, suffices to give the accurate atomic weight if the accurate equivalent is known.

Example 11. The oxide of an element contains 53·24 per cent of oxygen. The vapour density of the fluoride of the element is about 52. What is the probable atomic weight of the element?

$$\text{The equivalent of the element} = \frac{46{\cdot}72}{53{\cdot}28} \times 8{\cdot}000 = 7{\cdot}018.$$

The *accurate* atomic weight of the element $= 7{\cdot}018 \times n$ where $n =$ the valency of the element in the oxide. The valency can be deduced in two ways.

(1) Since the equivalent of the element is 7·018 and that of fluorine is 19·00, the percentage of the element in the fluoride

$$= \frac{7{\cdot}018}{(7{\cdot}018 + 19{\cdot}00)} \times 100 = 26{\cdot}98.$$

(Note that we have assumed that the element exerts the same valency in the oxide and the fluoride and has, therefore, the same equivalent in both compounds.)

∴ The proportion of one molecular weight of the fluoride which is due to the presence of the element is approximately $104 \times 0{\cdot}27 = 28$. If, therefore, we assume that one molecule of the fluoride contains only one atom of the element, the approximate atomic weight of the element is 28 and the accurate atomic weight is $7{\cdot}018 \times 4 = 28{\cdot}07$.

(2) Alternatively, we may assign varying valencies to the element and calculate the corresponding molecular weights of the fluoride, comparing them with the value given as shown in the following table:

Valency	Atomic weight of the element	Formula of the fluoride	Molecular weight	Vapour density
1	7·02	XF	26·02	13·01
2	14·04	XF_2	52·04	26·02
3	21·06	XF_3	78·06	39·03
4	28·08	XF_4	104·08	52·04

The element, therefore, has an atomic weight approximately 28 and valency 4.

In the questions given at the end of this chapter, it has been assumed that the student is acquainted with the practical details of the following methods for determining vapour densities :

(1) Dumas' method, (2) Victor Meyer's method, (3) Hofman's method, (4) Regnault's method.

A modification of the last method is discussed below.

* 3. Method of limiting densities

The methods usually employed for the determination of molecular weights by comparison of vapour densities give only approximate results (cf. p. 14). Regnault's method, consisting as it does of the direct weighing of a measured volume of a gas, can be used to give very accurate values for the vapour densities of those substances which are gaseous at ordinary temperatures. Molecular weights obtained from these values will still, however, be only approximate since gases at ordinary temperature and pressure do not obey the gas laws rigorously; under these conditions, therefore, Avogadro's law cannot be exact, unless, indeed, all gases showed the same deviations from the gas laws which, in fact, they do not.

At very low pressures, however, all gases conform more closely to the perfect gas equation so that by a comparison of their vapour densities at these pressures, accurate values for molecular weights can be obtained.

The **normal density** of a gas is defined as its density at 0° and 760 mm. pressure. Then if 1 litre of the gas, A, measured at 0° and 760 mm. has a mass, W_A gm., the normal density of the gas is W_A gm. per litre. If, now, this mass of gas is brought to a very low pressure, p, where $p \to 0$, the gas will conform rigidly to the gas equation $pv = kRT$ where k = the number of gm.-molecules of the gas. Assume that the accurate molecular weight of the gas is M_A. Then since W_A gm. of the gas $= W_A/M_A$ gm.-molecules $= k$, the gas equation can be written :

$$_A(pv)_0 = kRT = \frac{W_A}{M_A} \cdot RT, \quad \text{.....................(1)}$$

where $_A(pv)_0$ is the limiting value of pv when $p \to 0$.

But $W_A = D_A$ where D_A is the normal density of the gas, A.

$$\therefore\ M_A = \frac{D_A}{{}_A(pv)_0} \cdot RT, \quad \text{.....................}(2)$$

where $D_A/{}_A(pv)_0$ is, by definition, the **limiting density** of the gas, A.

For a gas B, we have, similarly:

$$M_B = \frac{D_B}{{}_B(pv)_0} \cdot RT,$$

$$\therefore\ \frac{M_A}{M_B} = \frac{D_A}{{}_A(pv)_0} \bigg/ \frac{D_B}{{}_B(pv)_0} = \frac{D_A \times {}_B(pv)_0}{D_B \times {}_A(pv)_0}. \quad \text{...........}(3)$$

The ratio of the **accurate** molecular weights of gases, therefore, is given by the ratio of their limiting densities.

* **Example 12.** The normal densities of oxygen and carbon monoxide are 1·4290 and 1·2504 gm. per litre respectively. The limiting value of pv $(p \to 0)$ for 1 litre of oxygen, measured at *N.T.P.*, is 1·00096, and the corresponding value for carbon monoxide is 1·00081. What value for the atomic weight of carbon is given by these figures?

As in equation:

$$\frac{M_{CO}}{M_{O_2}} = \frac{1{\cdot}2504 \times 1{\cdot}00096}{1{\cdot}4290 \times 1{\cdot}00081},$$

where M_{CO} and M_{O_2} are the accurate molecular weights of carbon monoxide and oxygen respectively.

But since the atomic weight of oxygen is taken as the standard and equal to 16·0000, $M_{O_2} = 32{\cdot}0000$.

$$\therefore\ M_{CO} = \frac{1{\cdot}2504 \times 1{\cdot}00096 \times 32{\cdot}0000}{1{\cdot}4290 \times 1{\cdot}00081} = 28{\cdot}04.$$

$\therefore$ Atomic weight of carbon $= 28{\cdot}04 - 16{\cdot}00 = \mathbf{12{\cdot}04}$.

* 4. Compressibility coefficient of a gas

The compressibility coefficient, α, of a gas (sometimes called the **bulk modulus**) is defined by the equation:

$$\alpha = -\frac{1}{pv} \cdot \frac{d}{dp}(pv) \quad \text{.......................}(4)$$

measurements being taken at 0°. For gases other than hydrogen pv decreases with increase of p and $\frac{d}{dp}(pv)$ is negative;

the compressibility coefficient of these gases is, therefore, positive.

Assuming that the compressibility coefficient remains constant over a given pressure range, the equation given above can be written in the form (obtained by integration) :

$$\frac{(pv)_a - (pv)_b}{(pv)_a} = \alpha p_1, \quad \ldots\ldots\ldots\ldots\ldots\ldots\ldots(5)$$

where p_1 = change of pressure between the limits for which pv has values $(pv)_a$ and $(pv)_b$ respectively.†

If, initially, $p=1$ and is then brought to $p \to 0$, then :

$$\frac{(pv)_0 - (pv)_1}{(pv)_0} = \alpha p = \alpha, \quad \ldots\ldots\ldots\ldots\ldots\ldots\ldots(6)$$

since p = change of pressure $\doteq$ 1 and $(pv)_0$ and $(pv)_1$ denote the values of pv at $p \to 0$ and $p=1$ respectively.

Let the mass of gas (W) be such that it occupies 1 litre at 1 atmosphere pressure.

Then $\dfrac{W}{(pv)_1} = D_n$ = the normal density of the gas,

and $\dfrac{W}{(pv)_0} = D_l$ = the limiting density of the gas.

Substituting these values in equation :

$$\frac{\frac{W}{D_l} - \frac{W}{D_n}}{\frac{W}{D_l}} = \alpha. \quad \ldots\ldots\ldots\ldots\ldots\ldots\ldots(7)$$

From which :

$$\mathbf{D_l = D_n(1 - \alpha)}. \quad \ldots\ldots\ldots\ldots\ldots\ldots\ldots(8)$$

* **Example 13.** The normal density of oxygen is 1·4290 gm. per litre and its compressibility coefficient is 0·00094. For nitrous oxide the corresponding figures are 1·9777 gm. per litre and 0·00747. Calculate the atomic weight of nitrogen.

† The integration is effected by noting that $(pv)_a - (pv)_b$ is very small in comparison with $(pv)_a$; as an approximation put $pv = k$, integrate, $\alpha = -\frac{1}{k}\frac{d}{dp}(pv)$ and substitute $(pv)_a$ for k.

Let D_l = the limiting density of oxygen,
and D_l' = the limiting density of nitrous oxide.
Then $D_l = 1{\cdot}4290(1 - 0{\cdot}00094) = 1{\cdot}4267$,
and $D_l' = 1{\cdot}9777(1 - 0{\cdot}00747) = 1{\cdot}9629$.

Then, as in example 12 :

Molecular weight of nitrous oxide

$$= \frac{32{\cdot}0000 \times 1{\cdot}9629}{1{\cdot}4267} = 44{\cdot}002.$$

$$\therefore \text{ Atomic weight of nitrogen} = \frac{44{\cdot}002 - 16{\cdot}000}{2} = \mathbf{14{\cdot}001.}$$

* The compressibility coefficient is often calculated by measuring the normal density and the density at a pressure of half an atmosphere, or by observations of the value of pv at 1 atmosphere pressure and at half that pressure.

Let a mass of gas, W_a, occupying 1 litre at *N.T.P.* be brought to a pressure of half an atmosphere, and let the density of the gas at this pressure be denoted by $D_{\frac{1}{2}}$. Then in equation (5) :

$$\frac{(pv)_0 - (p_a v_a)_{\frac{1}{2}}}{(pv)_0} = \alpha p_a, \quad \text{.........................(9)}$$

where $(p_a v_a)_{\frac{1}{2}}$ = the product of the pressure and the volume at half an atmosphere for a mass of gas originally occupying 1 litre at a pressure of 1 atmosphere.

But $$(pv)_0 = \frac{W_a}{D_l},$$

where D_l = the limiting density of the gas, and since

$p_a = \frac{1}{2}$, both in the product $(p_a v_a)_{\frac{1}{2}}$ and αp_a, and $v_a = \dfrac{W_a}{D_{\frac{1}{2}}}$.

$$\therefore \frac{(pv)_0 - (p_a v_a)_{\frac{1}{2}}}{(pv)_0} = \frac{\dfrac{W_a}{D_l} - \dfrac{1}{2} \cdot \dfrac{W_a}{D_{\frac{1}{2}}}}{\dfrac{W_a}{D_l}} = \alpha \times \frac{1}{2}.$$

$$\therefore \mathbf{D_l = 2D_{\frac{1}{2}}\left(1 - \frac{\alpha}{2}\right)}. \quad \text{.....................(10)}$$

This result can be combined with equation (8), to give both α and D_l.

* **Example 14.** The density of nitrous oxide in gm. per litre is 1·9777 at 760 mm. and 0°. At 380 mm. and 0° its density is 0·98853 gm. per litre. What is the compressibility coefficient of nitrous oxide? Calculate the atomic weight of nitrogen given that the limiting density of oxygen is 1·4276 gm. per litre.

Then, as in equations (8) and (10):

$$D_l = D_n(1-\alpha) = 1{\cdot}9777\,(1-\alpha),$$

$$D_l = 2D_{\frac{1}{2}}\left(1-\frac{\alpha}{2}\right) = 2\times 0{\cdot}98853\left(1-\frac{\alpha}{2}\right).$$

$$\therefore\ 1{\cdot}9777\,(1-\alpha) = 2\times 0{\cdot}98853\left(1-\frac{\alpha}{2}\right).$$

From which: $\boldsymbol{\alpha = 0{\cdot}000648}$.

$$\therefore\ D_l = 1{\cdot}9777\,(1-0{\cdot}000648) = 1{\cdot}9751.$$

Then, as in example 12:

$$\text{molecular weight of nitrous oxide} = \frac{32{\cdot}0000\times 1{\cdot}9751}{1{\cdot}4276} = 44{\cdot}20.$$

$\therefore$ Atomic weight of nitrogen = **14·10.**

* 5. Determination of limiting density by graphical method

The limiting value of p_0v_0 when $p\to 0$ can be obtained by plotting observed values of pv against the corresponding pressures. If we assume that pv varies in a linear manner with p (as has been done in para. 4, p. 19), it is only necessary to plot a few values and continue the straight line joining them until it cuts the axis at $p=0$.

* **Example.** The volume of a quantity of ethylene was measured at different pressures and at constant temperature, 0°, with the following results:

p (atmospheres)	1·0	0·8	0·6	0·4	0·2
v (c.c.) - -	156·33	195·69	235·20	392·50	768·15

Calculate the molecular weight of ethylene ($O_2 = 32{\cdot}00$).

The values of pv are:

p (atmospheres)	1·0	0·8	0·6	0·4	0·2
pv (c.c.—atmospheres) -	156·33	156·55	156·80	157·0	157·23

When these values are plotted (as in Fig. 1) extrapolation of the resulting straight line to $p=0$ gives $p_0v_0=157{\cdot}46$.

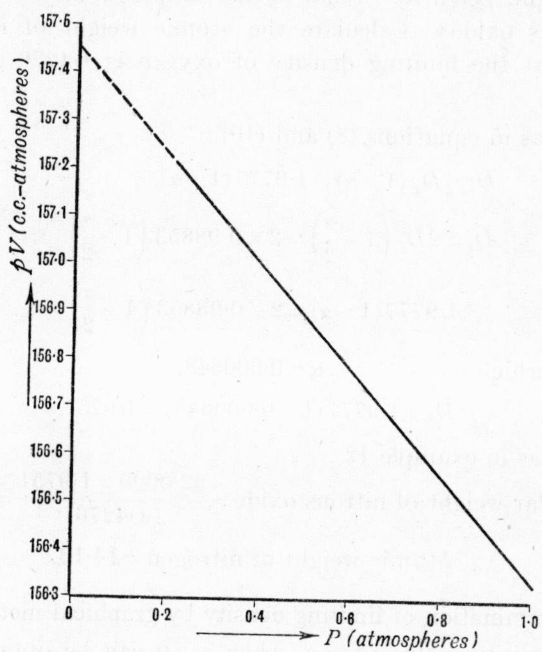

FIG. 1. Graphical method of determining compressibility coefficient of a gas.

∴ As in equation (6):

$$\text{compressibility coefficient} = 0{\cdot}0072.$$

The normal density of ethylene $=1{\cdot}2606$, and the limiting density of oxygen $=1{\cdot}4267$.

∴ If M = molecular weight of ethylene,

$$\frac{M}{32{\cdot}00} = \frac{1{\cdot}2606(1-0{\cdot}0072)}{1{\cdot}4267}.$$

$$\therefore \text{M} = 28{\cdot}07.$$

* Alternatively, the density, d, at different pressures less than 1 atmosphere may be plotted against the pressure. The value of $\dfrac{d_0}{p_0}$, that is the limiting value when $p=0$, can then be obtained by extrapolation. Then if d_1 and p_1 are the density at 1

atmosphere pressure and p_1 = the pressure = 1 atmosphere and m = the fixed mass of gas :

$$\frac{d_1/p_1}{d_0/p_0}=\frac{m/p_1v_1}{m/p_0v_0}=\frac{p_0v_0}{p_1v_1}=\frac{1}{1-\alpha}\doteq 1+\alpha \text{ (since } \alpha \text{ is small)}. \quad \ldots(11)$$

6. The gram-molecular volume

The accurate value for the gram-molecular-volume is easily obtained from the value of the limiting density of oxygen. Since all atomic weights are referred to O = 16 and O_2 = 32 (exactly), then :

$$\text{gm.-molecular-volume}=\frac{32}{\text{limiting density of oxygen}}$$

$$=\frac{32}{1{\cdot}4276} \text{ litres} = \mathbf{22{\cdot}415 \text{ litres}}.$$

7. Determination of vapour density by microbalance

The microbalance was originally constructed in order to determine the vapour densities of the inert gases at a time when only very small amounts were available. Essentially, it consists of a very light and small balance, made entirely of quartz and enclosed in an air-tight container; one arm of the balance carries a bulb so that, by adjusting the pressure of the gas in the case, small weighings can be obtained from the change in the buoyancy factor. The bulb is evacuated and the container is filled with a standard gas and the pressure is adjusted until the pointer is in the zero position, after which the container is filled with the gas whose density is required and the pressure again adjusted to bring the balance to the zero point.

Then if :

d_s = density of the standard gas at 760 mm. and 0°,

and d_x = density of the other gas at 760 mm. and 0°,

and T = constant temperature of the case and its gaseous contents,

p_s = pressure of standard gas required to bring the balance to zero position, and p_x = pressure of the other gas required to bring the balance to the zero position,

and V = the volume of the bulb :

weight of standard gas displaced by the bulb

$$= V \times d_s \times \frac{p_s}{760} \times \left(\frac{273}{273+T}\right),$$

where V = volume of the bulb.

Similarly, for the gas whose density is required :

$$\text{Weight of gas displaced} = V \times d_x \times \frac{p_x}{760} \times \frac{273}{(273+T)}.$$

But these two weights must be equal.

$$\therefore \ d_x = \frac{d_s \times p_s}{p_x}. \quad \ldots\ldots\ldots\ldots\ldots\ldots\ldots\ldots(12)$$

Example 15. At 16° it was found that the pressure of pure carbon dioxide required to bring the balance to zero position was 12·54 mm. What is the molecular weight of a gas which used, similarly, at 16°, was at a pressure of 13·76 mm.?

$$\text{Vapour density of the gas} = \text{vapour density of } CO_2 \times \frac{12{\cdot}54}{13{\cdot}76}.$$

$$= \frac{22{\cdot}00 \times 12{\cdot}54}{13{\cdot}76} = 20{\cdot}08,$$

and molecular weight of the gas = **40·16.**

Alternatively, the principle of the microbalance may be embodied in an apparatus in which a bulb of known capacity is filled with a gas whose density is required, the weight of the gas being determined directly by suitable adjustment of the buoyancy factor.

Example 16. With the bulb, of capacity 3·52 c.c., evacuated it is found that the balance is in the zero position when the pressure of dry air in the case is 737·2 mm., its uniform temperature being 15°. A quantity of a pure gaseous compound is then admitted to the bulb at a pressure of 2·17 mm. and at 15°. To restore the balance to its neutral position, it is found necessary to increase the pressure of air in the case 744·0 mm. What is the molecular weight of the gaseous compound?

Density of dry air at 0° and 760 mm. $=0{\cdot}001293$ gm. per c.c.

$\therefore$ Density of dry air at 15° and 737·2 mm.

$$=0{\cdot}001293 \times \frac{273}{288} \times \frac{737{\cdot}2}{760} = 0{\cdot}001190 \text{ gm. per c.c.}$$

$\therefore$ Weight of air displaced by the bulb at 15° and 737·2 mm.

$$=3{\cdot}52 \times 0{\cdot}001190 = \mathbf{0{\cdot}004187} \textbf{ gm.}$$

Similarly, weight of air displaced by the bulb at 15° and 744·0 mm. pressure

$$=0{\cdot}001293 \times \frac{273}{288} \times \frac{744{\cdot}0}{760} \times 3{\cdot}52 = \mathbf{0{\cdot}004224} \textbf{ gm.}$$

$\therefore$ Weight of gas in the bulb

$$=0{\cdot}004224 - 0{\cdot}004187 = \mathbf{0{\cdot}000037} \textbf{ gm.}$$

But 3·52 c.c. of gas, measured at 2·17 mm. and 15°

$$=0{\cdot}00953 \text{ c.c. at } N.T.P.$$

$$\therefore \text{ Weight of 22,400 c.c. at } N.T.P. = \frac{0{\cdot}000037}{0{\cdot}00953} \times 22{,}400 \text{ gm.}$$

$$=87 \text{ gm. (with sufficient accuracy).}$$

$\therefore$ Molecular weight of the gaseous compound $=87$.

8. Determination of molecular weights of gases by diffusion

The rates at which gases diffuse (under comparable conditions of temperature and pressure) are inversely proportional to the square roots of their vapour densities (Graham's law).

For vapour densities we may use absolute densities (gm. per c.c.) or molecular weights, since these are directly proportional to the vapour densities. The theoretical basis of Graham's law according to the kinetic theory of gases is discussed on p. 31.

Example 17. The gaseous fluoride of an element contains 26·92 per cent of the element. 50 c.c. of the gas diffuses under certain conditions in 25 seconds. Under the same conditions 100 c.c. of oxygen diffuses in 27·7 seconds. What is the probable atomic weight of the element?

The molecular weight of the gas is obtained from the equation:

$$\frac{R_g}{R_{O_2}} = \frac{\sqrt{\text{molecular weight of oxygen}}}{\sqrt{\text{molecular weight of the gas}}},$$

where R_g = rate of diffusion of the gaseous fluoride
and R_{O_2} = rate of diffusion of oxygen under the same conditions.

But $$R_g = \frac{50}{25} \quad \text{and} \quad R_{O_2} = \frac{100}{27{\cdot}7}$$

Also, the molecular weight of oxygen = 32.

∴ If M = the molecular weight of the gaseous fluoride, then :

$$\frac{\frac{50}{25}}{\frac{100}{27{\cdot}7}} = \frac{\sqrt{32}}{\sqrt{M}}.$$

$$\therefore \; M = 104.$$

Therefore, the approximate atomic weight of the element $= 106 \times 0{\cdot}2692 \doteq 28$ (assuming that the fluoride contains only one atom of the element per molecule).

But the accurate equivalent $= \frac{26{\cdot}92}{73{\cdot}08} \times 19{\cdot}00 = 7{\cdot}000$.

∴ Accurate atomic weight of the element $= 7{\cdot}000 \times 4 = \mathbf{28{\cdot}00}$.

9. Use of the ratio C_p/C_v

When the density of a gas (assumed to be an element) and consequently the molecular weight of the gas have been *accurately* determined, the atomic weight of the element can be obtained from the relationship :

$$\text{Atomic weight} = \frac{\text{molecular weight}}{\text{atomicity}}.$$

(Note that the atomicity of a gas is the number of atoms contained in one molecule of that gas.)

The atomicity can be deduced from the ratio of the specific heat of a gas at constant pressure (C_p) to the specific heat at constant volume (C_v). The ratio C_p/C_v has the following approximate values (see also p. 151) :

1·67 for monatomic gases, for example, the inert gases ;

1·41 for diatomic gases (elements or compounds), for example, H_2, O_2, HCl.

1·28 for triatomic gases (elements or compounds), for example, O_3, H_2O, CO_2.

Although atomic weights are usually derived from the accurate determination of equivalents (see p. 13), accurate values for atomic weights can be obtained from gas densities by the method given on p. 17.

Example 18. The specific heat of chlorine at constant volume is 0·082 and at constant pressure, 0·115. One litre of the gas at *N.T.P.* weighs 3·151 gm. Calculate the approximate atomic weight of chlorine.

22·4 litres of chlorine at *N.T.P.* weigh

$$3{\cdot}151 \times 22{\cdot}4 \text{ gm.} = 70{\cdot}58 \text{ gm.}$$

$$\therefore \text{ Molecular weight} = 70{\cdot}58.$$

$$\text{But ratio } C_p/C_v = \frac{0{\cdot}115}{0{\cdot}082} = 1{\cdot}40.$$

$$\therefore \text{ Chlorine is diatomic and its atomic weight} = \frac{70{\cdot}58}{2} = 35{\cdot}29.$$

Example 19. A gaseous oxide of an element contains 42·85 per cent of the element. 0·2 gm. of the gas occupies 160 c.c. at *N.T.P.* The ratio of the specific heat of the gas at constant pressure to that at constant volume is 1·43. What is the atomic weight of the element?

$$\text{Chemical equivalent of the element} = \frac{42{\cdot}85}{57{\cdot}15} \times 8{\cdot}000 = 6{\cdot}000.$$

But the molecular weight of the gaseous oxide is

$$\frac{0{\cdot}2}{160} \times 22{,}400 = 28.$$

Since, however, $C_p/C_v = 1{\cdot}43$, the gaseous oxide must contain only two atoms per molecule. Therefore, if X denote one atom of the element, the formula for the oxide is XO and the element is divalent.

$$\therefore \text{ Atomic weight of the element} = 6{\cdot}000 \times 2 = \mathbf{12{\cdot}000}.$$

Alternatively, the approximate atomic weight may be obtained as follows:

Weight of the element in one gm.-molecule of the oxide

$$= 28 \times 0{\cdot}4285 = 12{\cdot}00.$$

But since there is only one atom of X in one molecule of the compound, this value is also the approximate atomic weight.

The accurate atomic weight can then be obtained from the accurate equivalent.

Example 20. A gaseous hydride of an element X, gave $C_p/C_v=1{\cdot}30$. When 3·082 gm. of the hydride was completely oxidised, 1·632 gm. of water was formed. What is the probable atomic weight of the element?

Fraction by weight of hydrogen in water $=\dfrac{2{\cdot}016}{18{\cdot}016}$.

∴ Weight of hydrogen in 3·082 gm. of the hydride of the element $=\dfrac{2{\cdot}016}{18{\cdot}016}\times 1{\cdot}632=0{\cdot}1872$ gm.

∴ Chemical equivalent of the element

$$=\frac{3{\cdot}082-0{\cdot}1827}{0{\cdot}1827}\times 1{\cdot}008=15{\cdot}99.$$

But since the gaseous hydride gave $C_p/C_v=1{\cdot}30$, it is almost certainly triatomic and its probable formula is H_2X. The element, therefore, is divalent.

∴ Probable atomic weight $=15{\cdot}99\times 2=$ **31·98.**

10. Direct use of Avogadro's hypothesis in determining molecular formulae

Molecular formulae can often be deduced from the observed volumes of reacting gases by applying the converse of Avogadro's hypothesis, namely, that equal numbers of molecules of all gases must occupy equal volumes (allowing for deviations from the gas laws), the conditions of temperature and pressure being assumed to be constant. It follows that the number of molecules in a gas is proportional to its volume.

Example 21. On heating 60 c.c. of a mixture of equal volumes of chlorine and an oxide of chlorine and cooling to atmospheric temperature, the resulting gas measured 75 c.c. Treatment of this gas with caustic soda solution resulted in a contraction to 15 c.c. Assuming that all measurements were made at the same temperature and pressure, deduce the formula of the oxide. (H.S.C., London.)

Let the formula of the oxide of chlorine be denoted by Cl_xO_y. Then since the mixture is composed of equal volumes of chlorine and the oxide of chlorine, that is, there are 30 c.c. of each, the action of heat on the mixture is represented by the equations :

$$\underset{30\text{ c.c.}}{Cl_2} = \underset{30\text{ c.c.}}{Cl_2} \text{ (unchanged by heat) ......(1)}$$

$$\underset{30\text{ c.c.}}{Cl_xO_y} = \underset{(x/2\times 30)\text{ c.c.}}{x/2Cl_2} + \underset{(y/2\times 30)\text{ c.c.}}{y/2O_2} \text{ ....(2)}$$

Equation (2) follows from the fact that if 1 molecule of a gas gives $x/2$ molecules of another gas, then 1 volume must give $x/2$ volumes, the unit of volume here being 30 c.c. Since the chlorine gas is completely absorbed by caustic soda, the residual gas (15 c.c.) must be oxygen.

$$\therefore\ y/2\times 30=15.$$

$$\therefore\ y=1.$$

But, after heating, 30 c.c. of the oxide of chlorine increased to 45 c.c. (since the 30 c.c. of chlorine originally present is unchanged by the action of heat).

$$\therefore\ (x/2\times 30)+(y/2\times 30)=45.$$

$$\therefore\ x/2\times 30=45-(y/2\times 30)=30 \text{ (since } y=1).$$

$$\therefore\ x=2.$$

$\therefore$ Formula for the oxide = $\mathbf{Cl_2O}$.

Example 22. 10 c.c. of a mixture of hydrogen, carbon monoxide and carbon dioxide was mixed with 15 c.c. of oxygen and exploded. The resulting mixture of gases was cooled to the original room temperature and pressure and measured 19 c.c. On shaking with potash a further contraction to 12 c.c. took place. Deduce the percentage composition of the mixture.

Let x c.c. = volume of hydrogen,

y c.c. = volume of carbon monoxide,

and z c.c. = volume of carbon dioxide.

Then, on explosion, the following reactions occur :

$$\underset{x\text{ c.c.}}{2H_2} + \underset{\frac{1}{2}x\text{ c.c.}}{O_2} = \underset{\text{(condensed to occupy a negligible volume)}}{2H_2O}$$

$$\underset{y\text{ c.c.}}{2CO} + \underset{\frac{1}{2}y\text{ c.c.}}{O_2} = \underset{y\text{ c.c.}}{2CO_2}$$

$$\underset{z\text{ c.c.}}{CO_2} = \underset{z\text{ c.c.}}{CO_2}$$

Since the contraction on shaking with potash is due solely to the absorption of carbon dioxide, then :

$$y+z=19-12=7.$$

But $x+y+z=10$ (from the original volume of the mixture).

$$\therefore\ x=3.$$

The equations can now be rewritten :

$$\underset{3\ \text{c.c.}}{2H_2} + \underset{1\frac{1}{2}\ \text{c.c.}}{O_2} = \underset{\text{(condensed)}}{2H_2O}$$

$$\underset{y\ \text{c.c.}}{2CO} + \underset{\frac{1}{2}y\ \text{c.c.}}{O_2} = \underset{y\ \text{c.c.}}{2CO_2}$$

$$\underset{z\ \text{c.c.}}{CO_2} = \underset{z\ \text{c.c.}}{CO_2}$$

$\therefore$ Volume of oxygen required for complete combustion $=(1\frac{1}{2}+y/2)$ c.c., and since 15 c.c. of oxygen were originally present and 12 c.c. of oxygen remain,

$$\therefore\ 1\tfrac{1}{2}+y/2=3.\quad \therefore\ y=3.\quad \therefore\ z=4.$$

$\therefore$ Percentage composition of the mixture is :

$$H_2,\ 30;\ \ CO,\ 30;\ \ CO_2,\ 40.$$

Alternatively, having found x, we can obtain y and z from the observed contraction on explosion. Since the volume of carbon dioxide originally present in the mixture remains unaltered by the combustion, the only change of volume results from the equations :

$$\underset{3\ \text{c.c.}}{2H_2} + \underset{1\frac{1}{2}\ \text{c.c.}}{O_2} = \underset{0}{2H_2O}\ \text{(condenses so that its volume may be ignored)}$$

$$\underset{y\ \text{c.c.}}{2CO} + \underset{\frac{1}{2}y\ \text{c.c.}}{O_2} = \underset{y\ \text{c.c.}}{2CO_2}$$

$$\therefore\ (3+1\tfrac{1}{2}+y+\tfrac{1}{2}y)\ \text{c.c.}-y\ \text{c.c.}=\text{contraction on explosion}$$
$$=(25-19)\ \text{c.c.}=6\ \text{c.c.}$$

From which : $y=3$.

* 11. Kinetic theory of gases

If p = the pressure of a gas,
n = the number of molecules of the gas per c.c.,
m = the mass of one molecule,
and $\bar{u}$ = *root mean square* velocity of the molecules,

then, according to the kinetic theory of gases:

$$p=\tfrac{1}{3}nm\bar{u}^2;$$

$$\therefore\ \bar{u}=\sqrt{\frac{3p}{nm}}\ .\ \dots\dots\dots\dots\dots\dots\dots\dots(13)$$

But nm = the mass of 1 c.c. of the gas at temperature, T, and pressure, p = absolute density (d).

$$\therefore\ \bar{u}=\sqrt{\frac{3p}{d}}\ .$$

$$\therefore\ \bar{u}\propto\sqrt{\frac{1}{d}}\ \text{ or }\ \frac{1}{\sqrt{d}}\ .$$

Assuming then that the rate of diffusion of a gas is proportional to $\bar{u}$, then rate of diffusion is inversely proportional to the density of the gas (Graham's law).

* **Example 23.** Calculate (*a*) the root mean square velocity of the hydrogen molecule at *N.T.P.*, (*b*) the root mean square velocity of the molecule of methane at 100°.

From equation (13):

$$\bar{u}=\sqrt{\frac{3p}{nm}}\ .$$

But nm = mass of 1 c.c. of gas = absolute density of the gas (d).

For hydrogen at *N.T.P.*, $d \doteq 0{\cdot}00009$ gm. per c.c.

Since d is expressed in gm. per c.c. and u in cm. per sec., then the pressure, p, must be expressed in *C.G.S.* units, that is, in dynes per sq. cm., so that at a pressure of 76 cm. of mercury:

$$p=76\times\underset{\text{(density of mercury)}}{13{\cdot}6}\times\underset{\text{(acceleration due to gravity)}}{981}$$

$$\therefore\ \bar{u}=\sqrt{\frac{3\times76\times13{\cdot}6\times981}{0{\cdot}00009}}\ \text{cm. per sec.}$$

$$\doteq 180{,}000\ \text{cm. per sec.}$$

The molecular weight of methane (CH_4) is 16 and its vapour density is 8. At 100°, therefore, the absolute density of methane (assuming pressure to be normal) is equal approximately to $0{\cdot}00009 \times 8 \times \frac{273}{373}$ gm. per c.c.

$$\therefore\ \bar{u}=\sqrt{\frac{3\times 76\times 13{\cdot}6\times 981\times 373}{0{\cdot}00009\times 8\times 273}}$$

$$\doteqdot \mathbf{68{,}000\ cm.\ per\ sec.}$$

Although the pressure of the gas has been used in the foregoing calculations, the root mean square velocity of a molecule of any gas is independent of the pressure. If M is the molecular weight of the gas and p is its pressure, then $pV=RT$ where V = volume occupied by M gm. of the gas at pressure, p, and at absolute temperature, T.

But if d is the density of the gas at this temperature and pressure :

$$d=\frac{M}{V}=\frac{M\times p}{RT},$$

$$\therefore\ \bar{u}=\sqrt{\frac{3p}{d}}=\sqrt{\frac{3p\times RT}{M\times p}}=\sqrt{\frac{3RT}{M}},$$

and is, therefore, independent of p.

In using the equation $\bar{u}=\sqrt{\frac{3RT}{M}}$, the gas constant, R, must be expressed in ergs per degree. For an ideal gas, the molecular weight in gm. occupies 22,400 c.c. at 76 cm. and 0°.

$$\therefore\ R=\frac{pV}{T}=\frac{76\times 981\times 13{\cdot}6\times 22{,}400}{273}$$

$$=8{\cdot}32\times 10^7 \text{ ergs per degree.} \qquad (14)$$

* 12. Internal energy of a gas

According to the kinetic theory of gases, the kinetic energy of a gas can be identified with its internal energy. If this internal energy is denoted by U per gm.-molecule of gas, then :

$$U=\tfrac{1}{2}M\bar{u}^2, \qquad (15)$$

where M = the molecular weight of the gas expressed in gm.

But $p=\frac{1}{3}nm\bar{u}^2=\frac{1}{3}d\bar{u}^2$ where d = density of the gas in gm. per c.c.

∴ If V c.c. is the volume occupied by 1 gm.-molecule of the gas at pressure, p, and absolute temperature, T:

$$pV=\tfrac{1}{3}Vd\bar{u}^2=\tfrac{1}{3}M\bar{u}^2\,; \qquad \text{(16)}$$

$$\therefore\; U=\tfrac{1}{2}M\bar{u}^2=pV\times\tfrac{3}{2}=\tfrac{3}{2}\mathrm{RT}. \qquad \text{(17)}$$

QUESTIONS ON CHAPTER II

[In questions 1, 2 and 3 use H = 1 and 1 litre of hydrogen at *N.T.P.* weighs 0·09 gm. The nature of the other questions will determine whether or not the gm.-molecular-volume must be taken as 22·4 litres at *N.T.P.*]

1. Calculate the vapour densities of the substances, A, B and C, to which the following figures obtained by Dumas' method refer :

	A	*B*	*C*
Weight of bulb - - -	40·73 gm.	35·09 gm.	47·26 gm.
Temperature of sealing -	100°	140°	100°
Weight of bulb + vapour -	40·86 gm.	35·32 gm.	48·04 gm.
Temperature of the laboratory	15°	15°	18°
Barometric height - - -	750 mm.	763 mm.	756 mm.
Weight of bulb full of water	213 gm.	189 gm.	238 gm.

[1 c.c. of air at *N.T.P.* weighs 0·001293 gm.]

2. Calculate the molecular weights of the substances, D, E and F, to which the following figures obtained by Victor Meyer's method refer :

	D	*E*	*F*
Weight of substance - -	0·207 gm.	0·158 gm.	0·193 gm.
Volume of air displaced -	46·0 c.c.	52·3 c.c.	33·7 c.c.
Laboratory temperature -	17°	15°	18°
Barometric height - -	755 mm.	762 mm.	751 mm.
Pressure of aqueous vapour at laboratory temperature -	14·4 mm.	12·7 mm.	15·4 mm.

3. 0·107 gm. of a liquid was vaporised as in Hofmann's method at 78° over mercury. The volume of the vapour was 52·3 c.c., while the height of the column of mercury in the eudiometer was 393 mm. Ignoring the change of density of the mercury, calculate the vapour density of the liquid, given that the barometric height was 756 mm.

4. An element, X, forms two gaseous oxides containing 36·3 per cent and 53·3 per cent of oxygen respectively. At 0° and 760 mm., one gm. of each of these oxides occupies 505 c.c. and 735 c.c. respectively. Calculate the equivalent weights of X and its probable atomic weight. (1st M.B., London.)

5. A compound has the percentage composition : C = 54·5; H = 9·2 ; O = 36·3 ; and 0·208 gm. of the compound displaced, by

Victor Meyer's method, 56·3 c.c. of air measured over water at 15° and 754 mm. atmospheric pressure. What is the molecular formula of the compound? [Vapour tension of water at 15° = 12·7 mm.]

6. Four compounds of an element contain 27·3 per cent, 80·0 per cent, 81·8 per cent and 42·8 per cent of the element respectively. 1 litre of each of these compounds in the form of a vapour at *N.T.P.* weigh respectively 1·964 gm., 1·340 gm., 1·964 gm. and 1·250 gm. Deduce the probable atomic weight of the element.

7. A compound has the percentage composition: C = 14·3; H = 1·2; Cl = 84·5. 1 gm. of the compound was vaporised at 120° and 752 mm. pressure and then occupied 194 c.c. What is the molecular formula of the compound?

8. Four compounds of an element contain respectively 10·04 per cent, 7·79 per cent, 24·24 per cent and 21·17 per cent of the element. The corresponding weights of 1 litre of the vapour of each of these compounds, measured at 100° and 760 mm., were 3·904 gm., 5·032 gm., 3·235 gm. and 5·555 gm. What is the probable atomic weight of the element?

9. 0·256 gm. of the sulphate of a certain element yielded 0·525 gm. of barium sulphate, when it was treated in aqueous solution with barium chloride. The vapour density of the chloride of the element was about 67. Suggest possible values for the atomic weight of the element. (O. and C.)

10. Under comparable conditions of temperature and pressure 100 c.c. of hydrogen and 100 c.c. of a gas, *X*, diffuse respectively in 10 sec. and 55·3 sec. What is the approximate molecular weight of the gas, *X*?

11. The oxide of an element contains 27·27 per cent of the element. Four compounds of the element have vapour densities 15, 8, 78 and 22 respectively. The corresponding percentages of the element in these compounds are 80, 75, 77·9 and 81·8. What is the most probable value for the accurate atomic weight of the element?

12. 2·000 gm. of the chloride of an element was completely hydrolysed to hydrochloric acid and a compound containing no chlorine. The hydrochloric acid was precipitated by the addition of an excess of silver nitrate and the resulting silver chloride was found to weigh 6·258 gm. The chloride of the element was volatile and its vapour density was about 69. Calculate the probable atomic weight of the element.

13. 10 gm. of nitric oxide are passed slowly over a weighed quantity of heated copper filings. Assuming that the whole of the gas is decomposed, calculate (*a*) the increase in the weight of the copper, (*b*) the volume of the gas produced if measured at 14° and 754 mm. (H.S.C., London.)

14. 14·8 c.c. of a mixture of carbon dioxide and carbon monoxide was mixed with 20 c.c. of oxygen and sparked until there was no further change in volume. After cooling to the original room temperature and pressure, the volume of the residual gas was 29·5 c.c. Calculate the percentage by volume of the original mixture.

15. A gaseous oxide of carbon contains 72·72 per cent of oxygen. 1 litre of the gas at 27° and 720 mm. weighs 1·694. The specific heat of the gas at constant pressure is 0·202 and at constant volume, 0·160. Deduce the atomic weight of carbon.

16. The equivalent weight of a volatile metal is 100·3. The specific heat of the metal is 0·033. 0·25 gm. of the metal occupies 79·5 c.c. at 500° and 760 mm. Calculate the atomic weight of the metal and the molecular weight of the vapour. What value would you expect to find for the ratio of the specific heat of the metallic vapour at constant pressure to that at constant volume? (C.H.L.)

17. The chloride of an element contains 92·21 per cent of chlorine. Three gaseous compounds of the element are found to contain 75 per cent, 80 per cent and 42·9 per cent of the element. When 100 c.c. each of these three gaseous compounds are allowed to diffuse under comparable conditions the times taken were respectively 14·2 seconds, 19·4 seconds and 18·7 seconds. Under the same conditions 100 c.c. of oxygen diffused in 20 seconds. What are (*a*) the approximate molecular weights of the gaseous compounds, (*b*) the probable accurate atomic weight of the element?

18. If a solid element burns in oxygen without permanent change in gaseous volume, and if the pure gaseous product has a density of 32, what is the equivalent of the element? (1st M.B., London.)

19. Calculate the volume and the composition of the gaseous products of the following reactions: (*a*) 100 c.c. of hydrogen, measured at 18° and 760 mm., is mixed with 50 c.c. of oxygen, measured at 0° and 740 mm., the mixture being then exploded and the gaseous product measured at 120° and 380 mm.; (*b*) 50 c.c. of carbon monoxide, measured at 17° and 738 mm., is mixed with 20 c.c. of oxygen, measured at 15° and 758 mm., and exploded, the residual gas being measured at 0° and 760 mm.

20. 0·2561 gm. of the gaseous hydride of an element was completely decomposed into its elements and the hydrogen formed, when absorbed in metallic palladium, was found to weigh 0·0161 gm. The ratio of the specific heats of the gaseous hydride at constant pressure and constant volume was 1·30. Deduce the probable atomic weight of the element. [H = 1·008.]

21. The specific heat of a metallic element, *M*, was found to be 0·0304 and when 0·898 gm. of its anhydrous bromide was heated in hydrogen, 0·418 gm. of the metal was left. The specific heats of a gaseous element, *G*, were found to be 0·0385 at constant pressure and 0·0231 at constant volume, and 150 c.c. of the gas at 750 mm.

pressure and 16° weighed 0·812 gm. Explain briefly but clearly what conclusions you can draw about the elements *M* and *G* and why. (C.U.O.S.)

22. A mixture of 4·5 c.c. of a gas, *X*, and 95·5 c.c. of oxygen diffused in 101·3 seconds. Under the same conditions 100 c.c. of oxygen diffused in 100 seconds. What is the molecular weight of *X*?

23. The anhydrous sulphate of a metal contains 8·588 per cent of the metal. The vapour density of the chloride of the metal is 40. What is the probable atomic weight of the metal?

24. 2 litres of the hydride of an element, measured at 12° and 748 mm., were passed slowly over heated black copper oxide and the water formed weighed 1·516 gm. The vapour density of the gas was 17·1. The ratio of the specific heats of the gas at constant pressure and constant volume was 1·28. Deduce the approximate equivalent and atomic weight of the element. [Density of hydrogen = 0·087 gm. per litre.]

25. A glass bulb when filled with ozonised oxygen was found to weigh 0·0108 gm. more than when filled with pure oxygen. The sphere was then opened under turpentine of density 0·8692 gm. per c.c. On reweighing it was found that 13·67 gm. of turpentine had entered the sphere. The experiments were conducted at 17° and 770 mm. pressure. Calculate the vapour density of ozone. [1 litre of hydrogen at *N.T.P.* weighs 0·087 gm.] (C.U.O.S.)

26. What is the percentage composition by volume of a mixture of nitrogen, hydrogen and carbon monoxide which gave the following results? 13·2 c.c. of the mixture was placed in a eudiometer with 10 c.c. of oxygen and ignited. The volume after explosion was 15·4 c.c. Treatment with caustic potash removed 3 c.c. of the residual gas. [All measurements were made at the same room temperature and pressure.]

27. A mixture of 20 c.c. of an oxide of nitrogen and 10 c.c. of nitrogen was heated, the mixture being thereby completely converted into nitrogen and oxygen. The volume of the gas, after cooling to the original room temperature and pressure, was 40 c.c. Treatment with alkaline pyrogallol reduced the volume to 30 c.c. What is the molecular formula of the oxide of nitrogen?

28. 10 c.c. of a mixture of carbon monoxide and hydrogen was exploded with an excess of oxygen and the contraction was found to be 11 c.c., all volumes being measured at constant room temperature and pressure. What is the percentage volume of carbon monoxide in the mixture?

29. On reduction 0·1250 gm. of the oxide of a metal, *M*, yielded 0·0930 gm. of the metal. By Victor Meyer's method the vapour density of the volatile compound $M(CH_3)_n$ gave a value 58 (hydrogen = 1). What is (*a*) the atomic weight of *M*, (*b*) the formula of its oxide? (N.U.J.B.)

30. 20 c.c. of a mixture of ammonia and hydrogen was completely decomposed by sparking into nitrogen and hydrogen. 20 c.c. of oxygen were then added and the mixture was sparked again. After cooling to room temperature, the mixture of gases was shaken with alkaline pyrogallol and a contraction of 7 c.c. was observed. Deduce the percentage by volume of ammonia in the original mixture.

31. 0·5360 gm. of the carbide of an element reacted with an excess of water to give 267 c.c. of methane (CH_4) measured at 17° and 754 mm. pressure. The bromide of the element had a vapour density of approximately 133. What conclusions can be drawn about the atomic weight of the element?

32. An element forms a hydrated chloride containing 46·69 per cent of chlorine and 47·34 per cent of water of crystallisation. The specific heat of the element is 0·38 at 0° and 0·62 at 500°. 0·200 gm. of the anhydrous chloride occupied in the form of a vapour 110 c.c. at 250° and 740 mm. Deduce (*a*) the atomic weight of the element, (*b*) the formula for the hydrated chloride.

33. What deductions concerning the molecular formula of a gas can be drawn from the following data? Mixed with an excess of oxygen and sparked it was converted completely into carbon dioxide, the volumes before and after the explosion being the same. 1 litre of the gas at *N.T.P.* weighs 3·11 gm.

34. Deduce the percentage composition by volume of a mixture of hydrogen, carbon monoxide and nitrogen which gave the following results. 14·5 c.c. of the mixture of gases was exploded with an excess of oxygen, the products being brought to the original room temperature and pressure; the observed contraction was 11·75 c.c. Treatment of the residual gases with potash gave a further contraction of 5·5 c.c.

35. 100 c.c. of a mixture of nitrous oxide and nitric oxide were slowly passed over red hot copper. The resulting gas occupied 85 c.c. Another 100 c.c. of the same mixture were maintained at 100°, 20 c.c. of oxygen (measured at 100°) were added and the total volume of the gases contracted to 99·85 c.c., measured at 100°. Deduce the composition of the remaining mixture. (C.U.O.S.)

HINT: Note that the addition of oxygen to nitric oxide produces nitrogen peroxide which will contain a mixture of NO_2 and N_2O_4 molecules.

36. What conclusions concerning the molecular formula of a gas can be drawn from the following data? 20 c.c. of the gas was exploded with 60 c.c. of oxygen and a contraction of 15 c.c. was observed. Treatment of potash reduced the volume to 45 c.c., and of this residual gas 35 c.c. was absorbed by alkaline pyrogallol. [All volumes were measured at the constant room temperature and pressure.]

37. The hydrated sulphate of an element, X, contains 48·64 per cent of water of crystallisation. When 0·6318 gm. of the hydrated sulphate was treated in solution with an excess of ammonium hydroxide 0·0967 gm. of the corresponding metallic oxide was obtained. The specific heat of the metal is 0·22. What deductions can be made as to the atomic weight of the metal and the formula of the hydrated sulphate?

38. 45 c.c. of a mixture of carbon monoxide, carbon dioxide and oxygen was sparked until there was no further change of volume and the carbon monoxide was completely converted into carbon dioxide. The volume of the gaseous mixture was then 40 c.c. Treatment with aqueous potash reduced the volume to 15 c.c. What was the percentage composition of the original mixture?

39. 50 c.c. of a mixture of nitrogen, ammonia and oxygen was sparked until there was no further decrease in volume, the ammonia being converted entirely into water and nitrogen. The volume of the product at the original room temperature and pressure was 25 c.c. Treatment with alkaline pyrogallol removed 5 c.c. of the residual gaseous mixture. What was the volume composition of the original mixture?

40. 3·000 gm. of the hydrated sulphate of a metal, X, was heated to a constant weight at 120° and the resulting decrease in weight, due solely to the loss of water of crystallisation, was 1·677 gm. The anhydrous sulphate was dissolved in water and on treatment with an excess of barium chloride solution gave 2·172 gm. of barium sulphate. The metal forms an oxide, A, containing 40·9 per cent of oxygen which when treated with an excess of water evolves oxygen and leaves the hydroxide of X corresponding with the hydrated sulphate, the amount of oxygen obtained in this way from 1 gm. of the oxide being 155 c.c. at 15° and 740 mm. Suggest formulae for the hydrated salt and the oxide, A. What is the probable atomic weight of the element?

* **41.** Calculate the root mean square velocity of (*a*) the molecule of carbon dioxide at 0°, (*b*) the molecule of propane (C_3H_8) at 100°.

* **42.** The root mean square velocity of the molecule of hydrogen iodide at a certain temperature and pressure is $2{\cdot}6 \times 10^4$ cm. per sec. What is the velocity of the molecule of ozone at the same temperature and pressure?

[In the following questions 5-figure or 7-figure logarithms are required.]

* **43.** A quantity of nitrous oxide occupies 108·72 c.c. at 1 atmosphere pressure and at 0°. At the same temperature but a pressure of $\frac{1}{2}$ an atmosphere its volume is 218·26 c.c. What is the compressibility coefficient of nitrous oxide?

* **44.** The following figures give the volume occupied by a fixed mass of hydrogen chloride at varying pressures and at 0° C.:

pressure (atmospheres)	1	0·8	0·6	0·4	0·2
volume (c.c.) - -	182·52	228·47	305·12	458·35	918·05

Determine the compressibility coefficient of hydrogen chloride by a graphical method.

* **45.** The volume of a quantity of oxygen at 0° was measured at 607·97 mm. and 204·30 mm. pressure; the corresponding pv products (in arbitrary units) were found to be 56, 267 and 56, 296 respectively. Assuming that $d(pv)/dp$ is constant between the pressure limits 0 and 1 atmosphere and that the normal density of oxygen is 1·4290, calculate the limiting density. (Manchester Hons. Chem.)

* **46.** The density of carbon dioxide at various pressures is given below:

p (mm. Hg) - -	580·73	375·41	115·80
d (gm. per litre) -	1·5060	0·9732	0·2999

Find graphically the compressibility coefficient of carbon dioxide and hence calculate the atomic weight of carbon, given that the normal density of oxygen is 1·4290 gm. per litre and that the compressibility coefficient of oxygen is 0·00094.

* **47.** The density of methyl fluoride is 1·5454 and 1·0241 gm. per litre at pressures of 1 atmosphere and $\frac{2}{3}$ atmosphere respectively (both observations at 0°). Calculate the molecular weight of methyl fluoride, using the data for oxygen given in Q. 46.

48. When the bulb of a microbalance was surrounded by oxygen it was found that the balance was at its zero position at a pressure of oxygen = 35·36 mm. What is the molecular weight of a gas, X, which used similarly was at a pressure = 27·09 mm.?

CHAPTER III

VAPOUR PRESSURES

1. Vapour pressure of immiscible liquids

The vapour pressure of two (or more) liquids which are mutually insoluble is the sum of the separate vapour pressures of the constituents, that is,

$$p = p_1 + p_2 + p_3 + \dots , \qquad \qquad (18)$$

where p = total vapour pressure of the mixture at a given temperature and p_1, p_2, p_3, etc., are the respective vapour pressures of the constituents at the same temperature.

Example 24. The vapour pressures of chloroform and benzene at various temperatures are as follows :

	20°	30°	40°	50°	60°
Chloroform -	160 mm.	248 mm.	369 mm.	535 mm.	755 mm.
Benzene -	75 mm.	119 mm.	181 mm.	275 mm.	389 mm.

At what temperature would a mixture of these two liquids begin to boil at an atmospheric pressure of 760 mm., assuming that they are completely insoluble in each other?

The total pressure of the mixture at any temperature is obtained by adding the two pressures and is then plotted against the temperature (see Fig. 2). The temperature at which the combined pressures = 760 mm. can then be read from the curve. [Boiling point = 49°.]

2. Principle of distillation in steam

When a liquid, immiscible with water, is distilled in steam, the principle given above can be employed to follow the course of the distillation. Assume that, at the temperature of distillation, the vapour pressure of water is denoted by P_w and that of the other liquid by P_x. Then, if the mixture is boiling against an atmospheric pressure = 760 mm. :

$$P_w + P_x = 760.$$

Also weight of water (W_w) which distils in a given time = number of molecules of water × weight of one molecule of water.

But : number of molecules distilling in a given time is proportional to the vapour pressure, P_w. Also, weight of one molecule of water is proportional to its molecular weight (M_w).

$$\therefore \quad W_w = k \times P_w \times M_w.$$

Similarly, $$W_x = k \times P_x \times M_x,$$

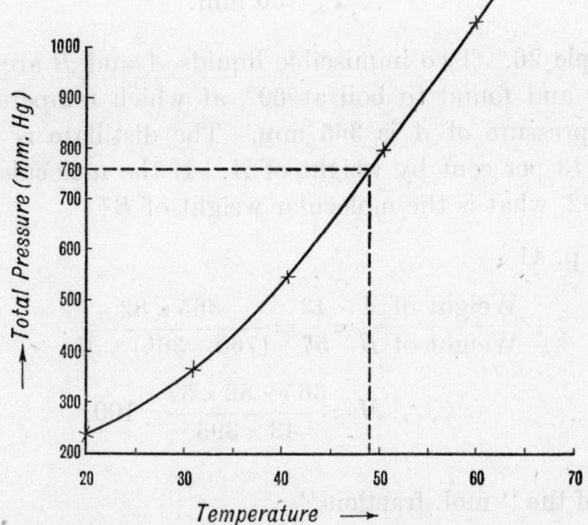

FIG. 2. Graphical method of determining the boiling point of a mixture of mutually insoluble liquids.

where W_x = weight of the liquid, X, which distils in the same time as W_w gm. of water, and M_x = the molecular weight of X.

$$\therefore \frac{W_w}{W_x} = \frac{P_w \times M_w}{P_x \times M_x} = \frac{P_w \times M_w}{(760 - P_w) \times M_x} \text{..........(19)}$$

Since P_x is often very small in comparison with P_w, the equation can usually be used in the approximate form :

$$\frac{W_w}{W_x} \doteq \frac{760 \times M_w}{P_x \times M_x} = \frac{760 \times 18}{P_x \times M_x}, \text{ ....(20)}$$

since M_w = the molecular weight of water in the form of a vapour.

Example 25. When aniline (molecular weight, 93) is steam-distilled the distillate is found to contain 26·5 per cent by weight of aniline. What is the approximate vapour pressure of aniline at the temperature of the distillation? (O. and C.)

Then, as in equation (20):

$$\frac{73{\cdot}5}{26{\cdot}5}=\frac{760\times 18}{P_A\times 93},$$

where P_A = the vapour pressure of aniline at the temperature of the distillation.

$$\therefore\ \mathbf{P_A=50\ mm.}$$

Example 26. Two immiscible liquids A and B are distilled together and found to boil at 60°, at which temperature the vapour pressure of A is 365 mm. The distillate is found to contain 43 per cent by weight of A. If the molecular weight of A is 82, what is the molecular weight of B?

As on p. 41:

$$\frac{\text{Weight of } A}{\text{Weight of } B}=\frac{43}{57}=\frac{365\times 82}{(760-365)\times M}.$$

$$\therefore\ M=\frac{365\times 82\times 57}{43\times 395}=\mathbf{100.}$$

3. Use of the "mol.-fraction"

For many purposes in calculations in physical chemistry it is convenient to express the concentration of each of the constituents of a system in molecular proportions (instead of weights).

If we suppose, for example, that a solution contains W_b gm. of a solute dissolved in W_a gm. of the solvent, then the total number of gm.-molecules of solvent and solute $=\left(\frac{W_a}{M_a}+\frac{W_b}{M_b}\right)$, where M_a and M_b are the molecular weights of the solvent and solute respectively. Then, by definition:
mol.-fraction of the solvent

$$=\frac{\text{no. of gm.-molecules of solvent}}{\text{total no. of gm.-molecules of solvent and solute}}$$

$$=\frac{\dfrac{W_a}{M_a}}{\dfrac{W_a}{M_a}+\dfrac{W_b}{M_b}}\ \ldots\ldots\ldots\ldots\ldots\ldots\ldots\ldots\ldots\ldots\ldots\ldots(21)$$

Similarly, mol.-fraction of the solute

$$=\frac{\frac{W_b}{M_b}}{\frac{W_a}{M_a}+\frac{W_b}{M_b}}. \quad \text{.........................(22)}$$

Clearly, if n_1, n_2, n_3, etc., represent the mol.-fractions of the constituents of any system, then :

$$n_1+n_2+n_3+\ldots=1. \quad \text{......................(23)}$$

For the simplest case of a *dilute* solution of a solute, b, in a solvent, a, equation (22) can be written :

$$\text{mol.-fraction of solute}=\frac{\frac{W_b}{M_b}}{\frac{W_a}{M_a}+\frac{W_b}{M_b}}\doteqdot\frac{\frac{W_b}{M_b}}{\frac{W_a}{M_a}}, \quad \text{........(24)}$$

since $\frac{W_a}{M_a}$ is large compared with $\frac{W_b}{M_b}$.

Example 27. What is the mol.-fraction of the solute in the solution obtained by dissolving 5 gm. of urea (molecular weight =60) in 100 gm. of water?

From equation (22) :

$$\text{mol.-fraction of urea}=\frac{\frac{5}{60}}{\frac{5}{60}+\frac{100}{18}}=0{\cdot}0148.$$

From equation (24) :

$$\text{approximate mol.-fraction of urea}=\frac{\frac{5}{60}}{\frac{100}{18}}=0{\cdot}0150.$$

It is clear that the approximation is sufficiently accurate in this example.

* 4. Partial molal quantities

In many calculations it is desirable to know how a particular property of a system varies with the addition of the separate constituents. Since this effect will depend upon the composition of the mixture, the change of property, for example, volume, must be expressed as a rate of change when the quantity of the added constituent is infinitesimally small. The method of calculation can be illustrated by considering partial molal volumes.

For a binary mixture of two substances, A and B, the partial molal volumes, $\bar{V}_A$ and $\bar{V}_B$, respectively are defined by the equations :

$$\bar{V}_A = \left(\frac{\partial V}{\partial n_A}\right)_B^{\dagger} \quad \text{and} \quad \bar{V}_B = \left(\frac{\partial V}{\partial n_B}\right)_A, \qquad \text{............(25)}$$

that is, $\bar{V}_A$ is the rate of increase of volume per gm.-molecule of A when a small quantity, dn_A moles, of A is added and the amount of B remains constant. $\bar{V}_B$ is defined similarly.

Then if ΔV = the small increase in volume when small amounts, dn_A and dn_B, of A and B respectively are added simultaneously :

$$\Delta V = \bar{V}_A \, dn_A + \bar{V}_B \, dn_B. \qquad \text{......................(26)}$$

$\bar{V}_A$ and $\bar{V}_B$ depend solely on the composition of the mixture (temperature constant). Therefore, if the constituents are added simultaneously in the same proportion as that in which they are already present, that is, n_A gm.-molecules of A and n_B gm.-molecules of B, then :

$$V = \bar{V}_A \, n_A + \bar{V}_B \, n_B. \qquad \text{........................(27)}$$

We may, in this way, add a total of 1 gm.-molecule. Then :

$$V = \bar{V}_A \, n'_A + \bar{V}_B \, n'_B, \qquad \text{.....................(28)}$$

where n'_A and n'_B are the mol.-fractions of A and B in the original mixture and V is the volume occupied by 1 gm.-molecule of that mixture.

* **Example 28.** A solution of ethyl alcohol in water has a density of 0·8494, the mol.-fraction of the water being 0·4. If the partial molal volume of the alcohol in the solution is 57·5 c.c., calculate that of water. (Manchester Hons. Chem.)

Let V = volume of the solution containing 0·4 gm.-molecule of water and 0·6 gm.-molecule of ethyl alcohol.

Then weight of solution = $[(0{\cdot}4 \times 18) + (0{\cdot}6 \times 46)]$ gm. (the molecular weights of water and ethyl alcohol being respectively 18 and 46).

$$\therefore \ V = \frac{[(0{\cdot}4 \times 18) + (0{\cdot}6 \times 46)]}{0{\cdot}8494} = 40{\cdot}97 \text{ c.c.}$$

Then, from equation (27) :

$$V = \bar{V}_a \, n_a + \bar{V}_w \, n_w,$$

† See p. 428.

where subscripts refer to alcohol and water respectively.

$$\therefore \ 40{\cdot}97 = (57{\cdot}5 \times 0{\cdot}6) + (\bar{V}_w \times 0{\cdot}4);$$

$$\therefore \ \bar{V}_w = 16{\cdot}18 \text{ c.c.}$$

*** 5. Vapour pressure of miscible liquids**

The vapour pressure of each of the constituents of a mixture of miscible liquids (see p. 40 for immiscible liquids) is proportional to its mol.-fraction (Raoult's law). In a mixture of two such liquids, A and B, then :

$$p_A \propto \frac{N_A}{N_A + N_B} \quad \text{and} \quad p_B \propto \frac{N_B}{N_A + N_B}, \quad \text{..........(29)}$$

where p_A = vapour pressure of A,

p_B = vapour pressure of B,

N_A = number of gm.-molecules of A in the mixture,

and N_B = number of gm.-molecules of B in the mixture.

$$\therefore \ p_A = k\frac{N_A}{N_A + N_B} \quad \text{and} \quad p_B = k\frac{N_B}{N_A + N_B}, \quad \text{......(30)}$$

the proportionality constant being the same for each substance at a given temperature. Then p'_A denotes the vapour pressure of pure A at a given temperature :

$$p'_A = k \cdot \frac{N_A}{N_A + N_B} = k \quad (\text{since } N_B = 0);$$

$$\therefore \ p_A = p'_A \cdot \frac{N_A}{N_A + N_B} = p'_A\, n_A, \quad \text{......................(31)}$$

where n = the mol.-fraction of A. Similarly :

$$p_B = p'_B \times n_B = p'_B(1 - n_A).$$

$\therefore$ Total pressure exerted by a mixture of the two liquids

$$= p_A + p_B = \mathrm{p'_A n_A + p'_B(1 - n_A)}. \quad \text{..............(32)}$$

Mixtures of liquids which obey equation (32) are said to behave *ideally*, and the observed vapour pressure-composition curve is a straight line (Fig. 3, p. 47). The total vapour pressure at any temperature can be calculated from the known vapour pressures of the pure constituents and the composition of the mixture.

* **Example 29.** What is the percentage by weight of ethyl acetate in a mixture of ethyl acetate and propyl acetate which at 60° exerts a vapour pressure of 250 mm.? (Vap. press. of ethyl acetate at 60° = 415 mm. Vap. press. of propyl acetate at 60° = 172 mm.)

Let x = the mol.-fraction of ethyl acetate in the mixture.

Then $$(x \times 415) + (1 - x)\,172 = 250$$

and $$x = 0{\cdot}321.$$

The molecular weights of ethyl acetate and propyl acetate are 88 and 102 respectively.

$$\therefore\ x = \text{mol.-fraction of acetyl acetate} = \frac{\dfrac{X}{88}}{\dfrac{X}{88} + \dfrac{1 - X}{102}},$$

where X = fraction of ethyl acetate by weight.

From which $X = 0{\cdot}289$.

Percentage weight of ethyl acetate = 28·9.

The equation given on p. 49 for the vapour pressures of solutions of non-volatile solutes can be derived from Raoult's law as follows:

As in equation (31):

$$p_A = p'_A \cdot \frac{N_A}{N_A + N_B},$$

$$\therefore\ \frac{p_A}{p'_A} = \frac{N_A}{N_A + N_B},$$

$$\therefore\ 1 - \frac{p_A}{p'_A} = 1 - \frac{N_A}{N_A + N_B},$$

$$\therefore\ \frac{p'_A - p_A}{p'_A} = \frac{N_B}{N_A + N_B}, \quad \ldots\ldots\ldots\ldots (33)$$

that is, the relative lowering of vapour pressure = mol.-fraction of the solute (since p_B and p'_B of equation (32) are negligible for a non-volatile solute).

In general, mixtures of volatile liquids do not rigidly obey Raoult's law, but give vapour pressure curves of the type shown in Fig. 3. The observed vapour pressure is then either greater (positive deviation) or less (negative deviation) than that calculated by Raoult's law. When the deviation is very pronounced, mixtures having a greater or less vapour pressure than either constituent may be obtained.

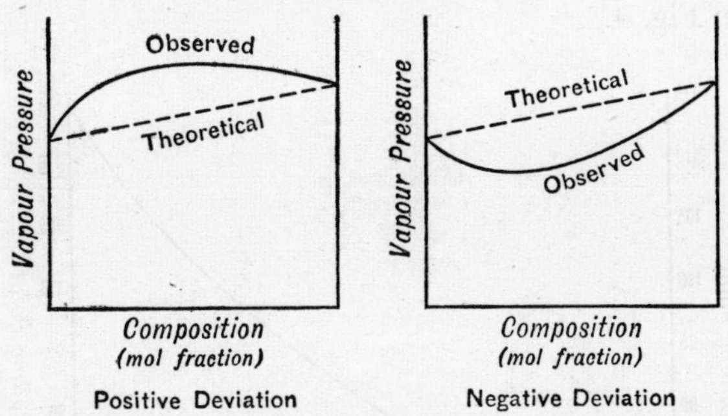

Fig. 3. Vapour pressure curves for mixtures of liquids which do not behave ideally.

* **Example 30.** State Raoult's law for the partial and total vapour pressures of a mixture of two ideal liquids. The vapour pressures of carbon tetrachloride and tin tetrachloride are shown below for various temperatures. Construct a boiling point-composition diagram for the two-component system, assuming ideal behaviour :

		$t°$	77°	80°	90°	100°	110°	114°
Carbon tetrachloride, *V.P.* (mm.)	- -	p_1	760	836	1112	1450	1880	
Stannic chloride, *V.P.* (mm.)	- -	p_2		258	362	499	673	760

Describe briefly the types of deviation from ideal behaviour, and indicate what conclusions about the interaction of the two components may be drawn from them.

(London B.Sc. Special)

Any mixture of the two liquids will boil when the vapour pressure = 760 mm. But assuming ideal behaviour, the vapour pressure of a mixture of the two liquids is given by equation (32).

Then if x = the mol.-fraction of stannic chloride in a mixture which boils at a given temperature :

$$p_{SnCl_4}(x) + p_{CCl_4}(1-x) = 760.$$

For example, at 80° :

$$258x + 836(1-x) = 760.$$

The following values are thus obtained :

Boiling point of mixture -	77°	80°	90°	100°	110°	114
Mol.-fraction of $SnCl_4$ -	0	0·132	0·470	0·726	0·928	1

The plot of boiling point against mol.-fraction of $SnCl_4$ is shown in Fig. 4.

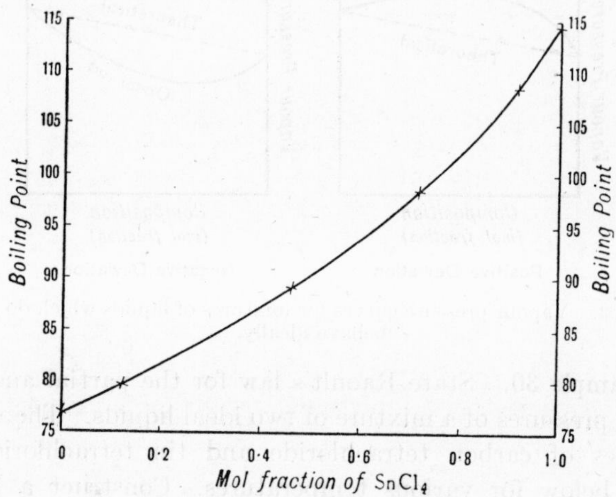

FIG. 4. Ideal boiling point-composition curve for mixtures of carbon tetrachloride and stannic chloride.

Deviation from ideal behaviour can be related to the differences in the forces of intra-molecular attraction, for information upon which the student should consult the appropriate books on Physical Chemistry.

6. Vapour pressures of solutions of non-volatile solutes

A non-volatile solute can be defined as one whose vapour pressure, over the given range of temperature, may be regarded as negligible in comparison with the vapour pressure of the solvent. The total vapour pressure of the solution is then the vapour pressure of the solvent in the presence of the solute. If, then, the mol.-fraction of the solvent is denoted by n_1, then, according to Raoult's law, the vapour pressure of the solvent (=total vapour pressure) is proportional to its mol.-fraction :

$$p_1 = kn_1,$$

where p_1 = the vapour pressure of the solvent.

But the vapour pressure of the pure solvent (at the same temperature) is given by the equation :

$$p_0 = k,$$

since for the pure solvent, n (the mol.-fraction) $=1$;

$$\therefore \; p_1 = p_0 n_1,$$

$$\therefore \; \frac{p_1}{p_0} = n_1 \quad \text{and} \quad \frac{p_0 - p_1}{p_0} = 1 - n = n_2, \; \ldots\ldots\ldots\ldots (34)$$

where $n_2 =$ the mol.-fraction of the solute.

Since $\frac{p_0 - p_1}{p_0}$ is, by definition, the relative lowering of vapour pressure, we have :

Relative lowering of vapour pressure
$=$ the mol.-fraction of the solute.

Example 31. What is the vapour pressure at 100° of the solution obtained by dissolving 3·08 gm. of cane sugar in 35·0 gm. of water?

Let $p_1 =$ the required vapour pressure, and
$p_0 =$ the vapour pressure of the pure solvent at 100°
$= 760$ mm.

Then, putting $x = p_0 - p_1$:

$$\frac{x}{760} = \text{mol.-fraction of the solute} \doteq \frac{\frac{3{\cdot}08}{342}}{\frac{35{\cdot}0}{18}},$$

the molecular weight of cane sugar being 342.

$$\therefore \; x = 3{\cdot}52 \text{ mm.}$$

$$\therefore \; p_1 = p_0 - x = 760 - 3{\cdot}52 \text{ mm.} = \mathbf{756{\cdot}48 \text{ mm.}}$$

Example 32. The vapour pressure of diethyl ether ($C_4H_{10}O$) is 440·0 mm. at 20°. A solution of 5 gm. of a non-volatile solute in 100 gm. of ether had a vapour pressure of 412·7 mm. What was the molecular weight of the solute?

Using equation :

$$\frac{p_0 - p_1}{p_0} = \text{mol.-fraction of solute} \doteq \frac{\frac{5}{X}}{\frac{100}{74}},$$

where X = the molecular weight of the solute and molecular weight of ether = 74.

$$\therefore \frac{440{\cdot}0 - 412{\cdot}7}{440{\cdot}0} = \frac{\frac{5}{X}}{\frac{100}{74}},$$

$$\therefore X = 59{\cdot}6.$$

7. Calculation of molecular weights of non-volatile substances in solution (method of elevation of boiling point)

Since a solution of a non-volatile solute has a lower vapour pressure than the pure solvent, it must have a higher boiling point. Inspection of Fig. 5, which gives the vapour pressure-temperature curves for the pure solvent and two solutions, shows that if the curves are assumed to be approximately parallel (as, in fact, they are) in the immediate region of the boiling point, then :

$$\frac{XK}{XM} = \frac{XL}{XN},$$

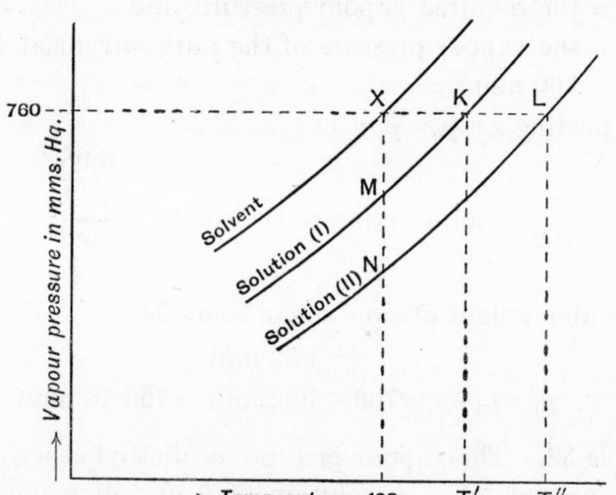

FIG. 5. Relation between boiling points and vapour pressures of solutions.

that is, the elevation of boiling point (ΔT) is directly proportional to the lowering of vapour pressure.

Using the notation of para. 6, p. 48, we have for any one solution:

$$\Delta T = k(p_0 - p_1).$$

Also, for any particular solvent, p_0 is constant for a given temperature and may be denoted by k_1.

$$\therefore \frac{p_0 - p_1}{p_0} = \frac{k\Delta T}{k_1} = k_2 \Delta T.$$

But, for dilute solutions :

$$\frac{p_0 - p_1}{p_0} \doteq \frac{\dfrac{W_x}{M_x}}{\dfrac{W_s}{M_s}},$$

where W_x and W_s are the weights of the solute and solvent respectively, and M_x and M_s are the corresponding molecular weights.

$$\therefore \frac{\dfrac{W_x}{M_x}}{\dfrac{W_s}{M_s}} = k_2 \Delta T. \qquad \text{.........................(35)}$$

If, now, we put $W_x = M_x$ and $W_s = 100$, then :

$$\Delta T = \frac{M_s}{100 k_2} = k_3 \text{ (another constant),}$$

since M_s is constant for a given solvent.

The constant, k_3, is the **boiling-point constant** for a given solvent, and is the elevation of boiling point which would be obtained theoretically † by dissolving one gm.-molecule of any non-volatile substance in 100 gm. of the solvent.

Equation (35) can be rewritten :

$$\frac{W_x}{M_x} \times \frac{M_s}{W_s} = k_2 \Delta T = \frac{M_s \,.\, \Delta T}{100 k_3},$$

since $$k_3 = \frac{M_s}{100 k_2},$$

$$\therefore \Delta T = \mathbf{k}_3 \cdot \frac{100 \times \mathbf{W_x}}{\mathbf{W_s} \times \mathbf{M_x}}, \qquad \text{....................(36)}$$

or $$M_x = \mathbf{k}_3 \cdot \frac{100 \times \mathbf{W_x}}{\mathbf{W_s} \times \Delta \mathbf{T}}. \qquad \text{....................(37)}$$

† Equation (35) has been derived for dilute solutions and would not, therefore, apply to a solution containing one gm.-molecule in 100 gm. of solvent. Provided, however, that the experimental data refer to dilute solutions, the constant k_3 can be used to indicate mathematical proportionality.

Example 33. A solution of 1·35 gm. of urea in 72·3 c.c. of water boiled at a temperature 0·162° higher than that of pure water. What is the molecular weight of urea? [$K=5{\cdot}2$.]

Problems of this nature are most accurately solved by proportion; the results can, of course, be checked by means of equation (37).

Let M = the required molecular weight.

Then since K = the boiling-point constant = 5·2.

$\therefore$ M gm. of urea in 100 gm. of water would theoretically give an elevation of boiling point = 5·2°.

Remembering that the elevation of boiling point is directly proportional to the concentration of the solute, then:

1·35 gm. of the solute in 100 gm. of water would give an elevation $=\left(\dfrac{5{\cdot}2}{M}\times 1{\cdot}35\right)^{\circ}$.

$\therefore$ 1·35 gm. of the solute in 72·3 gm. of water would give an elevation $=\left(\dfrac{5{\cdot}2}{M}\times 1{\cdot}35\times\dfrac{100}{72{\cdot}3}\right)^{\circ}$.

But this is the observed elevation;

$$\therefore \quad \frac{5{\cdot}2\times 1{\cdot}35\times 100}{72{\cdot}3\times M}=0{\cdot}162.$$

$$\therefore \quad M=\frac{5{\cdot}2\times 1{\cdot}35\times 100}{72{\cdot}3\times 0{\cdot}162}=\mathbf{60{\cdot}0}.$$

8. Calculation of the molecular weights of non-volatile substances in solution (method of freezing point)

Inspection of Fig. 6 shows that, assuming the vapour pressure-temperature curves of a pure solvent and dilute solutions in this solvent to be approximately parallel, the lowering of freezing point is directly proportional to fall of vapour pressure.

By a similar reasoning to that used in para. 7, p. 50, therefore, we obtain the equation:

$$M_x=k_3\cdot\frac{100\times W_x}{W_s\times\Delta T}, \qquad \text{.......................(38)}$$

where ΔT = the depression of freezing point of a solvent due to the presence of a non-volatile solute, k_3 = the freezing point, and the other symbols have the same significance as in para. 7,

p. 50. The method of calculation, therefore, is the same as that shown in Example 33.

Both the boiling-point constant and freezing-point constant

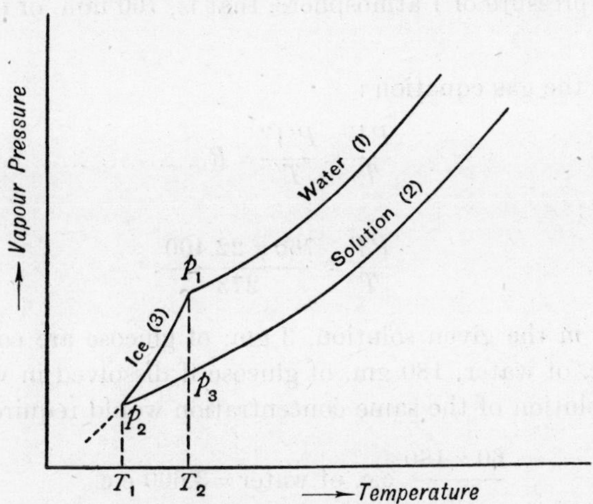

FIG. 6. Relation between lowering of vapour pressure and depression of freezing point.

can be calculated from the latent heat of evaporation and latent heat of fusion, respectively, of the solvent (see p. 324).

9. Calculations on osmotic pressure

The osmotic pressure of a solution containing a solute which behaves normally (see p. 119) can be obtained from the equation

$$P=\frac{KT}{V}, \qquad \ldots\ldots\ldots\ldots\ldots\ldots\ldots\ldots(39)$$

where P = the osmotic pressure, V = volume of the solution containing 1 gm.-molecule of the solute, T = the temperature in $°A$, and K = a constant identical with the gas constant R of the perfect gas equation $PV=RT$. By analogy with gas pressures, it follows that if 1 gm.-molecule of a solute is contained in 22·4 litres of a solvent, the osmotic pressure of the solution will be 1 atmosphere at 0°.

Example 34. Calculate the osmotic pressure of a solution containing 3 gm. of glucose in 60 c.c. of water at 15°. [Molecular weight of glucose = 180.]

Since the molecular weight of glucose is 180 : ∴ 180 gm. of glucose dissolved in 22,400 c.c. of water (the total volume of the solution may be assumed also to be 22,400 c.c.) exerts an osmotic pressure of 1 atmosphere, that is, 760 mm. of mercury, at 0°.

∴ In the gas equation :

$$\frac{PV}{T}=\frac{P'V'}{T'}=R, \quad\text{........................(40)}$$

we have :

$$\frac{PV}{T}=\frac{760\times 22{,}400}{273}.$$

Since, in the given solution, 3 gm. of glucose are contained in 60 c.c. of water, 180 gm. of glucose if dissolved in water to give a solution of the same concentration would require

$$\frac{60\times 180}{3}\text{ c.c. of water}=3{,}600\text{ c.c.}$$

If, then, for V' we write 3,600 c.c., that is, the volume of the given solution containing 1 gm.-molecule of glucose, and for T', the new temperature, 288 (in °A), the osmotic pressure, P', of the given solution is obtained from the equation :

$$\frac{760\times 22{,}400}{273}=\frac{P'\times 3{,}600}{288}.$$

From which $P'=4987$ mm.

Alternatively, remembering that the osmotic pressure is directly proportional both to the concentration of the solution and to the absolute temperature of the solution, the following method of working may be employed.

180 gm. of glucose in 22,400 c.c. of water at 0° gives an osmotic pressure = 760 mm.

∴ 3 gm. of glucose in 22,400 c.c. at 0° gives an osmotic pressure $=760\times\frac{3}{180}$ mm.

∴ 3 gm. of glucose in 60 c.c. at 0° gives an osmotic pressure $=760\times\frac{3}{180}\times\frac{22{,}400}{60}$ mm.

∴ 3 gm. of glucose in 60 c.c. of water at 15° gives an osmotic pressure $=760 \times \frac{3}{180} \times \frac{22,400}{60} \times \frac{288}{273}$ mm. $=4987$ mm.

It is preferable to use the latter method when calculating molecular weights from the observed osmotic pressures of solutions.

Example 35. 4·068 gm. of a substance dissolved in 82·3 c.c. of water gave an osmotic pressure of 6·15 atmospheres at 22°. What is the molecular weight of the substance?

Let M = the molecular weight of the substance.

Then, M gm. of the substance in 22,400 c.c. of water at 0° gives an osmotic pressure of 1 atmosphere.

Then, by proportion, as in the foregoing example:

4·068 gm. of the substance dissolved in 82·3 c.c. of water at 22° would give an osmotic pressure

$$=\frac{4 \cdot 068 \times 22,400 \times 295}{M \times 82 \cdot 3 \times 273} \text{ atmospheres.}$$

But the observed osmotic pressure = 6·15 atmospheres.

$$\therefore \frac{4 \cdot 068 \times 22,400 \times 295}{M \times 82 \cdot 3 \times 273} = 6 \cdot 15.$$

$$\therefore M = \frac{4 \cdot 068 \times 22,400 \times 295}{82 \cdot 3 \times 273 \times 6 \cdot 15} = 194 \cdot 5.$$

Example 36. What is the concentration (gm. per 100 c.c.) of a solution of glucose, $C_6H_{12}O_6$, which at 20° is isotonic with a solution of cane sugar, $C_{12}H_{22}O_{11}$, containing 8·36 gm. of cane sugar in 123 c.c. of water at 10°?

Two solutions are said to be **isotonic** when they have equal osmotic pressures.

Let the concentration of the glucose solution be x gm. per 100 c.c. The molecular weight of glucose, corresponding with the formula, $C_6H_{12}O_6$, is 180.

∴ 180 gm. of glucose in 22,400 c.c. of water at 0° gives an osmotic pressure of 1 atmosphere.

∴ x gm. of glucose in 100 c.c. of water will give, at 20°, an osmotic pressure

$$=\frac{x}{180} \times \frac{22,400}{100} \times \frac{293}{273} \text{ atmospheres.}$$

The osmotic pressure of the cane sugar solution (molecular weight for $C_{12}H_{22}O_{11}=342$)

$$=\frac{8{\cdot}36}{342}\times\frac{22{,}400}{123}\times\frac{283}{273}\text{ atmospheres.}$$

$\therefore$ Since the two osmotic pressures are equal :

$$\frac{x}{180}\times\frac{22{,}400}{100}\times\frac{293}{273}=\frac{8{\cdot}36}{342}\times\frac{22{,}400}{123}\times\frac{283}{273}.$$

$$\therefore\ x=3{\cdot}455\text{ gm.}$$

10. Relation between osmotic pressure and lowering of vapour pressure. (Approximate treatment)

In Fig. 7 all air is assumed to have been removed from the system, so that the solution is in equilibrium with the aqueous vapour. Then the aqueous vapour pressure at the point A must be the same inside and outside the tube.

$$\therefore\ P'=P''.$$

Let the density of the vapour over the pure solvent be d_v and, as an approximation, assume that this density remains the same over the height h, that is, over the small pressure range P to P''.

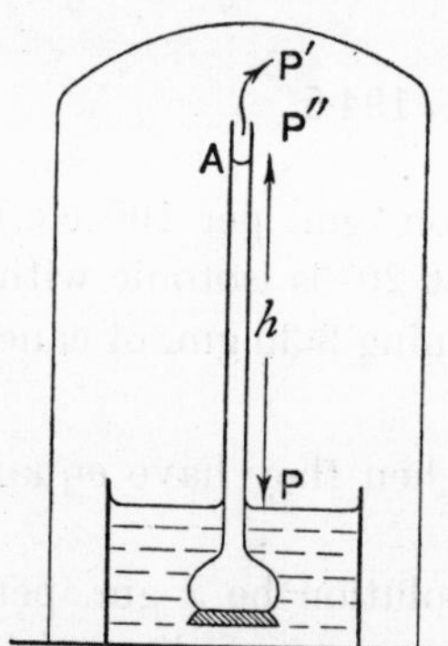

FIG. 7. Relation between lowering of vapour pressure and osmotic pressure (method 1).

Then, if d_s = density of the solution and P_0 = osmotic pressure :

$$P_0=h\,d_s\,g.$$

But $$P=P''+h\,d_v\,g=P'+h\,d_v\,g.$$

$$\therefore\ \frac{P_0}{d_s}=\frac{P-P'}{d_v}.$$

$$\therefore\ \frac{\mathrm{P}-\mathrm{P}'}{\mathrm{P}_0}=\mathrm{d}_v,\ \ldots\ldots\ldots\ldots\ldots\ldots\ldots(40)$$

since for dilute solutions $d_s \doteqdot 1$.

* **Example 37.** What is the vapour pressure of a solution of glucose which has an osmotic pressure of 3 atmospheres at 20°? [The vapour pressure of water at 20° = 17·39 mm.]

The density (gm. per c.c.) of water vapour at 20° and 17·39 mm. pressure is :

$$\underset{\substack{\text{(density of}\\ \text{hydrogen}\\ \text{at } N.T.P.)}}{0{\cdot}00009} \times \underset{\substack{\text{(vapour}\\ \text{density}\\ \text{of water)}}}{9} \times \frac{273}{293} \times \frac{17{\cdot}39}{760}$$

$$= 0{\cdot}0000173 \text{ gm. per c.c.}$$

Writing $P - P' = \Delta P$:

$$\frac{\Delta P}{3 \times 760} = 0{\cdot}0000173.$$

$$\therefore \Delta P = 0{\cdot}0394 \text{ mm.}$$

$$\therefore P' = P - \Delta P = 17{\cdot}39 - 0{\cdot}039 = \mathbf{17{\cdot}351 \text{ mm.}}$$

Alternatively, we may deduce the mol.-fraction of the solution from the observed osmotic pressure, and obtain the vapour pressure of the solution by using the relation given on p. 49.

The osmotic pressure of the glucose solution is $3 \times \frac{273}{293}$ atmospheres at 0°.

But if M is the molecular weight of glucose, M gm. of glucose in 22·4 litres of solution gives an osmotic pressure of 1 atmosphere at 0°.

Also M gm. of glucose in 22·4 litres produces a solution of molality $\frac{1}{22{\cdot}4}$.

$\therefore$ A solution which gives an osmotic pressure of 1 atmosphere at 0° must have a molality $= \frac{1}{22{\cdot}4}$.

$\therefore$ A solution of glucose which gives an osmotic pressure of $3 \times \frac{273}{293}$ atmospheres at 0° must, by proportion, have a molality

$$= \frac{1}{22{\cdot}4} \times 3 \times \frac{273}{293}.$$

But this is the number of gm.-molecules of glucose per 1000 c.c. of solution.

$$\therefore \text{Mol.-fraction of the solute} \doteqdot \frac{m}{M},$$

where m = number of gm.-molecules of glucose and M = number of gm.-molecules of water.

$$\therefore \text{ Mol.-fraction of the solute} = \frac{m}{M} = \frac{\dfrac{1}{22{\cdot}4} \times 3 \times \dfrac{273}{293}}{\dfrac{1000}{18}},$$

$$\therefore \frac{\Delta P}{P} = \frac{\Delta P}{17{\cdot}39} = \frac{1}{22{\cdot}4} \times 3 \times \frac{273}{293} \times \frac{18}{1000}.$$

$$\therefore \Delta P = 0{\cdot}0391 \text{ mm.}$$

$\therefore$ Vapour pressure of the solution at 20° = 17·351 mm.

* 11. Relation between osmotic pressure and lowering of vapour pressure

Let Fig. 8 represent a column of vapour of height h as in Fig. 7. The density of the vapour will vary with the pressure. Assume that at a height x, the density of the vapour is ρ. Then, considering the small element, dx, of Fig. 8 and assuming the column of vapour to be of unit cross-section, the difference in pressure due to the increase of height dx = the weight of vapour contained in the small element of volume dx.

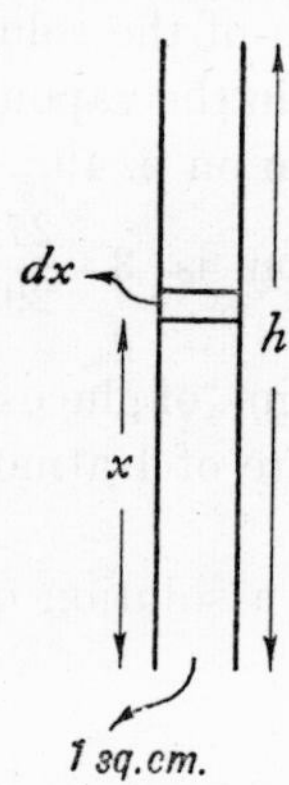

FIG. 8. Relation between lowering of vapour pressure and osmotic pressure (method 2).

$\therefore dP = -\rho \,.\, g \,.\, dx$ (the minus sign indicating that the pressure decreases as x increases and ρ = density of vapour at pressure P).

For 1 gm.-molecule of a gas which has a molecular weight, M, and occupies V c.c. :

$$\rho = M/V.$$

But $PV = RT$ and $V = RT/P$.

$$\therefore \rho = \frac{M}{V} = \frac{M}{RT} \times P.$$

$$\therefore dP = -\frac{M}{RT} \times P \times g \times dx,$$

or

$$\frac{dP}{P} = -\frac{Mg}{RT} \cdot dx.$$

Integrating between P and P' and 0 and h :

$$\log_e \left(\frac{P}{P'}\right) = \frac{Mg}{RT} \cdot h.$$

But $h\,g\,d_s = P_0$ (the osmotic pressure of the solution).

$$\therefore \ \log_e\left(\frac{P}{P'}\right) = \frac{Mg}{RT} \times \frac{P_0}{g\,d_s} = \frac{M}{RT\,d_s} \times P_0.$$

$$\therefore \ \mathbf{RT}\log_e\left(\frac{\mathbf{P}}{\mathbf{P'}}\right) = \frac{\mathbf{M}}{\mathbf{d_s}} \times \mathbf{P_0} = \mathbf{V_s} \times \mathbf{P_0}. \quad \text{..................(41)}$$

where V_s = the volume occupied by 1 gm.-molecule of the liquid solvent, since for dilute solutions the density of the solution can be taken as very nearly equal to the density of the pure solvent.

Equation (41) can be identified with equation (40) by the following approximation.

$$\text{Log}_e\left(\frac{P}{P'}\right) \equiv \log_e\left(1 + \frac{P - P'}{P'}\right)^{\dagger} \doteqdot \frac{P - P'}{P'} \doteqdot \frac{P - P'}{P},$$

$$\therefore \ \frac{P - P'}{P} = \frac{P_0 M}{RT\,d_s}.$$

$$\therefore \ \frac{\mathbf{P} - \mathbf{P'}}{\mathbf{P_0}} = \frac{\mathbf{PM}}{\mathbf{RT\,d_s}} = \frac{\mathbf{M}}{\mathbf{V}} = \boldsymbol{\rho},$$

since $d_s \doteqdot 1$.

12. Determination of molecular weights (Ostwald's method)

The method consists in allowing a stream of dry air to pass through (1) bulbs containing an aqueous solution of a non-volatile solute (2) through pure water. Then loss of weight (w_1) in (1) $\propto p_1$ (the vapour pressure of the solution) and loss of weight (w_2) in (2) $\propto (p_0 - p_1)$ where p_0 = the vapour pressure of the pure solvent at the same temperature.

$$\therefore \ \frac{w_2}{w_1} = \frac{p_0 - p_1}{p_1} \doteqdot \frac{p_0 - p_1}{p_0}.$$

$\therefore$ As on p. 49 :

$$\frac{p_0 - p_1}{p_0} = n_2 \text{ (the mol.-fraction of the solute).}$$

Example 38. Dry air was passed in succession through bulbs containing (*a*) 9·20 gm. of glucose in 89·5 gm. of water, (*b*) pure water. The loss of weight in the first series of bulbs was 5·21 gm., and the corresponding loss of weight in the second bulbs was 0·0528 gm. Deduce the molecular weight of glucose.

† $\text{Log}_e(1+x) = x - \frac{1}{2}x^2 + \frac{1}{3}x^3 - \frac{1}{4}x^4$, etc. $\doteqdot x$ when x is small.

Then, as above :

$$\frac{0{\cdot}0528}{9{\cdot}20}=\frac{p_0-p_1}{p_0}=n_2=\frac{\frac{9{\cdot}20}{X}}{\frac{89{\cdot}5}{18}},$$

where X = molecular weight of glucose.

$\therefore$ **X** = 183.

13. Relative lowering of solubility

If two liquids, L_A and L_B, are shaken together (L_B being sparingly soluble in L_A), then, on standing, the mixture separates into two layers consisting of (*a*) the solution of L_B in L_A, and (*b*) the excess of L_B (Fig. 9). Let p_B = the vapour pressure of pure L_B at the temperature of mixing, then if S = solubility of L_B in L_A at the same temperature, $S=kp_B$ where k = a constant.

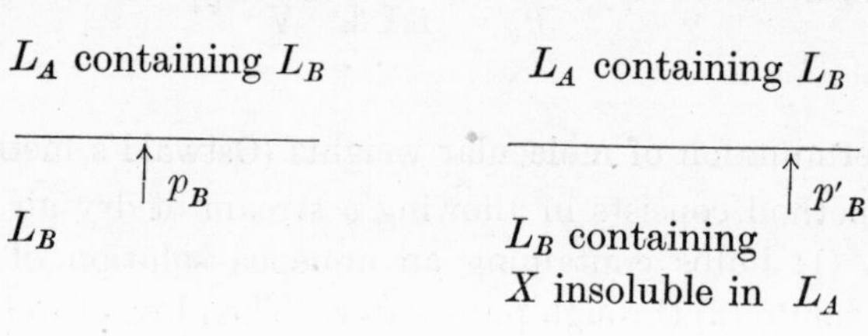

FIG. 9. Relative lowering of stability.

If, now, a substance, X, soluble in L_B, is added, the vapour pressure of L_B is reduced to a value, p'_B, given by the equation $p'_B=p_B\times N_B$, where N_B = mol.-fraction of L_B in the solution of X in L_B.

$$\therefore \frac{p_B-p'_B}{p_B}=\frac{N_X}{N_X+N_B}\doteq\frac{N_X}{N_B},$$

where N_X = the mol.-fraction of X in the solution of X in L_B. Since the solubility of L_B in L_A is proportional to the partial pressure of L_B, the new value of the solubility, S', is given by $S'=kp'_B$.

$$\therefore \frac{S-S'}{S}=\frac{p_B-p'_B}{p_B}\doteq\frac{N_X}{N_B}. \qquad \text{.................(42)}$$

Example 39. *L* is a liquid which is sparingly soluble in water. When 0·386 gm. of a solute *S* is dissolved in 8·26 gm. of *L*, *S* being insoluble in water, the effect of this is to diminish the solubility of *L* in water in the ratio of 10·5 to 9·9. What is the molecular weight of *S*, the molecular weight of *L* being 102? (C.U.O.S.)

Let $M =$ molecular weight of *S*.

Then
$$\frac{10{\cdot}5 - 9{\cdot}9}{10{\cdot}5} = \frac{\dfrac{0{\cdot}386}{M}}{\dfrac{8{\cdot}26}{102}}.$$

$$\therefore M = \frac{0{\cdot}386 \times 102 \times 10{\cdot}5}{0{\cdot}6 \times 8{\cdot}26} = 83.$$

QUESTIONS ON CHAPTER III

[A list of boiling point and freezing point constants is given on p. 431.]

1. A substance, *A*, immiscible with water, is distilled in steam and it is found that the mixture boils at 99°, at which temperature the vapour pressure of water is 732 mm. If the distillate is found to contain 18 per cent by weight of *A* and the atmospheric pressure is 760 mm., what is the molecular weight of *A*?

2. What is the approximate vapour pressure, at the temperature of distillation, of a liquid *A* which has a molecular weight 172 and which, on distillation in steam at 760 mm. atmospheric pressure, gave a distillate containing 7·2 per cent by weight of *A*?

3. A liquid, *X*, of density 1·086 gm. per c.c., was distilled in steam and the distillate was collected in a graduated receiver. The volumes of water and *X* were read at suitable intervals of time and the corresponding volumes were:

Volume of water (c.c.)	Volume of *X* (c.c.)
25·5	5·4
39·4	8·4
57·2	12·0
85·1	17·0
123·2	26·2

Given that the mixture distils at 98·6°, at which temperature the vapour pressure of water is 698 mm., and that the atmospheric pressure was 752 mm., calculate the molecular weight of *X*.

4. An amount of 0·300 gm. of a substance dissolved in 15 c.c. of water lowered the freezing point by 0·109°. Calculate the molecular weight of the substance. (Inter. B.Sc., London.)

5. A solution of 1·238 gm. of glucose in 26·2 c.c. of water boiled at a temperature 0·136° higher than that of pure water. Calculate the molecular weight of glucose.

6. It was found that 20·2 gm. of an aqueous solution containing 0·2 gm. of hydrogen peroxide had a freezing point 0·544° lower than that of water. Calculate the molecular weight of hydrogen peroxide. (1st M.B., London.)

7. Calculate the osmotic pressure of one per cent aqueous solution of dextrose, $C_6H_{12}O_6 . H_2O$, at 0°. (Inter. B.Sc., London.)

8. Calculate the osmotic pressure of a solution of cane sugar, $C_{12}H_{22}O_{11}$, containing 150 gm. per litre at 0°. (N.U.J.B.)

9. Calculate the molecular weights of the compounds, *A*, *B*, *C* and *D*, from the following values for the depression of freezing points in the solvents mentioned.

Substance	Weight of solute (gm.)	Volume of solvent (c.c.)	Density of the solvent at the freezing point	Observed depression of freezing point
A	1·502	25·6 (benzene)	0·89	2·35°
B	0·932	16·8 (water)	1·00	1·87°
C	2·306	30·0 (acetic acid)	1·05	2·14°
D	1·563	18·2 (phenol)	1·06	7·52°

10. 1·802 gm. of dinitrobenzene, $C_6H_4(NO_2)_2$, was dissolved in 28·3 c.c. of benzene, the density of benzene at the temperature at which its volume was measured being 0·890 gm. per c.c. At what temperature should the solution begin to solidify if the melting point of pure benzene is 5·53°?

11. A solution containing 3·761 gm. of an organic compound in 56·0 c.c. of acetic acid begins to freeze at 14·79°, the density of acetic acid being 1·05 gm. per c.c. If the freezing point of pure acetic acid is 16·71°, what is the molecular weight of the compound?

12. Two solutions, containing respectively 7·5 gm. of urea, CON_2H_4, and 42·75 gm. of a substance, *X*, in 1000 gm. of water freeze at the same temperature. Calculate the molecular weight of *X*. (H.S.C., London.)

13. When 2·062 gm. of a compound, *A*, of molecular weight 213, is dissolved in 43·2 gm. of benzene, the solution boiled at a temperature 0·605° higher than that of pure benzene. What is the molecular weight of a substance, *B*, 1·839 gm. of which when dissolved in 74·7 gm. of benzene raises its boiling point by 0·541°?

14. A solution of 8·55 gm. of cane sugar ($C_{12}H_{22}O_{11}$) in 100 gm. of water froze at −0·472° and a solution of 7·24 gm. of unknown substance in 100 gm. of water at −0·930°. Calculate the molecular weight of the unknown substance. (O. and C.)

15. Calculate the osmotic pressures (in cm. of mercury) of the following solutions, *A*, *B*, *C* and *D*, in which solutes of known molecular weights are dissolved at the stated temperatures and dilutions:

Solution	Molecular weight of the solute	Weight of solute (gm.)	Total volume of aqueous solution (c.c.)	Temperature of the solution
A	180	5·2	206	0°
B	342	1·382	50	27°
C	60	3·061	672	18°
D	126	0·569	18·3	21°

16. A solution contains 50 gm. of glycerol ($C_3H_8O_3$) per litre. Calculate its osmotic pressure in cm. of mercury at 17°. (H.S.C., London.)

17. What is the molecular weight of a non-electrolyte (see p. 122) of which a solution containing 2·18 gm. in 88·6 c.c. of water gave an osmotic pressure of 9·80 atmospheres at 16°?

18. A solution of 42 gm. of mannitol in one litre of water was found to have an osmotic pressure of 5·55 atmospheres at 20°. Calculate the molecular weight of mannitol. (N.U.J.B.)

19. Ice begins to separate at −0·744° from a solution containing 2·4 gm. of a non-electrolyte in 100 gm. of water. Calculate the molecular weight of the non-electrolyte and the osmotic pressure which the solution would exert at 20°. (1st M.B., London.)

20. At what temperature will a 4 per cent solution of cane sugar ($C_{12}H_{22}O_{11}$) be isotonic with a solution obtained by dissolving 3·42 gm. of glucose ($C_6H_{12}O_6$) in 168 c.c. of water at 15°?

21. An aqueous solution of an acid, which is so weak that it can be assumed to be practically unionised, boiled at 100·4° at normal pressure. 25·0 c.c. of the solution was neutralised by 38·5 c.c. of normal sodium hydroxide. The " boiling-point constant " for water

is 5·2 per 100 gm. Determine (*a*) the volume containing the equivalent weight in gm. of the acid, (*b*) the volume containing the molecular weight in gm. of the acid, and hence (*c*) the basicity of the acid. (1st M.B., London.)

22. Calculate the mol.-fraction of cane sugar in a solution containing 5 gm. of cane sugar ($C_{12}H_{22}O_{11}$) in 100 gm. of water. What will be the vapour pressure of this solution at 100°?

23. What is the vapour pressure of a solution containing 6·32 gm. of glycerol, $C_3H_8O_3$, in 48·6 gm. of water at 25°? [Vapour pressure of water at 25° = 23·62 mm.]

24. What is the osmotic pressure at 30° of a solution containing 48·2 gm. of urea in 650 c.c. of water? What is the vapour pressure of this solution at 100°?

25. 100 gm. of a cane sugar solution is cooled to −0·5°. What weight of ice will have separated at this temperature, assuming that the solution started to freeze at −0·38°?

26. The osmotic pressure of a solution of dextrose in water is 2·53 atmospheres at 25°. Calculate the vapour pressure of the solution at 25°, assuming that the vapour pressure of pure water at this temperature is 23·6 mm.

27. Dry air was passed slowly and successively through (*a*) bulbs containing a 10 per cent aqueous solution of a non-volatile solute, *X*, (*b*) bulbs containing pure water. The loss of weight in the first series of bulbs was 0·836 gm., and the corresponding loss of weight in the second series was 0·025 gm. Calculate the molecular weight of *X*.

28. Show theoretically that solutions of different substances in the same solvent have identical vapour pressures if their osmotic pressures possess the same value. At 20° the vapour pressure of ether is 442 mm. of mercury. When 6·1 gm. of a substance is dissolved in 50 gm. of ether, the vapour pressure fell to 410 mm. What is the molecular weight of the substance? (C.U.O.S.)

29. Dry air was passed in succession through two series of bulbs containing (*a*) a solution of 12·6 gm. of glucose, $C_6H_{12}O_6$, in 88 c.c. of water; (*b*) pure water. Compare the loss of weight in the first series of bulbs with that in the second series.

30. The vapour pressure of a solution of urea is 736·2 mm. at 100°. What is the osmotic pressure of this solution at 15°? At what temperature would the solution begin to freeze?

31. Pure liquid copper solidifies at 1083°. Liquid copper containing 3·45 per cent by weight of cuprous oxide in solution begins to solidify at 1063°. Calculate the freezing point of liquid copper containing 0·64 per cent by weight of sulphur dioxide, assuming that the reaction

$$6Cu + SO_2 \rightleftharpoons Cu_2S + 2Cu_2O$$

proceeds to completion. (C.U.O.S.)

32. L is a liquid which is sparingly soluble in water. When 0·386 gm. of a solute S is dissolved in 8·26 gm. of L, S being insoluble in water, the effect of this is to diminish the solubility of L in water in the ratio 10·5 to 9·9. What is the molecular weight of S, the molecular weight of L being 102? (C.U.O.S.)

33. An aqueous solution of cane sugar (M.W. = 342) has an osmotic pressure of 1·5 atmospheres at 18°. What will be the vapour pressure of this solution at 40°? If 100 gm. of this solution is cooled to −3·0°, what weight of ice should have separated out?

34. A litre of an aqueous solution contains 40 gm. of cane sugar, $C_{12}H_{22}O_{11}$. The solute is undergoing inversion according to the equation:

$$C_{12}H_{22}O_{11} + H_2O = \underset{\text{(dextrose)}}{C_6H_{12}O_6} + \underset{\text{(laevulose)}}{C_6H_{12}O_6}$$

What will be the approximate osmotic pressure of the solution at 15° when 28 gm. of the cane sugar has been converted into dextrose and laevulose?

*** 35.** Construct an ideal boiling point-composition curve for mixtures of ethyl acetate and ethyl propionate, using the following data of vapour pressures:

Ethyl Acetate

T	20	40	60	80
p (mm.)	72·8	186	415	833

Ethyl Propionate

T	20	40	60	80	100
p (mm.)	27·7	78	188	404	785

*** 36.** 100 c.c. of an organic liquid, A, of density 0·92 gm. per c.c. and molecular weight 46, was shaken with 100 c.c. of water in which it is partially soluble. It was then found that the freezing point of the water saturated with A was −2·65°. 5 gm. of an organic compound, soluble in A but insoluble in water, was added, and it was found that, after the compound had completely dissolved in A, the freezing point of the aqueous solution was −2·32°. Deduce the molecular weight of the compound.

*** 37.** The vapour pressure of a liquid A (mol. wt. = 72) is 38·96 mm. at 0° and that of liquid B (mol. wt. = 87) is 27·32 mm. at 0°. Assuming that the liquids are completely miscible and that the mixture behaves ideally, calculate the vapour pressure at 0° of a mixture of 20 gm. of A and 40 gm. of B.

*** 38.** The vapour pressure of methyl butyrate at 80° is 361 mm. and that of ethyl acetate at the same temperature is 833 mm. What is the percentage by weight of ethyl acetate in a mixture of ethyl acetate and methyl butyrate which boils at 80°, assuming that Raoult's law is obeyed?

* **39.** The vapour pressures of benzene and water at various temperatures are given below. At what temperature will a mixture of these two liquids (which are immiscible) boil at an atmospheric pressure of 754 mm., and what will be the percentage by weight of benzene in the distillate?

WATER

T - - -	20	40	60	80
p (mm. Hg) -	17·5	55·1	149	355·1

BENZENE

T - - -	20	40	60	80
p (mm. Hg) -	74·6	181	389	754

* **40.** Using equation (40) calculate the vapour pressure of a solution of urea at 40° given that its osmotic pressure is 1000 mm. at 18°. [Vap. press. of water at 40° = 55·13 mm.]

* **41.** Using the data of Q. 35, calculate the vapour pressure at 54° of a mixture of 20 gm. of ethyl acetate and 35 gm. of ethyl propionate. What is the mol.-fraction of ethyl acetate in a mixture of ethyl acetate and ethyl propionate which boils at 78°?

* **42.** An aqueous mixture containing 75 per cent of formic acid and 25 per cent of water has a boiling point lower than pure water or pure formic acid. If an aqueous solution of formic acid containing 40 per cent of the acid by weight is separated into a residue and a distillate by continued fractionation, what would be the weights of residue and distillate respectively?

* **43.** The density of a 5 per cent solution of potassium bromide is 1·0354 gm. per c.c. at 18° and its vapour pressure at this temperature is 15·259 mm. The vapour pressure of pure water at 18° is 15·460 mm. What is the osmotic pressure of the potassium bromide solution at 18°?

* **44.** In the following table are given the compositions (in gm. % chloroform) of the liquid and the vapour phases which are in equilibrium at various temperatures under 1 atmosphere pressure in the system acetone-chloroform.

Temp. -	55·0	58·6	60·5	61·8	62·8	63·5
Liquid -	0	13	29	38	47	54
Vapour -	0	10	20	30	40	50
Temp. -	64·0	63·9	63·6	63·0	61·2	
Liquid -	62	65	71	82	100	
Vapour -	62	70	80	90	100	

(*a*) At what temperature will a solution containing 40 per cent of chloroform begin to boil, and what is the composition of the vapour first evolved?

(*b*) What is the minimum number of simple fractional distillations (without column) which will yield a small specimen containing 90 per cent of acetone?

(*c*) What will be the composition of the residue left after prolonged distillation with an efficient column of a solution initially containing 40 per cent of chloroform?

(*d*) A solution containing 40 per cent of chloroform was distilled with a column, the rate of distillation being so adjusted that the thermometer at the top of the column remained steady at 58·6° until $\frac{1}{2}$ the liquid had distilled over. What would you expect the composition of the residue to be at this stage?

(Manchester Hons. Chem.)

*** 45.** A mixture of ethyl alcohol and water in which the mol.-fraction of alcohol is 0·82 has a density 0·8461 gm. per c.c. If the partial molal volume of water in this mixture is 15·7, calculate that of ethyl alcohol.

CHAPTER IV

SOLUBILITIES, PARTITION LAW, CONGRUENT MELTING POINTS

1. Solubility of solids

The solubility of a solid is usually obtained by the direct method of evaporating a weighed quantity of a saturated solution to dryness; alternatively, the solubility may be determined by a chemical method as in the following example.

Example 40. Deduce the solubility of oxalic acid crystals, $C_2O_4H_2 . 2H_2O$, in water at 15°, using the following data: 15·03 gm. of a saturated solution of the crystals at 15° was diluted to 500 c.c. 25 c.c. of the diluted solution required for complete neutralisation 25·4 c.c. of 0·093 N sodium hydroxide, phenolphthalein being used as indicator.

$$\text{Normality of the diluted solution} = \frac{25{\cdot}4 \times 0{\cdot}093}{25}.$$

∴ Number of gm. of oxalic acid crystals (molecular weight 126, and equivalent 63)

$$= \frac{25{\cdot}4 \times 0{\cdot}093}{25} \times \frac{63 \times 500}{1000} = 2{\cdot}98 \text{ gm.}$$

∴ (15·03 − 2·98) gm. of water dissolve 2·98 gm. of oxalic acid crystals.

∴ With sufficient accuracy 100 gm. of water dissolve $\frac{2{\cdot}98}{12{\cdot}05} \times 100$ gm. = **24·7 gm.** of oxalic acid crystals.

∴ Solubility of oxalic acid crystals at 15° = **24·7.**

For the determination of the solubilities of sparingly soluble substances the student is referred to pp. 196 and 361.

2. Solubility of gases

The solubility of a gas is expressed as the number of c.c. of that gas, measured at N.T.P., which will dissolve in 1 c.c. of a liquid under stated conditions of temperature and pressure (see p. 70). If the gas is moderately soluble, its solubility can be determined by exposing a fixed volume of it to a measured volume of a solvent, as in an absorption pipette, and noting the decrease in the volume of the gas. The solubility of extremely soluble gases, for example, ammonia, hydrogen chloride, is determined by an indirect chemical method.

Example 41. A small glass bulb containing 5·01 gm. of a saturated aqueous solution of ammonia was crushed in a beaker containing 100 c.c. of normal sulphuric acid. It was found that the excess of acid required 28·2 c.c. of normal sodium hydroxide for neutralisation. What is the solubility of ammonia in water under the conditions of the experiment?

The weight of ammonia in 5·01 gm. of saturated solution is equivalent to (100 – 28·2) c.c. = 71·8 c.c. N H_2SO_4.

$\therefore$ Weight of ammonia $= \frac{71 \cdot 8}{1000} \times 17$ (since the equivalent of ammonia = 17) = 1·22 gm.

$\therefore$ Weight of water = (5·01 – 1·22) gm. = 3·79 gm.

$\therefore$ 1 c.c. of water dissolves $\frac{1 \cdot 22}{3 \cdot 79}$ gm. of ammonia

$$= \frac{1 \cdot 22}{3 \cdot 79} \times \frac{22{,}400}{17} \text{ c.c. of ammonia at } N.T.P.$$

$$= \mathbf{424 \text{ c.c. at N.T.P.}}$$

3. Henry's law

The quantity (mass) of a gas dissolved by a given volume of a solvent at a given temperature is directly proportional to the pressure of the gas.

The law may also be stated:

(*a*) The volume of gas, measured at *N.T.P.*, which is absorbed by a given volume of a solvent is proportional to the pressure of the gas.

(*b*) The volume of a gas absorbed by a given volume of a solvent is the same at all pressures, provided the gas is measured at the pressure at which it dissolves.

If, for example, 100 c.c. of a given solvent dissolves 1 c.c. of a gas under a pressure of 760 mm., then it will dissolve twice that *mass* of gas under a pressure of 1520 mm., that is, twice the initial pressure. If this gas is measured at 1520 mm., it will occupy only 1 c.c. This mass of gas, if measured at 760 mm., would occupy 2 c.c. The *volume* of the gas dissolved, *measured at* 760 *mm.*, is, therefore, proportional to the pressure.

In applying Henry's law it is assumed (*a*) that the gas is only moderately soluble, (*b*) that the molecular state of the gas is the same in the gaseous and liquid phase and that there is no chemical combination between the gas and the solvent. The law would not, therefore, be true for gases such as sulphur dioxide, ammonia and hydrogen chloride.

Example 42. What volume of nitrogen, measured at *N.T.P.*, would be dissolved by 100 c.c. of water exposed to nitrogen at 400 mm. pressure and 0°? The coefficient of absorption of nitrogen at 0° is 0·02.

The coefficient of absorption is the volume of a gas, measured at *N.T.P.*, which would be absorbed by 1 c.c. of a liquid from the gas at normal pressure and the stated temperature. In this example, therefore, 1 c.c. of water will absorb 0·02 c.c. of nitrogen at 0° and 760 mm. pressure.

∴ 100 c.c. will absorb 2 c.c. at 0° and 760 mm. pressure.

∴ By Henry's law :

Volume of nitrogen, measured at 0° and 760 mm., which would be absorbed by 100 c.c. of water exposed to nitrogen at 0° and 400 mm. pressure

$$= 2{\cdot}00 \times \frac{400}{760} \text{ c.c.} = 1{\cdot}05 \text{ c.c.}$$

The solubility of a gas can also be expressed by its **solubility coefficient**, which is the volume of a gas absorbed by 1 c.c. of water at the temperature and pressure at which it dissolves, the volume being measured at this temperature and pressure. The relation between the absorption coefficient and the solubility coefficient can readily be deduced.

If V_1 = volume of gas absorbed by 1 c.c. of water, this volume being measured at the pressure and temperature of the gas, then $C_s = V_1$ where C_s = the solubility coefficient. If the pressure of the gas $= p$ mm. and the temperature at which it dissolves is $T°\ A$, then the absorption coefficient (C_a) is obtained by correcting V_1 to *N.T.P.*

$$\therefore\ C_a = V_1 \times \frac{273}{T} \times \frac{p}{760},$$

and $$C_a = C_s \times \frac{273}{T} \times \frac{p}{760};$$

or, if p is expressed in atmospheres,

$$C_a = C_s \times \frac{273}{T} \times p.$$

Example 43. Into a flask of capacity 1000 c.c. and containing nothing but 950 c.c. of water is put at 20° a volume of oxygen which when separately measured at 20° and 1 atmosphere pressure had occupied 50 c.c. The flask is then closed and well shaken. Calculate the pressure of the residual gaseous oxygen in the flask given that 100 c.c. of water at 20° exposed to oxygen kept at 1 atmosphere will dissolve 3·4 c.c. of the gas.

(Dur. Ent. Schol.)

Let P = the final pressure in the flask. Then, by Henry's law, the volume of oxygen dissolved by 100 c.c. of water

$$= \frac{P}{760} \times 3{\cdot}4 \text{ c.c.} = x \text{ c.c.}$$

But since the flask originally contained 50 c.c. of oxygen at 760 mm. (since temperature remains constant and the volume of the flask not occupied by water = (1000 − 950) c.c. = 50 c.c. = volume of oxygen at 760 mm. and 20°), and x c.c., measured at 760 mm., have dissolved, the residual gas would occupy a volume of $(50 - x)$ c.c. at 760 mm. But this volume of gas actually occupies 50 c.c. at pressure P.

$$\therefore\ 760(50 - x) = P \times 50.$$

Substituting for x:

$$(760 \times 50) - \left(P \times \frac{950}{100} \times 3{\cdot}4\right) = P \times 50.$$

From which $P = 461{\cdot}7$ mm.

When a mixture of gases is exposed to a liquid each dissolves in proportion to its partial pressure.

4. Dalton's law of partial pressures

The total pressure exerted by a mixture of gases is equal to the sum of the partial pressures of its constituents, the partial pressure of each gas being the pressure it would exert if it alone occupied a volume equal to the total volume of the mixture.

Example 44. 200 c.c. of oxygen, measured at 15° and 740 mm. pressure, and 50 c.c. of nitrogen, measured at 30° and 770 mm. pressure, were led into a previously evacuated flask of capacity 250 c.c. which was maintained at 20°. What are the partial pressures of oxygen and nitrogen respectively, and what is now the total pressure in the flask?

Let P_O = the partial pressure of the oxygen. Then this is the pressure exerted by a quantity of oxygen, initially occupying 200 c.c. at 15° and 740 mm., when it is made to occupy 250 c.c. at 20°.

But for a fixed mass of gas:

$$\frac{pv}{T} = \text{a constant},$$

where p, v and T are the corresponding pressure, volume and temperature (in ° absolute).

$$\therefore \frac{740 \times 200}{288} = \frac{P_O \times 250}{293}.$$

$$\therefore P_O = \frac{740 \times 200 \times 293}{288 \times 250} = 602{\cdot}3 \text{ mm.}$$

Similarly, if P_N denote the partial pressure of the nitrogen:

$$\frac{770 \times 50}{303} = \frac{P_N \times 250}{293},$$

and

$$P_N = \frac{770 \times 50 \times 293}{303 \times 250} = 148{\cdot}9 \text{ mm.}$$

∴ Total pressure in the flask

$$= P_O + P_N = 602{\cdot}3 + 148{\cdot}9 = 751{\cdot}2 \text{ mm.}$$

A common example of the use of the law of partial pressures is the correction of the volume of a gas for pressure when it is collected over water.

Example 45. What is the volume at *N.T.P.* of a quantity of a gas which when collected over water at 20° occupies a volume of 52·65 c.c., the barometric height being 754·7 mm.?

The vapour pressure of water at 20° = 17·4 mm.

Then, if P_g represent the actual pressure exerted by the gas:

$$P_g + 17{\cdot}4 = 754{\cdot}7,$$

since the barometric pressure must be balanced by the sum of the partial pressures of the gas and water vapour.

$$\therefore\ P_g = 754{\cdot}7 - 17{\cdot}4 = 737{\cdot}3 \text{ mm.}$$

$$\therefore \text{ Volume of the gas at } N.T.P. = 52{\cdot}65 \times \frac{273}{293} \times \frac{737{\cdot}3}{760}$$

$$= 47{\cdot}60 \text{ c.c.}$$

Example 46. A mixture of hydrogen and oxygen, containing 20 per cent of oxygen by volume, stands at a total pressure of 1000 mm. over water at 15°. Calculate the percentage composition of the gas absorbed from this mixture.

Coefficient of absorption of hydrogen at 15° = 0·019.

" " " oxygen " " = 0·032.

Since the total pressure of the mixed gases is 1000 mm., the partial pressure of the hydrogen $= \frac{4}{5} \times 1000$ mm. = 800 mm.

$$\therefore \text{ 1 c.c. of water will absorb } \frac{800}{760} \times 0{\cdot}019$$

$$= 0{\cdot}0200 \text{ c.c. of hydrogen.}$$

This is the volume of hydrogen measured at 760 mm. and 15°, although it has been absorbed at a pressure of 800 mm.

Similarly, the volume of oxygen, measured at 760 mm. and 15°, which will be absorbed by 1 c.c. of water at 15° and under a partial pressure of 200 mm. ($\frac{1}{5} \times 1000$ mm.)

$$= \frac{200}{760} \times 0{\cdot}032 = 0{\cdot}0084 \text{ c.c.}$$

$\therefore$ Total volume of gas dissolved by 1 c.c. of water

$$= 0{\cdot}0200 + 0{\cdot}0084$$

$$= 0{\cdot}0284 \text{ c.c. at 760 mm. and 15°.}$$

$\therefore$ Percentage of hydrogen in the dissolved gas

$$= \frac{0{\cdot}0200}{0{\cdot}0284} \times 100 = \mathbf{70{\cdot}4 \text{ per cent.}}$$

It is clear that it is not necessary to know the total pressure of the mixed gases. Thus, if, in the above calculation, the total pressure is denoted by P, the same result is obtained.

5. Adsorption† of gases by solids

The relation between the quantity of a gas adsorbed by porous solids such as wood charcoal is given by the **Freundlich isotherm**:

$$\frac{x}{m}=ap^{1/n}, \qquad (43)$$

where x = mass of gas adsorbed, m = the mass of adsorbing material (adsorbent), p = pressure of the gas, and a and n are constants for a given system at constant temperature. This equation can also be used for the adsorption of substances from aqueous solution, for example, of oxalic acid by charcoal.

The **Langmuir isotherm**, which refers to the adsorption of gases on smooth, that is, non-porous, surfaces, is the equation :

$$\frac{x}{m}=\frac{ap}{1+bp}, \qquad (44)$$

where a and b are constants. This equation is derived by assuming that the surface of the solid is only partially covered with the gas, and that the upper limit of adsorption corresponds with a layer of the gas one molecule thick.

6. The partition (or distribution) law

When a substance is soluble in two liquids, A and B, which are, themselves, immiscible, a given weight of that substance will distribute itself between the two liquids so that :

$$\frac{C_A}{C_B}=\text{a constant,}$$

where C_A = the concentration of the substance in the solvent, A,
and C_B = the concentration of the substance in the solvent, B.

It is assumed (a) that neither of the solvents is saturated with the substance, and (b) that the molecular state of the dissolved substance is the same in each solvent (see p. 77).

The ratio $\frac{C_A}{C_B}$ is called the **partition coefficient** or **distribution coefficient.**

† The term "adsorption" in reference to a gas taken up by a solid is used in varying senses. The student should consult the appropriate books on Physical Chemistry for the meaning of the following terms as they are used to describe adsorption phenomena: absorption, sorption, Van der Waal's adsorption, chemisorption.

Example 47. The partition coefficient of a substance, X, between ether and water is 3, the substance being more soluble in the ether. 100 c.c. of an aqueous solution containing 10 gm. of X is shaken with 100 c.c. of ether. A further 100 c.c. of the aqueous solution is shaken with two successive quantities of 50 c.c. of ether. Calculate the weight of X left in the aqueous solution after each experiment.

$$\frac{\text{Concentration of } X \text{ in ether}}{\text{Concentration of } X \text{ in water}} = \frac{3}{1}.$$

But concentration = mass of solute per c.c.

∴ Quantity of solute in volume (V c.c.) of any solvent $= V \times c$, where c = the concentration.

$$\therefore \frac{\text{Weight of } X \text{ in ether}}{\text{Weight of } X \text{ in water}} = \frac{V_e \times c_e}{V_w \times c_w} = \frac{V_e}{V_w} \times \frac{c_e}{c_w},$$

where V_e = volume of ether,

V_w = " " water,

c_e = concentration in ether,

c_w = " " water.

In the first experiment in which a single 100 c.c. quantity of either is used:

$$\frac{\text{Weight of } X \text{ in ether}}{\text{Weight of } X \text{ in water}} = \frac{V_e}{V_w} \times \frac{c_e}{c_w} = \frac{100}{100} \times \frac{3}{1} = \frac{3}{1}.$$

∴ X is distributed between the ether and the water so that 3 parts are in the 100 c.c. of ether and 1 part in the 100 c.c. of water.

∴ Only $\frac{1}{4}$ of the total original weight of X is left in aqueous solution.

∴ Weight of X left in aqueous solution $= \frac{1}{4} \times 10$ gm. $= 2{\cdot}5$ gm.

With two successive extractions using 50 c.c. quantities of ether, the calculation is as follows:

1*st extraction.*

$$\frac{\text{Weight of } X \text{ in ether}}{\text{Weight of } X \text{ in water}} = \frac{50}{100} \times \frac{3}{1} = \frac{3}{2}.$$

∴ The first extraction removes $\frac{3}{5}$ of X and leaves $\frac{2}{5}$.

2nd extraction.

As before :

$$\frac{\text{Weight of } X \text{ in ether}}{\text{Weight of } X \text{ in water}} = \frac{3}{2}.$$

$\therefore$ $\frac{3}{5}$ of the remaining $\frac{2}{5}$ is extracted.

$\therefore$ Fraction of X remaining in aqueous solution

$$=\{1 - \tfrac{3}{5} - (\tfrac{3}{5} \times \tfrac{2}{5})\} = \tfrac{4}{25}.$$

$\therefore$ Weight of X remaining in aqueous solution

$$= \tfrac{4}{25} \times 10 = 1{\cdot}6 \text{ gm.}$$

This result is an illustration of the general rule that successive extractions with small quantities of a solvent will remove more of the solute than a single extraction with the same total volume of solvent.

* Problems involving the calculation of the quantity of solute extracted by a large number of successive extractions can be solved as follows :

Let W_0 = the original weight of solute in a given volume of solution, and w_1, w_2, w_3, etc. = weights of the solute left after 1, 2, 3, etc., extractions with a constant volume of another solvent.

Assume that the first extraction removes a fraction, x, of the original solute. Then, in every subsequent extraction, the same fraction of the residual solute will be removed.

$$\therefore\ w_1 = W_0 - W_0 x = W_0(1-x),$$

$$w_2 = w_1 - w_1 x \quad = w_1(1-x) = W_0(1-x)^2,$$

$$w_3 = w_2 - w_2 x \quad = w_2(1-x) = W_0(1-x)^3\ ;$$

$$\therefore\ w_n = W_0(1-x)^n,$$

where w_n = the weight of the solute remaining after n successive extractions.

Let V = the volume of the original solution

and $\quad v$ = the volume of the liquid used in each extraction.

Then, after the first extraction :

$$\frac{\text{Weight of solute in extracting liquid}}{\text{Weight of solute left in original liquid}} = \frac{v \times K}{V} = \frac{x}{1-x},$$

where K = the partition coefficient and x, as above, is the fraction extracted.

$$\therefore \; x = \frac{vK}{(V+vK)}.$$

Substituting this value for x:

$$w_n = W_0\left(1 - \frac{vK}{V+vK}\right)^n = \mathbf{W}_0\left(\frac{\mathbf{V}}{\mathbf{V}+\mathbf{vK}}\right)^{\mathbf{n}} \text{.........(45)}$$

* **Example 48.** 500 gm. of water contain 100 gm. of succinic acid in solution. Calculate what weight of succinic acid would be removed from the water (*a*) by a single extraction with 500 c.c. of ether, (*b*) by ten successive extractions with 50 c.c. of ether. [The distribution coefficient of succinic acid between water and ether is 6 : 1, the acid is more soluble in water.] (C.U.O.S.)

By the method given in Example 47:
Weight of succinic acid removed in operation (*a*)

$$= \tfrac{1}{7} \times 100 = \mathbf{14{\cdot}28\ gm.}$$

For the first extraction in operation (*b*):

$$\frac{\text{Weight of succinic acid in ether}}{\text{Weight of succinic acid in water}} = \frac{1}{6} \times \frac{50}{500} = \frac{1}{60}.$$

$\therefore$ Fraction extracted in one operation $= \frac{1}{61}$.

Then, as in equation (45):

$$w_n = W_0(1-x)^n = 100\left(1 - \frac{1}{61}\right)^{10} = 84{\cdot}9 \text{ gm.}$$

$\therefore$ Weight of succinic acid removed $= 100 - 84{\cdot}9 = \mathbf{15{\cdot}1\ gm.}$

Where the molecular states of the solute in the two solvents are different, the ratio, C_A/C_B, is not constant. If, for example, a compound has a molecular formula denoted by X in one solvent, A, and associates to form a compound of molecular formula X_n in the other solvent, B, then : $\frac{C_A{}^n}{C_B} = K$, as indicated by the application of the Mass law (cf. Chap. V) to the equation

$$\underset{(\text{solvent } A)}{nX} \rightleftharpoons \underset{(\text{solvent } B)}{X_n}$$

The commonest examples are where $n = 2$, and then:

$$\frac{C_A{}^2}{C_B} = K.$$

Example 49. Varying amounts of acetic acid were shaken with a mixture of benzene and water and the following figures show how the acid distributed itself between the two liquids, concentrations being expressed in gm./litre. Assuming that acetic acid has the molecular formula CH_3COOH in water, deduce its molecular formula in benzene.

	Benzene C_B	*Water* C_W
(1)	0·620	3·750
(2)	0·893	4·530
(3)	1·600	6·070
(4)	2·810	8·030

The ratio C_W/C_B has the following values: (1) 6·05 ; (2) 5·07 ; (3) 3·79 ; (4) 2·86. It is clearly not constant.

For $C_W{}^2/C_B$ the ratios are: (1) 22·7 ; (2) 23·0 ; (3) 23·0 ; (4) 22·9. These ratios are approximately constant.

Acetic acid exists, therefore, in benzene solution as the double molecule $(CH_3COOH)_2$, the equilibrium between acetic acid in benzene solution and aqueous solution being represented by the equation :

$$\underset{\text{(benzene solution)}}{(CH_3COOH)_2} \rightleftharpoons \underset{\text{(aqueous solution)}}{2CH_3COOH}$$

7. Congruent melting points (dystectics)

The term congruent melting point is used in apposition to eutectic point. In Fig. 10, where the melting points of ferric chloride (Fe_2Cl_6) solutions are plotted against the composition of the mixture, *A*, *B*, *C* and *D* are the eutectic points. The curve has several maxima, *E*, *F*, *G* and *H* ; these are the **congruent melting points** or **dystectics.** At the point, *E*, the whole solution solidifies at 37°. At this point, the composition of the mixture is 60 per cent of ferric chloride and 40 per cent of water. Dividing these percentages by the molecular weights of ferric chloride ($Fe_2Cl_6 = 325$) and water (18) respectively, we obtain :

$$\frac{\text{Number of molecules of ferric chloride}}{\text{Number of molecules of water}} = \frac{60/325}{40/18} = \frac{0{\cdot}19}{2{\cdot}22} = 1 : 12.$$

The solid formed at *E* corresponds, therefore, with the formula, $Fe_2Cl_6 . 12H_2O$.

A solution of ferric chloride, containing 60 per cent of ferric chloride and 40 per cent of water, may be regarded as a single compound. If either water or ferric chloride is added to a mixture of this composition, the melting point of the mixture

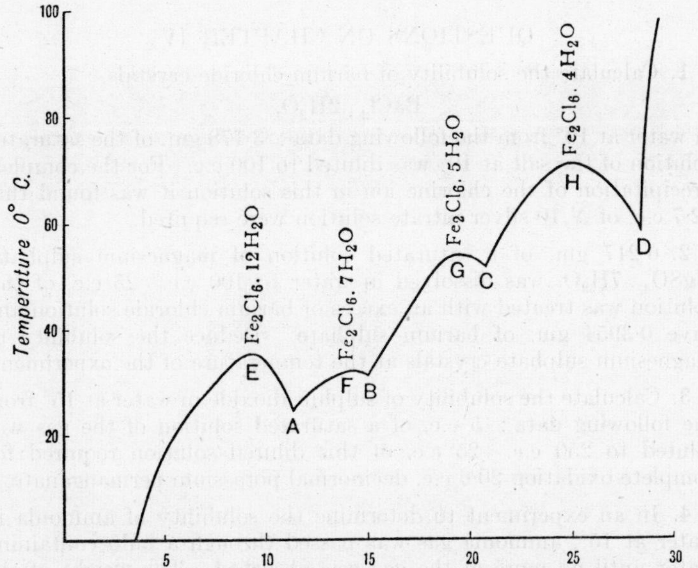

FIG. 10. Congruent melting points of the system $Fe_2Cl_6 - H_2O$.

falls in much the same way that the freezing point of water is lowered by the addition of sodium chloride.

The maxima on the curve correspond, therefore, with the existence of pure hydrates, and the formulae of such hydrates can be calculated by reading off the composition of the mixture at these points.

As another example, we can take the point, *F*. At this point, the composition is 71·7 per cent ferric chloride and 28·3 per cent of water.

∴ Ratio of Fe_2Cl_6 molecules to H_2O molecules

$$=\frac{71{\cdot}7/325}{28{\cdot}3/18}=\frac{1}{7}.$$

∴ The hydrate is $Fe_2Cl_6 \cdot 7H_2O$.

Similarly, if the melting point of alloys are plotted against their composition, the occurrence of dystectics indicates the formation of definite compounds (the so-called *intermetallic* compounds) between the metals.

QUESTIONS ON CHAPTER IV

1. Calculate the solubility of barium chloride crystals,

$$BaCl_2 . 2H_2O,$$

in water at 10° from the following data : 3·778 gm. of the saturated solution of the salt at 10° was diluted to 100 c.c. For the complete precipitation of the chlorine ion in this solution it was found that 22·7 c.c. of $N/10$ silver nitrate solution were required.

2. 6·217 gm. of a saturated solution of magnesium sulphate, $MgSO_4 . 7H_2O$, was dissolved in water to 100 c.c. 25 c.c. of this solution was treated with an excess of barium chloride solution and gave 0·3954 gm. of barium sulphate. Deduce the solubility of magnesium sulphate crystals at the temperature of the experiment.

3. Calculate the solubility of sulphur dioxide in water at 15° from the following data : 5 c.c. of a saturated solution of the gas was diluted to 250 c.c. 25 c.c. of this diluted solution required for complete oxidation 20·6 c.c. decinormal potassium permanganate.

4. In an experiment to determine the solubility of ammonia in water at 15°, ammonia gas was passed through a bulb containing water until no more of the gas was absorbed. The weight of the bulb when empty was 3·926 gm., while the weight of the bulb and the saturated solution of ammonia was 6·944 gm. The bulb and its contents were then crushed under 50 c.c. of normal sulphuric acid, and it was found that the unchanged acid required 10·4 c.c. of normal sodium hydroxide for neutralisation. Calculate the solubility of ammonia in water at 15°.

5. 100 c.c. of oxygen, measured at *N.T.P.*, and 100 c.c. of nitrogen, measured at 0° and 380 mm., were introduced into a flask of capacity 500 c.c. which was kept at 0°. What is the final pressure in the flask, and what are the partial pressures of the two gases?

6. The following volumes of gases were measured separately at the stated temperatures and pressures :

300 c.c. of nitrogen at 15° and 760 mm.
250 c.c. of oxygen at 22° and 745 mm.
500 c.c. of hydrogen at 18° and 780 mm.

The three volumes of gases were then led into a previously evacuated flask of capacity 1000 c.c., which was stoppered and maintained at 17°. Calculate (*a*) the final pressure in the flask, (*b*) the partial pressure of each gas.

7. 100 c.c. of oxygen, measured at 15° and 742 mm., and 150 c.c. of nitrogen, measured at 25° and 775 mm., were contained in a flask of capacity 250 c.c. The total pressure in the flask was found to be 765 mm. What was the temperature of the flask and its contents? What were the partial pressures of the oxygen and the nitrogen at this temperature?

8. 2 gm. of chloroform ($CHCl_3$) and 1 gm. of ethyl alcohol (C_2H_6O) were vaporised at 100° in a previously evacuated litre flask. Calculate (*a*) the total pressure in the flask, and (*b*) the partial pressure of the vapours of alcohol and chloroform respectively.

9. 100 c.c. of ammonia, originally at 15° and 760 mm., was sparked until no further decomposition occurred, at which point 98 per cent of the gas had been decomposed. If the final volume of the mixed gases was 150 c.c. at 20°, what were (*a*) the total pressure of the gas, (*b*) the partial pressures of ammonia, nitrogen and hydrogen respectively?

10. Assuming air to be a mixture of 80 per cent of nitrogen and 20 per cent of oxygen by volume, calculate the percentage of oxygen in the mixture of gases dissolved by water from air at 15°.

[Coefficient of absorption of oxygen at 15° = 0·038.
„ „ „ „ nitrogen „ = 0·018.]

11. What are the volumes of gases dissolved by 100 c.c. of water when shaken at *N.T.P.* with an excess of a mixture containing the following proportions by volume: Nitrogen, 78; Oxygen, 21; Argon, 1? [Coefficients of absorption: Nitrogen, 0·02; Oxygen, 0·05; Argon, 0·05.] (Inter. B.Sc., London.)

12. An aqueous solution contains 10 gm. of a solute per litre. When 1 litre of a solution is extracted with 100 c.c. of ether, 6 gm. of the solute are extracted. How much more of the solute would be extracted from the aqueous residue by a further 100 c.c. of ether? (C.H.L.)

13. The following are the melting points of copper-antimony alloys. Draw a melting point-composition curve and make what deductions you can from it.

Sb per cent	*M.P.*	*Sb per cent*	*M.P.*
0	1084°	50	675°
10	1008°	55	650°
15	950°	60	620°
20	870°	70	540°
25	775°	75	500°
29	660°	80	521°
35	684°	85	540°
40	695°	90	575°
45	690°	100	630°

14. Using the following data of the melting points of magnesium-zinc alloys, deduce the formula of the compounds formed between them :

Zn per cent	*M.P.*	*Zn per cent*	*M.P.*
0	650°	60	417°
10	612°	70	500°
20	555°	80	560°
30	495°	90	535°
40	440°	95	390°
50	348°	100	419°

15. The freezing points of solutions of sulphuric acid vary with the concentration of the acid according to the figures given below. What evidence do these figures give of the existence of hydrates of sulphuric acid?

H_2SO_4 *per cent*	*F.P.*	H_2SO_4 *per cent*	*F.P.*
0	0°	60	−46°
10	− 9°	63	−41°
20	−24°	66	−43°
30	−53°	70	−14°
40	−47°	75	5°
50	−28°	80	− 2°
55	−40°	83	−22°
58	−57°	90	8°

16. The following figures denote the solubility of barium acetate in water :

Temperature °	Gm. of barium acetate dissolved by 100 gm. of water
0	58
8	62
18	70
25	77
35	76
40	78
50	77
60	75
70	74
80	74

Express these results graphically and interpret the form of the curve, noting that the crystals which separate from the saturated solutions contain the following percentages of barium, viz. below 24° C., 44·3 per cent ; between 25° and 40°, 50·2 per cent ; above 41° C., 53·7 per cent. (O. and C.)

17. 2 gm. of a weak tribasic acid of molecular weight 150 was shaken with a mixture of 100 c.c. of benzene and 50 c.c. of water at 15°. 25 c.c. of the aqueous layer was then found to require 14·5 c.c. of normal sodium hydroxide for neutralisation. Assuming that the acid has the same molecular state in the two solvents, calculate the partition coefficient of the acid between water and benzene at 15°.

18. In an experiment to determine the distribution of benzoic acid between water and benzene, 100 c.c. of water and 100 c.c. of benzene were placed in each of four bottles. Varying amounts of benzoic acid were then added, and the bottles were shaken and allowed to stand at 20° so that equilibrium was reached. 25 c.c. portions of the aqeuous layer and the benzene layer were then removed from each bottle and titrated against standard sodium hydroxide solution with the following results :

	25 c.c. of aqueous layer (no. of c.c. of $N/10$ NaOH required)	25 c.c. of benzene layer (no. of c.c. of $N/10$ NaOH required)
(1)	2·45	3·45
(2)	3·60	7·45
(3)	4·35	10·90
(4)	4·55	11·90

What conclusions do you draw from these figures?

19. 100 c.c. of an aqueous solution contains 10 gm. of a solute, A. The partition coefficient of A between ether and water is 3 : 1, the substance A being more soluble in ether. Compare the weights of A extracted by (*a*) 100 c.c. of ether, (*b*) two successive 50 c.c. quantities of ether.

20. Given that acetic acid has a molecular weight, 60, calculate its apparent molecular weight in chloroform from the data :

C -	0·30	0·40	0·79	1·10	1·40
W -	4·90	5·70	8·00	9·50	10·7

where C and W, in gm.-molecules per litre, represent the equilibrium concentrations of acetic acid in chloroform and water respectively in five different mixtures at one temperature. (O. and C.)

21. Comment on the following results obtained in a distribution experiment :

Gm. benzoic acid in 10 c.c. water	Gm. benzoic acid in 10 c.c. benzene
0·0150	0·242
0·0195	0·412
0·0289	0·970

(N.U.J.B. Schol.)

22. The partition coefficient of a substance, A, between ether and water is 5 : 1, the substance being more soluble in ether. 1 litre of an aqueous solution contains 40 gm. of A. Calculate (*a*) the weight of A extracted by one extraction with 500 c.c. of ether, (*b*) the weight of A extracted by ten successive extractions with 50 c.c. quantities of ether.

23. An organic compound, A, when shaken with a mixture of chloroform and water distributes itself so that :

$$\frac{\text{concentration of } A \text{ in chloroform}}{\text{concentration of } A \text{ in water}} = \frac{4 \cdot 2}{1}.$$

2 gm. of the compound is shaken with 50 c.c. of chloroform and 100 c.c. of water. What is the concentration of A in the water? What volume of the chloroform solution would contain 0·5 gm. of A?

24. The Table below is a record of an experiment in which the viscosities of a series of mixtures of ethyl alcohol and water were measured (the experimental error did not exceed 0·1 per cent). Describe, carefully and critically, the conclusions you would draw from these figures. Mention any independent method by which you could test your conclusion.

Percentage of alcohol (gm. of alcohol in 100 gm. of mixture)	Viscosity	Percentage of alcohol (gm. of alcohol in 100 gm. of mixture)	Viscosity
100	0·0123	35	0·0206
66	0·0175	33	0·0208
50	0·0250	32	0·0215
48	0·0260	31	0·0220
44	0·0266	30	0·0207
42	0·0250	20	0·0193
40	0·0244	0	0·0111

(C.U.O.S.)

***25.** A flask of capacity 1000 c.c. was evacuated and kept at 15°. 500 c.c. of water, also at 15°, was then allowed to enter the flask and was followed by a quantity of gas which measured 500 c.c. at 15° and 760 mm. The flask was stoppered and shaken well, and the final pressure of the gas was found to be 742 mm. Deduce the absorption coefficient of the gas in water at 15°.

***26.** 1 c.c. of water dissolves 0·034 c.c. of oxygen at 0° and 760 mm. pressure of oxygen. A litre flask contains 500 c.c. of water, but no other substance. 1200 c.c. of oxygen, measured at 15° and 760 mm. is then forced into the flask. Calculate the final pressure in the flask, assuming that the flask and its contents remain at 0°.

* 27. The partition coefficient of an organic acid between ether and water is 3 : 1, the acid being more soluble in the ether. 100 c.c. of an aqueous solution of the acid is extracted with successive quantities of 25 c.c. of ether. Calculate the minimum number of such extractions required so that less than 1 per cent of the organic acid remains in aqueous solution.

* 28. The following figures record the solubility of sodium iodide in water at various temperatures. Plot the solubility diagram and discuss what information can be obtained from the curves.

Temperature °	Gm. NaI in 100 gm. solution	Temperature °	Gm. NaI in 100 gm. solution
140	77·0	40	67·2
120	76·3	30	65·5
100	75·4	10	62·8
80	74·7	−10	60·3
60	72·0	−15·2	57·2
50	69·5	−20	51·0
		−30	40·0

(C.U.O.S.)

* 29. A mass of gas which occupies 10 c.c. at 0° and 760 mm. is contained over dry mercury at 15°. A quantity of chloroform, sufficient to leave an excess of the liquid, is then introduced and it is found that the mixture of air and chloroform vapour now occupy 14·1 c.c., the pressure on the mixture being 575 mm. Deduce the vapour pressure of chloroform at 15°.

* 30. Derive and discuss the Langmuir adsorption isotherm. Test the validity of the isotherm using the following data referring to the adsorption of a gas on charcoal:

Pressure, mm. - - - -	100	200	500	900
Gas adsorbed, milligrams per gram	1·57	1·96	2·30	2·42

(A.R.I.C.)

CHAPTER V

LAW OF MASS ACTION

1. Active mass of a reacting substance

The rate of a chemical reaction is directly proportional to the active masses of the reacting substances (law of mass action).

It is assumed that the student is acquainted with the use of the term " active mass " as it applies to solids, miscible and immiscible liquids and gases. Thus, in the reactions represented by the following equations, the active masses of the reacting substances are as stated :

$$(1)\ CaCO_3 \rightleftharpoons CaO + CO_2.$$

Active mass of calcium carbonate = active mass of a solid = a constant at a given temperature.

Active mass of carbon dioxide = mass per unit volume, denoted by square brackets, $[CO_2] = kp$ where p = the pressure of the gas at a given temperature and k = a proportionality constant.

$$(2)\ N_2O_4 \rightleftharpoons 2NO_2.$$

Active mass of $N_2O_4 = [N_2O_4] = k_1 p_{N_2O_4}$, where $p_{N_2O_4}$ = the partial pressure (cf. p. 71) of N_2O_4 in the mixture.

Active mass of $NO_2 = [NO_2]^2 = [k_2 p_{NO_2}]^2 = k_3 p^2_{NO_2}$, where k_2 and k_3 are constants and p_{NO_2} = the partial pressure of NO_2 in the mixture.

It is also assumed that the student is familiar with the use of the terms " velocity constant " and " equilibrium constant " as applied to simple reactions. In the reaction given by equation (2), for example, the velocity constants and equilibrium constant are as follows :

Velocity of reaction from left to right $= k_1[N_2O_4]$, where k_1 = velocity constant.

Velocity of reaction from right to left $= k_2[NO_2]^2$, where $k_2 =$ velocity constant.

$$\frac{[NO_2]^2}{[N_2O_4]} = K = \text{the equilibrium constant.}$$

Since $[NO_2]$ is proportional to the partial pressure of NO_2 and $[N_2O_4]$ is proportional to the partial pressure of N_2O_4,

$$\frac{(p_{NO_2})^2}{(p_{N_2O_4})} = \text{a constant} = K_1.$$

When active masses are expressed in gm.-molecules per litre, the equilibrium constant is denoted by K_c; an equilibrium constant involving partial pressures is denoted by K_p.

Thus:

$$\frac{[NO_2]^2}{[N_2O_4]} = K_c; \quad \frac{(p_{NO_2})^2}{(p_{N_2O_4})} = K_p.$$

The general relation between K_c and K_p is given on p. 96.

The following examples indicate how the mass law can be applied to the determination of the concentration of reacting substances under equilibrium conditions. The student should be familiar with the experimental details of methods of illustrating the law of mass action by the determination of velocity constants and equilibrium constants.

2. Miscellaneous worked examples

Example 50. If a given quantity of phosphorus pentachloride is heated to 250° and allowed to come to equilibrium at atmospheric pressure, it is found to be dissociated to the extent of 80 per cent into phosphorus trichloride and chlorine. If, now, the pressure on this mixture is increased so that finally the equilibrium mixture occupies only one half of its original volume (temperature remaining constant), what will be the percentage dissociation at the new pressure?

The reaction is expressed by the equation:

$$PCl_5 \rightleftharpoons PCl_3 + Cl_2.$$

We assume that initially there is 1 gm.-molecule of phosphorus pentachloride, and that when equilibrium is reached at 250° and 1 atmosphere pressure the total volume of the mixture is V litres. Then, since the dissociation is 80 per cent :

$$\text{Active mass of } PCl_5 = \frac{1-0{\cdot}8}{V} \text{ gm.-molecules per litre.}$$

Similarly :

$$\text{Active mass of } PCl_3 = \frac{0{\cdot}8}{V} \text{ gm.-molecules per litre.}$$

$$\text{Active mass of } Cl_2 = \frac{0{\cdot}8}{V} \text{ gm.-molecules per litre.}$$

The equilibrium constant, K_c, is given by the equation :

$$K_c = \frac{[PCl_3] \times [Cl_2]}{[PCl_5]}.$$

Substituting the known values :

$$K_c = \frac{\frac{0{\cdot}8}{V} \times \frac{0{\cdot}8}{V}}{\frac{0{\cdot}2}{V}} = \frac{3{\cdot}2}{V}.$$

Let x = the fraction dissociated when the total volume of the system has been reduced to half its initial value, that is, to $\frac{V}{2}$.

Then, active mass of $PCl_5 = \frac{1-x}{V/2} = \frac{2(1-x)}{V}$,

and ,, ,, ,, $PCl_3 = \frac{x}{V/2} = \frac{2x}{V}$,

and ,, ,, ,, $Cl_2 = \frac{x}{V/2} = \frac{2x}{V}$.

Since the equilibrium constant must remain unchanged at a fixed temperature,

$$\therefore \frac{\frac{2x}{V} \times \frac{2x}{V}}{2\left(\frac{1-x}{V}\right)} = \frac{2x^2}{(1-x)V} = K = \frac{3{\cdot}2}{V},$$

$$\therefore x^2 + 1{\cdot}6x - 1{\cdot}6 = 0.$$

The roots of this equation are $-2{\cdot}3$ and $0{\cdot}69$. The negative root must clearly be ignored.

$\therefore\ x = 0{\cdot}69$ and percentage dissociation $= 69$.

Example 51. If 1 mole of acetic acid and 1 mole of ethyl alcohol are mixed and the reaction proceeds to equilibrium, the concentration of the acid and water are found to be $\frac{1}{3}$ and $\frac{2}{3}$ mole. If 1 mole of ester and 3 moles of water are mixed, how much ester is present when equilibrium is reached? ($\sqrt{52} = 7{\cdot}21$).

(O. and C.)

The equation for the reaction is :

$$C_2H_5OH + CH_3COOH \rightleftharpoons CH_3COOC_2H_5 + H_2O.$$

Let V = total volume of the reaction mixture at equilibrium.

From the equation, 1 mol. of ethyl alcohol reacts with 1 mol. of acetic acid to form 1 mol. of ethyl acetate and 1 mol. of water (assuming the reaction to be complete).

But at equilibrium only $\frac{2}{3}$ mol. of acetic acid had been converted into ethyl acetate ($\frac{2}{3}$ mol. of water had been formed).

$\therefore$ At equilibrium :

Number of mols. of acetic acid $= \frac{1}{3}$.

" " ethyl alcohol $= \frac{1}{3}$.

" " ethyl acetate $= \frac{2}{3}$.

" " water $= \frac{2}{3}$.

Therefore, the corresponding active masses (= concentrations in gm.-molecules per litre) are as shown under the equation :

$$\underset{\frac{1/3}{V}}{C_2H_5OH} + \underset{\frac{1/3}{V}}{CH_3COOH} \rightleftharpoons \underset{\frac{2/3}{V}}{CH_3COO_2H_5} + \underset{\frac{2/3}{V}}{H_2O}.$$

$\therefore$ At equilibrium :

$$\frac{[CH_3COOC_2H_5] \times [H_2O]}{[C_2H_5OH] \times [CH_3COOH]} = \frac{\frac{\frac{2}{3}}{V} \times \frac{\frac{2}{3}}{V}}{\frac{\frac{1}{3}}{V} \times \frac{\frac{1}{3}}{V}} = 4 = K_c,$$

where K_c = the equilibrium constant for the reaction at the temperature of the experiment.

When 1 mol. of ester and 3 mols. of water are mixed and allowed to come to equilibrium, x mols. of ester will be converted into ethyl alcohol and acetic acid. If V_1 is the total volume of the mixture at equilibrium, then the concentrations of the reacting substances are as shown :

$$\begin{array}{cccc} C_2H_5OH + & CH_3COOH \rightleftharpoons & CH_3COOC_2H_5 + & H_2O. \\ \frac{x}{V_1} & \frac{x}{V_1} & \frac{1-x}{V_1} & \frac{3-x}{V_1} \end{array}$$

$$\therefore \frac{\frac{1-x}{V_1} \times \frac{3-x}{V_1}}{\frac{x}{V_1} \times \frac{x}{V_1}} = 4.$$

$$\therefore \frac{(1-x)(3-x)}{x^2} = 4 \quad \text{or} \quad (1-x)(3-x) = 4x^2.$$

$$\therefore 3x^2 + 4x - 3 = 0.$$

$$\therefore x = \frac{-4 \pm \sqrt{52}}{7} = +0{\cdot}53 \quad \text{or} \quad -1{\cdot}87.$$

Ignoring the negative root :

$$x = 0{\cdot}53 \text{ mol.}$$

$\therefore$ Amount of ester present at equilibrium $= (1-x)$ mol.

$$= 0{\cdot}47 \text{ mol.}$$

Example 52. When 1 gm.-molecule of ethyl alcohol and 1 gm.-molecule of acetic acid are mixed and allowed to come to equilibrium at 25°, the equilibrium mixture contains $\frac{2}{3}$ gm.-molecule of ethyl acetate. How many gm.-molecules of ethyl alcohol must be mixed with 1 gm.-molecule of acetic acid in order that the equilibrium mixture at 25° shall contain $\frac{3}{4}$ gm.-molecule of ethyl acetate?

As in the previous example :

$$\begin{array}{cccc} C_2H_5OH + & CH_3COOH \rightleftharpoons & CH_3COOC_2H_5 + & H_2O, \\ \frac{\frac{1}{3}}{V} & \frac{\frac{1}{3}}{V} & \frac{\frac{2}{3}}{V} & \frac{\frac{2}{3}}{V} \end{array}$$

where V = volume of mixture at equilibrium,

$$\frac{\frac{\frac{2}{3}}{V} \times \frac{\frac{2}{3}}{V}}{\frac{\frac{1}{3}}{V} \times \frac{\frac{1}{3}}{V}} = 4 = K_c.$$

Let n gm.-molecules of ethyl alcohol be required to produce $\frac{3}{4}$ gm.-molecule of ethyl acetate at equilibrium. Then, equilibrium concentrations are as shown (V_1 being the volume of the reaction mixture):

$$\underset{\frac{n-\frac{3}{4}}{V_1}}{C_2H_5OH} + \underset{\frac{1-\frac{3}{4}}{V_1}}{CH_3COOH} \rightleftharpoons \underset{\frac{\frac{3}{4}}{V_1}}{CH_3COOC_2H_5} + \underset{\frac{\frac{3}{4}}{V_1}}{H_2O}$$

For equilibrium:

$$\frac{[CH_3COOC_2H_5]\times[H_2O]}{[C_2H_5OH]\times[CH_3COOH]}=4.$$

Substituting active masses:

$$\frac{\frac{\frac{3}{4}}{V_1}\times\frac{\frac{3}{4}}{V_1}}{\frac{n-\frac{3}{4}}{V_1}\times\frac{\frac{1}{4}}{V_1}}=\frac{9}{4\left(n-\frac{3}{4}\right)}=4.$$

From which $n=1\frac{5}{16}$ gm.-molecules.

Weights given in gm. must be converted into gm.-molecules before being used in equations derived from the mass law. Thus, in the equilibrium discussed in Examples 51 and 52, a quantity of ethyl alcohol expressed in gm. would be divided by 46 (the molecular weight of ethyl alcohol), the weight of acetic acid being divided similarly by 60 (the molecular weight of acetic acid). For example, a mixture of 92 gm. of ethyl alcohol and 90 gm. of acetic acid would give the following concentrations when expressed in gm.-molecules per litre:

$$\text{concentration of ethyl alcohol}=\frac{92/46}{V}=\frac{2}{V},$$

$$\text{,, \quad ,, acetic acid}=\frac{90/60}{V}=\frac{3/2}{V}.$$

Example 53. What weight of ethyl acetate will be formed by the interaction of 138 gm. of ethyl alcohol and 240 gm. of acetic acid at 25°?

$$\text{138 gm. of ethyl alcohol}=\frac{138}{46}=3 \text{ gm.-molecules.}$$

$$\text{240 gm. of acetic acid}=\frac{240}{60}=4 \quad \text{,,} \quad \text{,,}$$

Then if x gm.-molecules of ethyl acetate are formed at equilibrium, the concentrations of the reacting substances at equilibrium are as shown in the equation :

$$\underset{\frac{3-x}{V}}{C_2H_5OH} + \underset{\frac{4-x}{V}}{CH_3COOH} \rightleftharpoons \underset{\frac{x}{V}}{CH_3COOC_2H_5} + \underset{\frac{x}{V}}{H_2O}.$$

∴ Using the value for the equilibrium constant given in Example 51 :

$$\frac{x^2}{(3-x)(4-x)} = 4.$$

From which $x = 2{\cdot}27$ gm.-molecules.

But the molecular weight of ethyl acetate = 88.

∴ Number of gm. of ethyl acetate at equilibrium

$$= 2{\cdot}27 \times 88 = \mathbf{199{\cdot}8\ gm.}$$

Example 54. A mixture of 7·8 gm. of ethyl alcohol and 10 gm. of acetic acid was kept at a constant temperature until equilibrium was established when 2·7 gm. of acetic acid remained in the mixture. Calculate the equilibrium constant of the reaction correct to one decimal place. Determine also the equilibrium mixture formed by allowing 12 gm. of ethyl alcohol, 8·1 gm. of acetic acid, 4 gm. of ethyl acetate and 10·8 gm. of water to react under the given circumstances.

(A.R.I.C.)

Converting the given weights to gm.-molecules, the concentrations of ethyl alcohol and acetic acid in gm.-molecules per litre are respectively $\frac{7{\cdot}8}{46}\Big/V$ and $\frac{10}{60}\Big/V$, where V is the total volume of the reaction mixture in litres. Then, if at equilibrium x gm.-molecules of ethyl alcohol have undergone reaction, the equilibrium concentrations are those shown in the equation :

$$\underset{\frac{\left(\frac{7{\cdot}8}{46}-x\right)}{V}}{C_2H_5OH} + \underset{\frac{\left(\frac{10}{60}-x\right)}{V}}{CH_3COOH} \rightleftharpoons \underset{\frac{x}{V}}{CH_3COOC_2H_5} + \underset{\frac{x}{V}}{H_2O}\ ;$$

$$\therefore\ K_c = \frac{\frac{x}{V} \times \frac{x}{V}}{\frac{\left(\frac{7\cdot8}{46} - x\right)}{V} \times \frac{\left(\frac{10}{60} - x\right)}{V}} = \frac{x^2}{\left(\frac{7\cdot8}{46} - x\right)\left(\frac{10}{60} - x\right)}.$$

But $\left(\frac{10}{60} - x\right)$ = number of gm.-molecules of acetic acid in V litres at equilibrium

$$= \frac{2\cdot7}{60}.$$

$$\therefore\ -x = \frac{2\cdot7}{60} - \frac{10}{60} = -\frac{7\cdot3}{60} \quad \text{and} \quad x = \frac{7\cdot3}{60}.$$

$$\therefore\ K_c = \frac{\frac{7\cdot3}{60} \times \frac{7\cdot3}{60}}{\left(\frac{7\cdot8}{46} - \frac{7\cdot3}{60}\right)\left(\frac{10}{60} - \frac{7\cdot3}{60}\right)} = 6\cdot8.$$

To determine the equilibrium concentrations from the given initial amounts of reactants, we write :

$$\begin{array}{cccc} C_2H_5OH & + \ CH_3COOH & \rightleftharpoons CH_3COOC_2H_5 + & H_2O \\ \frac{\left(\frac{12}{46} - x\right)}{V} & \frac{\left(\frac{8\cdot1}{60} - x\right)}{V} & \frac{\left(\frac{4}{88} + x\right)}{V} & \frac{\left(\frac{10\cdot8}{18} + x\right)}{V} \end{array}$$

It is well to determine the sign of x at this stage.

If $\dfrac{\frac{4}{88} \times \frac{10\cdot8}{18}}{\frac{12}{46} \times \frac{8\cdot1}{60}} > 6\cdot8,$ then x is $-$ve and the reaction proceeds from right to left.

If $\dfrac{\frac{4}{88} \times \frac{10\cdot8}{18}}{\frac{12}{46} \times \frac{8\cdot1}{60}} < 6\cdot8,$ then x is $+$ve and the reaction proceeds from left to right.

But $\dfrac{\frac{4}{88} \times \frac{10\cdot8}{18}}{\frac{12}{46} \times \frac{8\cdot1}{60}} \doteqdot 0\cdot8.$ $\therefore$ x is $+$ve.

$$\therefore\ \frac{\left(\frac{4}{88} + x\right)\left(\frac{10\cdot8}{18} + x\right)}{\left(\frac{12}{46} - x\right)\left(\frac{8\cdot1}{60} - x\right)} = 6\cdot8.$$

Solutions to this equation are $x = 0{\cdot}072$ or $0{\cdot}5$, and the smaller value must be taken since x cannot exceed 12/46.

$$\left.\begin{aligned} \therefore\ [C_2H_5OH] &= \left(\frac{12}{46} - 0{\cdot}072\right) \times 46 \text{ gm.} = 8{\cdot}7 \text{ gm.} \\ [CH_3COOH] &= \left(\frac{8{\cdot}1}{60} - 0{\cdot}072\right) \times 60 \text{ gm.} = 3{\cdot}8 \text{ gm.} \\ [CH_3COOC_2H_5] &= \left(\frac{4}{88} + 0{\cdot}072\right) \times 88 \text{ gm.} = 10{\cdot}34 \text{ gm.} \\ [H_2O] &= \left(\frac{10{\cdot}8}{18} + 0{\cdot}072\right) \times 18 \text{ gm.} = 12{\cdot}1 \text{ gm.} \end{aligned}\right\} \text{all in } V \text{ litres.}$$

In gaseous reactions it is often convenient to use the partial pressures of the reactants instead of the actual concentrations in gm.-molecules per litre (see p. 87). Since, at a given temperature, the partial pressure of a gas is proportional to the number of molecules per c.c., it must also be proportional to the concentration expressed in gm.-molecules per litre.

Example 55. At a pressure of 1 atmosphere and at 40°, nitrogen peroxide contains 60 per cent by volume of NO_2 molecules. Calculate the percentage dissociation of N_2O_4 and the equilibrium constant in terms of the partial pressures of N_2O_4 and NO_2. Hence deduce the percentage dissociation at the same temperature but under a pressure of 5 atmospheres.

The equation is :

$$\underset{1-x}{N_2O_4} \rightleftharpoons \underset{2x}{2NO_2}$$

Then, as shown on p. 119, if x = fraction of N_2O_4 dissociated, $2x$ gm.-molecules of NO_2 are formed and the percentage of NO_2 by volume $= \dfrac{2x}{1+x} \times 100$.

$$\therefore\ \frac{2x}{1+x} \times 100 = 60.$$

$\therefore$ Percentage dissociation $= 100x =$ **42·8 per cent.**

To derive the mass law equation, let $p_{N_2O_4}$ and p_{NO_2} denote the partial pressures of N_2O_4 and NO_2 respectively :

$$\underset{p_{N_2O_4}}{N_2O_4} \rightleftharpoons \underset{p_{NO_2}}{2NO_2}$$

According to the mass law :

$$\frac{[NO_2]^2}{[N_2O_4]} = K_c.$$

Substituting partial pressures :

$$\frac{(p_{NO_2})^2}{p_{N_2O_4}} = K_p.$$

To find the partial pressures we note that the total pressure of the gaseous mixture is 1 atmosphere. But there are 60 per cent of NO_2 molecules.

$$\therefore\ p_{NO_2} = 1 \times \frac{60}{100} = 0{\cdot}6 \text{ atmosphere,}$$

$$p_{N_2O_4} = 0{\cdot}4 \text{ atmosphere.}$$

$$\therefore\ K_p = \frac{0{\cdot}6 \times 0{\cdot}6}{0{\cdot}4} = 0{\cdot}9.$$

Let p'_{NO_2} = the partial pressure of NO_2 at the same temperature but at a pressure of 5 atmospheres and $p'_{N_2O_4}$ = the partial pressure of N_2O_4 at 5 atmospheres.

Then
$$\frac{(p'_{NO_2})^2}{p'_{N_2O_4}} = 0{\cdot}9.$$

But :
$$p'_{NO_2} + p'_{N_2O_4} = 5.$$

$$\therefore\ \frac{(p'_{NO_2})^2}{5 - p'_{NO_2}} = 0{\cdot}9.$$

$$\therefore\ p'_{NO_2} = 1{\cdot}738 \text{ atmospheres.}$$

Then, if x_1 = fraction by weight of N_2O_4 dissociated into NO_2 :

$$\frac{2x}{1+x} = \frac{\text{no. of gm.-molecules of } NO_2}{\text{total no. of gm.-molecules}}$$

$$= \frac{\text{partial pressure of } NO_2}{\text{total pressure}}.$$

$$\therefore\ \frac{2x}{1+x} = \frac{1{\cdot}738}{5}.$$

$$\therefore\ x = 0{\cdot}214 \text{ and percentage dissociation} = 21{\cdot}4.$$

*** 3. Relation between K_c and K_p**

In the reversible reaction :

$$aA+bB+cC+\ldots \rightleftharpoons qQ+rR+sS+\ldots,$$

where A, B, C, etc., and Q, R, S, etc., are the molecular formulae of the reacting substances and a, b, c, etc., and q, r, s, etc., are the corresponding numbers of the molecules taking part in the reaction, then the order of the reaction from left to right $=a+b+c+\ldots$, and the order of the reaction from right to left $=q+r+s+\ldots$.

The equilibrium constant, K_c (see p. 87), is given by the expression :

$$K_c=\frac{[Q]^q\times[R]^r\times[S]^s\times\ldots}{[A]^a\times[B]^b\times[C]^c\times\ldots},$$

where square brackets denote concentrations in gm.-molecules per litre. As a matter of convention the equilibrium constants (K_c and K_p) are always expressed with the active masses of the resultants as the numerator, in this instance, the substances represented by Q, R, S, etc.

If P_A, P_B, P_C, P_Q, P_R, P_S denote the partial pressures of the substances indicated by the subscripts when equilibrium is reached, then the equilibrium constant, K_p, is given by the equation :

$$K_p=\frac{[P_Q]^q\times[P_R]^r\times[P_S]^s\times\ldots}{[P_A]^a\times[P_B]^b\times[P_C]^c\times\ldots}.$$

The relation between K_c and K_p can then be obtained in the following manner.

Since $[A]$=number of gm.-molecules of A per litre,

$$\therefore\ [A]=\frac{1}{V_A},$$

where V_A is the volume in litres of the gaseous mixture containing 1 gm.-molecule of A.

If, then, P_A is the partial pressure of A :

$$[A]=\frac{1}{V_A}=\frac{P_A}{RT},$$

assuming that A obeys the gas equation.

Similarly :

$$[B]=\frac{P_B}{RT};\quad [C]=\frac{P_C}{RT};\quad [Q]=\frac{P_Q}{RT},\text{ etc.}$$

$$\therefore\ K_c=\frac{[Q]^q\times[R]^r\times[S]^s\times\ldots}{[A]^a\times[B]^b\times[C]^c\times\ldots}$$

$$=\frac{\left(\frac{P_Q}{RT}\right)^q\times\left(\frac{P_R}{RT}\right)^r\times\left(\frac{P_S}{RT}\right)^s\times\ldots}{\left(\frac{P_A}{RT}\right)^a\times\left(\frac{P_B}{RT}\right)^b\times\left(\frac{P_C}{RT}\right)^c\times\ldots}$$

$$=\frac{(P_Q)^q\times(P_R)^r\times(P_S)^s\times\ldots}{(P_A)^a\times(P_B)^b\times[P_C]^c\times\ldots}\times(RT)^{a+b+c+\ldots-q-r-s-\ldots}$$

$$=\mathbf{K_p(RT)^{\Sigma n}}. \qquad (46)$$

where Σn = the algebraic sum of the number of molecules taking part in the reaction as given by the stoichiometric equation, the numbers of the molecules of **products** being taken as negative.

The values for K_p and Σn are given in the following table of various reactions :

Reaction	K_p	Σn
$H_2+Cl_2=2HCl$	$\frac{(p_{HCl})^2}{(p_{H_2})\times(p_{Cl_2})}$	0
$2H_2+O_2=2H_2O$ (gas)	$\frac{(p_{H_2O})^2}{(p_{H_2})^2\times(p_{O_2})}$	+ 1
$2H_2O=2H_2+O_2$	$\frac{(p_{H_2})^2\times(p_{O_2})}{(p_{H_2O})^2}$	− 1
$2NH_3=N_2+3H_2$	$\frac{(p_{N_2})\times(p_{H_2})^3}{(p_{NH_3})^2}$	− 2

It should be noted that when the reaction does not involve a change in the total number of molecules (and, consequently, in the total volume), then

$$\Sigma n=0,\quad (RT)^{\Sigma n}=(RT)^0=1,\quad\text{and}\quad K_c=K_p.$$

* **Example 56.** At 400° and at a total pressure of 10 atmospheres, ammonia is dissociated to the extent of 98 per cent. Calculate K_p and K_c for this reaction at 400°.

The equation for the reaction is :

$$\underset{(1-x)}{2NH_3} \rightleftharpoons \underset{x/2}{N_2} + \underset{3x/2}{3H_2}$$

If x is the fraction of ammonia dissociated at equilibrium, then, from equation, total number of gm.-molecules of all gases at equilibrium $=(1+x)$. If, therefore, P is the total pressure of the mixture at equilibrium :

$$\text{partial pressure of ammonia} = \left(\frac{1-x}{1+x}\right) \times P,$$

$$\text{,, ,, ,, nitrogen} = \left(\frac{x/2}{1+x}\right) \times P,$$

$$\text{,, ,, ,, hydrogen} = \left(\frac{3x/2}{1+x}\right) \times P.$$

But at equilibrium :

$$\frac{P_{N_2} \times P^3_{H_2}}{P^2_{NH_3}} = K_p \text{ where } \begin{cases} P_{N_2} = \text{partial pressure of } N_2, \\ P_{H_2} = \text{ ,, ,, ,, } H_2, \\ P_{NH_3} = \text{ ,, ,, ,, } NH_3. \end{cases}$$

Substituting the values given above :

$$K_p = \frac{\left\{\left(\frac{x/2}{1+x}\right) \times P\right\} \times \left\{\left(\frac{3x/2}{1+x}\right) \times P\right\}^3}{\left\{\frac{(1-x)}{(1+x)} \times P\right\}^2} = \frac{27x^4P^2}{16(1+x)^2(1-x)^2}.$$

From which, since $x=0{\cdot}98$ and $P=10$ atmospheres :

$$K_p = \frac{27 \times (0{\cdot}98)^4 \times 100}{16 \times (1{\cdot}98)^2 \times (0{\cdot}02)^2} = 9{\cdot}92 \times 10^4.$$

To calculate K_c, assume that the total volume of the equilibrium mixture is V litres and that there was originally 1 gm.-molecule of ammonia. Then the equilibrium concentration, in gm.-molecules per litre, are as shown in the equation:

$$\underset{\left(\frac{1-x}{V}\right)}{2NH_3} \rightleftharpoons \underset{\left(\frac{x/2}{V}\right)}{N_2} + \underset{\left(\frac{3x/2}{V}\right)}{3H_2}$$

$$\therefore K_c = \frac{\left(\frac{x/2}{V}\right)\left(\frac{3x/2}{V}\right)^3}{\left(\frac{1-x}{V}\right)^2} = \frac{27x^4}{16(1-x)^2} \times \frac{1}{V^2}.$$

But if a total of $(1+x)$ gm.-molecules of a gas occupy a volume V litres at a pressure P and temperature $T°$ A, then :

$$PV=(1+x)\,RT,$$

since $PV=nRT$ where n = number of gm.-molecules of gas.

$$\therefore\ V=\frac{(1+x)\,RT}{P}.$$

Substituting this value :

$$K_c=\frac{27x^4}{16(1-x)^2}\times\frac{P^2}{(1+x)^2}\times\frac{1}{(RT)^2}$$

$$=K_p\times(RT)^{-2}.\ \ldots\ldots\ldots\ldots\ldots\ldots\ldots\ldots\ldots\ldots(47)$$

The term $(RT)^{-2}$ results from the increase in volume in which 2 gm.-molecules of ammonia form four gm.-molecules of a mixture of hydrogen and nitrogen (cf. p. 97).

To evaluate R in equation (47), we note that the pressure is in atmospheres and the volume in litres. But for 1 gm.-molecule of any gas :

$$PV=RT \quad\text{and}\quad R=\frac{PV}{T},$$

and since 1 gm.-molecule of any gas occupies 22·4 litres at *N.T.P.* :

$$\therefore\ R=\frac{1\times 22{\cdot}4}{273}.$$

$$\therefore\ K_c=K_p\times(RT)^{-2}=K_p\times\left(\frac{1\times 22{\cdot}4\times 673}{273}\right)^{-2}$$

$$=\frac{K_p\times(273)^2}{(22{\cdot}4\times 673)^2}=32{\cdot}55.$$

The same result may be obtained directly by considering the active masses, in gm.-molecules per litre, of the reacting gases.

Let V = volume in litres at 400°, that is, at 673° A, and 10 atmospheres, occupied by the equilibrium mixture which results from 1 gm.-molecule of ammonia. These active masses are as shown in the equation :

$$\begin{array}{ccccc} 2NH_3 & \rightleftharpoons & N_2 & + & 3H_2 \\ \frac{1-x}{V} & & \frac{x/2}{V} & & \frac{3x/2}{V} \end{array}$$

Total number of gm.-molecules $=(1+x)=1{\cdot}98$. But 1 gm.-molecule of a gas occupies 22·4 litres at *N.T.P.*

$\therefore$ 1·98 gm.-molecules of a gas occupy

$$22 \cdot 4 \times \frac{673}{273} \times \frac{1}{10} \times 1 \cdot 98 \text{ litres} \quad \text{at } 400^\circ \text{ and } 10 \text{ atmospheres}$$

$$= 10 \cdot 93 \text{ litres.}$$

$$\therefore \text{ Concentration of ammonia} = \frac{1-x}{V}$$

$$= \frac{0 \cdot 02}{10 \cdot 93} \text{ gm.-molecules per litre.}$$

$$\text{Concentration of nitrogen} = \frac{x/2}{V}$$

$$= \frac{0 \cdot 49}{10 \cdot 93} \text{ gm.-molecules per litre.}$$

$$\text{Concentration of hydrogen} = \frac{3x/2}{V}$$

$$= \frac{1 \cdot 47}{10 \cdot 93} \text{ gm.-molecules per litre.}$$

$$\therefore K_c = \frac{\left(\frac{0 \cdot 49}{10 \cdot 93}\right) \times \left(\frac{1 \cdot 47}{10 \cdot 93}\right)^3}{\left(\frac{0 \cdot 02}{10 \cdot 93}\right)^2} = 32 \cdot 55.$$

Example 57. Nitrogen peroxide is dissociated to the extent of 53 per cent at 60° and at a total pressure of 1 atmosphere. Calculate (*a*) the percentage dissociation at 60° and at a total pressure of 2000 mm. of mercury, (*b*) the pressure at which nitrogen peroxide would be dissociated to the extent of 67 per cent at the same temperature.

The equation for the dissociation is :

$$\underset{(1-x)}{N_2O_4} \rightleftharpoons \underset{2x}{2NO_2}$$

If x = fraction dissociated, then total number of molecules is $(1+x)$ and, as on p. 98 :

$$\text{Partial pressure of } N_2O_4(p_{N_2O_4}) = \left(\frac{1-x}{1+x}\right) \times P,$$

$$\text{,, \quad ,, \quad ,, } NO_2(p_{NO_2}) = \left(\frac{2x}{1+x}\right) \times P,$$

where P = total pressure = 760 mm.

$$\therefore\ K_p=\frac{p^2_{NO_2}}{p_{N_2O_4}}=\frac{\left(\frac{2x}{1+x}\right)^2\times P^2}{\left(\frac{1-x}{1+x}\right)\times P}=\frac{4x^2P}{(1+x)(1-x)}$$

$$=\frac{4\times0\cdot53\times0\cdot53\times760}{1\cdot53\times0\cdot47}=\mathbf{1\cdot19\times10^3}.$$

Let x = fraction dissociated at 2000 mm. pressure.

Then $$\frac{4x^2\times2000}{(1+x)(1-x)}=1\cdot19\times10^3.$$

From which $x=0\cdot36$ or 36 per cent.

Let P = pressure in mm. at which the dissociation is 67 per cent.

Then :

$$K_p=1\cdot19\times10^3=\frac{4x^2P}{(1+x)(1-x)}=\frac{4\times0\cdot67\times0\cdot67\times P}{1\cdot67\times0\cdot33}.$$

From which : $P=365$ mm.

* 4. Irreversible first order reactions

Monomolecular or first order reactions are of the type :

$$A\rightarrow mB$$

or

$$A\rightarrow mC+nD+\ldots.$$

Assume, in each case, that the concentration of A, at the beginning of the reaction, is a gm.-molecules per litre. Then, since the reaction is monomolecular, a is also the active mass of A. After a time t (in arbitrary units) we may assume that x gm.-molecules have undergone reaction, leaving the concentration of unchanged A equal to $(a-x)$ gm.-molecules per litre.

Then, by the Mass Law :

$$\text{Rate of change of } A=\frac{dx}{dt}=k(a-x),$$

where k is the velocity constant.

$$\therefore\ \int\frac{dx}{(a-x)}=\int k\,dt+C.$$

$$\therefore\ -\log_e(a-x)=kt+C.$$

But when $t=0$, $x=0$;

$$\therefore\ C=-\log_e a.$$

$$\therefore\ k=\frac{-\log_e(a-x)+\log_e a}{t}=\frac{1}{t}\log_e\left(\frac{a}{a-x}\right)\ \ldots\ldots(48)$$

* **Example 58.** A solution of cane sugar is hydrolysed to the extent of 20 per cent after 30 minutes. After what time, from the beginning of the reaction, would the solution be hydrolysed to the extent of 75 per cent, assuming the conditions of the experiment to remain the same?

The equation for the reaction is:

$$C_{12}H_{22}O_{11}+H_2O=C_6H_{12}O_6 \quad + \quad C_6H_{12}O_6$$

(equimolecular proportions of glucose and fructose)

The reaction from left to right is, therefore, theoretically bimolecular.

Starting with a gm.-molecules of cane sugar and b gm.-molecules of water, the rate of reaction is given, initially, by the equation:

$$\frac{dx}{dt}=k\left(\frac{a}{V}\right)\left(\frac{b}{V}\right),$$

where V = the total volume in litres of the cane sugar solution.

After a time, t, x gm.-molecules of the cane sugar have been hydrolysed so that:

$$\frac{dx}{dt}=k\left(\frac{a-x}{V}\right)\left(\frac{b-x}{V}\right),$$

assuming that V remains constant.

Since, however, water is in large excess, its active mass may be considered constant, so that x may be ignored in comparison with b.

Denoting the active mass of the water by K, a constant:

Rate of hydrolysis of cane sugar after a time, t,

$$=\frac{dx}{dt}=k\left(\frac{a-x}{V}\right)K=k_1(a-x),$$

since V is also a constant for a given experiment and

$$k_1=\frac{kK}{V}=\text{a constant.}$$

$\therefore$ After a time t minutes:

$$\frac{dx}{dt}=k_1(a-x),$$

and

$$k_1t=\log_e\left(\frac{a}{a-x}\right) \quad \ldots\ldots\ldots\ldots\ldots\ldots\ldots (49)$$

At the end of 30 minutes, 20 per cent of the cane sugar is hydrolysed, so that assuming the reaction to have been started with a gm.-molecules, the amount of hydrolysis after 30 minutes is $a/5$ gm.-molecules.

Substituting in equation (49):

$$k_1 \times 30 = \log_e \frac{a}{(a - \frac{1}{5}a)} = \log_e \tfrac{5}{4}.$$

If t minutes is the time required for 75 per cent hydrolysis, then $x = \frac{3}{4}a$.

$$\therefore\ k_1 \times t = \log_e \frac{a}{(a - \frac{3}{4}a)} = \log_e 4. \qquad \text{.............(50)}$$

Eliminating k_1 between equations (49) and (50):

$$\frac{t}{30} = \frac{\log_e 4}{\log_e \frac{5}{4}} = \frac{\log_e 10 \times \log_{10} 4}{\log_e 10 \times \log_{10} \frac{5}{4}} = \frac{0{\cdot}6021}{0{\cdot}0969}.$$

From which:

$$t = 186{\cdot}4 \text{ minutes.}$$

* **Example 59.** In an experiment on the inversion of cane sugar the following polarimeter readings (α) were taken at the stated times (t). Show that the observed rate of reaction corresponds with a reaction of the first order. After what time would you expect a zero reading on the polarimeter?

t (min.)	0	60	120	180	360	∞
α°	$+13{\cdot}1$	$+11{\cdot}6$	$+10{\cdot}2$	$+9{\cdot}0$	$+5{\cdot}87$	$-3{\cdot}8$

As in Fig. 11, let α_0 = polarimeter reading at the beginning of the experiment and α_∞ = the reading when $t = \infty$, that is, when the inversion is complete (using the common convention angles measured to the right of the zero are positive, those measured to the left of the zero are negative).

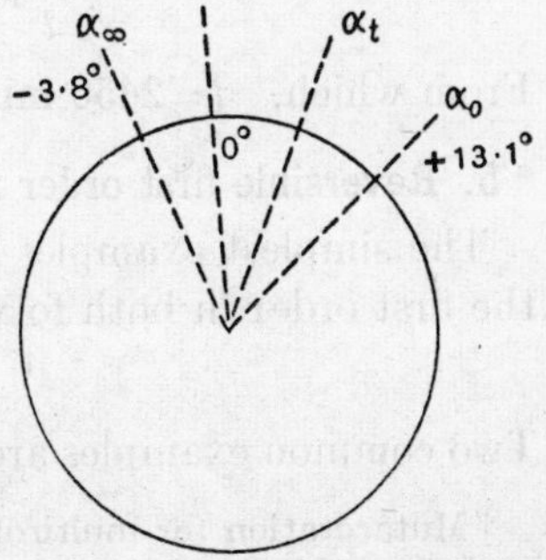

Fig. 11. Use of polarimeter in calculating the velocity constant of inversion of cane sugar.

Then the total amount of inversion which can take place is proportional to the arithmetical sum of the two angles α_0 and α_∞, that is, the algebraic sum of their difference, $\alpha_0 - \alpha_\infty$,

$$= 13{\cdot}1^\circ + 3{\cdot}8^\circ = 16{\cdot}9^\circ.$$

Similarly, the amount of inversion which still has to take place after a time, t, is proportional to the arithmetical sum of α_t and α_∞ that is, to their algebraic difference, $\alpha_t - \alpha_\infty$.

Therefore, by comparison with equation (48):

$$k = \frac{1}{t} \log_e \frac{\alpha_0 - \alpha_\infty}{\alpha_t - \alpha_\infty} \quad \text{.......................(51)}$$

Since it is sufficient to show that k is constant, we can use the equation:

$$k_1 = \frac{1}{t} \log_{10} \frac{\alpha_0 - \alpha_\infty}{\alpha_t - \alpha_\infty}.$$

Let k_{60} denote the value of k, obtained from the reading after 60 minutes.

Then $$k_{60} = \frac{1}{60} \log_{10} \frac{(13{\cdot}1 + 3{\cdot}8)}{(11{\cdot}6 + 3{\cdot}8)} = 0{\cdot}000673.$$

Similarly:

$$k_{120} = \frac{1}{120} \log_{10} \frac{(13{\cdot}1 + 3{\cdot}8)}{(10{\cdot}2 + 3{\cdot}8)} = 0{\cdot}000681,$$

$$k_{180} = \frac{1}{180} \log_{10} \frac{(13{\cdot}1 + 3{\cdot}8)}{(9{\cdot}0 + 3{\cdot}8)} = 0{\cdot}000667,$$

$$k_{360} = \frac{1}{360} \log_{10} \frac{(13{\cdot}1 + 3{\cdot}8)}{(5{\cdot}87 + 3{\cdot}8)} = 0{\cdot}000673.$$

The reaction is clearly monomolecular, the average value of k being 0·000673. To determine the time of zero reading, we put $\alpha_t = 0$ in equation (51), and obtain t from the known value of the velocity constant.

$$\therefore \; \frac{1}{t} \log_{10} \frac{16{\cdot}9}{3{\cdot}8} = 0{\cdot}000673.$$

From which, $t = 2450$ **minutes.**

* 5. Reversible first order reactions

The simplest examples are those in which the reaction is of the first order in both forward and reverse directions:

$$A \rightleftharpoons B.$$

Two common examples are mutarotation † and the formation of

† Mutarotation (or multirotation) can be defined as a change in the optical activity of a solution due to structural change in the dissolved substance. The classical example is glucose, which in water can be represented as an equilibrium mixture of α- and β-glucose, the specific rotations of which are 111·2° and 17·5° respectively, while the equilibrium mixture has a specific rotation of 52·5°.

lactones.† If, in a reaction such as the above, we assume that the initial concentration of A is a gm.-molecules per litre and that after a time t, x gm.-molecules of B are present, then the rate of the forward reaction is given by the equation :

$$\frac{dx}{dt}=k_1(a-x).$$

The rate of the opposing reaction is similarly :

$$-\frac{dx}{dt}=k_2x,$$

(the minus sign to show that the equation gives the rate of conversion of B to A).

The observed rate of reaction from left to right is clearly the difference in the rates of the forward and opposing reactions.

$$\therefore \frac{dx}{dt}=k_1(a-x)-k_2x.$$

Let e denote the value of x when equilibrium is reached. Since the rates of the forward and opposing reactions are then equal :

$$k_1(a-e)=k_2e\ ;$$

$$\therefore\ a=\frac{k_1+k_2}{k_1}\cdot e.$$

Substituting in equation :

$$\frac{dx}{dt}=(k_1+k_2)e-(k_1+k_2)x\ ;$$

$$\therefore \int\frac{dx}{(e-x)}=\int(k_1+k_2)\,dt+C\ ;$$

$$\therefore\ -\log_e(e-x)=(k_1+k_2)t+C.$$

When $x=0$, $t=0$, so that $C=-\log_e e$;

$$\therefore\ k_1+k_2=\frac{1}{t}\log_e\frac{e}{(e-x)}\ \dots\dots\dots\dots\dots\dots(51a)$$

† Lactones are the inner anhydrides of γ- and δ- hydroxy acids

$$CH_2OH\,.\,CH_2\,.\,CH_2\,.\,COOH \rightleftharpoons \underbrace{CH_2\,.\,CH_2\,CH_2\,C}_{O}{=}O+H_2O$$

γ-hydroxy butyric acid — butyrolactone

In aqueous solution, the active mass of water may be taken as constant, so that the formation of a lactone reduces to the simple reversible reaction of the type :

$$A\rightleftharpoons B.$$

The expression is easily remembered by noting that it is of the same form as the ordinary monomolecular equation, but that k_1+k_2 replaces k and e replaces a.

* **Example 60.** An optically active substance undergoing mutarotation gave the following readings. Show that the reaction is an opposing monomolecular one.

t (mins.)	0	180	300	420	1440	∞
$\alpha°$	189	169	156	146	84·5	31·3

For an opposing monomolecular reaction:

$$\frac{1}{t}\log_e\frac{e}{(e-x)}=\text{a constant.}$$

Inspection of Fig. 12 shows that

$$e \propto A\hat{O}C \quad \text{and} \quad x \propto B\hat{O}C\,;$$

$$\therefore \frac{1}{t}\log_e\frac{e}{e-x}=\frac{1}{t}\log_e\frac{\alpha_0-\alpha_e}{\alpha_t-\alpha_e}=\frac{1}{t}\log_e\frac{\alpha_0-\alpha_\infty}{\alpha_t-\alpha_\infty}.$$

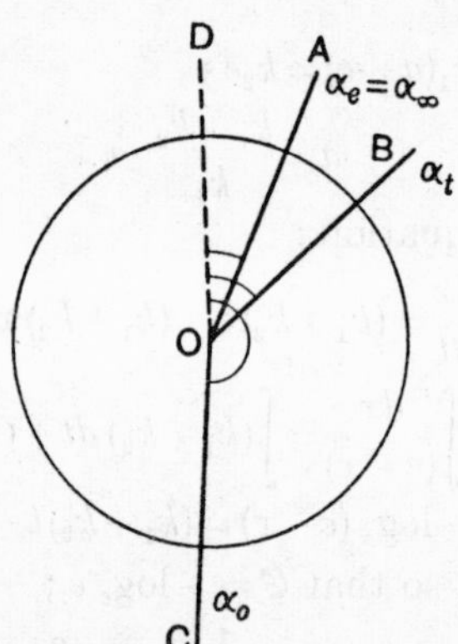

FIG. 12. Use of polarimeter for studying reversible reactions of the first order. $\widehat{DOC}=189°$; $\widehat{DOA}=31·3°$.

Since it is sufficient to show that the expression is constant, we can tabulate the values of $\frac{1}{t}\log_{10}\frac{\alpha_0-\alpha_\infty}{\alpha_t-\alpha_\infty}$ as follows.

For $t=180$,

$$\frac{1}{t}\log_{10}\frac{\alpha_0-\alpha_\infty}{\alpha_t-\alpha_\infty}=\frac{1}{180}\log_{10}\frac{157·7}{137·7}=3·272\times10^{-4}.$$

For $t=300$,

$$\frac{1}{t}\log_{10}\frac{\alpha_0-\alpha_\infty}{\alpha_t-\alpha_\infty}=\frac{1}{300}\log_{10}\frac{157{\cdot}7}{124{\cdot}7}=3{\cdot}39\times10^{-4}.$$

Similarly, for $t=420$ and $t=1440$, the corresponding values are $3{\cdot}29\times10^{-4}$ and $3{\cdot}28\times10^{-4}$ respectively in good agreement with a monomolecular constant.

* 6. Irreversible second order reactions

These reactions are of the type :

$$A+B=mC+nD+\ldots\ldots\ldots\ldots\ldots\ldots \quad (52)$$

or

$$2A=mC+nD+\ldots\ldots\ldots\ldots\ldots\ldots \quad (53)$$

The Mass Law applied to a reaction of the type represented by equation (52) gives, for the velocity of reaction at any time, the equation :

$$\frac{dx}{dt}=k(a-x)(b-x),$$

where a and b are the initial concentrations in gm.-molecules of A and B and x is the number of gm.-molecules per litre of A which have undergone reaction with an equal number of gm.-molecules of B, after a time, t, from the beginning of the reaction.

$$\therefore \frac{dx}{(a-x)(b-x)}=k\,dt.$$

$$\therefore \int\frac{dx}{(a-x)(b-x)}=\int k\,dt+C.$$

Putting $x=0$, when $t=0$, and substituting in the integral :

$$\frac{1}{(b-a)}\log_e\frac{(b-x)}{(a-x)}=kt+C,$$

we find

$$C=\frac{1}{(b-a)}\log_e\left(\frac{b}{a}\right).$$

$$\therefore kt=\frac{1}{(b-a)}\log_e\frac{(b-x)}{(a-x)}-\frac{1}{(b-a)}\log_e\left(\frac{b}{a}\right)$$

$$=\frac{1}{(b-a)}\log_e\left\{\frac{a(b-x)}{b(a-x)}\right\}.$$

$$\therefore k=\frac{1}{t}\cdot\frac{1}{(b-a)}\log_e\left\{\frac{a(b-x)}{b(a-x)}\right\}.\ \ldots\ldots\ldots\ldots\ldots\ldots(54)$$

Similarly, for equation (53):

$$\frac{dx}{dt}=k(a-x)^2,$$

from which:

$$\int\frac{dx}{(a-x)^2}=\int k\,dt+C,$$

and

$$\frac{1}{(a-x)}=kt+C.$$

Putting $x=0$ when $t=0$:

$$C=\frac{1}{a}.$$

$$\therefore\ k=\frac{1}{t}\cdot\frac{x}{a(a-x)}\ \ldots\ldots\ldots\ldots\ldots\ldots\ldots(55)$$

In many reactions, the observed order of the reaction may differ from that expected from the chemical (stoichiometric) equation. This may be due to a variety of causes, one of which may be that the total reaction is the result of two or more consecutive reactions; in this case, the observed order is that of the slowest or slower reaction.

* **Example 61.** A definite volume of hydrogen peroxide undergoing spontaneous decomposition required 22·8 c.c. of standard permanganate solution for titration. After 10 minutes and 20 minutes respectively the volumes of permanganate required were 13·8 c.c. and 8·25 c.c. Find the order of reaction in the decomposition of hydrogen peroxide. How may the result be explained? (London B.Sc. Special.)

The equation for the reaction is usually written:

$$2H_2O_2=2H_2+O_2.$$

According to this equation, the reaction is bimolecular and the given data should, therefore, satisfy the equation:

$$k=\frac{1}{t}\cdot\frac{x}{a(a-x)}.\quad\text{(See above)}$$

$$\therefore\ \frac{1}{t_1}\cdot\frac{x_1}{a(a-x_1)}\ \text{should equal}\ \frac{1}{t_2}\cdot\frac{x_2}{a(a-x_2)},$$

where x_1 and x_2 are respectively the amounts of decomposition corresponding with times t_1 and t_2.

Since the permanganate readings may be taken as directly proportional to the concentrations of the hydrogen peroxide, we have :

$$t_1=10\,;\quad a=22{\cdot}8\,;\quad x_1=\ 9{\cdot}0\,;\quad (a-x_1)=13{\cdot}8.$$

$$t_2=20\,;\quad a=22{\cdot}8\,;\quad x_2=14{\cdot}55\,;\quad (a-x_2)=\ 8{\cdot}25.$$

$$\therefore\ \frac{1}{t_1}\cdot\frac{x_1}{a(a-x_1)}=\frac{1}{10}\cdot\frac{9{\cdot}0}{22{\cdot}8\times13{\cdot}8}=2{\cdot}86\times10^{-3},$$

and
$$\frac{1}{t_2}\cdot\frac{x_2}{a(a-x_2)}=\frac{1}{20}\cdot\frac{14{\cdot}55}{22{\cdot}8\times8{\cdot}25}=3{\cdot}82\times10^{-3}.$$

The reaction is clearly not bimolecular.

Considering the chemical properties of hydrogen peroxide, a reasonable alternative is to assume two consecutive reactions, represented by the equations :

$$H_2O_2=H_2O+O,$$
$$2O=O_2.$$

If it is further assumed that the second reaction is faster than the first (a reasonable assumption on purely chemical grounds), then the observed order of reaction, being that of the slower reaction, should be monomolecular.

Then, using subscripts as above :

$$\frac{1}{t_1}\log_e\frac{a}{(a-x_1)}\ \text{should equal}\ \frac{1}{t_2}\log_e\frac{a}{(a-x_2)},$$

or
$$\frac{1}{t_1}\log_{10}\frac{a}{(a-x_1)}\quad ,,\quad ,,\quad \frac{1}{t_2}\log_{10}\frac{a}{(a-x_2)}.$$

Substituting the given values :

$$\frac{1}{t_1}\log_{10}\frac{a}{(a-x_1)}=\frac{1}{10}\log_{10}\frac{22{\cdot}8}{13{\cdot}8}=2{\cdot}18\times10^{-2},$$

$$\frac{1}{t_2}\log_{10}\frac{a}{(a-x_2)}=\frac{1}{20}\log_{10}\frac{22{\cdot}8}{8{\cdot}25}=2{\cdot}21\times10^{-2}.$$

These values may be considered as in good agreement and the reaction is, therefore, monomolecular.

* 7. Use of the "half-time" value

For a monomolecular reaction :

$$k=\frac{1}{t}\log_e\frac{a}{(a-x)}.$$

Putting $x = a/2$, that is, assuming half of the original substance to have undergone reaction :

$$k = \frac{1}{t} \log_e \frac{a}{a/2} = \frac{1}{t} \log_e 2 = \frac{1}{t} \times 0{\cdot}6936.$$

Therefore, whatever the units in which time and concentration are expressed, the time ($t_{\frac{1}{2}}$) for half-reaction in a molecular reaction is given by the equation :

$$\mathbf{k t_{\frac{1}{2}} = 0{\cdot}6936.} \qquad \ldots\ldots\ldots\ldots\ldots\ldots\ldots\ldots (56)$$

Since k is independent of a (the initial concentration), it follows that the time for half-decomposition in a monomolecular reaction is also independent of the initial concentration.

For a second order reaction of the type $2A \rightarrow$, we have :

$$k = \frac{1}{t} \cdot \frac{x}{a(a-x)}.$$

Putting $x = a/2$:

$$k = \frac{1}{t} \cdot \frac{a/2}{a \times a/2} = \frac{1}{ta}.$$

$$\therefore \mathbf{k t_{\frac{1}{2}} = \frac{1}{a}} \ldots\ldots\ldots\ldots\ldots\ldots\ldots\ldots\ldots\ldots (57)$$

For a bimolecular reaction, therefore, the time of half-reaction is inversely proportional to the initial concentration.

The velocity constant of a termolecular reaction of the type $3A \rightarrow$ is given by the equation :

$$k = \frac{1}{2t} \left\{ \frac{x(2a-x)}{a^2(a-x)^2} \right\},$$

and the time for half-decomposition is related to the velocity constant by the equation :

$$kt_{\frac{1}{2}} = 3/2 \, . \, 1/a^2 \, ;$$

$$\therefore \mathbf{k t_{\frac{1}{2}} \propto \frac{1}{a^2}} \ldots\ldots\ldots\ldots\ldots\ldots\ldots\ldots (58)$$

In general, the half-time value for an nth order reaction is inversely proportional to the $(n-1)$th power of the initial concentration. This result may be applied to the experimental determination of the order of a reaction. Thus, assuming that the reaction is of the nth order and we determine the half-time values t_a and t_b corresponding with initial concentrations denoted by a and b respectively, then :

$$t_a \propto \frac{1}{a^{n-1}} \quad \text{and} \quad t_b \propto \frac{1}{b^{n-1}}. \quad \ldots\ldots\ldots\ldots\ldots\ldots(59)$$

Since also the proportionality constant for a reaction of any given order is the same for the two expressions :

$$\frac{t_a}{t_b} = \frac{b^{n-1}}{a^{n-1}}.$$

$$\therefore \log\left(\frac{t_a}{t_b}\right) = (n-1)\log b - (n-1)\log a$$

$$= (n-1)(\log b - \log a).$$

$$\therefore n = \frac{\log t_a - \log t_b}{\log b - \log a} + 1. \quad \ldots\ldots\ldots\ldots\ldots\ldots(60)$$

An inspection of the equations given above will show that it is not necessary to determine the time for half-reaction.

The same equation, (60), holds for the times taken for any fixed fraction of the original concentration; for example, we could use the " third-time " or " tenth-time ".

*** Example 62.** Determine the order of reaction:

$$\underset{\text{(ammonium cyanate)}}{NH_4CNO} \rightarrow \underset{\text{(urea)}}{CO(NH_2)_2}$$

from the following data :

Initial concentration of ammonium cyanate in gm.-molecules/litre	Time for half-conversion into urea (hours)
0·05	37·03
0·10	19·15
0·20	9·45

The order of reaction to be expected from the equation is unity :

$$NH_4CNO = CO(NH_2)_2.$$

The reaction, however, is obviously not monomolecular, since the time for half-conversion is dependent upon the initial concentration.

Taking the first two sets of figures and using equation we have :

$$\text{order of the reaction} = \frac{\log 37{\cdot}03 - \log 19{\cdot}15}{\log 0{\cdot}10 - \log 0{\cdot}05} + 1$$

$$= 1{\cdot}95.$$

Similarly, by taking the last two readings, we have :

$$\text{order of the reaction} = \frac{\log 19{\cdot}15 - \log 9{\cdot}45}{\log 0{\cdot}20 - \log 0{\cdot}10} + 1$$

$$= 2{\cdot}02.$$

The reaction is, therefore, bimolecular :

$$2NH_4CNO = 2CO(NH_2)_2.$$

This result may be confirmed by calculating the bimolecular constant for the three given values :

$$(1)\ k = \frac{1}{t_1} \cdot \frac{x_1}{a(a - x_1)} = \frac{1}{37{\cdot}03} \times \frac{0{\cdot}025}{0{\cdot}05 \times 0{\cdot}025} = 0{\cdot}54.$$

$$(2)\ k = \frac{1}{t_2} \frac{x_2}{a(a - x_2)} = \frac{1}{19{\cdot}15} \times \frac{0{\cdot}05}{0{\cdot}10 \times 0{\cdot}05} = 0{\cdot}52.$$

$$(3)\ k = \frac{1}{t_3} \frac{x_3}{a(a - x_3)} = \frac{1}{9{\cdot}45} \times \frac{0{\cdot}10}{0{\cdot}20 \times 0{\cdot}10} = 0{\cdot}53.$$

QUESTIONS ON CHAPTER V

[For method of solving a cubic equation, see p. 429.]

1. If one gm.-molecule of acetic acid is treated with one gm.-molecule of ethyl alcohol, reaction proceeds until two-thirds of the alcohol is esterified. Calculate the additional quantity of alcohol which is esterified when another gm.-molecule of acetic acid is introduced into the system. (C.H.L.)

2. At 40°, nitrogen peroxide is 38 per cent dissociated into NO_2 molecules. Given that the total pressure of the mixture is 1 atmosphere, calculate the equilibrium constant in terms of the partial pressures in atmospheres.

3. The equilibrium constant for the reaction

$$CH_3COOH + C_2H_5OH \rightleftharpoons CH_3COOC_2H_5 + H_2O$$

is 4·0 at 25°, the concentrations of ethyl acetate and water in gm.-molecules per litre being the numerators. If 5 gm.-molecules of acetic acid and 1 gm.-molecule of ethyl alcohol are mixed and allowed to reach equilibrium at 25°, how many gm.-molecules of ethyl acetate will be formed?

4. Using the equilibrium constant given in Q. 3, calculate the weight of ethyl acetate which will be formed when 92 gm. of ethyl alcohol and 180 gm. of acetic acid are allowed to come to equilibrium at 25°.

5. Starting with equimolecular quantities of ethyl alcohol and acetic acid, the position at equilibrium consists (in molecular quantities) of $\frac{1}{3}$ alcohol, $\frac{1}{3}$ acid, $\frac{2}{3}$ ester and $\frac{2}{3}$ water. In what molecular proportions must the acid and alcohol be mixed in order to obtain a 90 per cent yield of ester from the quantity of alcohol used? (O. and C.)

6. Using the value for the equilibrium constant given in Q. 3, calculate the weight of acetic acid which must be allowed to react with 92 gm. of ethyl alcohol in order to obtain 166 gm. of ethyl acetate at equilibrium at 25°.

7. At 65° and at normal atmospheric pressure, nitrogen tetroxide is dissociated to the extent of 60 per cent into nitrogen dioxide according to the equation:

$$\underset{\substack{\text{40 per cent}\\\text{by weight}}}{N_2O_4} \rightleftharpoons \underset{\substack{\text{60 per cent}\\\text{by weight}}}{2NO_2}$$

If the temperature remains constant but the pressure is adjusted so the total volume of the gas is reduced to one-half of its initial value, what will be the percentage by weight of nitrogen tetroxide in the mixture?

8. At a pressure of 2 atmospheres, N_2O_4 is 35 per cent dissociated into NO_2. Calculate K_p (the equilibrium constant in terms of partial pressures). (C.U.O.S.)

9. At 2000° under atmospheric pressure, carbon dioxide is 1·80 per cent dissociated according to the equation:

$$2CO_2 \rightleftharpoons 2CO + O_2.$$

Calculate the equilibrium constant for this reaction, using partial pressures in atmospheres. (O. and C.)

10. Show that for the dissociation of hydrogen iodine according to the equation:

$$2HI \rightleftharpoons H_2 + I_2,$$

the equilibrium constant in terms of gm.-molecules per litre, K_c, is the same as the equilibrium constant in terms of partial pressures, K_p.

11. Experiment shows that the equilibrium constant of the reaction:

$$C_2H_5OH + CH_3COOH \rightleftharpoons CH_3COOC_2H_5 + H_2O$$

is 2·8 at room temperature, and the velocity constant of the forward reaction is 0·002. When a catalyst is added this velocity constant is increased to 0·0045. What is now the velocity constant of the backward reaction? (C.U.O.S.)

12. If phosphorus pentachloride is heated to 250° and allowed to reach chemical equilibrium, 80 per cent of the pentachloride is dissociated. Calculate how many gm.-molecules of chlorine must be mixed with one gm.-molecule of phosphorus pentachloride to reduce the dissociation to 40 per cent. The volume of the system remains constant throughout. (Inter. B.Sc., London.)

13. The vapour density of phosphorus pentachloride at 250° and at 760 mm. pressure is 55·6. Calculate the percentage dissociation at this temperature and pressure. One gm.-molecule of phosphorus pentachloride was heated to 250° at 760 mm. pressure. Two gm.-molecules of chlorine were then introduced and the pressure was adjusted to twice its original value, the temperature remaining constant. What percentage of the pentachloride remains undissociated at the new equilibrium?

14. The vapour density of nitrogen peroxide at 60° and 760 mm. is 28·3. Calculate the percentage dissociation at this temperature and pressure. What is the equilibrium constant in terms of the partial pressures of N_2O_4 and NO_2? At what pressure, temperature remaining constant, would the gaseous mixture have a vapour density of 32·5?

15. When pure ammonia is maintained at 480° and a pressure of 1 atmosphere, it dissociates to give a gas containing 20 per cent of ammonia by volume. Determine (*a*) the degree of dissociation, (*b*) the equilibrium constant at this temperature (in terms of partial pressures), (*c*) the composition at the same temperature but under a pressure of 5 atmospheres. (C.U.O.S.)

16. After two solutions, each containing silver and mercurous salts, had stood in contact with silver amalgam until equilibrium was established, the final concentrations were found to be :

	Silver ion	Mercurous ion
Solution 1 -	0·004*M*	0·20*M* if the ion is Hg^+ or 0·10*M* if the ion is $(Hg-Hg)^{++}$
Solution 2 -	0·002*M*	0·05*M* if the ion is Hg^+ or 0·025*M* if the ion is $(Hg-Hg)^{++}$

The active masses of the metals were the same in the two experiments. According to the assumption made as to the nature of the mercurous ion, the reaction would be represented as :

$$Hg^+ + Ag \rightleftharpoons Hg + Ag^+,$$

or

$$Hg_2^{++} + 2Ag \rightleftharpoons 2Hg + 2Ag^+.$$

Formulate the corresponding expressions for the equilibrium constant, and ascertain which of the assumptions gives consistent values for the supposed equilibrium constant. (N.U.J.B. Schol.)

17. A quantity of solid ammonium hydrosulphide, NH_4HS, was heated in a closed flask and when equilibrium was established the total pressure of the mixed gases was 47 cm. The dissociation takes place according to the equation: $NH_4HS \rightleftharpoons NH_3 + H_2S$. Ammonia gas was then introduced into the flask until the total pressure was 54·2 cm. What was the partial pressure of the hydrogen sulphide when the new equilibrium had been reached?

18. Calculate the percentage of nitric oxide in air heated to 2200° *A* given that the equilibrium constant of the reaction

$$N_2 + O_2 \rightleftharpoons 2NO$$

at this temperature is $8·8 \times 10^{-4}$, the nitric oxide term being the numerator and quantities being expressed in gm.-molecules. (C.U.O.S.)

19. Ammonium carbamate, NH_2COONH_4, dissociates on heating into ammonia and carbon dioxide. The vapour pressure of the undissociated salt is small compared with those of the two gases. The salt was heated in a closed vessel at constant temperature and the total pressure noted. Ammonia was then introduced into the vessel in such amount that when equilibrium had been restored the partial pressure of the ammonia was equal to the initial total pressure. Find the ratio of the final and initial total pressures. (C.U.O.S.)

20. Using the value for the equilibrium constant given in Q. 3, calculate the weight of ethyl acetate present when the following reactants are allowed to come to equilibrium: 10 gm. of ethyl alcohol, 10 gm. of acetic acid, 5 gm. of ethyl acetate, 20 gm. of water.

21. When a mixture of 1 gm.-molecule of hydrogen chloride and 0·5 gm.-molecule of oxygen is allowed to come to equilibrium at 400°, 0·39 gm.-molecule of chlorine is formed, the total pressure of the reaction mixture at equilibrium being 1 atmosphere. The reaction takes place according to the equation:

$$4HCl + O_2 \rightleftharpoons 2Cl_2 + 2H_2O.$$

Calculate the partial pressures of the reactants at equilibrium and the equilibrium constant in terms of the partial pressures in atmospheres.

22. 2·54 gm. of iodine was heated in a closed flask of capacity 2000 c.c. to 200°. The pressure exerted was 185 mm. What was the percentage dissociation at this temperature? If the pressure were increased to such a degree that the volume was reduced to 500 c.c., what would be the percentage dissociation?

23. The equilibrium constant (in terms of partial pressures in atmospheres) for the dissociation $Se_6 \rightleftharpoons 3Se_2$ is 0·20 at 700°. Calculate the percentage dissociation of selenium vapour maintained at 700° and at a pressure of 600 mm.

24. At 400° and at a total pressure of 10 atmospheres, the equilibrium mixture, $N_2 + 3H_2 \rightleftharpoons 2NH_3$, contains 4 per cent by volume of ammonia. Calculate the equilibrium constant in partial pressures in atmospheres and hence deduce the percentage by volume of ammonia in the equilibrium mixture at the same temperature but at a total pressure of 30 atmospheres.

* **25.** When a gm.-molecules of iodine (vapour) are allowed to react with b gm.-molecules of hydrogen an equilibrium $H_2 + I_2 \rightleftharpoons 2HI$ is set up and $2x$ gm.-molecules of HI are formed. Show that the equilibrium constant, K_c, is equal to the equilibrium constant, K_p, and that each is equal to $\frac{4x^2}{(a-x)(b-x)}$. If $K_p = K_c = 50{\cdot}4$ at 454°, calculate the number of gm.-molecules of HI formed at equilibrium from initial quantities of 8·10 gm.-molecules of hydrogen and 2·94 gm.-molecules of iodine.

* **26.** In an experiment on the decomposition of hydrogen peroxide by means of colloidal silver as catalyst, 15 c.c. of the peroxide solution were decomposed and the oxygen evolved was collected and measured at suitable intervals of time. The concentration of the hydrogen peroxide was such that the complete decomposition of 15 c.c. into water and oxygen gave 6·18 c.c. of oxygen at *N.T.P.* The following volume-time readings were obtained :

Time (minutes)	Vol. of oxygen at *N.T.P.*
2	1·24 c.c.
4	2·36 c.c.
6	3·36 c.c.
8	3·98 c.c.
14	5·23 c.c.

Show graphically or by calculation that the reaction is monomolecular. Calculate the average velocity constant expressing time in seconds and concentration as c.c. of available oxygen.

* **27.** It was found that a solution of cane sugar was hydrolysed to the extent of 25 per cent in 1 hour. Calculate the time taken for the sugar to be 50 per cent hydrolysed, assuming that the reaction is monomolecular. (C.U.O.S.)

* **28.** In the hydrolysis of propyl acetate in the presence of dilute hydrochloric acid in dilute aqueous solution the following data were recorded :

Time from start in minutes - -	60	350
Percentage of ester decomposed -	18·17	69·12

Calculate the time in which half the ester was decomposed. (B.Sc. Special, London.)

* **29.** The decomposition of hydrogen peroxide in the presence of colloidal silver is a monomolecular reaction. 50 c.c. of a solution of hydrogen peroxide (which if completely converted into water and oxygen would have given 39·56 c.c. of oxygen at *N.T.P.*) was decomposed by colloidal silver and gave 12·81 c.c. of oxygen at *N.T.P.* in six minutes. How much longer will it be before a further 12·00 c.c. of oxygen are evolved?

* **30.** 4·4 gm. of ethyl acetate and 500 c.c. of $N/10$ sodium hydroxide (which are exactly equivalent quantities) were mixed and allowed to react at 25°. After reaction had taken place for 30 minutes it was found that 100 c.c. of the mixture required 72·8 c.c. of $N/10$ hydrochloric acid for neutralisation. Calculate the time taken for half the ester to undergo saponification. Calculate also the velocity constant of the reaction, expressing time in minutes and concentrations in gm.-molecules per litre.

* **31.** The percentage dissociation of hydrogen chloride at 700° is $1{\cdot}2 \times 10^{-3}$ and that of water vapour at the same temperature is $1{\cdot}4 \times 10^{-7}$. Calculate K_p for each of these reactions, and hence deduce K_c for the Deacon reaction:

$$4HCl + O_2 \rightleftharpoons 2Cl_2 + 2H_2O$$

at the same temperature.

* **32.** A quantity of ethyl acetate is mixed with an excess of sodium hydroxide at 25°. 100 c.c. of the mixture is immediately titrated against 0·05 N hydrochloric acid, of which 68·2 c.c. were required for neutralisation. After 30 minutes, 100 c.c. of the mixture required, similarly, 49·7 c.c. of the acid. When the reaction was complete 100 c.c. of the mixture required 15·6 c.c. of the acid. Calculate the velocity constant of the reaction, using concentration in gm.-molecules per litre and time in minutes.

* **33.** A quantity of hydrogen peroxide on decomposition in the presence of a catalyst gave 23·5 c.c. of oxygen in 10 minutes and 37·0 c.c. in 20 minutes. Assuming the reaction to be monomolecular, what volume of oxygen should be evolved in 15 minutes?

* **34.** An aqueous solution of an optically active compound gave the following results. Show that the reaction is an opposing monomolecular reaction, and determine $(k_1 + k_2)$ where k_1 = velocity constant of the forward reaction and k_2 = velocity constant of the opposing reaction (express time in minutes).

Initial polarimeter reading = 115·6°.
Final (steady) polarimeter reading = 23·5°.

t (hours)	3	6	9	15
Polarimeter reading	102·0°	90·5°	80·6°	65·1°

* **35.** Obtain an expression for a termolecular reaction of the type: $3A \rightarrow$, and show how the time taken for $\frac{1}{3}$ of complete reaction is related to the initial concentration of A.

*** 36.** A quantity of an aqueous solution of a diazonium salt, which, if completely decomposed, would give 60·0 c.c. of nitrogen, undergoes spontaneous decomposition to give the following results. Determine the order of the reaction and calculate the average velocity constant (*t* in minutes, concentrations as volumes of nitrogen).

t (mins.) - - - -	116	180	518	1354
Vol. of N_2 evolved (c.c.) -	9·7	15·3	32·6	53·9

*** 37.** A gas, *A*, is soluble in water with which it partly combines according to the general equation : $A + nH_2O = A.nH_2O$.

Show that, for such a system, Henry's law takes the form :

$$\frac{p}{c_1 + c_2} = K \text{ (a constant)},$$

where p = the pressure of the gas, c_1 = the concentration of single molecules of *A* in the solution, and c_2 = the concentration of the $A.nH_2O$ molecules.

*** 38.** In two separate experiments a quantity of a diazonium salt was decomposed as in Q. 36. The results obtained were as follows :

Experiment 1		Experiment 2	
50 c.c. of the solution gave on complete decomposition 160 c.c. of N_2 at *N.T.P.*		50 c.c. of the solution gave on complete decomposition 132 c.c. of N_2 at *N.T.P.*	
Time (minutes)	Vol. of N_2 at *N.T.P.* (c.c.)	Time (minutes)	Vol. of N_2 at *N.T.P.* (c.c.)
10	14·5	10	12·0
25	33·7	25	27·3
50	60·3	50	49·0
100	97·9	100	80·5
150	120·9	150	99·6

Determine the order of the reaction, using a graphical method.

*** 39.** Acetaldehyde is decomposed by heat to give methane and carbon monoxide, and since the decomposition entails an increase in volume at constant pressure the rate of the reaction can be followed by the increase of pressure if the volume is kept constant. The following results were obtained at 518°. Initial pressure = 363 mm. Δp = *increase* of pressure.

t (sec.)	Δp (mm.)
42	34
242	134
840	244
1440	284

Determine the order of the reaction.

CHAPTER VI

ABNORMALITY

1. Causes of abnormality

Abnormal experimental results, that is, results which apparently do not agree with the simple laws of gases and solutions, such as those of Avogadro and Raoult, are due to three main causes :

(1) In gases : Thermal dissociation.

(2) In solution : (*a*) Electrolytic dissociation ;

(*b*) Association.

2. Abnormality of gases

Assuming that abnormal vapour densities are due entirely to thermal dissociation, the amount of dissociation can be calculated from the observed vapour density.

As the simplest case, we can consider a gaseous substance, A, dissociating, in part, to two substances, B and C, which are also gases.

$$A \rightleftharpoons B + C.$$

Assume that, at a given temperature and pressure, one gm.-molecule of A would, if it did not dissociate, occupy a volume, V. If x represent the fraction of this gm.-molecule which actually dissociates at the same temperature and pressure, then total number of gm.-molecules of A, B and $C = (1 + x)$, as shown in the equation :

$$\underset{1-x}{A} \rightleftharpoons \underset{x}{B} + \underset{x}{C}$$

$$\begin{aligned}\text{Total number of gm.-molecules} &= 1 - x + x + x \\ &= 1 + x.\end{aligned}$$

Assume that the volume occupied by the dissociated mixture $= V'$. Then, since pressure and temperature are constant :

$$V' = V(1 + x).$$

Let D = the density of A, assuming no dissociation, and D' = the density of the dissociation mixture. Then, since the *mass* of 1 gm.-molecule of A is unchanged by dissociation :

$$V \times D = V' \times D' = V(1+x) \times D'.$$

$$\therefore \ (1+x) = \frac{D}{D'}. \quad \ldots\ldots\ldots\ldots\ldots\ldots\ldots\ldots (61)$$

Since vapour densities are in the same ratio as absolute densities, we may write :

$$(1+x) = \frac{D_V}{D_V'},$$

where D_V and D'_V are the vapour densities corresponding with D and D'.

Similarly, if X = the percentage dissociation :

$$\frac{(100+X)}{100} = \frac{D_V}{D_V'}. \quad \ldots\ldots\ldots\ldots\ldots\ldots (62)$$

Example 63. The vapour density of nitrogen peroxide is 30·0 at 60°. Calculate the percentage dissociation of the gas, expressing your result as (*a*) the percentage dissociation by weight, (*b*) the percentage of NO_2 molecules in the equilibrium mixture.

The equation for the dissociation is :

$$\underset{100-X}{N_2O_4} \rightleftharpoons \underset{2X}{2NO_2}$$

The vapour density of N_2O_4, assuming no dissociation,

$$= \frac{(2 \times 14) + (4 \times 16)}{2} = 46.$$

Then, if X = percentage dissociation :

$$\frac{100+X}{100} = \frac{46}{30}.$$

From which $X = \mathbf{53{\cdot}3}$.

In $(100+X)$ molecules, $2X$ molecules are NO_2 molecules.

∴ Percentage of NO_2 molecules by volume

$$= \frac{2X}{(100+X)} \times 100 = \frac{106{\cdot}6}{153{\cdot}3} \times 100 = \mathbf{69{\cdot}5}.$$

Example 64. 1 litre of the vapour of phosphorus pentachloride, measured at 200° and 760 mm., weighs 4·26 gm. What is the percentage dissociation of phosphorus pentachloride at this temperature and pressure?

1 litre of the vapour of phosphorus pentachloride at 200° and 760 mm.

$$= 1 \times \frac{273}{473} \text{ litre at } N.T.P. = 0{\cdot}578 \text{ litre.}$$

$$\therefore \ 22{\cdot}4 \text{ litres at } N.T.P. \text{ weigh } \frac{4{\cdot}26}{0{\cdot}578} \times 22{\cdot}4 \text{ gm.} = 162{\cdot}9 \text{ gm.}$$

But the true molecular weight of $PCl_5 = 208{\cdot}5$.

The equation for the dissociation is:

$$\underset{100-X}{PCl_5} \rightleftharpoons \underset{X}{PCl_3} + \underset{X}{Cl_2}$$

and since molecular weights can replace vapour densities in equation (62):

$$\frac{100+X}{100} = \frac{208{\cdot}5}{162{\cdot}9}.$$

$$\therefore \ \mathbf{X = 28{\cdot}0.}$$

The general equation for thermal dissociation, in which a gaseous substance dissociates so that 1 molecule of the substance produces n molecules of the dissociated mixture, is quite clearly:

$$\frac{\mathbf{100 + X(n-1)}}{\mathbf{100}} = \frac{\mathbf{D_V}}{\mathbf{D_V'}},$$

where X = percentage dissociation, D_V = "normal" vapour density, and D_V' = observed vapour density.

3. Abnormality in solution

In solution the following effects depend upon the total concentration of solute particles (molecules and ions):

(*a*) The lowering of vapour pressure.
(*b*) The lowering of freezing point.
(*c*) The elevation of boiling point.
(*d*) The osmotic pressure.

Abnormal values will be obtained when the solute is either dissociated or associated.

4. Abnormality due to dissociation

The simplest example is that of a binary electrolyte, that is, one which dissociates into two ions, as in the equation :

$$\underset{1-x}{AB} \rightleftharpoons \underset{x}{A^+} + \underset{x}{B^-}$$

Assume that a gm.-molecular weight of AB is dissolved in 100 gm. of solvent. Then the lowering of freezing point of this solution $=k$ (the freezing point constant). But if the degree of dissociation $=x$, then total number of gm.-molecules and gm.-ions in 100 gm. of the solvent $=(1+x)$.

$$\therefore \text{ Depression of freezing point} = k(1+x).$$

$$\therefore \frac{\text{Observed depression of freezing point}}{\text{Calculated depression of freezing point}}$$

$$= \frac{k(1+x)}{k} = 1 + x = i, \quad \text{......................(63)}$$

where i is called the Van't Hoff factor.

Example 65. The cryoscopic constant for water is 18·7 and the freezing point of a decinormal solution of sodium chloride is 0·342°. What is the percentage ionisation for such a solution? (O. and C.)

The percentage dissociation obtained in this and similar calculations is the apparent dissociation based on the Arrhenius theory of electrolytes. The theory of complete dissociation recognises that strong electrolytes such as sodium chloride are ionised in the solid state and that increase in the " apparent " degree of dissociation is due, not to the increase in the number of ions, but to their increased freedom or mobility as the solution becomes more dilute. For " abnormal " results of osmotic pressure, vapour pressure and associated phenomena such as boiling point elevation :

$$\frac{\text{observed value}}{\text{calculated value}} = \text{osmotic coefficient} = f_0.$$

According to the Arrhenius theory of partial dissociation : $f_0 = 1 + (n-1)x$, where $x =$ the fraction of dissociation of an electrolyte dissociating into n ions.

Assuming complete dissociation, the equation obtained by Debye and Hückel is :

$$1-f_0=w\frac{e^2}{6\epsilon kT}\sqrt{\frac{4\pi Ne^2}{\epsilon kT}\cdot\frac{1}{1000}}\sqrt{nc},$$

where e = the charge on an electron, ϵ = the dielectric constant of the solvent, k = the Boltzmann constant $=\frac{R}{N}$, where R = the gas constant and N = the Avogadro number, T = the absolute temperature, n = number of ions produced by the dissociation of one molecule of the electrolyte, c = the concentration of the electrolyte in gram-molecules per litre, w = a constant determined by the charges on the ions. (See also p. 184.)

Assuming, then, that the apparent ionisation is due to the dissociation of sodium chloride according to the equation :

$$\underset{1-x}{NaCl} \rightleftharpoons \underset{x}{Na^+} + \underset{x}{Cl^-}$$

then $$\frac{1+x}{1}=\frac{0{\cdot}342}{0{\cdot}187}=1{\cdot}829.$$

$\therefore$ $x=0{\cdot}829$ and the percentage dissociation $=82{\cdot}9$.

For a ternary electrolyte, that is, one which dissociates into three ions :

$$i=1+2x,$$

as shown in the following equation for the dissociation of barium chloride :

$$\underset{1-x}{BaCl_2} \rightleftharpoons \underset{x}{Ba^{++}} + \underset{2x}{2Cl^-}$$

Total number of gm.-molecules and gm.-ions $=1+2x$.

In general, for an electrolyte which dissociates into n ions, the equation is :

$$\underset{1-x}{M} \rightleftharpoons \underset{nx}{nN}$$

$$i=1-x+nx=1+(n-1)x. \quad \ldots\ldots\ldots\ldots\ldots\ldots(64)$$

Example 66. Calculate the vapour pressure of a solution of 5·61 gm. of anhydrous sodium sulphate in 100 gm. of water at 100°, assuming that the salt is 85 per cent dissociated.

The calculated vapour pressure is obtained from the equation :

$$\frac{P-P'}{P}=\frac{n}{N}. \quad \text{(See p. 49.)}$$

Since the molecular weight of anhydrous sodium sulphate is 142 :

$$\frac{760 - P'}{760} = \frac{5{\cdot}61/142}{100/18}.$$

From which the lowering of vapour pressure $= 760 - P' = 5{\cdot}40$ mm.

Since the sodium sulphate is 85 per cent dissociated :

$$\underset{1-x}{Na_2SO_4} \rightleftharpoons \underset{2x}{2Na^+} + \underset{x}{SO_4^{--}}$$

$$\therefore\ i = 1 + 2x = 2{\cdot}7.$$

$\therefore$ Observed depression of vapour pressure

$$= 5{\cdot}40 \times 2{\cdot}7 \text{ mm.} \doteqdot 14{\cdot}6 \text{ mm.}$$

$\therefore$ Vapour pressure of the solution $= (760 - 14{\cdot}6)$ mm.

$$= 745{\cdot}4 \text{ mm.}$$

Example 67. What weight of glucose, $C_6H_{12}O_6$, when dissolved in 50 c.c. of water at 15° (assuming no change of volume) will give a solution whose osmotic pressure will be equal to that of the solution obtained by dissolving 1·80 gm. of sodium chloride in 70 c.c. of water (assuming no change of volume) at 18° ; the sodium chloride has an apparent dissociation of 83 per cent at the stated temperature and dilution.

Assuming no dissociation, the calculated value for the sodium chloride solution

$$= \frac{1{\cdot}80 \times 22{,}400 \times 291}{58{\cdot}5 \times 70 \times 273} \text{ atmospheres.}$$ (See p. 53.)

Since sodium chloride is 83 per cent dissociated in the solution :

$$i = 1{\cdot}83.$$

$\therefore$ Observed osmotic pressure

$$= \frac{1{\cdot}80 \times 22{,}400 \times 291}{58{\cdot}5 \times 70 \times 273} \times 1{\cdot}83 \text{ atmospheres.}$$

Let x gm. = weight of glucose.

Then the osmotic pressure of the glucose solution

$$= \frac{x \times 22{,}400 \times 288}{180 \times 50 \times 273} \text{ atmospheres.}$$

$$\therefore \frac{1{\cdot}80 \times 22{,}400 \times 291 \times 1{\cdot}83}{58{\cdot}5 \times 70 \times 273} = \frac{x \times 22{,}400 \times 288}{180 \times 50 \times 273}.$$

From which $x = 7{\cdot}32$ gm.

The relation between the true molecular weight and the apparent molecular weight for a binary electrolyte may be deduced in the following manner. For a solution containing a fixed weight of solute, the depression of the freezing point is inversely proportional to the molecular weight of the solute. Then, if $(\Delta t)_c$ = the calculated depression and M is the true molecular weight corresponding with the undissociated molecule:

$$(\Delta t)_c \propto \frac{1}{M}. \quad \therefore (\Delta t)_c = \frac{K}{M},$$

where K = the proportionality constant.

Similarly, if $(\Delta t)_0$ = observed depression of freezing point and M' = the apparent molecular weight:

$$(\Delta t)_0 = \frac{K}{M'}.$$

$$\therefore (\Delta t)_c \times M = (\Delta t)_0 \times M'.$$

But
$$(\Delta t)_0 = (\Delta t)_c \times (1 + x);$$

$$\therefore M = M'(1 + x). \quad \text{.....................(65)}$$

Example 68. A solution of 5·5 gm. of sodium nitrate in 76·2 c.c. of water begins to freeze at $-2{\cdot}852°$. Calculate (*a*) the apparent molecular weight of the solute, (*b*) its apparent degree of dissociation.

From Chapter III:

$$\text{Apparent molecular weight} = \frac{18{\cdot}6 \times 5{\cdot}5 \times 100}{76{\cdot}2 \times 2{\cdot}852}$$

$$= 47{\cdot}1.$$

The true molecular weight of sodium nitrate = 85.

$$\therefore 47{\cdot}1\,(1 + x) = 85.$$

$\therefore x = 0{\cdot}805$ and apparent percentage dissociation = 80·5.

For the general case of an electrolyte dissociating into n ions, the true and apparent molecular weights are clearly related by the equation:

$$\mathrm{M} = \mathrm{M}'\{1 + (\mathrm{n} - 1)\mathrm{x}\}, \quad \text{.....................(66)}$$

where M = normal molecular weight, M' = apparent molecular weight.

5. Abnormality due to association

When association of the solute occurs, the observed value will be less than the "normal" value and the factor "i" is less than unity.

Thus, in the case of a molecule, M, associating in solution according to the equation :

$$\underset{100-X}{2M} \rightleftharpoons \underset{X/2}{M_2}$$

then the factor $i = \frac{100 - X + X/2}{100} = \frac{100 - X/2}{100} < 1.$

Example 69. 0·5 gm. of acetic acid when dissolved in 20 gm. of benzene depresses the freezing point by 1·04°. From these data make what deductions you can concerning the constitution of acetic acid dissolved in benzene. (The cryoscopic constant for 100 gm. of benzene is 50.) (C.U.O.S.)

The calculated value for the depression of freezing point, assuming that acetic acid, CH_3COOH (molecular weight$=60$), behaves normally, is 2·08. (See Chap. III).

Assuming that acetic acid associates to form double molecules, then :

$$\underset{100-X}{2CH_3COOH} \rightleftharpoons \underset{X/2}{(CH_3COOH)_2}$$

$$\therefore \quad \frac{100 - X/2}{100} = i = \frac{1{\cdot}04}{2{\cdot}08}.$$

$$\therefore X = \mathbf{100}.$$

Therefore, acetic acid, if it associates only to form double molecules, is 100 per cent associated in benzene solution.

Alternatively, we may use the data given in the question to calculate the apparent molecular weight of acetic acid in benzene. By the method given in Chap. III :

Apparent molecular weight$=120$.

But the molecular weight of acetic acid corresponding with the formula, CH_3COOH, is 60.

∴ Acetic acid probably consists entirely of double molecules, $(CH_3COOH)_2$, in benzene solution.

For the general type of association :

$$\underset{1-x}{nM} \rightleftharpoons \underset{x/n}{(M)_n}$$

$$i = 1 - x + x/n = \frac{n - x(n-1)}{n} \quad \text{.................(67)}$$

* 6. Abnormal behaviour of pure liquids

The standard methods for the determination of the molecular weight of a liquid substance give the molecular weight in the form of a vapour ; this may be different from the molecular weight as a liquid. The molecule of any substance in which the positive and negative charges are unsymmetrically distributed has an electrical moment called the dipole moment. If the " effective centre " of all the negative charges be assumed to be at a point A while the corresponding centre of the equal and opposite positive charges is at a point B, then the dipole moment is measured by the product $e \times d$ where e = the total negative charge = total positive charge and d = the distance between the points A and B. The dipole moment is calculated for one molecule and then has the order of magnitude 10^{-18} electrostatic units (e.s.u.). It is usual to express the value of a dipole moment in Debye units in which the actual value per molecule is multiplied by 10^{18}. For ethyl alcohol the value is $1{\cdot}7 \times 10^{-18}$ e.s.u. or 1·7 Debye units. The presence of a high dipole moment may lead to association, comparable with the association of acetic acid molecules in benzene solution (cf. p. 126).

For a large number of liquids, in which it is believed association does not occur, the equation of Eötvös satisfactorily gives the relation between the surface tension of a liquid and its temperature. The equation can be written :

$$\gamma(Mv)^{2/3} = K(t_0 - t), \quad \text{.....................(68)}$$

where M = the molecular weight of the liquid (assumed to be the same as the vapour), γ = the surface tension at temperature, $t°$, v = the volume occupied by 1 gm. of the liquid (specific volume), t_0 = the temperature at which the surface tension becomes zero (the critical temperature approximately) and K = a constant.

For measurements at two temperatures, t_1 and t_2, equation can be written :

$$\frac{\gamma_2(Mv_2)^{2/3} - \gamma_1(Mv_1)^{2/3}}{t_2 - t_1} = K, \quad \text{.................(69)}$$

where v_1 and v_2 are the specific volumes at temperatures t_1 and t_2 respectively and γ_1 and γ_2 are the corresponding values for the surface tension.

$$\therefore\ M = \left\{\frac{K(t_2 - t_1)}{\gamma_2 v_2^{2/3} - \gamma_1 v_1^{2/3}}\right\}^{3/2}. \quad \text{.................(70)}$$

K has the value $\doteq -2{\cdot}12$.

Example 70. The surface tension of carbon disulphide is 33·6 at 19·4° and 29·4 at 46·1°. The densities of carbon disulphide at 19·4° and 46·1° are 1·264 gm. per c.c. and 1·223 gm. per c.c. respectively. What conclusion concerning the molecular weight of liquid carbon disulphide can be drawn from these data?

In equation (70) :

$$v_2 = \frac{1}{1{\cdot}223}\ \text{c.c.}\ ; \quad v_1 = \frac{1}{1{\cdot}264}\ \text{c.c.}$$

$$\therefore\ M = \left\{\frac{-2{\cdot}12\,(46{\cdot}1 - 19{\cdot}4)}{[29{\cdot}4 \times (1/1{\cdot}223)^{2/3}] - [33{\cdot}6 \times (1/1{\cdot}264)^{2/3}]}\right\}^{3/2}$$

$$= 81{\cdot}5.$$

The molecular weight of carbon disulphide corresponding with the formula $CS_2 = 76$. The agreement is sufficiently close to assume that carbon disulphide is unassociated in the liquid state since the value of K is only approximate, being an average for a number of " normal " liquids for which K varies from 2·2256–2·0419.

For associated liquids the value of K obtained by substituting the normal value of the molecular weight is very much lower than 2·12, but approaches the normal value as the temperature rises, an indication that the degree of association decreases with increase of temperature. Examples are water ($K = 0{\cdot}9$–$1{\cdot}2$) and alcohols ($K = 1{\cdot}0$–$1{\cdot}6$).

It would appear from equation (70) that the degree of association, x, could be obtained from the equation :

$$\gamma_2\left(\frac{M}{1 - x/2} \cdot v_2\right)^{2/3} - \gamma_1\left(\frac{M}{1 - x/2} \cdot v_1\right)^{2/3} = K(t_2 - t_1), \quad \text{.....(71)}$$

since, from equation (67) (p. 126), the apparent molecular weight of a substance associating to form double molecules

$$=M/(1-x/2),$$

where M = the molecular weight of the single molecule. Attempts to calculate the degree of association by this method do not, however, give reliable results.

* 7. Determination of critical temperature by Eötvös method

According to the Eötvös equation as it is given on p. 127, the straight line obtained by plotting $\gamma(Mv)^{2/3}$ against t should, on extrapolation to $\gamma(Mv)^{2/3}=0$, give t_c, the critical temperature. It is found that critical temperatures obtained in this way differ from the directly observed values by about 6° and that the Eötvös equation is, therefore, more correctly written :

$$\gamma(Mv)^{2/3}=(t_c-t-a), \quad\text{.....................(72)}$$

where a = a constant for a particular liquid and may be taken as $\doteqdot 6$. Extrapolation to $\gamma(Mv)^{2/3}=0$ then gives a temperature $\doteqdot (t_c-6)$. The critical temperature is obtained, therefore, by adding 6° to the value of t when $\gamma(Mv)^{2/3}=0$.

QUESTIONS ON CHAPTER VI

[A list of boiling point and freezing point constants is given on p. 431.]

1. The density of nitrogen peroxide at 27° is 38·3. What is the composition of the vapour? (1st M.B., London.)

2. What is the percentage dissociation of phosphorus pentachloride when its vapour density is 75·3?

3. 1 litre of nitrogen peroxide at 30° and 760 mm. weighs 2·81 gm. Calculate the apparent molecular weight of the gas (O_2 = 32·00). Using this value of the molecular weight, calculate the percentage dissociation of the gas at 30° and 760 mm.

4. A normal solution of hydrochloric acid was found to be in equilibrium with ice at −3·53°. Calculate the degree of dissociation of the acid in this solution. (Inter. B.Sc., London.)

5. Calculate the vapour density of phosphorus pentachloride at the temperature at which it is dissociated to the extent of 68·7 per cent. [Take 1 litre of hydrogen at *N.T.P.* weighs 0·087 gm.]

6. A solution of 6·39 gm. of sodium nitrate in 75 c.c. of water freezes at −3·04°. What conclusions can be drawn from this fact? (C.U.O.S.)

7. Calculate the osmotic pressure at 15° of a decinormal solution of potassium chloride, assuming that the salt is 85 per cent dissociated at this temperature and pressure.

8. A solution containing 0·8461 gm. of sodium chloride in 25·85 gm. of water boiled at 100·57°. Calculate the percentage dissociation of the salt.

9. If the solution obtained by dissolving 5 gm. of potassium nitrate in 100 gm. of water has a degree of ionisation 0·95, calculate the freezing point of the solution. (N.U.J.B.)

10. The freezing-point constant of water is 18·58. A 0·585 per cent solution of sodium chloride lowers the freezing point of water by 0·350°. What interpretation do you place on this result? (C.U.O.S.)

11. Calculate the freezing point of a solution obtained by dissolving 5 gm. of acetic acid in 75 gm. of benzene, assuming that acetic acid is 95 per cent associated in a benzene solution of this concentration. (Freezing point of benzene = 5·53°.)

12. Calculate the vapour pressure of a solution of sodium chloride, containing 5·6 gm. of sodium chloride in 63·2 gm. of water at 100°, assuming that the solute is 92 per cent dissociated at this temperature and dilution.

13. Assuming complete dissociation of all soluble salts, calculate (*a*) the osmotic pressure of $M/5$ barium chloride solution at 15°, (*b*) the osmotic pressure of the solution obtained by mixing equal volumes of $M/5$ barium chloride and $M/5$ sodium sulphate at 30°.

14. The osmotic pressure of a 4 per cent solution of potassium chloride at 15° is 22·8 atmospheres. What percentage dissociation is indicated by these figures?

15. A solution of barium chloride containing 10 gm. of the anhydrous salt per litre has an apparent dissociation into $Ba^{++} + 2Cl^-$ of 85 per cent. What would be the osmotic pressure of this solution at 17°?

16. A chloride of mercury contains 26·2 per cent of chlorine and has a vapour density of 138. When 1 gm. of the chloride is dissolved in 100 gm. of water the freezing point is lowered by 0·0677°. What deductions can be drawn from these results? (C.U.O.S.)

17. The vapour pressure of a normal solution of sodium chloride at 100° is 735·4 mm. What value does this figure give for the percentage dissociation of the salt?

18. A decinormal solution of potassium chloride was found to exert an osmotic pressure of 4·44 atmospheres at 17°. Calculate (*a*) the apparent molecular weight, (*b*) the amount of ionisation of the dissolved salt. (1st M.B., London.)

19. Calculate the weight of one litre of nitrogen peroxide at 80° and 740 mm. pressure, assuming 75 per cent dissociation.

20. The vapour pressure of a 5 per cent solution of sodium chloride at 100° is 739·9 mm. Deduce the percentage dissociation of sodium chloride at this temperature and concentration.

21. A solution containing 0·5638 gm. of barium bromide, $BaBr_2$, in 25·29 gm. of water gave an osmotic pressure of 3565 mm. at 20°. What is the apparent degree of dissociation of barium bromide into barium ion and bromine ion?

22. What is the concentration of a solution of cane sugar, $C_{12}H_{22}O_{11}$, in gm. per 100 gm. of water, which has a vapour pressure of 750 mm. at 100°? What concentration of sodium nitrate would give the same vapour pressure at 100°, assuming complete dissociation of the salt?

23. The freezing point of nitrobenzene is 3·0°. A solution of 1·20 gm. of chloroform in 100 gm. of nitrobenzene freezes at 2·3°. A solution of 0·6 gm. of acetic acid in 100 gm. of nitrobenzene freezes at 2·64°. From these data make what deductions you can concerning the molecular state of acetic acid when dissolved in nitrobenzene. (C.U.O.S.)

24. What concentration (gm. per 100 c.c. solution) of urea (molecular weight = 60) would be isotonic at 15° with a solution of glucose (molecular weight = 180) containing 5·63 gm. of glucose in 85 c.c. of solution at 30°?

What concentration of sodium chloride (assuming complete dissociation) would, at 20°, be isotonic with these solutions?

25. When 1·62 gm. of urea was dissolved in 25 c.c. of water, the freezing point of water was depressed by 2·01°. A normal solution of potassium chloride began to freeze at a temperature 3·42° lower than the freezing point of pure water. Calculate the apparent degree of dissociation in N KCl solution.

26. In a series of six experiments with hydrogen iodide, 0·96 gm. of the latter in each experiment was entirely converted into vapour at the given temperature and constant pressure and then quickly cooled. The amount of iodine liberated in each experiment was determined by titration with $0{\cdot}1N$ sodium thiosulphate, and the volumes of the latter for corresponding temperatures were as follows:

250°	290°	330°	360°	400°	420°
13·25 c.c.	12·4 c.c.	12·0 c.c.	12·9 c.c.	14·6 c.c.	15·7 c.c.

Calculate the percentage of hydrogen iodide dissociated at each temperature; express your results in the form of a graph. What conclusions do you draw from the form of the curve? (N.U.J.B.)

27. A tenth molar solution of mercuric chloride ($HgCl_2$) gave an osmotic pressure of 2·24 atmospheres at 0°. 2·72 gm. of the salt when vaporised occupied 552 c.c. at 400° and 760 mm. pressure. What conclusions can be drawn from these results?

28. A solution of 8·5 gm. of sodium nitrate in 1000 c.c. of water begins to freeze at −0·342°. What is the percentage dissociation of the salt? Assuming that the percentage dissociation remains unaltered by change of temperature, calculate the vapour pressure of the solution at 100°.

29. The vapour pressure of pure benzene at 40° is 181 mm. When 10 gm. of a monobasic organic acid of molecular weight 138 is dissolved in 100 gm. of benzene, the vapour pressure of the solution is 175·8 mm. at 40°. Calculate the apparent molecular weight of the acid in benzene solution. What conclusion can be drawn from the value so obtained?

30. The freezing points of certain aqueous solutions, each containing 1 gm. of substance per 100 gm. of solvent, are as follows:

1% glucose ($C_6H_{12}O_6$) - - - - - - −0·103°
1% sodium chloride - - - - - - - −0·604°
1% potassium iodide - - - - - - - −0·213°
1% potassium iodide (containing also 1·372% mercuric iodide) - - - - - - - −0·2234°

Explain the conclusions you draw from these data.

(N.U.J.B. Schol.)

31. A solution of 5·92 gm. of potassium nitrate in 95·6 c.c. of water at 15° is isotonic with a solution of 5·63 gm. of urea ($CO(NH_2)_2$) in 81·2 c.c. of water at 20°. Calculate the percentage dissociation of potassium nitrate at the dilution and the temperature stated.

* **32.** The surface tension of silicon tetrachloride at 18·9° and 45·5° is respectively 16·31 dynes/cm. and 13·66 dynes/cm. The corresponding densities are 1·486 gm./c.c. and 1·429 gm./c.c. Calculate the molecular surface energy at each temperature, and hence show that silicon tetrachloride is not associated.

* **33.** The surface tension of liquid oxygen was determined at several temperatures by observing its rise in a capillary tube.† The following results were obtained:

Temperature, °A	Height to which liquid rose h (cm.)	Radius of the capillary tube r (cm.)	Density of the liquid d (gm./c.c.)
76·20	2·000	0·014090	1·2096
85·41	1·783	0·014112	1·1650
86·41	1·758	0·014117	1·1602
87·43	1·733	0·014121	1·1552
88·92	1·701	0·014122	1·1482

† Use $T = \frac{1}{2}hrgd$ where T = the surface tension (dynes per cm.), h = the height to which the liquid rises, r = internal radius of the capillary tube, g = acceleration due to the earth's gravitational force and d = the density of the liquid.

Calculate the surface tension at each temperature, and hence deduce the temperature coefficient of molecular surface energy for liquid oxygen. What conclusion can you draw from these results?

* 34. Using the values obtained in question 33, calculate the critical temperature of oxygen.

* 35. The following results were obtained for the rise of propyl alcohol in a capillary tube (the nomenclature is the same as in question 33). Obtain the average value for the rate of change of surface energy with temperature, and hence show that propyl alcohol is strongly associated.

Temperature	h (cm.)	r (cm.)	d (gm./c.c.)
16·4	4·22	0·01425	0·8073
46·3	3·89	0·01425	0·7831
78·3	3·54	0·01425	0·7546

CHAPTER VII

THERMOCHEMISTRY

1. The law of constant heat summation

It is assumed that the student is acquainted with the experimental methods of illustrating Hess's law of constant heat summation, which may be stated as follows :

(1) The heat exchange during a chemical reaction depends solely upon the chemical and physical states of the initial substances and of the products ; it is independent of the manner in which the reaction takes place, or

(2) The **heat content** (or **intrinsic energy**) of a substance depends solely upon its physical state and chemical composition ; it is independent of its method of preparation.†

The heat exchanges involved in various physical and chemical changes are defined as follows :

(*a*) **Heat of formation.**

The heat of formation of a compound is the heat evolved or absorbed when 1 gm.-molecule of that compound is synthesised from its elements ; the physical state of the compound and the elements from which it is formed must be given, since these will affect the observed heat of formation. Thus, the heat of formation of water, the water being liquid at 0°, is much greater than the heat evolved if the water is formed as steam at 100°.

Where heat is *absorbed* during a chemical reaction, this is indicated by a minus sign. In the synthesis of carbon disulphide, for example, 26,000 calories per gm.-molecule are absorbed ; the heat of formation of carbon disulphide, therefore, is negative and equal to − 26,000 calories.

(*b*) **Heat of combustion**

The heat of combustion of a substance is the heat evolved when a fixed quantity (usually 1 gm.-molecule unless otherwise

† No absolute value can be assigned to the heat content of a system. If, however, the heat contents of a system in two different states are denoted by H_1 and H_2, then $H_1 - H_2$ is constant, depending only on the initial and final states of the system.

stated) is burnt to give products whose physical and chemical nature are given. Thus, the combustion of a fixed amount of methane will give rise to two different quantities of heat, according as the gas is oxidised to water and carbon dioxide or water and carbon monoxide. It is assumed, usually, that when a value is given for a heat of combustion, then this value is the heat evolved when a substance is completely oxidised, that is, it is burnt in the presence of an excess of oxygen.

(*c*) **Heat of neutralisation**

The heat of neutralisation of an acid or an alkali is the heat evolved when 1 *gm.-equivalent* is neutralised, the dilutions of the reacting solutions being stated.

(*d*) **Heat of solution**

The heat of solution of a substance is the heat evolved or absorbed when 1 gm.-molecule of that substance is dissolved in a stated quantity of the solvent.

(*e*) **Heat of dilution**

The heat of dilution of a substance is the heat evolved or absorbed when a given volume of a solution, containing 1 gm.-molecule of the substance, is diluted to another stated volume.

Example 71. The heat of combustion of ethylene, C_2H_4, is 333,000 cal. Given that the heats of combustion of carbon and hydrogen are 97,300 cal. and 68,400 cal. respectively, calculate the heat of formation of ethylene.

It is usual to denote the heat content of a substance by enclosing the formula of that substance in curved brackets, { }. Thus, $\{C_2H_4\}$ represents the heat content of ethylene under stated conditions. Although no absolute value can be assigned to the heat content of a substance, a difference of heat contents can be expressed as an amount of heat evolved or absorbed.

The equation for the combustion of ethylene is :

$$C_2H_4 + 3O_2 = 2CO_2 + 2H_2O. \quad \ldots\ldots\ldots\ldots\ldots\ldots (a)$$

$$\therefore \{C_2H_4\} + \{3O_2\} - \{2CO_2\} - \{2H_2O\} = 333{,}000 \text{ cal.} \ \ldots (b)$$

Similarly :

$$\{C\} + \{O_2\} - \{CO_2\} = 97{,}300 \text{ cal.} \quad \ldots\ldots\ldots\ldots\ldots (c)$$

and

$$\{H_2\} + \{\tfrac{1}{2}O_2\} - \{H_2O\} = 68{,}400 \text{ cal.} \quad \ldots\ldots\ldots\ldots\ldots (d)$$

Then, if Q denote the required heat of formation of ethylene :

$$\{2C\} + \{2H_2\} - \{C_2H_4\} = Q.$$

To find Q, therefore, we have to eliminate $\{O_2\}$, $\{H_2O\}$ and $\{CO_2\}$ from equations (*b*), (*c*) and (*d*).

If equations (*c*) and (*d*) are multiplied respectively by 2 and added, then :

$$2\{C\} + 2\{O_2\} - 2\{CO_2\} + 2\{H_2\} + \{O_2\} - 2\{H_2O\}$$
$$= [(2 \times 97{,}300) + (2 \times 68{,}400)] \text{ cal.}$$
$$= 331{,}400 \text{ cal.} \quad \ldots\ldots\ldots\ldots (e)$$

By subtracting corresponding sides of equation (*a*) from equation (*e*) :

$$2\{C\} + 2\{O_2\} - 2\{CO_2\} + 2\{H_2\} + \{O_2\} - 2\{H_2O\}$$
$$- \{C_2H_4\} - \{3O_2\} + \{2CO_2\} + \{2H_2O\}$$
$$= 331{,}400 - 333{,}000 = -1600 \text{ cal.} \quad \ldots\ldots\ldots\ldots (f)$$

But the left-hand side of equation (*f*) reduces to :

$$\{2C\} + \{2H_2\} - \{C_2H_4\}.$$
$$\therefore \{2C\} + \{2H_2\} - \{C_2H_4\} = -1600 \text{ cal.}$$

In the formation of one gm.-molecule of ethylene from its elements, therefore, 1600 calories of heat are *absorbed*.

Provided that it is remembered that a thermochemical equation involves heat contents, it is not necessary to write the equations with brackets. Care should be taken, however, to ensure that the correct sign for the heat exchange is obtained.

An alternative method of working is often preferred. Using the data of Example 71 :

$$\{C_2H_4\} + \{3O_2\} = \{2CO_2\} + \{2H_2O\} + 333{,}000 \text{ cal.}$$

But $\quad \{CO_2\} = \{C\} + \{O_2\} - 97{,}300 \text{ cal.}$

and $\quad \{H_2O\} = \{H_2\} + \{\tfrac{1}{2}O_2\} - 68{,}400 \text{ cal.}$

Substituting these values :

$$\{C_2H_4\} + \{3O_2\} = 2[\{C\} + \{O_2\} - 97{,}300 \text{ cal.}] + 2[\{H_2\} + \{\tfrac{1}{2}O_2\}$$
$$- 68{,}400 \text{ cal.}] + 333{,}000 \text{ cal.}$$
$$\therefore \{C_2H_4\} - \{2C\} - \{2H_2\} = +1{,}600 \text{ cal.}$$
$$\therefore \{2C\} + \{2H_2\} = \{C_2H_4\} - 1{,}600 \text{ cal.}$$

Example 72. The heats of combustion of hydrogen, carbon, acetylene and ethane are 68,400 cal., 97,300 cal., 310,000 cal. and 370,500 cal. respectively. Calculate (*a*) the heat of formation of acetylene, (*b*) the heat of formation of ethane, (*c*) the heat exchange when 1 gm.-molecule of acetylene is reduced to ethane.

The reactions are written :

$$C + O_2 = CO_2 + 97,300 \text{ cal.}, \quad \ldots\ldots (a)$$

$$H_2 + \tfrac{1}{2}O_2 = H_2O + 68,400 \text{ cal.}, \quad \ldots\ldots (b)$$

$$C_2H_2 + 2\tfrac{1}{2}O_2 = 2CO_2 + H_2O + 310,000 \text{ cal.}, \quad \ldots\ldots (c)$$

$$C_2H_6 + 3\tfrac{1}{2}O_2 = 2CO_2 + 3H_2O + 370,500 \text{ cal.} \quad \ldots\ldots (d)$$

Note that the heats of combustion are given in each for the combustion of 1 gm.-molecule and that the heats of combustion of carbon and hydrogen respectively are identical with the heats of formation of carbon dioxide and water.

Let Q cal. = the heat of formation of acetylene.

Then $\quad 2C + H_2 = C_2H_2 + Q$ cal.

To determine Q, equations (*a*), (*b*) and (*c*) must be manipulated so as to eliminate O_2, CO_2 and H_2O.

Multiplying equation (*a*) by 2 and adding corresponding sides of equation (*b*) :

$$2C + H_2 + 2\tfrac{1}{2}O_2 = 2CO_2 + H_2O + (2 \times 97,300) \text{ cal.} + 68,400 \text{ cal.}$$

$$= 2CO_2 + H_2O + 263,000 \text{ cal.} \quad \ldots\ldots (f)$$

Subtracting equation (*c*) from equation (*f*) :

$$2C + H_2 + 2\tfrac{1}{2}O_2 - C_2H_2 - 2\tfrac{1}{2}O_2 = (263,000 - 310,000) \text{ cal.}$$

$$\therefore\ 2C + H_2 = C_2H_2 - 47,000 \text{ cal.}$$

$\therefore$ The heat of formation of acetylene is negative, being equal to $-47,000$ cal. In the formation of 1 gm.-molecule of acetylene, therefore, 47,000 cal. are absorbed.

To determine the heat of formation of ethane, multiply equation (*a*) by 2, and equation (*b*) by 3 ; adding corresponding sides of the resulting equations :

$$2C + 2O_2 + 3H_2 + 1\tfrac{1}{2}O_2 = 2CO_2 + 3H_2O + (2 \times 97,300) \text{ cal.} + (3 \times 68,400) \text{ cal.}$$

$$= 2CO_2 + 3H_2O + 399,800 \text{ cal.} \quad \ldots\ldots (h)$$

Subtracting equation (*d*) from equation (*h*):

$$2C + 3H_2 - C_2H_6 = (399{,}800 - 370{,}500) \text{ cal.}$$
$$= \mathbf{29{,}300 \text{ cal.}}$$

The heat of formation of ethane is, therefore, +29,300 cal., and this amount of heat is evolved when 1 gm.-molecule of ethane is synthesised from its elements.

To calculate the heat of reduction of acetylene to ethane, we use the equations :

$$2C + H_2 = C_2H_2 - 47{,}000 \text{ cal.}, \quad \ldots\ldots\ldots\ldots\ldots\ldots(i)$$
$$2C + 3H_2 = C_2H_6 + 29{,}300 \text{ cal.} \quad \ldots\ldots\ldots\ldots\ldots\ldots(j)$$

Subtracting (*i*) from (*j*) :

$$2H_2 = C_2H_6 - C_2H_2 + 76{,}300 \text{ cal.}$$
$$\therefore\ C_2H_2 + 2H_2 = C_2H_6 + \mathbf{76{,}300 \text{ cal.}}$$

In the reduction of 1 gm.-molecule of acetylene to ethane, therefore, 76,300 cal. of heat are evolved.

In the foregoing calculation, the physical state of the carbon, for example, whether graphite or diamond, and of the hydrogen, for example, its pressure and temperature, have been ignored. As mentioned on p. 134, the heat exchange will vary with the physical states of the reacting substances and of the products.

2. Work of expansion of a gas (pressure and temperature constant)

When the volume of a system changes during a reaction, for example, a gas is evolved, the observed heat of the reaction differs from the true heat of the reaction ; the system will either do work against the opposing pressure or will have work done on it (if it contracts), and the heat equivalent of this work must enter into the thermochemical equation.

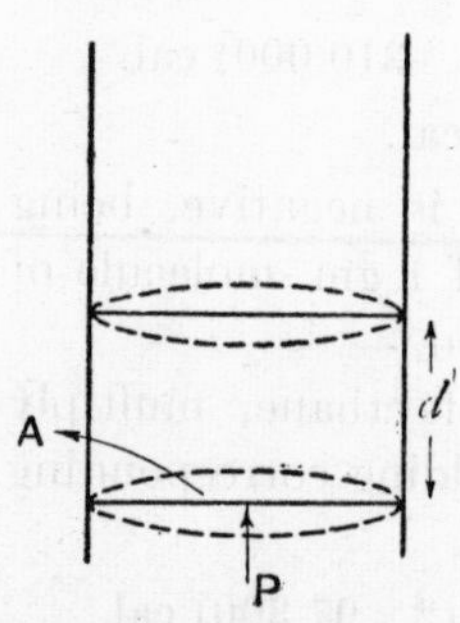

FIG. 13. Work of isothermal expansion of a gas (pressure constant).

As the simplest case we may consider a reaction in which the volume of the system increases against a constant pressure. Allow the expansion to take place as in Fig. 13. Then if P = the constant pressure on the gas, then this is the force on unit area of the piston. If, then, the piston moves through a distance, d, work done *per unit area* of the piston $= P \times d$.

But the area of the piston $= A$ units of area.

$\therefore$ Total work done $= P \times d \times A = PV$ where $V =$ increase in volume.

If, now, the expansion is produced as a result of the formation of 1 gm.-molecule of gas, then $PV = RT$ where $T =$ temperature ($°A$) of the system.

Example 73. In a chemical reaction it is found that the volume of the system increases by 1000 c.c. at a constant atmospheric pressure of 740 mm. Calculate the work of expansion in (*a*) ergs, (*b*) calories.

$P = 740$ mm. of Hg $= 74$ cm.

$\therefore$ P (dynes) $= 74 \times 13{\cdot}6$ (density of mercury) $\times 981$ (acceleration due to gravity)

$\therefore$ Work done in ergs $= P \times V = 74 \times 13{\cdot}6 \times 981 \times 1000$

$= 9{\cdot}87 \times 10^8$ ergs.

But 1 cal. $\equiv 4{\cdot}2 \times 10^7$ ergs.

$$\therefore \text{ Work done in cal.} = \frac{9{\cdot}87 \times 10^8}{4{\cdot}2 \times 10^7} = 23{\cdot}5 \text{ cal.}$$

For the particular case in which 1 gm.-molecule of a gas is produced at constant pressure, $PV = RT$, so that the work done must be RT cal. provided the value of R is obtained in the appropriate units. Since 1 gm.-molecule of any gas occupies 22,400 c.c. at 760 mm. pressure and 0°, we have :

$$P = 76 \times 13{\cdot}6 \times 981 \text{ dynes.}$$

$$V = 22{,}400 \text{ c.c.}$$

$$\therefore PV = 76 \times 13{\cdot}6 \times 981 \times 22{,}400 \text{ ergs.}$$

$$\therefore \frac{PV}{T} = \frac{76 \times 13{\cdot}6 \times 981 \times 22{,}400}{273} \text{ ergs per degree}$$

$$= \frac{76 \times 13{\cdot}6 \times 981 \times 22{,}400}{273 \times 4{\cdot}2 \times 10^7} \text{ cal. per degree}$$

$$\doteq 2 = R.$$

$\therefore$ Work done $\doteq$ **2 T cal.**, where T can have any value.

Example 74. The heat of formation of carbon monoxide at constant volume at 18° is 29,600 cal. Calculate the heat of formation of the gas under constant pressure at 18°.

At constant volume :

$$C + \tfrac{1}{2}O_2 = CO + 29{,}600 \text{ cal.},$$

or

$$2C + O_2 = 2CO + 59{,}200 \text{ cal.}$$

When, however, the reaction is conducted at constant pressure, the volume of the system increases ; ignoring the volume of the carbon, the increase in the volume of the system is 22·4 litres at 0° and 760 mm. pressure for the formation of 2 gm.-molecules of carbon monoxide. The reaction, therefore, does work against the applied pressure, and the heat equivalent of this work must be subtracted from the heat evolved when the reaction takes place at constant volume.

From reasoning outlined on p. 138, the work done in the production of 1 gm.-molecule of a gas is $2T$ cal. whatever the pressure.

∴ Work done *by* the gas in reaction (2)

$$= 2 \times 291 = 582 \text{ cal.}$$

∴ Work done in formation of 1 *gm.-molecule* of carbon dioxide $= 219$ cal.

∴ Heat of formation of carbon monoxide (1 gm.-molecule)

$$= 29{,}600 - 291 \doteqdot 29{,}310 \text{ cal.}$$

3. First law of thermodynamics

The energy exchange in any system as a result of physical or chemical change is given by the equation :

$$\Delta U = Q - W, \qquad \text{......................... (73)}$$

where ΔU = the *increase* in the energy of the system, Q = the heat *absorbed* in the reaction, and W = the work (in cal.) done *by* the system, for example, work due to expansion or electrical work.

Where the system does no work or has no work done on it, as in a gaseous reaction at constant volume, $W = 0$ and $\Delta U = Q$.

For gaseous reactions at constant pressure in which the volume of the system may change, as in the reaction :

$$2CO + O_2 = 2CO_2,$$

work is done, either *on* the system by contraction or *by* the system during expansion. Assuming no other work is done, then :

$$\Delta U = Q - p\Delta V, \quad \text{.......................(74)}$$

where p = the constant pressure and ΔV = the *increase* in volume of the system during the change.

If the equation is written :

$$Q = \Delta U + p\Delta V, \quad \text{.......................(75)}$$

the sum of the two terms, ΔU and $p\Delta V$, gives the total heat exchange of the reaction.

Writing :

$$Q = \Delta U + p\Delta V = \Delta H, \quad \text{...................(76)}$$

ΔH = *increase* in the *heat content* of the system. The sign of a change of heat content in relation to heat of reaction should be noted carefully. In the combustion of carbon to form carbon dioxide (at constant pressure) 29,310 cal. are evolved :

$$C + \tfrac{1}{2}O_2 = CO_2 + 29{,}310 \text{ cal.}$$

The heat of formation of carbon dioxide is, therefore, +29,310 cal. The heat content change = −29,310, since this amount of heat is lost to the surroundings.

Since p is constant, the term $p\Delta V$ depends solely on the initial and final states of the system, as does, therefore, the term ΔH (see Hess's law, p. 134).

When no work is done :

$$Q = \Delta U = \Delta H. \quad \text{.......................(77)}$$

* 4. Work of isothermal expansion of a gas (pressure variable)

The work of isothermal expansion of a gas (pressure constant), that is, the work done by increase in volume as a result of a change in the number of gm.-molecules of a gas, has been discussed on p. 138.

It is also of importance to calculate the work done by the isothermal expansion of a given mass of gas from a volume, V_1, to volume, V_2. Since the volume is varying continuously, the pressure on the gas will undergo a corresponding continuous decrease from its initial value, p_1, to its final value, p_2.

$$\therefore \text{ Work done} = \int_{V_1}^{V_2} p\,dV.$$

For any mass of gas at constant temperature, $pV = kT$, where k is a constant depending upon the mass of gas.

$$\therefore \text{ Work done} = \int_{V_1}^{V_2} p\,dV = \int_{V_1}^{V_2} \frac{kT}{V}\,dV$$

$$= kT \int_{V_1}^{V_2} \frac{dV}{V} = \mathbf{kT \log_e \frac{V_2}{V_1}}, \quad \text{.......................(78)}$$

where T is constant (isothermal expansion). For 1 gm.-molecule of a gas, $k = R$, and work done $= RT \log_e \frac{V_2}{V_1} \doteq \mathbf{2T \log_e \frac{V_2}{V_1}}$ **cal.**†

*** Example 75.** Calculate the work done by 1 litre of hydrogen initially at 0° and 760 mm. pressure in expanding to a volume of 2 litres also at 0°.

$$\text{Work done} = kT \log_e \frac{V_2}{V_1} = 2{\cdot}303 kT \log_{10} \frac{V_2}{V_1}.$$

For a mass of gas which occupies 1 litre at $N.T.P.$:

$$pV = kT \text{ where } k = \frac{R}{22{\cdot}4}.$$

$$\therefore \text{ Work done} = \frac{RT}{22{\cdot}4} \times 2{\cdot}303 \times \log_{10} \frac{V_2}{V_1}$$

$$= \frac{2 \times 273 \times 2{\cdot}303 \times \log_{10} 2}{22{\cdot}4} \text{ cal.}$$

$$= \mathbf{16{\cdot}9 \text{ cal.}} \text{ (since } R = 2 \text{ cal. per degree).}$$

$$\text{Work done in ergs} = 16{\cdot}9 \times 4{\cdot}2 \times 10^7$$

$$= \mathbf{7{\cdot}00 \times 10^8 \text{ ergs.}}$$

* 5. Work of expansion of gas (adiabatic)

When a gas expands adiabatically no heat enters or leaves the system. The work is done at the expense of the internal energy of the gas whose temperature must, therefore, fall. The work of adiabatic expansion is not of direct importance in calculating heats of reaction, but the result obtained below is of importance in the development of the second law of thermodynamics (see p. 303).

† This is the **maximum work** of expansion (see p. 296).

For any adiabatic change, the pressure of a gas and its corresponding volume are related by the equation

$$p \times V^{\gamma} = \text{a constant} = K, \quad \ldots\ldots\ldots\ldots\ldots\ldots \text{(79)}$$

where γ = the ratio of the specific heats of the gas at constant pressure and constant volume respectively. This relation can be obtained in the following manner.

For any gas, the amount of heat (dQ) entering the system is related to the increase in energy ($C_v\,dT$) and the work done ($p\,dV$) by the equation:

$$dQ = C_v\,dT + p\,dV.$$

But since $pV = RT$:

$$p\,dV + V\,dp = R\,dT.$$

By elimination of dT:

$$dQ = \frac{C_v + R}{R}\,p\,dV + \frac{C_v}{R}\,V\,dp.$$

But for adiabatic change, $dQ = 0$.

$$\therefore \frac{C_v + R}{R}\,p\,dV + \frac{C_v}{R}\,V\,dp = 0.$$

$$\therefore \frac{C_v + R}{C_v}\,p\,dV + V\,dp = 0.$$

But $$\frac{C_v + R}{C_v} = \frac{C_p}{C_v} \quad \text{(see p. 138).}$$

Denoting $\frac{C_v}{C_p}$ by γ:

$$\gamma p\,dV + V\,dp = 0.$$

$$\therefore \gamma \frac{dV}{V} + \frac{dp}{p} = 0.$$

Integration between the appropriate limits gives:

$$\gamma \log_e \frac{V_1}{V_2} + \log_e \frac{p_1}{p_2} = 0.$$

$$\therefore p_1 V_1^{\gamma} = p_2 V_2^{\gamma}.$$

If the mass of gas involved is 1 gm.-molecule, the pressure, temperature and volume are still related by the gas equation:

$$pV = RT.$$

For any mass of gas: $pV = kT$.

Then, as in para. 4, p. 141:

$$\text{Work done} = \int_{V_1}^{V_2} p\,dV = \int_{V_1}^{V_2} \frac{K}{V^\gamma}\,dV$$

$$= K\left[\frac{V^{1-\gamma}}{1-\gamma}\right]_{V_1}^{V_2} = K\left(\frac{V_2^{1-\gamma}}{1-\gamma} - \frac{V_1^{1-\gamma}}{1-\gamma}\right).$$

But $K = pV^\gamma = p_1V_1^\gamma = p_2V_2^\gamma$.

$$\therefore \text{Work done} = K\left(\frac{V_2^{1-\gamma}}{1-\gamma}\right) - K\left(\frac{V_1^{1-\gamma}}{1-\gamma}\right)$$

$$= \frac{p_2V_2^\gamma \times V_2^{1-\gamma}}{1-\gamma} - \frac{p_1V_1^\gamma \times V_1^{1-\gamma}}{1-\gamma}$$

$$= \frac{\mathbf{p_2V_2 - p_1V_1}}{\mathbf{1-\gamma}}. \qquad \text{.........(80)}$$

For 1 gm.-molecule of a gas:

$$\text{Work done} = \frac{p_2V_2 - p_1V_1}{1-\gamma} = \frac{\mathbf{R(T_2 - T_1)}}{\mathbf{1-\gamma}}. \qquad \text{........(81)}$$

* **Example 76.** Calculate the work done when (*a*) 5 litres of oxygen at 2 atmospheres pressure expands adiabatically to 20 litres, (*b*) 28 gm. of oxygen at 0° and 5 atmospheres expands adiabatically so that the final pressure is 1 atmosphere.

For oxygen, $\gamma \doteqdot 1{\cdot}4$ (see p. 26).

(*a*) Since $p_1V_1^\gamma = p_2V_2^\gamma$,

$$\therefore\ 2 \times 5^{1\cdot4} = p_2 \times 20^{1\cdot4}.$$

From which $p_2 = 0{\cdot}2872$ atmospheres.

$$\therefore \text{Work done} = \frac{(0{\cdot}2872 \times 20) - (2 \times 5)}{1 - 1{\cdot}4}$$

$$= \mathbf{10{\cdot}66\ litre\text{-}atmospheres.}$$

To convert litre-atmospheres to ergs and hence to calories, we note that:

$$1\ \text{litre-atmosphere} = 1000 \times 76 \times 981 \times 13{\cdot}6\ \text{ergs}$$

$$= \frac{1000 \times 76 \times 981 \times 13{\cdot}6}{4{\cdot}2 \times 10^7}\ \text{cal.}$$

$$= 24{\cdot}14\ \text{cal.}$$

$$\therefore \text{Work done in cal.} = 10{\cdot}66 \times 24{\cdot}14 = \mathbf{257\ cal.}$$

(*b*) Since 32 gm. of oxygen occupy 22·4 litres at *N.T.P.*:

∴ 28 gm. of oxygen at 0° and 5 atmospheres will occupy

$$\frac{22 \cdot 4}{5} \times \frac{28}{32} = 3 \cdot 92 \text{ litres.}$$

$$\therefore\ 5 \times 3 \cdot 92^{1 \cdot 4} = 1 \times V_2^{1 \cdot 4} \quad (\text{where } V_2 = \text{the final volume}).$$

$$\therefore\ V_2 = \sqrt[1 \cdot 4]{5 \times 3 \cdot 92^{1 \cdot 4}} = 10 \cdot 52 \text{ litres.}$$

$$\therefore \text{ Work done} = \frac{(1 \times 10 \cdot 52) - (5 \times 3 \cdot 92)}{1 - 1 \cdot 4}$$

$$= \mathbf{22 \cdot 7 \text{ litre-atmospheres.}}$$

$$\therefore \text{Work done in cal.} = 22 \cdot 7 \times 24 \cdot 14$$

$$= \mathbf{548 \text{ cal.}}$$

6. Heats of neutralisation and strengths of acids

The heats of neutralisation of strong acids and strong alkalis are constant and equal to 13,700 cal. per gm.-equivalent. This quantity of heat is the heat of formation of water from hydrogen ion and hydroxyl ion:

$$H^+ + OH^- = H_2O + 13{,}700 \text{ cal.}$$

Any variation from this figure, therefore, indicates that the acid (or alkali) is not completely dissociated. If the percentage dissociation is known, then the heat of dissociation can be calculated.

Example 77. The heat of neutralisation of a weak acid in normal solution by a strong alkali is 13,385 cal. Assuming that the acid is 14 per cent dissociated in normal solution, calculate the heat of dissociation of the acid.

If the acid had been 100 per cent dissociated, the amount of heat evolved would have been 13,700 cal.

∴ Amount of heat *absorbed* in the dissociation of 86 per cent of the acid = 13,700 − 13,385 = 315 cal.

∴ Heat of dissociation per gm.-equivalent

$$= -\frac{315 \times 100}{86} \text{ cal.} = \mathbf{-366 \text{ cal.}}$$

The strengths of two acids can be compared by determining the proportion in which 1 gm.-equivalent of a strong base divides itself when acted upon by a mixture of 1 gm.-equivalent each of two acids. This proportion can be calculated from the observed heat of such a reaction.

Example 78. The heats of neutralisation of two acids HA and HB are 13,650 cal. and 11,200 cal. respectively. When 1 gm.-equivalent of sodium hydroxide in dilute solution is added to a mixture of 1 gm.-equivalent of HA and 1 gm.-equivalent of HB, 12,960 cal. are evolved. Compare the strengths of the two acids, HA and HB.

Let a fraction n gm.-equivalents of the sodium hydroxide be neutralised by the acid HA.

$$\text{Then } n\text{H}A + n\text{NaOH} = n\text{Na}A + n\text{H}_2\text{O} + (n \times 13{,}650) \text{ cal.}$$

Since there is only 1 gm.-equivalent of NaOH, $(1-n)$ gm.-equivalents must have been neutralised by the acid, HB.

$$\therefore\ (1-n)\text{H}B + (1-n)\text{NaOH} = (1-n)\text{Na}B + (1-n)\text{H}_2\text{O} + [(1-n) \times 11{,}200] \text{ cal.}$$

But the observed heat of the reaction is 12,960 cal.

$$\therefore\ (n \times 13{,}650) + [(1-n)(11{,}200] = 12{,}960.$$

$$\therefore\ n = 0{\cdot}72 \text{ and } (1-n) = 0{\cdot}28.$$

$$\therefore\ \frac{\text{Strength of acid, H}A}{\text{Strength of acid, H}B} = \frac{0{\cdot}72}{0{\cdot}28} = \frac{2{\cdot}57}{1}.$$

* 7. The Kirchhoff Equation

The Kirchhoff equation gives the relation between the increase of energy, ΔU, or of heat content, ΔH (as a result

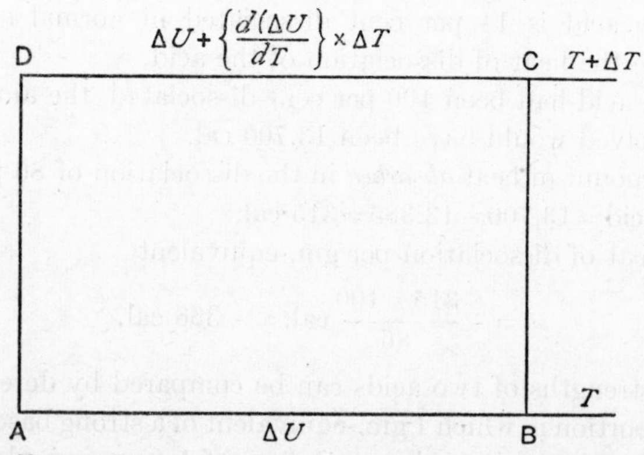

FIG. 14. Change of internal energy with temperature (Kirchhoff equation).

of a physical or chemical change) and the change of temperature.

If we assume that the reaction takes place at constant volume, then the change of energy, ΔU, is equal to the heat evolved or absorbed. Assume that at a temperature, T, the energy exchange is ΔU, the specific heat of the reactants being denoted by $(C_A)_v$ and that of the products by $(C_B)_v$.

At the higher temperature, $T+\Delta T$, the energy exchange will be denoted by

$$\left\{\Delta U + \left(\frac{d}{dT}(\Delta U) \,.\, \Delta T\right)\right\},$$

since $\frac{d}{dT}(\Delta U)$ is the variation of ΔU with temperature. If we assume further that the specific heats of the reactants and the products, respectively, remain constant over the small temperature range, ΔT, we can proceed from the state represented by A in Fig. 14 to that represented by C by either of the paths ADC or ABC.

The total increase in the energy of the system along the path ADC

= heat required to raise the reactants through ΔT + heat absorbed as a result of the reaction at temperature, $T+\Delta T$

$$=(C_A)_v \Delta T + \left[\Delta U + \left\{\frac{d}{dT}(\Delta U)\Delta T\right\}\right].$$

Similarly, total increase of energy along ABC

= heat absorbed as a result of the reaction taking place at T + heat required to raise the products through ΔT

$$=\Delta U + (C_B)_v \Delta T.$$

But since the energy exchange must be the same whatever the path :

$$(C_A)_v + \left[\Delta U + \left\{\frac{d}{dT}(\Delta U)\Delta T\right\}\right] = \Delta U + (C_B)_v \Delta T.$$

$$\therefore \frac{d}{dT}(\Delta U) = (C_B)_v - (C_A)_v,$$

$$\text{or} \quad \left\{\frac{\partial}{\partial T}(\Delta U)\right\}_v = (C_B)_v - (C_A)_v. \quad \ldots\ldots\ldots\ldots\ldots\ldots(82)$$

It can be shown, similarly, that for reactions taking place at constant pressure :

$$\left\{\frac{\partial}{\partial T}(\Delta H)\right\}_p = (C_B)_p - (C_A)_p. \quad \ldots\ldots\ldots\ldots\ldots(83)$$

* **Example 79.** The specific heat of liquid benzene is 0·412 cal. per gm. at 35° and that of benzene vapour at constant pressure at 35° is 0·300 cal. per gm. How does the heat of vaporisation of benzene vary with change of temperature?

Change of heat content of liquid benzene per degree at 35° = 0·412 × 78 cal. per gm.-molecule = 32·14 cal. Similarly, change of heat content of benzene vapour per gm.-molecule per degree = 0·300 × 78 = 23·4 cal.

$$\therefore \left\{\frac{\partial(\Delta H)}{\partial T}\right\}_p = (C_p)_{\text{gas}} - (C_p)_{\text{liquid}}$$

$$= 23{\cdot}4 - 32{\cdot}14 = -8{\cdot}74 \text{ cal. per degree.}$$

The latent heat of evaporation of benzene, therefore, **decreases** by 8·74 cal. per gm.-molecule per degree. The molecular heat of evaporation of benzene at 35° is 8520 cal. At 45°, therefore, the molecular heat of evaporation = 8520 − (10 × 8·74) = **8433 cal.** The sign of this result can be checked by applying the principles used in the derivation of the Kirchhoff equation.

In the foregoing example it has been assumed that the specific heats of liquid and gaseous benzene remain constant over the range 35°–45°. In general such specific heats vary with the temperature, and the quantity of heat over wide ranges of temperature is then obtained by integration.

* **Example 80.** The heat of combustion of carbon monoxide at constant pressure at 20° is 67,950 cal. per gm.-molecule. What is the heat of combustion at 300° given that the molecular specific heats of carbon monoxide, oxygen and carbon dioxide vary with temperature according to the following equations (T being the absolute temperature):

$$(C_p)_{CO} = 6{\cdot}5 + 0{\cdot}0010T,$$

$$(C_p)_{O_2} = 6{\cdot}5 + 0{\cdot}0010T,$$

$$(C_p)_{CO_2} = 7{\cdot}0 + 0{\cdot}0071T - 0{\cdot}00000186T^2.$$

In problems of this nature it is advisable to draw a diagram similar to that in Fig. 15.

The reaction is :

$$CO + \tfrac{1}{2}O_2 = CO_2.$$

Let Q_{293} = heat of reaction at 293° A, i.e. 20°,
and Q_{573} = ,, ,, ,, 573° A, i.e. 300°.

Then, as in Fig. 15, we may proceed from A to C by the alternative paths ABC and ADC, the heat exchange being the same in each case.

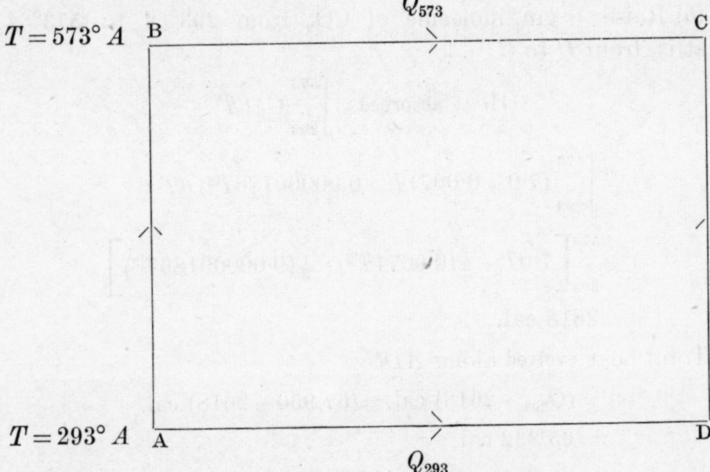

FIG. 15. Use of the Kirchhoff equation.

Along ABC

(*a*) Raise 1 gm.-molecule of carbon monoxide and $\frac{1}{2}$ gm.-molecule of oxygen from 293° A to 573° A, that is, from A to B.

Heat absorbed is :

(1) For 1 gm.-molecule of $CO = \int_{293}^{573} C_p \, dT$

$$= \int_{293}^{573} (6{\cdot}5 + 0{\cdot}0010T)\, dT$$

$$= \Big[6{\cdot}5T + \tfrac{1}{2}(0{\cdot}0010T^2) \Big]_{293}^{573} = 1942 \text{ cal.}$$

(2) For $\frac{1}{2}$ gm.-molecule of $O_2 = \frac{1}{2} \int_{293}^{573} C_p \, dT$

$$= \tfrac{1}{2} \int_{293}^{573} (6{\cdot}5 + 0{\cdot}0010T)\, dT = 971 \text{ cal.}$$

∴ Total heat absorbed along $AB = 1942 + 971$

$$= 2913 \text{ cal.}$$

(*b*) Now allow the reaction to proceed at 573° *A*, the heat evolved being Q_{573} cal.

$\therefore$ Total heat evolved along $ABC = (Q_{573} - 2913)$ cal.

Along ADC,

(*a*) Allow the reaction to take place at 293° *A*.

$$\text{Heat evolved} = Q_{293} = 67{,}950 \text{ cal.}$$

(*b*) Raise 1 gm.-molecule of CO_2 from 293° *A* to 573° *A*, that is, from *D* to *C*.

$$\text{Heat absorbed} = \int_{293}^{573} C_p\,dT$$

$$= \int_{293}^{573} (7{\cdot}0 + 0{\cdot}0071T - 0{\cdot}00000186T^2)\,dT$$

$$= \Big[7{\cdot}0T + \tfrac{1}{2}(0{\cdot}0071T^2) - \tfrac{1}{3}(0{\cdot}00000186T^3) \Big]_{293}^{573}$$

$$= 2618 \text{ cal.}$$

Total heat evolved along *ADC*

$$= (Q_{293} - 2618) \text{ cal.} = (67{,}950 - 2618) \text{ cal.}$$

$$= 65{,}332 \text{ cal.}$$

$$\therefore (Q_{573} - 2913) = 65{,}332.$$

$$\therefore Q_{573} = -\Delta Q_{573} = 68{,}245 \text{ cal.}$$

* 8. Ratio of the specific heats of gases

Let C_v = the specific heat of a gas at constant volume and C_p = the specific heat of the same gas at constant pressure.

From the definition of C_v, we have:

$$C_v \Delta T = \Delta U.$$

Similarly:

$$C_p \Delta T = \Delta H.$$

But

$$\Delta H = \Delta U + p\Delta V.$$

$$\therefore C_v = \frac{\Delta U}{\Delta T} = \left(\frac{\partial U}{\partial T}\right)_v$$

and

$$\therefore C_p = \frac{\Delta H}{\Delta T} = \left(\frac{\partial H}{\partial T}\right)_p = \left(\frac{\partial U}{\partial T}\right)_p + \left\{\frac{\partial (p\Delta V)}{\partial T}\right\}_p.$$

But, for a perfect gas, U is independent of the volume:

$$\therefore \left(\frac{\partial U}{\partial T}\right)_v = \left(\frac{\partial U}{\partial T}\right)_p;$$

$$\therefore C_p = \left(\frac{\partial U}{\partial T}\right)_v + \left\{\frac{\partial (p\Delta V)}{\partial T}\right\}_p.$$

But by the kinetic theory of gases, U for 1 gm.-molecule of any gas is related to R, the gas constant, and T, the absolute temperature, by the equation:

$U = 3/2 . RT$ (see p. 33).

$$\therefore C_v = \left(\frac{\partial U}{\partial T}\right)_v = 3/2 . R, \quad \ldots\ldots\ldots\ldots\ldots\ldots(84)$$

and $$C_p = \left(\frac{\partial U}{\partial T}\right)_v + \left\{\frac{\partial (p\Delta V)}{\partial T}\right\} = 3/2 . R + \left\{\frac{\partial (p\Delta V)}{\partial T}\right\}_p. \quad \ldots(85)$$

But for 1 gm.-molecule of any gas:

$$\left\{\frac{\partial (p\Delta V)}{\partial T}\right\}_p = \left\{\frac{\partial (RT)}{\partial T}\right\}_p = R. \quad \ldots\ldots\ldots\ldots\ldots\ldots(86)$$

$$\therefore C_p = 3/2 . R + R = 5/2 . R.$$

$$\therefore \frac{C_p}{C_v} = \frac{5/2 . R}{3/2 . R} = 5/3 = 1{\cdot}67.$$

This expression is derived, however, on the assumption that the energy of a gas is due solely to the translational velocity of the molecules and ignores energy changes such as might be caused by the energy of the atoms within the molecule. Denoting all such changes of internal energy by e:

$$C_v = 3/2 . R + e \text{ and } C_p = 5/2 . R + e.$$

$$\therefore \frac{C_p}{C_v} = \frac{5/2 . R + e}{3/2 . R + e} = \frac{5R + 2e}{3R + 2e}. \quad \ldots\ldots\ldots\ldots\ldots\ldots(87)$$

For monatomic gases, in which there is no energy of oscillation of the atoms within the molecule, $e = 0$ and $C_p/C_v = 1{\cdot}67$. Where e is not zero, $C_p/C_v < 1{\cdot}67$. For diatomic gases the ratio $\doteqdot 1{\cdot}42$, and for triatomic gases, the ratio $\doteqdot 1{\cdot}28$.

QUESTIONS ON CHAPTER VII

1. Calculate the heat of formation of methane, using the following data:

$$CH_4 + 2O_2 = CO_2 + 2H_2O + 212{,}000 \text{ cal.},$$
$$C + O_2 = CO_2 + 97{,}300 \text{ cal.},$$
$$H_2 + \tfrac{1}{2}O_2 = H_2O + 68{,}400 \text{ cal.}$$

2. Calculate the heat of formation of diethyl ether, $C_4H_{10}O$, from the following data :

$$C_4H_{10}O + 6O_2 = 4CO_2 + 5H_2O + 660{,}000 \text{ cal.},$$
$$C + O_2 = CO_2 + 97{,}000 \text{ cal.},$$
$$H_2 + \tfrac{1}{2}O_2 = H_2O + 68{,}400 \text{ cal.}$$

3. From the following data, calculate the heat of formation of carbon disulphide :

$$C + O_2 = CO_2 + 96{,}900 \text{ cal.},$$
$$S + O_2 = SO_2 + 71{,}000 \text{ cal.},$$
$$CS_2 + 3O_2 = CO_2 + 2SO_2 + 265{,}000 \text{ cal.}$$

(1st M.B., London.)

4. The heat of formation of carbon dioxide is 94,000 cal. and that of nitrous oxide is $-17{,}700$ cal. Calculate the heat of combustion of carbon in nitrous oxide. (H.S.C., London.)

5. The molecular heat of combustion of camphor, $C_{10}H_{16}O$, is 141,000 cal., the molecular heat of formation of carbon dioxide, 97,000 cal., the molecular heat of formation of water, 68,000 cal., all measured at constant pressure. Calculate the heat of formation of camphor from its elements at constant pressure.

(Inter. B.Sc., London)

6. The heats of formation of toluene, C_7H_8, carbon dioxide and water are -3500 cal., 97,000 cal. and 68,400 cal., respectively. What is the heat of complete combustion of 10 gm. of toluene?

7. When the following reaction takes place :

$$CH_2Cl_2 + O_2 = CO_2 + 2HCl,$$

106,800 cal. are evolved. The heats of formation of carbon dioxide and hydrogen chloride being 94,400 cal. and 22,000 cal., respectively, calculate the heat of formation of methylene chloride (CH_2Cl_2).

(1st M.B., London)

8. From the following data, calculate the heat evolved in the formation of 2·5 litres of carbon monoxide from its elements :

$$C + O_2 = CO_2 + 94{,}500 \text{ cal.},$$
$$2CO + O_2 = 2CO_2 + 136{,}000 \text{ cal.}$$

From your results, calculate the energy change in the reaction $CO_2 + C = 2CO$. (1st M.B., London)

9. Calculate the heat of formation of aniline, C_6H_7N, from the following data :

$$4C_6H_7N + 31O_2 = 24CO_2 + 14H_2O + 2N_2 + 3350 \text{ Cal.},$$
$$C + O_2 = CO_2 + 97 \text{ Cal.},$$
$$H_2 + \tfrac{1}{2}O_2 = H_2O + 68{\cdot}4 \text{ Cal.}$$

[1 Cal. = 1000 cal.]

10. Calculate the heat evolved in the combustion of 10 cubic feet of carbon monoxide, measured at *N.T.P.*, using the following data of heats of formation :

$$C + O_2 = CO_2 + 97{,}300 \text{ cal.},$$
$$C + \tfrac{1}{2}O_2 = CO + 29{,}300 \text{ cal.}$$

[1 cubic foot = 28·32 litres.]

11. The heat of combustion of propionic acid, C_2H_5COOH, is 387,000 cal. Calculate the heat of formation of the acid from its elements given that :

$$C + O_2 = CO_2 + 97{,}300 \text{ cal.},$$
$$H_2 + \tfrac{1}{2}O_2 = H_2O + 68{,}400 \text{ cal.}$$

12. From the following data, calculate the heat of formation of potassium hydroxide in aqueous solution :

$$KOH_{(aq.)} + HCl_{(aq.)} = KCl_{(aq.)} + H_2O + 13{,}700 \text{ cal.},$$
$$H_2 + Cl_2 = 2HCl_{(aq.)} + 78{,}600 \text{ cal.},$$
$$H_2 + \tfrac{1}{2}O_2 = H_2O_{(liquid)} + 68{,}400 \text{ cal.},$$
$$K + \tfrac{1}{2}Cl_2 = KCl_{(aq.)} + 102{,}000 \text{ cal.}$$

13. When 1 gm.-equivalent of an acid, A', is neutralised with 1 gm.-equivalent of sodium hydroxide in dilute solution the amount of heat evolved is 13,550 cal. A similar experiment using 1 gm.-equivalent of a different acid, A'', yielded 14,700 cal. When a mixture of 1 gm.-equivalent of each of the two acids, A' and A'', was allowed to react with 1 gm.-equivalent of sodium hydroxide, the amount of heat evolved was 14,350 cal. Compare the strengths of the two acids.

14. Calculate the calorific value, expressed in therms per 1000 cubic feet, of a gaseous fuel of the percentage composition : H_2, 30 ; CO, 20 ; CH_4, 40 ; N_2, 10, using the following data :

$$H_2 + \tfrac{1}{2}O_2 = H_2O + 68{,}400 \text{ cal.},$$
$$CH_4 + 2O_2 = CO_2 + 2H_2O + 212{,}000 \text{ cal.},$$
$$CO + \tfrac{1}{2}O_2 = CO_2 + 68{,}000 \text{ cal.}$$

[1 cubic foot = 28·32 litres ; 1 therm = $2{\cdot}52 \times 10^7$ cal.]

15. Assuming that 25 per cent of the heat generated is dissipated, calculate the proportion by volume of water vapour and air which will just maintain a mass of coke at 1000°.

$$2C + O_2 = 2CO + 58{,}000 \text{ cal.},$$
$$H_2O + C = CO + H_2 - 29{,}000 \text{ cal.}$$

(C.U.O.S.)

16. Calculate the heat of dissociation of calcium carbonate given that the heats of formation of calcium carbonate, calcium oxide and carbon dioxide are 270,000 cal., 135,000 cal. and 97,000 cal. respectively.

17. Calculate the heat of formation of hydrogen cyanide, HCN, using the following data :

$$2HCN + 2\tfrac{1}{2}O_2 = H_2O + 2CO_2 + N_2 + 323,000 \text{ cal.},$$
$$H_2 + \tfrac{1}{2}O_2 = H_2O + 68,400 \text{ cal.},$$
$$C + O_2 = CO_2 + 97,000 \text{ cal.}$$

18. Calculate the heat of the reaction : $C_2H_2 + H_2O = CH_3CHO$, given :

$$2C + H_2 = C_2H_2 - 47,800 \text{ cal.},$$
$$H_2 + \tfrac{1}{2}O_2 = H_2O + 68,400 \text{ cal.},$$
$$C + O_2 = CO_2 + 97,000 \text{ cal.},$$
$$CH_3CHO + 2\tfrac{1}{2}O_2 = 2CO_2 + 2H_2O + 282,000 \text{ cal.}$$

19. The heat evolved during the combustion of 1 gram-molecule of methane is 213 kilo-calories. If the heats absorbed during the following gaseous changes:

$$CO_2 \rightleftharpoons C + O_2,$$
$$H_2O \rightleftharpoons 2H + \tfrac{1}{2}O_2,$$

are 265 and 160 kilo-calories respectively, derive the energy of linkage of the carbon-hydrogen bond. (C.U.O.S.)

20. The heat of combustion of ethylene is 333,000 cal. that of acetylene is 312,000 cal. and that of hydrogen is 68,400 cal. Calculate the heat evolved or absorbed when 10 litres of acetylene is reduced to ethylene at constant volume, the acetylene being originally at *N.T.P*.

21. Calculate the heat of formation of orthophosphoric acid in aqueous solution from the following data :

$$PCl_5 + 4H_2O = H_3PO_{4\,(aq.)} + 5HCl_{(aq.)} + 123,400 \text{ cal.},$$
$$H_2 + Cl_2 = 2HCl_{(aq.)} + 78,600 \text{ cal.},$$
$$H_2 + \tfrac{1}{2}O_2 = H_2O_{(liq.)} + 68,400 \text{ cal.},$$
$$P + 2\tfrac{1}{2}Cl_2 = PCl_5 + 105,000 \text{ cal.}$$

22. The strengths of two acids, H*A* and H*B*, are in the ratio 2 : 3. The heats of neutralisation of the two acids, H*A* and H*B*, are 13,350 cal. and 13,700 cal. respectively. Calculate the heat of the reaction :

$$NaA + HB \rightleftharpoons HA + NaB.$$

23. Calculate the heat of the reaction :

$$SO_2Cl_2 + 2H_2O = H_2SO_{4\,(aq.)} + 2HCl_{(aq.)},$$

given that :

$$S + O_2 + Cl_2 = SO_2Cl_2 + 89,800 \text{ cal.},$$
$$\tfrac{1}{2}H_2 + \tfrac{1}{2}Cl_2 = HCl_{(aq.)} + 39,300 \text{ cal.},$$
$$H_2 + S + 2O_2 = H_2SO_{4\,(aq.)} + 210,000 \text{ cal.},$$
$$H_2 + \tfrac{1}{2}O_2 = H_2O_{(liq.)} + 68,400 \text{ cal.}$$

24. When 100 c.c. of a mixture of methane (CH_4) and ethylene (C_2H_4) was exploded with an excess of oxygen, the volume of carbon dioxide produced (measured at the same temperature and pressure) was 160 c.c. Calculate the heat evolved when 22·4 litres of the mixture of methane and ethylene (measured at *N.T.P.*) is completely oxidised to carbon dioxide and water at constant volume.

$$CH_4 + 2O_2 = CO_2 + 2H_2O + 212{,}000 \text{ cal.},$$

$$C_2H_4 + 3O_2 = 2CO_2 + 2H_2O + 333{,}000 \text{ cal.}$$

25. A monobasic acid is dissociated to the extent of 25 per cent in 0·1 normal solution. When a 0·1 normal solution of the acid was neutralised by a dilute solution of potassium hydroxide, the heat evolved per gm.-molecule of the acid was 14,200 cal. Calculate the heat of dissociation of the acid per gm.-molecule.

26. The heat of formation of carbon monoxide at constant pressure at 200° is 26,000 cal. What is the heat of formation at the same temperature but at constant volume?

27. 5 gm. of zinc is allowed to dissolve in an excess of dilute hydrochloric acid at 15° and at an atmospheric pressure of 750 mm. Calculate (*a*) in ergs, (*b*) in calories, the work done against the atmosphere by the escaping hydrogen. (Zn = 65.)

28. When CO, H_2 and CH_3OH are burnt completely in closed vessels, the heats evolved per gm.-molecule are 67,700, 68,400 and 170,600 cal. respectively. Calculate the heat evolved in the reaction:

$$CO + 2H_2 = CH_3OH.$$

If the reaction is carried out at atmospheric pressure at 300°, what work is done by the atmosphere per gm.-molecule of methyl alcohol produced? What effect will this have on the heat of reaction according as it occurs at constant volume or constant pressure? (C.U.O.S.)

29. The latent heat of evaporation of methyl alcohol (CH_3OH) is 8890 cal. per gm.-molecule at 40°. 20 gm. of methyl alcohol is vaporised at 40° and 700 mm. pressure. Calculate the change in internal energy.

30. The heat of formation of carbon dioxide from graphite at 15° and constant volume is 97,400 cal., and that of carbon monoxide under the same conditions is 25,400 cal. What heat should be evolved when 100 litres of carbon monoxide measured at N.T.P. is burnt in an excess of oxygen at a constant pressure of 400 mm., both reactants and products being at 15°?

* 31. Calculate the work done (*a*) in ergs, (*b*) in calories when 2 gm. of oxygen at 15° and 760 mm. pressure expands isothermally until its pressure is 100 mm.

* **32.** 5 gm. of a gas expands isothermally from an initial pressure of 2 atmospheres. If the molecular weight of the gas is 44, its constant temperature 100°, and 35·6 cal. are absorbed in the process, what is the final pressure of the gas?

* **33.** If W = work of isothermal expansion of a gas, obtain an expression for $\left(\frac{\partial W}{\partial V}\right)_T$.

* **34.** 100 c.c. of oxygen at 15° and 500 mm. pressure expands adiabatically to 200 mm. pressure. What is the final temperature of the gas?

* **35.** Calculate the molecular heat of evaporation of water at 80° given that the latent heat of evaporation at 100° is 540 cal. per gm. and that the mean specific heats of water and water vapour over the temperature range 60°–100° are 1·00 and 0·46 cal. per gm. respectively.

* **36.** To what pressure must a given volume of oxygen, originally at 100° and 1 atmosphere pressure, be adiabatically compressed in order to raise its temperature to 400°?

* **37.** The heat evolved in the conversion of 1 gm.-atom of β-sulphur into α-sulphur is 82 cal. at 25°. If the specific heats of α- and β-sulphur are 0·163 and 0·171 respectively, what is the heat of transition at 50°?

* **38.** Assuming that the latent heat of vaporisation of iodine is 24 cal. per gm. at 200°, calculate the heat of sublimation at 250° given that the specific heats of solid iodine and iodine vapour are 0·054 and 0·03 respectively.

* **39.** Derive the relation between the pressure and the temperature changes brought about by adiabatic compression of a perfect gas Helium is compressed isothermally at 25° from a pressure of 1 atmosphere to 10 atmospheres. It is then expanded adiabatically until the pressure is again 1 atmosphere. If both processes are carried out reversibly, calculate the fraction of the work expended during compression which is regained during expansion.

(London B.Sc. Special.)

* **40.** You are given $H_2 + \frac{1}{2}O_2 = H_2O$ (vap.) + 57,800 cal. at 15° and $CO + \frac{1}{2}O_2 = CO_2$ + 68,000 cal. at 15°. Find the heat change involved in the water-gas reaction: $H_2 + CO_2 = H_2O + CO$ at room temperature (15°), and, starting from the First Law of Thermodynamics, show how the heat change at any temperature can be calculated from the following data:

H_2, $C_p = 6{\cdot}50 + 0{\cdot}0009T$; CO_2, $C_p = 7{\cdot}0 + 0{\cdot}0071T - 0{\cdot}0000019T^2$;
CO, $C_p = 6{\cdot}50 + 0{\cdot}0010T$; H_2O (vap.), $C_p = 8{\cdot}81 - 0{\cdot}0019T + 0{\cdot}0000022T^2$.

Calculate its value at 2000° A. (Manchester Hons. Chem.)

* **41.** The formation of ammonia from nitrogen and hydrogen is an exothermic reaction :

$$N_2 + 3H_2 = 2NH_3\;;\quad \Delta H = -21{,}600 \text{ cal.},$$

the value of ΔH given in the equation being its value at 25°. Given that the variation in the specific heats are :

$$N_2\;;\quad C_p = 6{\cdot}50 + 0{\cdot}0010T$$
$$H_2\;;\quad C_p = 6{\cdot}50 + 0{\cdot}0009T$$
$$NH_3\;;\quad C_p = 8{\cdot}04 + 0{\cdot}0007T + 0{\cdot}0000051T^2,$$

calculate the heat of formation of ammonia at 1500°.

* **42.** The critical temperature of hydrogen sulphide is 100° and its critical pressure is 88 atmospheres. If a quantity of hydrogen sulphide originally at 20° and 1 atmosphere pressure is adiabatically compressed to 100 atmospheres pressures, will this pressure be sufficient to liquefy the gas?

* **43.** Calculate the heat of the reaction :

$$4NH_3 + 5O_2 = 4NO + 6H_2O$$

at 500° using the following data † :

$$N_2 + 3H_2 = 2NH_3 \quad \Delta H_{298} = -21{,}600 \text{ cal.}$$
$$H_2 + \tfrac{1}{2}O_2 = H_2O_{(gas)} \, \Delta H_{298} = -58{,}000 \text{ cal.}$$
$$\tfrac{1}{2}N_2 + \tfrac{1}{2}O_2 = NO \quad \Delta H_{298} = +21{,}600 \text{ cal.}$$
$$O_2\;;\quad C_p = 6{\cdot}50 + 0{\cdot}0010T.$$
$$H_2O\;;\quad C_p = 8{\cdot}81 - 0{\cdot}0019T + 0{\cdot}0000022T^2$$
$$NO\;;\quad C_p = 6{\cdot}50 + 0{\cdot}0010T.$$
$$NH_3\;;\quad C_p = 8{\cdot}04 + 0{\cdot}0007T + 0{\cdot}0000051T^2.$$

† It is usual in stating values of ΔH to specify the absolute temperature. Thus ΔH_{298} represents the change in heat content at 25° C.

CHAPTER VIII

THE MASS LAW AND IONIC THEORY

1. The mass law and solutions of electrolytes

The law of mass action can be used in problems involving weak electrolytes, that is, substances such as the weak organic acids which are only feebly ionised in aqueous solution. Compounds such as silver chloride which are only sparingly soluble in water, even though they may be regarded as completely dissociated, obey the Mass Law, that is, the active masses of the ions to which they give rise are the same as the actual concentrations of the ions.

Example 81. A weak monobasic acid is dissociated to the extent of 3 per cent in $N/50$ solution. What will be the percentage dissociation in $N/20$ solution?

Since the acid is monobasic, one molecule of it dissociates into one hydrogen ion† and one acidic ion (denoted by A^-):

$$\begin{array}{ccc} \mathrm{H}A & \rightleftharpoons & \mathrm{H}^+ + A^- \\ \frac{1-x}{V} & & \frac{x}{V} \quad \frac{x}{V} \end{array}$$

If the concentration of the acid before dissociation is one gm.-molecule in V litres, then the concentrations of the undissociated acid and the ions produced from it, when equilibrium is reached, are those written under the equation, namely:

$$\frac{1-x}{V} \text{ gm.-molecule per litre of H}A,$$

† In reactions in solution the term hydrogen ion is used to imply the oxonium ion formed between protons and the molecules of the solvent. For an aqueous solution of an acid the equilibrium is more correctly represented by the equation:

$$\mathrm{H}A + \mathrm{H_2O} \rightleftharpoons \mathrm{H_3O^+} + A^-.$$

Since the active mass of the water, however, remains constant, it is convenient to write the dissociation in the form:

$$\mathrm{H}A \rightleftharpoons \mathrm{H}^+ + A^-.$$

$\frac{x}{V}$ gm.-ions per litre of H^+,

$\frac{x}{V}$ gm.-ions per litre of A^-.

By the law of mass action:

$$k_1[HA]=k_2[H^+]\times[A^-],$$

where k_1 and k_2 are the velocity constants and square brackets denote concentrations (active masses).

$$\therefore\ \frac{[H^+]\times[A^-]}{[HA]}=\frac{\left(\frac{x}{V}\right)\times\left(\frac{x}{V}\right)}{\frac{1-x}{V}}=\frac{k_1}{k_2}=K_a, \quad \text{.........(88)}$$

where K_a = by definition, the **dissociation constant** of the acid.

If x is small, then:

$$\frac{\left(\frac{x}{V}\right)\times\left(\frac{x}{V}\right)}{\left(\frac{1-x}{V}\right)}\doteq\frac{x^2}{V}\doteq K_a.$$

When $V=50$ litres (that is, in $N/50$ solution) and $x=0{\cdot}03$,

then $$K_a=\frac{0{\cdot}03\times0{\cdot}03}{50}.$$

If x = fraction dissociated when $V=20$ (that is, in $N/20$ solution), then:

$$K_a=\frac{x^2}{20};$$

$$\therefore\ \frac{0{\cdot}03\times0{\cdot}03}{50}=\frac{x^2}{20}.$$

From which $x=0{\cdot}019$.

$\therefore$ Percentage dissociation $=100x=$ **1·9**.

The same result can be obtained more quickly by using **Ostwald's dilution law.**

Since $\frac{x^2}{V}=K_a$ where x = fraction dissociated, therefore

$$\frac{(100x)^2}{V}=\text{a constant.}$$

But $100x$ is the percentage dissociation (denote by X).

$$\therefore \frac{X^2}{V} = \text{a constant} = K, \quad \text{..................(89)}$$

which is the dilution law. Note carefully, however, that K is not equal to K_a; it is, in fact, $10{,}000K_a$.

Substituting in equation (89):

$$\frac{3^2}{50} = \frac{X^2}{20},$$

from which $X = 1{\cdot}9$ **per cent.**

The dilution law can also be written:

$$X = \sqrt{KV} = K_1\sqrt{V},$$

where $K_1 = \sqrt{K}$.

$\therefore X \propto \sqrt{V}$, that is, the percentage dissociation is directly proportional to the square root of the dilution.

Example 82. The dissociation constant of a weak monobasic acid is $1{\cdot}04 \times 10^{-5}$ at 20°. What is the concentration of hydrogen ion in $N/20$ solution of this acid at 20°?

As on p. 159:

$$K_a = \frac{[H^+] \times [A^-]}{[HA]} = \frac{[H^+]^2}{[HA]} = \frac{[H^+]^2}{\frac{1}{20}},$$

since $[H^+] = [A^-]$ and $[HA]$ can be taken as very roughly equal to the total concentration of the acid, that is, $\frac{1}{20}$ gm.-molecule per litre.

$$\therefore \frac{[H^+]^2}{\frac{1}{20}} = 1{\cdot}04 \times 10^{-5};$$

$$\therefore [H^+] = \sqrt{\frac{1{\cdot}04 \times 10^{-5}}{20}} = \mathbf{7{\cdot}2 \times 10^{-4}} \textbf{ gm.-ion/litre.}$$

2. Solubility product

A sparingly soluble electrolyte, for example, silver chloride, can be regarded as almost completely ionised even in its saturated solution. Since a solution, if saturated, must theoretically be in equilibrium with some of the undissolved solid, we have, for silver chloride:

$$\underset{\text{(solid)}}{AgCl} \rightleftharpoons \underset{\substack{\text{(dissolved}\\\text{but neglible)}}}{AgCl} \rightleftharpoons Ag^+ + Cl^-.$$

For equilibrium between solid AgCl and the dissolved salt, that is, the undissociated salt:

$$\underset{\text{dissolved}}{[\text{AgCl}]} = k\underset{\text{solid}}{[\text{AgCl}]} = K$$

(since the active mass of solid silver chloride is a constant at a given temperature).

For equilibrium between Ag^+, Cl^- and the dissolved AgCl:

$$[\text{Ag}^+] \times [\text{Cl}^-] = k_1 \underset{\text{dissolved}}{[\text{AgCl}]} = k_1 \times K = K_S.$$

K_S is the **solubility product** (denoted S.P.) and, for any salt,† is the product of the active masses of the ions. It is important to note that it is only for saturated solutions that the product of the active masses of the ions is equal to the solubility product.

Example 83. The solubility of calcium fluoride at 18° is 0·015 gm. What is the solubility product of calcium fluoride at this temperature?

Solubility of calcium fluoride (CaF_2; molecular weight, 78)

$$= \frac{0{\cdot}015}{78} \text{ gm.-molecules per litre.}$$

Each gm.-molecule of calcium fluoride gives 1 gm.-ion of calcium (Ca^{++}) and two gm.-ions of fluorine (F^-) according to the equation:

$$CaF_2 \rightleftharpoons Ca^{++} + 2F^-.$$

Assuming complete dissociation, therefore:

$$\text{concentration of calcium ion} = \frac{0{\cdot}015}{78} \text{ gm.-ion per litre,}$$

$$\text{concentration of fluorine ion} = \frac{2 \times 0{\cdot}015}{78} \text{ gm.-ion per litre,}$$

∴ Solubility product for calcium fluoride

$$= [\text{Ca}^{++}] \times [\text{F}^-]^2 = \frac{0{\cdot}015}{78} \times \left(\frac{2 \times 0{\cdot}015}{78}\right)^2$$

$$= 2{\cdot}8 \times 10^{-11}.$$

Example 84. The dissociation constant for hydrogen sulphide for dissociation into $2H^+$ and S^{--} is $1{\cdot}1 \times 10^{-22}$ at 18°.

† To which the law of mass action can be applied (see p. 159).

What is the concentration of hydrogen ion in a saturated solution of the gas, the molality of the saturated solution being 0·1? If the solubility product of cadmium sulphide is 4×10^{-29} at 18°, calculate the maximum concentration of cadmium ion which can remain in a solution of $N/10$ hydrochloric acid which has been saturated with hydrogen sulphide.

The dissociation of hydrogen sulphide is :

$$H_2S \rightleftharpoons 2H^+ + S^{--}.$$

$$\therefore \frac{[H^+]^2 \times [S^{--}]}{[H_2S]} = K_a$$

(the dissociation constant for H_2S for dissociation into $2H^+ + S^{--}$).

But since the amount of dissociation is small, $[H_2S] \doteqdot 0{\cdot}1$.

$$\therefore \frac{[H^+]^2 \times [S^{--}]}{0{\cdot}1} = 1{\cdot}1 \times 10^{-22}.$$

But, from the equation :

$$H_2S \rightleftharpoons 2H^+ + S^{--},$$

it is clear that $[S^{--}] = \frac{1}{2}[H^+]$.

$$\therefore [H^+]^2 \times [S^{--}] = \tfrac{1}{2}[H^+]^3 = 1{\cdot}1 \times 10^{-22} \times 0{\cdot}1 = 1{\cdot}1 \times 10^{-23}.$$

$$\therefore [H^+]^3 = 2{\cdot}2 \times 10^{-23} = 22 \times 10^{-24}.$$

$$\therefore [H^+] = \sqrt[3]{22 \times 10^{-24}} = 2{\cdot}8 \times 10^{-8} \text{ gm.-ion/litre.}$$

When $N/10$ hydrochloric acid is saturated with hydrogen sulphide, it may be assumed that the hydrochloric acid is completely dissociated and that the small hydrogen ion concentration resulting from the dissociation of the hydrogen sulphide may be ignored. The hydrogen ion concentration in the solution is, therefore, very approximately equal to 0·1 gm. ion per litre.

Substituting this value in the dissociation constant for hydrogen sulphide :

$$\frac{(0{\cdot}1)^2 \times [S^{--}]}{0{\cdot}1} = 1{\cdot}1 \times 10^{-22}.$$

$$\therefore [S^{--}] = 1{\cdot}1 \times 10^{-21}.$$

But for cadmium sulphide (CdS) :

$$\text{Solubility product} = [Cd^{++}] \times [S^{--}] = 4 \times 10^{-29}.$$

Substituting for $[S^{--}]$:

$$[Cd^{++}] = \frac{4 \times 10^{-29}}{1{\cdot}1 \times 10^{-21}} = 3{\cdot}63 \times 10^{-8} \text{ gm.-ion/litre.}$$

*** 4. Lowering of solubility produced by a common ion (general treatment)**

The simplest example is that of a sparingly soluble binary electrolyte *AB*, the solubility of which is lowered by the addition of a compound, *CB*, giving rise to a common ion, B^-.

Let S_1 = the solubility of *AB* before the addition of *CB*,
S_2 = the solubility of *AB* after the addition of *CB*,
α_1 = the degree of dissociation of *AB* before the addition of *CB*,
α_2 = the degree of dissociation of *AB* after the addition of *CB*,
C = the concentration of *CB* in the mixture,
and α_3 = the degree of dissociation of *CB*.

Then, before the addition of *CB* :

$$AB \rightleftharpoons A^+ + B^-,$$

and $[A^+] \times [B^-]$ = a constant (since the solution is saturated).

$$\therefore\ S_1\alpha_1 \times S_1\alpha_1 = S_1{}^2\alpha_1{}^2 = \text{a constant.}$$

After the addition of *CB*, the concentrations of A^+ and B^- are as shown :

$$\begin{array}{cccc} AB \rightleftharpoons & A^+ & + & B^- \\ & S_2\alpha_2 & & (S_2\alpha_2 + C\alpha_3). \end{array}$$

$$\therefore\ S_2\alpha_2(S_2\alpha_2 + C\alpha_3) = \text{a constant} = S_1{}^2\alpha_1{}^2.$$

Solving this equation for S_2 :

$$S_2{}^2\alpha_2{}^2 + S_2\alpha_2 C\alpha_3 - S_1{}^2\alpha_1{}^2 = 0,$$

and

$$S_2 = \frac{-\alpha_2 C\alpha_3 \pm \sqrt{\alpha_2{}^2 C^2\alpha_3{}^2 + 4\alpha_2{}^2 S_1{}^2\alpha_1{}^2}}{2\alpha_2{}^2}.$$

Ignoring the negative value of the root and writing the solution in its simplest form :

$$S_2 = -\frac{C\alpha_3}{2\alpha_2} + \sqrt{\frac{C^2\alpha_3{}^2}{4\alpha_2{}^2} + \frac{S_1{}^2\alpha_1{}^2}{\alpha_2{}^2}}. \quad \text{..............(90)}$$

*** Example 85.** The solubility of calcium sulphate in water at 15° is 0·013 mols. of the anhydrous salt per litre, and it may be assumed to be dissociated to the extent of 85 per cent. If 20 gm. of anhydrous sodium sulphate is added to 1 litre of saturated calcium sulphate solution at 15°, what weight of calcium sulphate would be precipitated, assuming that the degrees of dissociation of calcium sulphate and sodium sulphate in the mixed solutions are 0·56 and 0·70 respectively?

Before the addition of sodium sulphate:

$$[Ca^{++}] = [SO_4^{--}] = 0{\cdot}013 \times 0{\cdot}85 \text{ gm.-ion per litre.}$$

$$\therefore\ [Ca^{++}] \times [SO_4^{--}] = (0{\cdot}013 \times 0{\cdot}85)^2.$$

Let S = the solubility of calcium sulphate in gm.-molecules per litre after the addition of sodium sulphate. Then if $[SO_4^{--}]_{CaSO_4}$ denote the concentration of SO_4^{--} from the calcium sulphate:

$$[SO_4^{--}]_{CaSO_4} = [Ca^{++}] = S \times 0{\cdot}56.$$

But since the sodium sulphate (molecular weight = 142) is dissociated to the degree of 0·70, the sulphate ion concentration from the sodium sulphate = $(\frac{20}{142} \times 0{\cdot}70)$ gm.-ion per litre.

$$\therefore\ (S \times 0{\cdot}56) \times [(S \times 0{\cdot}56) + (\tfrac{20}{142} \times 0{\cdot}70)] = (0{\cdot}013 \times 0{\cdot}85)^2.$$

$$\therefore\ S = 0{\cdot}00105 \text{ gm.-molecules per litre.}$$

$\therefore$ Wt. of $CaSO_4$ precipitated

$$= (0{\cdot}013 - 0{\cdot}00105) \text{ gm.-molecules}$$

$$= 1{\cdot}612 \text{ gm.}$$

*** 5. The isohydric principle**

Two solutions are said to be isohydric when the amount of dissociation of each solute is unchanged by mixing the solutions.

The simplest example is that of two weak acids, solutions of which will have the hydrogen ion as the " common ion ". Let the equilibrium condition of the solutions of two such acids before mixing be as shown in the equations:

$$\begin{array}{ccccc} HA_1 & \rightleftharpoons & H^+ & + & A_1^-, \\ \dfrac{1-x_1}{V_1} & & \dfrac{x_1}{V_1} & & \dfrac{x_1}{V_1}, \end{array}$$

$$\begin{array}{ccccc} HA_2 & \rightleftharpoons & H^+ & + & A_2^-, \\ \dfrac{1-x_2}{V_2} & & \dfrac{x_2}{V_2} & & \dfrac{x_2}{V_2}. \end{array}$$

Before mixing :

$$\frac{1-x_1}{V_1}=k_1\left(\frac{x_1}{V_1}\right)\times\left(\frac{x_1}{V_1}\right),$$

and

$$\frac{1-x_2}{V_2}=k_2\left(\frac{x_2}{V_2}\right)\times\left(\frac{x_2}{V_2}\right).$$

If, after mixing, the dissociation of each acid is to remain unaltered, then :

$$\frac{1-x_1}{(V_1+V_2)}=k_1\left(\frac{x_1+x_2}{V_1+V_2}\right)\times\left(\frac{x_1}{V_1+V_2}\right),$$

and

$$\frac{1-x_2}{(V_1+V_2)}=k_2\left(\frac{x_1+x_2}{V_1+V_2}\right)\times\left(\frac{x_2}{V_1+V_2}\right).$$

Eliminating k_1 between these two equations :

$$\frac{x_1}{V_1}=\frac{x_2}{V_2}, \quad \text{.............................(91)}$$

that is, the volumes of the two solutions containing respectively 1 gm.-molecule of each acid must be in the same ratio as the fractions of dissociation of the two acids in these volumes. Alternatively, the hydrogen ion concentration must be the same in both acid solutions.

If $k_{a(1)}$ denote the dissociation constant of the first acid then :

$$k_{a(1)}=\frac{x_1^2}{(1-x_1)V_1}\doteq\frac{x_1^2}{V_1}$$

if the acid is weak.

Similarly, for the second acid :

$$k_{a(2)}=\frac{x_2^2}{(1-x_2)V_2}\doteq\frac{x_2^2}{V_2}.$$

$$\therefore \frac{x_1^2}{V_1^2}=\frac{k_{a(1)}}{V_1},$$

and

$$\frac{x_2^2}{V_2^2}=\frac{k_{a(2)}}{V_2}.$$

$\therefore$ If

$$\frac{x_1}{V_1}=\frac{x_2}{V_2},$$

then

$$\frac{k_{a(1)}}{V_1}=\frac{k_{a(2)}}{V_2} \quad \text{.............................(92)}$$

that is, the volumes of the two acids containing 1 gm.-molecule of each acid respectively must be in the same ratio as the dissociation constants of the two acids.

Example 86. What is the concentration of acetic acid which can be added to $N/2$ formic acid so that the percentage dissociation of both acids is unchanged? [K_a for acetic acid $=1{\cdot}85 \times 10^{-5}$; K_a for formic acid $=2{\cdot}4 \times 10^{-4}$.]

The concentration of hydrogen ion in $N/2$ formic acid is given by the equation :

$$\frac{[H^+] \times [COOH^-]}{[HCOOH]} = 2{\cdot}4 \times 10^{-4}.$$

But $$[HCOOH] \doteq 0{\cdot}5 \text{ and } [H^+] = [COOH^-];$$

$$\therefore [H^+]^2 \doteq 2{\cdot}4 \times 10^{-4} \times 0{\cdot}5 = 1{\cdot}2 \times 10^{-4}.$$

This equation gives, therefore, the concentration of hydrogen ion which must be present in the acetic acid solution before the two acids are mixed.

But $$\frac{[H^+] \times [CH_3COO^-]}{[CH_3COOH]} = \frac{[H^+]^2}{[CH_3COOH]} = 1{\cdot}85 \times 10^{-5}.$$

$$\therefore [CH_3COOH] = \frac{[H^+]^2}{1{\cdot}85 \times 10^{-5}} = \frac{1{\cdot}2 \times 10^{-4}}{1{\cdot}85 \times 10^{-5}}$$

$$= 6{\cdot}48 \text{ gm.-molecules per litre.}$$

6. The pH value

The concentration of hydrogen ion in a solution is conveniently expressed by the pH number, which can be calculated as follows.

Let the actual concentration of hydrogen in gm.-ion per litre be denoted by $[H^+]$.

Then $$[H^+] = 10^{-x},$$

where $x = p$H, by definition.

Thus, if the hydrogen ion concentration is $\frac{1}{1000}$ gm.-ion per litre, then :

$$\frac{1}{1000} = 10^{-x}.$$

$$\therefore 10^{-3} = 10^{-x}.$$

$$\therefore pH = x = 3.$$

It is apparent that the lower the hydrogen ion concentration of a solution, the higher will be its pH value.

Example 87. What is the pH of a solution which contains 0·019 gm. of hydrochloric acid per litre, assuming that the acid is completely dissociated?

Since the dissociation is complete,

$$[HCl]=[H^+],$$

that is, the concentration of hydrochloric acid in gm.-molecules per litre is the same as the concentration of hydrogen ion in gm.-ion per litre.

$$\therefore\ [H^+]=\frac{0{\cdot}019}{36{\cdot}5}.$$

$$\therefore\ \frac{0{\cdot}019}{36{\cdot}5}=10^{-x},\ \text{where } x=p\text{H value.}$$

Taking logarithms (base 10) of both sides :

$$\log_{10}\left(\frac{0{\cdot}019}{36{\cdot}5}\right)=-x.$$

$$\therefore\ x=-\log_{10}\left(\frac{0{\cdot}019}{36{\cdot}5}\right)=\log_{10}36{\cdot}5-\log_{10}0{\cdot}019$$

$$=3{\cdot}28.$$

Example 88. The pH of a solution is 5·6. What is the hydrogen ion concentration of this solution?

By definition :

$$[H^+]=10^{-pH}=10^{-5{\cdot}6}.$$

$$\therefore\ \log_{10}[H^+]=-5{\cdot}6=\bar{6}{\cdot}4.$$

$$\therefore\ [H^+]=2{\cdot}512\times10^{-6}\ \text{gm.-ion per litre.}$$

Example 89. The dissociation constant of a weak monobasic acid at 20° is $0{\cdot}8\times10^{-6}$. What is the pH of a decinormal solution of this acid?

As in example 82 :

$$[H^+]=\sqrt{0{\cdot}8\times10^{-6}\times0{\cdot}1}=2{\cdot}82\times10^{-4}.$$

$$\therefore\ 2{\cdot}82\times10^{-4}=10^{-x}.$$

From which $x=p\text{H}=3{\cdot}55$.

7. The ionic product for water

Pure water is very feebly dissociated into hydrogen ions and hydroxyl ions :

$$H_2O \rightleftharpoons H^+ + OH^-.$$

Since the active mass of the undissociated water molecules can be regarded as constant (the dissociation being small), the product of the active masses of the hydrogen ion and hydroxyl ion must also be constant at a given temperature :

$$\therefore \; [H^+] \times [OH^-] = \text{a constant} = K_w, \; \ldots\ldots\ldots\ldots (93)$$

where K_w = the ionic product for water.

From the measurement of the specific conductivity of pure water (cf. p. 197), the value obtained for the constant at 18° is

$$0{\cdot}8 \times 10^{-14},$$

or for rough work 1×10^{-14}.

$$\therefore \; [H^+] \times [OH^-] \doteqdot 10^{-14} \text{ (in any aqueous solution).}$$

The value of K_w depends upon the temperature and increases with rise of temperature.

The hydrogen ion concentration can be calculated from the hydroxyl ion concentration, and conversely the hydroxyl ion concentration can be obtained when the pH of a solution is known.

Example 90. What is the pH of a solution containing 2 gm. of sodium hydroxide per litre?

Assuming complete dissociation of the sodium hydroxide :

$$[OH^-] = \tfrac{2}{40} \text{ gm. ion per litre.}$$

$$\therefore \; [H^+] \times \tfrac{2}{40} = 10^{-14};$$

$$\therefore \; [H^+] = 2 \times 10^{-13} = 10^{-x},$$

where x = the pH of the solution.

From which $p\text{H} = 12{\cdot}7$.

* 8. The hydrolysis constant

The hydrolysis of a salt is represented by the equation :

$$BA + H_2O \rightleftharpoons BOH + HA,$$

where B = the metallic or electropositive radical and A = the acidic or electronegative radical.

Denoting active masses by square brackets, then :

$$\frac{[BOH] \times [HA]}{[BA] \times H_2O]} = K.$$

Since $[H_2O]$ may be considered constant for dilute solutions:

$$\frac{[BOH]\times[HA]}{[BA]}=K_h,$$

where K_h = the **hydrolysis constant** for the salt, BA.

If 1 gm.-molecule of the salt BA is dissolved in V litres of water and a fraction, x gm.-molecules, of the salt is hydrolysed, then (assuming amount of water to remain constant) concentrations at equilibrium are as shown in the equation:

$$\begin{array}{ccccccc} BA & + & H_2O & \rightleftharpoons & BOH & + & HA \\ \frac{1-x}{V} & & & & \frac{x}{V} & & \frac{x}{V} \end{array}$$

$$\therefore \quad \frac{\frac{x}{V}\times\frac{x}{V}}{\left(\frac{1-x}{V}\right)}=K_h.$$

If x is small, $1-x \doteqdot 1$ and $\frac{x^2}{V}=K_h$.

$$\therefore \quad x=\sqrt{K_h V}=k\sqrt{V}. \quad \text{.....................(94)}$$

At a given temperature, therefore, the percentage hydrolysis is directly proportional to the **square root of the dilution.**

* **Example 91.** The hydrolysis constant for an aqueous solution of potassium cyanide at 15° is $1{\cdot}35\times10^{-9}$. What is the percentage hydrolysis of potassium cyanide in (*a*) $M/10$ solution, (*b*) $M/20$ solution?

From equation (94):

$$x=\sqrt{K_h\times V}$$
$$=\sqrt{1{\cdot}35\times10^{-9}\times10}$$
$$=1{\cdot}17\times10^{-4}.$$

$\therefore$ Percentage hydrolysis $=100x=1{\cdot}17\times10^{-2}$.

Since the amount of hydrolysis $\propto \sqrt{V}$:

Percentage dissociation in $\frac{M}{20}$ solution

$$=1{\cdot}17\times\frac{\sqrt{20}}{\sqrt{10}}\times10^{-2}=1{\cdot}66\times10^{-2}.$$

*** 9. Relation between K_h, K_a and K_b**

The hydrolysis constant can be related to the ionic product of water and the dissociation constants of the acid and the base produced. Since the hydrolysis will only take place to any appreciable extent if either the acid or the base is weak (if both acid and alkali are weak, the hydrolysis is practically complete), we can consider first the case in which the hydrolysis produces a strong base and a weak acid.

As a first approximation, it may be assumed that the acid is so weak as to be unionised and that the base (since its concentration is very small) is completely dissociated, since the salt may also be assumed to be completely dissociated, the concentrations of the ions are as given in the equation :

$$\underset{\frac{1}{V}}{B^+} + \underset{\frac{1-x}{V}}{A^-} + H_2O \rightleftharpoons \underset{\frac{1}{V}}{B^+} + \underset{\frac{x}{V}}{OH^-} + \underset{\frac{x}{V}}{HA}$$

Note that since BA and BOH are completely dissociated, the concentration of B^+ is unaltered by the hydrolysis.

By definition :

$$K_h = \frac{[BOH] \times [HA]}{[BA]} = \frac{[OH^-] \times [HA]}{[BA]}, \quad \ldots\ldots\ldots\ldots(a)$$

$$K_w = [H^+] \times [OH^-], \quad \ldots\ldots\ldots\ldots(b)$$

$$K_a = \frac{[H^+] \times [A^-]}{[HA]}. \quad \ldots\ldots\ldots\ldots(c)$$

From equations (a) and (b) :

$$K_w = [H^+] \times [OH^-] = \frac{K_a}{[A^-]} \times [HA] \times [OH^-]$$

$$= K_a \times \frac{[HA] \times [OH^-]}{[BA]} = K_a \times K_h.$$

$$\therefore K_h = \frac{K_w}{K_a}. \quad \ldots\ldots\ldots\ldots(95)$$

For hydrolysis to a weak base and a strong acid, the equation is :

$$\underset{\frac{1-x}{V}}{B^+} + \underset{\frac{1}{V}}{A^-} + H_2O \rightleftharpoons \underset{\frac{x}{V}}{BOH} + \underset{\frac{x}{V}}{H^+} + \underset{\frac{1}{V}}{A^-}$$

$$\therefore\ K_h=\frac{[BOH]\times[HA]}{[BA]}=\frac{[BOH]\times[H^+]}{[BA]},$$

$$K_b=\frac{[B^+]\times[OH^-]}{[BOH]}.$$

$$\therefore\ K_w=[H^+]\times[OH^-]=[H^+]\times K_b\times\frac{[BOH]}{[B^+]}$$

$$=K_b\times\frac{[H^+]\times[BOH]}{[BA]}=K_b\times K_h.$$

$$\therefore\ \mathbf{K_h}=\frac{\mathbf{K_w}}{\mathbf{K_b}}\ .\ \dots\dots\dots\dots\dots\dots(96)$$

*** Example 92.** The dissociation constant of acetic acid is $1{\cdot}8\times10^{-5}$ at 18°. Deduce the percentage hydrolysis in $M/10$ solution of sodium acetate at 18°. ($K_w=10^{-14}$.)

Denoting the acetate ion by A^-, the equation and concentrations are :

$$\begin{array}{ccccccccc} Na^+ & + & A^- & + & H_2O & \rightleftharpoons & Na^+ & + & OH^- & + & HA \\ \frac{1}{V} & & \frac{1-x}{V} & & & & \frac{1}{V} & & \frac{x}{V} & & \frac{x}{V} \end{array}$$

Then, as on p. 170 :

$$K_h=\frac{K_w}{K_a}=\frac{10^{-14}}{1{\cdot}8\times10^{-5}}.$$

But $$K_h=\frac{[NaOH]\times[HA]}{[NaA]}=\frac{[OH^-]\times[HA]}{[NaA]}$$

$$=\frac{\frac{x}{V}\times\frac{x}{V}}{\frac{1}{V}}=\frac{x^2}{V}=\frac{x^2}{10}.$$

$$\therefore\ \frac{x^2}{10}=\frac{10^{-14}}{1{\cdot}8\times10^{-5}}\ \text{and}\ x=7{\cdot}45\times10^{-5}.$$

$$\therefore\ \text{Percentage hydrolysis}=\mathbf{7{\cdot}45\times10^{-3}}.$$

When a salt hydrolyses to produce a weak base *and* a weak acid, the degree of hydrolysis is independent of the concentration of the salt. The equation can be written :

$$\begin{array}{ccccccc} BA & + & H_2O & \rightleftharpoons & BOH & + & HA \\ \frac{1-x}{V} & & & & \frac{x}{V} & & \frac{x}{V}. \end{array}$$

Then $K_h = \frac{[HA] \times [BOH]}{[BA]} = \frac{x^2}{V(1-x)}$.

But $K_b = \frac{[B^+] \times [OH^-]}{[BOH]}$. $\therefore$ $[BOH] = \frac{[B^+] \times [OH^-]}{K_b}$.

And $K_a = \frac{[H^+] \times [A^-]}{[HA]}$. $\therefore$ $[HA] = \frac{[H^+] \times [A^-]}{K_a}$.

$$\therefore K_h = \frac{[H^+] \times [A^-] \times [B^-] \times [OH^-]}{K_b \times K_a \times [BA]} = \frac{[A^-] \times [B^+] \times K_w}{K_b \times K_a \times [BA]}$$

$$= \frac{K_w \times [BA]}{K_b \times K_a},$$

since BA is completely ionised and $[BA]=[A^-]=[B^+]$.

But $K_h = \frac{x^2}{(1-x)V}$ and $[BA] = \frac{1-x}{V}$.

$$\therefore \frac{x^2}{(1-x)V} = \frac{K_w \times \left(\frac{1-x}{V}\right)}{K_a \times K_b}.$$

$$\therefore \frac{x^2}{(1-x)^2} = \frac{K_w}{K_a \times K_b},$$

that is, x is independent of $[BA]$.

Alternatively, we may define a new hydrolysis constant (K_h') by means of the equation :

$$B^+ + A^- + H_2O \rightleftharpoons BOH + HA.$$

Then, by the mass law :

$$\frac{[BOH] \times [HA]}{[B^+] \times [A^-]} = \text{a constant} = K_h'.$$

Substitution, as above, then gives :

$$K_h' = \frac{[B^+] \times [OH^-] \times [H^+] \times [A^-]}{K_b \times K_a \times [B^+] \times [A^-]} = \frac{K_w}{K_a K_b}.$$

Example 92 (a). At 18° the dissociation constants of acetic acid and aniline are $1{\cdot}8 \times 10^{-5}$ and $4{\cdot}2 \times 10^{-10}$ respectively. What is the degree of hydrolysis in aqueous aniline acetate? What is the hydrogen ion concentration in this solution?

If x = the degree of hydrolysis, then :

$$\frac{x^2}{(1-x)^2} = \frac{K_w}{K_a K_b} = \frac{10^{-14}}{1{\cdot}8 \times 10^{-5} \times 4{\cdot}2 \times 10^{-10}} = \frac{10}{7{\cdot}56}.$$

From which $\mathbf{x = 0{\cdot}54}$.

The hydrogen ion concentration can be obtained as follows:

$$K_a = \frac{[H^+][A^-]}{[HA]}. \quad \therefore \ [H^+] = K_a \frac{[HA]}{[A^-]}.$$

But
$$\frac{[HA]}{[A^-]} = \frac{\frac{x}{V}}{\left(\frac{1-x}{V}\right)} = \frac{x}{(1-x)} = \sqrt{\frac{K_w}{K_a K_b}}.$$

$$\therefore \ [H^+] = K_a \sqrt{\frac{K_w}{K_a K_b}} = 2{\cdot}05 \times 10^{-5}.$$

* 10. Distribution of a strong alkali between two weak acids

As the most general case we may mix:

a_1 gm.-molecules of the acid, HA_1,
a_2 ,, ,, ,, ,, HA_2,
and b ,, ,, ,, base, BOH.

Assume that there is insufficient base to neutralise all the acid, that is, that $b < (a_1 + a_2)$. When equilibrium is reached, let the total volume of the mixture be V litres and assume that x gm.-molecules of the base have united with the acid HA_1 to form the salt, BA_1. Therefore, $(b - x)$ gm.-molecules of the base must have united with the acid HA_2 to form the salt, BA_2. The quantities of the acids and salts at equilibrium are, therefore:

$(a_1 - x)$ gm.-molecules of HA_1
$(a_1 - (b - x))$,, ,, ,, HA_2
x ,, ,, ,, BA_1
and $(b - x)$,, ,, ,, BA_2
} in V litres.

Let $K_{a(1)}$ denote the dissociation constant of the acid HA_1 and $K_{a(2)}$ that of the acid HA_2.

Then
$$K_{a(1)} = \frac{[H^+][A_1]}{[HA_1]} \text{ and } K_{a(2)} = \frac{[H^+][A_2]}{[HA_2]}.$$

But since the salts BA_1 and BA_2 can be regarded as completely dissociated while HA_1 and HA_2 are feebly dissociated:

$$[A_1] = [BA_1] = x/V;$$
$$[A_2] = [BA_2] = (b - x)/V;$$
$$[HA_1] = (a_1 - x)/V \text{ and } [HA_2] = [a_2 - (b - x)]/V.$$

$$\therefore\ K_{a(1)}=\frac{[H^+]\times\dfrac{x}{V}}{\dfrac{(a_1-x)}{V}},\ \ldots\ldots\ldots\ldots\ldots\ldots\ldots\ldots(97)$$

$$K_{a(2)}=\frac{[H^+]\times\dfrac{(b-x)}{V}}{\dfrac{[a_2-(b-x)]}{V}}.$$

Eliminating $[H^+]$:

$$\frac{K_{a(1)}}{K_{a(2)}}=\frac{x[a_2-(b-x)]}{(a_1-x)(b-x)}.$$

When $a_1=a_2=b=1$, that is, when the acids and the alkali are originally present in molecular proportions:

$$\frac{K_{a(1)}}{K_{a(2)}}=\frac{x^2}{(1-x)^2},$$

and

$$\frac{x}{1-x}=\frac{\sqrt{K_{a(1)}}}{\sqrt{K_{a(2)}}}.\ \ldots\ldots\ldots\ldots\ldots\ldots\ldots\ldots(98)$$

The alkali distributes itself, therefore, between the two acids in the ratio of the square roots of their dissociation constants.

Example 92 (b). An acid has $K_a=1{\cdot}46\times10^{-6}$. When 1 gm.-equivalent of sodium hydroxide is allowed to react with a mixture of 1 gm.-equivalent of the acid and 1 gm.-equivalent of another acid X, it is found that 53 per cent of the acid X is neutralised. Calculate the dissociation constant of the acid X. If the final volume of the mixed solutions is 1700 c.c., what is the hydrogen ion concentration of the mixture?

As in equation (98):

$$\frac{0{\cdot}47}{0{\cdot}53}=\frac{\sqrt{1{\cdot}46\times10^{-6}}}{\sqrt{K_{a_1}}},$$

where K_{a_1} = the dissociation constant of the acid X.

$$\therefore\ K_{a_1}=1{\cdot}85\times10^{-6}.$$

If $[H^+]$ = the hydrogen ion concentration, then by equation (97):

$$1{\cdot}46 \times 10^{-6} = \frac{[H^+] \times \dfrac{0{\cdot}47}{1{\cdot}7}}{\dfrac{0{\cdot}53}{1{\cdot}7}}.$$

$$\therefore\ [H^+] = \frac{1{\cdot}46 \times 10^{-6} \times 0{\cdot}53}{0{\cdot}47} = 1{\cdot}64 \times 10^{-6}.$$

*11. Indicators

An indicator (acid-alkali titrations) may be regarded as dissociating according to the equation:

$$HI_n \rightleftharpoons H^+ + I_n^-.$$

$$\therefore\ K_i = \frac{[H^+] \times [I_n^-]}{[HI_n]}, \quad \ldots\ldots\ldots\ldots\ldots\ldots\ldots(99)$$

where K_i = the **indicator constant.**

The ion, I_n^-, undergoes tautomeric change and K_i is, therefore, often termed the *apparent* indicator constant.

For an indicator ionising to produce a coloured cation, the indicator constant can be written:

$$K_i = \frac{[I_n^+] \times [OH^-]}{[I_nOH]}.$$

For use as an indicator, I_n^- must be sharply different in colour from HI_n. Rearranging equation (99):

$$[H^+] = K \times \frac{[HI_n]}{[I_n^-]}, \quad \ldots\ldots\ldots\ldots\ldots\ldots\ldots(100)$$

so that the ratio $[HI_n]/[I_n^-]$ is directly proportional to the hydrogen ion concentration.

Example 92 (c). The indicator constant for phenolphthalein is $1{\cdot}5 \times 10^{-10}$ and the dissociation constant of ammonium hydroxide is $1{\cdot}8 \times 10^{-5}$. Determine the ratio $[HI_n]/[I_n^-]$ for phenolphthalein when it is added in small amount to the solution obtained by mixing 200 c.c. of $0{\cdot}01N$ NH_4OH to 200 c.c. of $M/10$ NH_4Cl.

For ammonium hydroxide :

$$K_b = \frac{[NH_4^+] \times [OH^-]}{[NH_4OH]} = 1{\cdot}8 \times 10^{-5}.$$

For $[NH_4^+]$ we may write the concentration of NH_4Cl and, since the dissociation is small, $[NH_4OH]$ = total molality of ammonium hydroxide.

$$\therefore\ 1{\cdot}8 \times 10^{-5} = \frac{[\frac{1}{20}] \times [OH^-]}{[\frac{1}{200}]}.$$

$$\therefore\ [OH^-] = 1{\cdot}8 \times 10^{-5} \times \tfrac{1}{200} \times 20 = 1{\cdot}8 \times 10^{-6}.$$

$$\therefore\ [H^+] = \frac{10^{-14}}{1{\cdot}8 \times 10^{-6}} \doteqdot 5{\cdot}5 \times 10^{-9}.$$

$$\therefore\ [HI_n]/[I_n^-] = \frac{[H^+]}{K_i} = \frac{5{\cdot}5 \times 10^{-9}}{1{\cdot}5 \times 10^{-10}}$$

$$\doteqdot 36.$$

QUESTIONS ON CHAPTER VIII

1. The solubility of silver chloride is $1{\cdot}6 \times 10^{-6}$ gm.-molecules per litre at 18°. What is the solubility product of silver chloride at this temperature?

2. The solubility product of silver acetate at 20° is $3{\cdot}6 \times 10^{-3}$. Calculate the solubility of silver acetate in water at 20°, expressing your answer (*a*) in gm.-molecules per litre, (*b*) in gm. per 100 c.c. of solution.

3. A weak binary electrolyte is ionised to the extent of 2 per cent in decinormal solution. Calculate the degree of ionisation of this acid in $N/50$ solution. (O. and C.)

4. A weak monobasic acid is 3·5 per cent dissociated in $N/20$ solution at 15°. What is the dissociation constant of the acid at this temperature?

5. The dissociation constant of a weak monobasic acid is $1{\cdot}4 \times 10^{-5}$ at 25°. What is the concentration of hydrogen ion in an $N/20$ solution of this acid at 25°? What is the percentage dissociation of this acid in $N/20$ solution at 25°?

6. The solubility product of ferric hydroxide at 15° is $1{\cdot}1 \times 10^{-36}$. Express the solubility of ferric hydroxide in water at 15° as gm. of ferric hydroxide per 100 c.c. of saturated solution.

7. An aqueous solution of chloracetic acid containing 0·2 gm.-molecules per litre has a *p*H of 1·78. Calculate (*a*) the degree of ionisation, (*b*) the dissociation constant of the acid.

(1st M.B., Manch.)

8. The solubility product of ferrous hydroxide is $1{\cdot}5 \times 10^{-4}$ at 18°. Calculate the concentration of ferrous ion in a solution of ferrous sulphate in which a concentration of hydroxyl ion equal to $0{\cdot}1N$ is maintained.

9. The dissociation constant for hydrogen sulphide (dissociated into $2H^+$ and S^{--}) is $1{\cdot}1 \times 10^{-22}$ at 18°. What is the concentration of sulphide ion in a $0{\cdot}1N$ hydrochloric acid solution which is saturated with hydrogen sulphide at 18°, assuming that the concentration of H_2S is $0{\cdot}1M$?

10. Calculate the pH of (*a*) $N/10$ hydrochloric acid, (*b*) a solution containing 0·014 gm. of sulphuric acid per litre. Assume that the solute is completely dissociated in each case.

11. What is the pH of a $0{\cdot}01N$ solution of an acid which at that dilution is ionised to the extent of 85·5 per cent? (1st M.B., London)

12. The pH of a solution is 3·7. What is the hydrogen ion concentration per litre?

13. Calculate the hydrogen ion concentration in gm. per litre of an aqueous solution of which $p\text{H} = 2{\cdot}143$. (1st M.B., London)

14. The ionic product for water ($[OH^-] \times [H^+]$) is approximately 10^{-14} at 20°. What is the pH of $N/1000$ sodium hydroxide solution, assuming complete dissociation of the sodium hydroxide?

15. The pH of a decinormal solution of a weak monobasic acid is 2·5. Find the dissociation constant of this acid. What is the hydrogen ion concentration in a $N/25$ solution of the acid? What is the percentage dissociation of the acid in $N/25$ solution?

16. Assuming complete dissociation of all the solutes, calculate the pH of the solution obtained by mixing equal volumes of $N/10$ NaOH and $N/20$ HCl.

17. The following is a record of a laboratory experiment: Concentrated hydrochloric acid (37·04 gm. in 100 c.c.) was dropped slowly into a nearly saturated solution of barium chloride (276 gm. in 1000 c.c.) until a crystalline precipitate was formed. For the first titration 20 c.c. of barium chloride were used; after the precipitate had formed, 5 c.c. of water were added and the experiment repeated, and so on with increments of water in the way shown in the table.

Total water added in c.c.	HCl added in c.c.
0	1·9
5	4·5
10	7
20	12·8

What conclusions can you draw from these results? [Express your concentrations in gm.-molecules per litre and neglect any contraction on mixing.] (C.U.O.S.)

18. The dissociation constant of hydrogen sulphide for dissociation into $2H^+$ and S^{--} is $1{\cdot}1 \times 10^{-22}$ at 18°. What is the maximum concentration of lead ion which can exist in $N/10$ hydrochloric acid previously saturated with hydrogen sulphide (concentration of saturated hydrogen sulphide is $0{\cdot}1M$)? [The solubility product for lead sulphide at 18° is $3{\cdot}6 \times 10^{-28}$.]

19. 5·85 gm. of sodium chloride were dissolved in 1 litre of saturated silver chloride. Calculate the weight of silver chloride precipitated. [The solubility product of silver chloride at room temperature is 1×10^{-5} gm.-molecules per litre.] (C.U.O.S.)

20. The dissociation constant of acetic acid at 18° is $1{\cdot}8 \times 10^{-5}$. What is the pH of a $N/50$ solution of acetic acid at this temperature?

21. The dissociation of a weak monobasic acid at 18° is such that in $N/20$ solution, the pH of the solution is 3·11. What is the dissociation constant of the acid at this temperature?

22. The concentration of silver ion in a solution of silver acetate saturated at 20° was found by titration with a standard solution of potassium thiocyanate to be 6·69 gm. per litre. 4·78 gm. of anhydrous sodium acetate were dissolved in one litre of such a solution and, after allowing to settle, the clear solution was found to contain 4·28 gm. of silver per litre. When a similar experiment was performed using 9·48 gm. of the anhydrous sodium acetate, the concentration of the silver ion was found to be 2·92 gm. per litre. How do you account for these experimental results? Are your conclusions generally applicable? (C.U.O.S.)

23. The dissociation constant of acetic acid at 18° is $1{\cdot}85 \times 10^{-5}$. If 2 gm. of sodium acetate is added to 300 c.c. of $N/10$ acetic acid, what is (*a*) the hydrogen ion concentration, (*b*) the pH of the resulting solution?

24. What weight of anhydrous potassium acetate must be added to a decinormal solution of acetic acid in order to give a solution of $p\text{H} = 5{\cdot}2$, assuming the dissociation constant of acetic acid to be $1{\cdot}85 \times 10^{-5}$?

* 25. The dissociation constants of two monobasic acids are $1{\cdot}65 \times 10^{-4}$ and $8{\cdot}38 \times 10^{-5}$ respectively. Aqueous solutions of these acids are made to contain $\frac{1}{10}$ of a gm.-molecule respectively of these acids. If the solutions are now mixed and it is found that the hydrogen ion concentration remains unaltered, in what proportions were the volumes of the original solutions?

* 26. The dissociation constant of acetic acid is $1{\cdot}85 \times 10^{-5}$ and of propionic acid $1{\cdot}45 \times 10^{-5}$. What is the concentration of acetic acid which can be added to $N/10$ propionic acid so that the percentage dissociation of the propionic acid remains unchanged?

* **27.** The dissociation constant of benzoic acid is $6{\cdot}2 \times 10^{-5}$. What is the degree of hydrolysis in a solution containing 5·58 gm. of sodium benzoate per litre? [Use $K_w = 10^{-14}$.]

* **28.** If the hydroxyl ion concentration in a $M/10$ solution of the sodium salt of a weak monobasic acid is $1{\cdot}3 \times 10^{-4}$, what is the dissociation constant of the acid? What would be the approximate hydroxyl ion concentration in $M/50$ solution of the sodium salt?

* **29.** The dissociation constant of ammonium hydroxide is $1{\cdot}8 \times 10^{-5}$. What is the pH of the solution obtained by dissolving 10 gm. of ammonium chloride in 500 c.c. of $N/10$ NH_4OH, assuming no change in volume?

* **30.** It is desired to prepare a buffer solution of $p\text{H} = 4{\cdot}5$ using acetic acid and sodium acetate. Assuming $K_a = 1{\cdot}85 \times 10^{-5}$ for acetic acid, calculate the weight of sodium acetate which must be added to 1 litre of N acetic acid in order to obtain a solution of the required acidity.

* **31.** What volume of $0{\cdot}1N$ sodium hydroxide must be added to 200 c.c. of $0{\cdot}1N$ acetic acid ($K_a = 1{\cdot}85 \times 10^{-5}$) so that the resulting solution shall have a pH value $= 7$?

* **32.** Two monobasic acids have molecular weights 60 and 74 respectively and their dissociation constants are $1{\cdot}85 \times 10^{-5}$ and $1{\cdot}40 \times 10^{-5}$ respectively. 2 gm. of the first acid is contained in 200 c.c. of its aqueous solution and 1 gm. of the second acid in 50 c.c. of its aqueous solution. If the solutions are now mixed, what is the pH of the mixture?

* **33.** A solution of sodium phenate has $p\text{H} = 10$. What is the molality of the solution? [K_a for phenol $= 1 \times 10^{-10}$.]

* **34.** The partition coefficient of aniline between benzene and water at 20° is 11·3, the aniline being more soluble in benzene. In an experiment to determine the hydrolysis constant of aniline hydrochloride 15 gm. of the salt was shaken with 1000 c.c. of water and 100 c.c. of benzene until equilibrium was established and 50 c.c. of the benzene layer was then found to contain 0·2360 gm. of aniline. Deduce the hydrolysis constant of aniline hydrochloride at 20°.

* **35.** The solubility of hydrogen sulphide in water is such that when the pressure of the gas is 1 atmosphere the saturated solution is 0·1 molar. Taking $K_1 (H_2S \rightleftharpoons H^+ + HS^-)$ to be $9{\cdot}5 \times 10^{-8}$ and $K_2 (HS^- \rightleftharpoons H^+ + S^{--})$ to be $1{\cdot}2 \times 10^{-15}$, calculate the sulphide ion concentration of a solution if the pH is 5·2.

* **36.** The indicator constant of phenolphthalein is approximately 10^{-10}. A solution is prepared by adding 100·01 c.c. of $0{\cdot}01N$ sodium hydroxide to 100·00 c.c. of $0{\cdot}01N$ hydrochloric acid. If a few drops of phenolphthalein are now added, what fraction of the indicator is converted to its coloured form?

37. Calculate the equivalent point of the titration of $0{\cdot}1N$ sodium phenoxide with hydrochloric acid. The dissociation constant of phenol is $1{\cdot}2 \times 10^{-10}$. (A.R.I.C.)

* **38.** Carbon dioxide was passed for a short time through a suspension of calcium carbonate in water. The partial pressure of carbon dioxide over the resulting solution was 0·1422 atmospheres and the concentration of calcium bicarbonate was $0{\cdot}533 \times 10^{-2}$ mol. per litre. Calculate the solubility product of calcium carbonate given that the first (apparent) and the second (true) dissociation constants of a solution of carbon dioxide in water are respectively $3{\cdot}04 \times 10^{-7}$ and $1{\cdot}295 \times 10^{-11}$; the degree of dissociation of calcium bicarbonate at the above concentration is 0·87 and the solubility of carbon dioxide in water is 0·04354 mols. per litre under 1 atmosphere pressure. (Manchester Hons. Chem.)

* **39.** Calculate the hydrogen ion concentrations of the solutions respectively obtained by adding to separate 100 c.c. lots of 0·01 N acetic acid 99·5 c.c., 100 c.c. and 100·5 c.c. of 0·01 N sodium hydroxide. [K_a for acetic acid is $1{\cdot}85 \times 10^{-5}$.]

* **40.** 100 c.c. of a solution of acetic acid was titrated with $N/10$ potassium hydroxide, using methyl red as the only indicator available. After the addition of 50·0 c.c. of the potassium hydroxide solution the transformed fraction of the indicator was found to be 0·60. What was the original normality of the acetic acid?

[The indicator constant of methyl red $= 10^{-5{\cdot}20}$.

The dissociation constant of acetic acid $= 10^{-4{\cdot}73}$.]

(Manchester Hons. Chem.)

* **41.** By constructing suitable mass-law equations show that the percentage hydrolysis of a salt BA, formed from a weak base BOH and a weak acid HA, is independent of the concentration of the solution. Hence deduce the percentage hydrolysis in a solution of ammonium acetate given that K_b for ammonium hydroxide is $1{\cdot}80 \times 10^{-5}$ and K_a for acetic acid is $1{\cdot}85 \times 10^{-5}$.

CHAPTER IX

ELECTROCHEMISTRY

1. Faraday's laws of electrolysis

(*a*) The amount of chemical action is the same at all parts of a completed circuit and is proportional to the amount of electricity (current $\times$ time) which flows through the circuit.

(*b*) The masses of ions liberated by the passage of the same quantity of electricity are in the same ratio as their chemical equivalents. The number of gm. of an ion liberated by the passage of one coulomb (one ampère-second) is the electrochemical equivalent of that ion. To liberate 1 gm.-equivalent of any ion requires the passage of 96,540 coulombs, a quantity of electricity sometimes called the faraday.

Example 93. During the electrolysis of brine in a Castner-Kellner cell 1000 gm. of chlorine were liberated. What quantity of electricity is required to do this? Calculate (*a*) the weight of sodium hydroxide, (*b*) the volume of hydrogen measured at 15° and 745 mm. pressure liberated by the same current. (H.S.C., London.)

The chemical equivalent of chlorine is 35·5. To liberate 35·5 gm. of chlorine 96,540 coulombs are required.

$\therefore$ 1000 gm. of chlorine will be liberated by the passage of

$$\frac{96{,}540}{35{\cdot}5} \times 1000 \text{ coulombs} = \mathbf{2{\cdot}72 \times 10^6 \text{ coulombs.}}$$

For every atom of chlorine liberated during the electrolysis, one atom of sodium reacts with water to form one molecule of sodium hydroxide :

$$NaCl \begin{cases} \nearrow \underset{35\cdot5}{Cl} \\ \searrow \underset{40}{NaOH} \end{cases}$$

Then, if 35·5 gm. of chlorine is formed, 40 gm. of sodium hydroxide is produced at the same time.

∴ Weight of sodium hydroxide formed at the same time as 1000 gm. of chlorine

$$=\frac{1000}{35{\cdot}5}\times 40 \text{ gm.}=1127 \text{ gm.}$$

Similarly, corresponding with the liberation of 35·5 gm. of chlorine, 1 gm. of hydrogen would be obtained.

But 1 gm. of hydrogen may be taken as occupying approximately 11·2 litres at *N.T.P.*

∴ Volume of hydrogen corresponding with the liberation of 1000 gm. of chlorine

$$=\frac{11{\cdot}2\times 1000}{35{\cdot}5} \text{ litres at } N.T.P.$$

$$=\frac{11{\cdot}2\times 1000}{35{\cdot}5}\times\frac{288}{273}\times\frac{760}{745} \text{ litres at } 15°, \text{ and } 745 \text{ mm.}$$

$$=330 \text{ litres.}$$

Example 94. A current of 0·56 ampère flows through a copper voltameter for 160 minutes with the deposition of 1·824 gm. of copper.

In another experiment, a current of 0·48 ampère was allowed to flow through a solution of silver nitrate with the deposition of 3·863 gm. of silver in 120 minutes. Calculate (*a*) the electro-chemical-equivalent of copper, (*b*) the chemical equivalent of copper. [Ag = 107·9.]

The electro-chemical equivalent (*E.C.E.*) of copper = number of gm. of copper deposited by 1 coulomb

$$=\frac{1{\cdot}824}{0{\cdot}56\times 160\times 60}=0{\cdot}0003392.$$

Similarly,

$$E.C.E. \text{ of silver}=\frac{3{\cdot}863}{0{\cdot}48\times 120\times 60}=0{\cdot}001118.$$

But since the chemical equivalents are in the same ratio as the electro-chemical equivalents :

$$\frac{X}{107{\cdot}9}=\frac{0{\cdot}0003392}{0{\cdot}001118},$$

where X = the chemical equivalent of copper in cupric salts.

$$\therefore\ X=32{\cdot}75.$$

2. Specific conductivity, molecular conductivity and equivalent conductivity

It is assumed that the student is acquainted with the use of the following definitions and the experimental methods employed:

(*a*) The specific conductivity of a solution is the inverse of the specific resistance (resistivity) and is measured in reciprocal ohms, that is, $ohms^{-1}$ or mhos.

(*b*) The molecular conductivity of a solution is the product of the specific conductivity and the volume, measured in c.c., of the solution which contains 1 gm.-molecule of the solute.

(*c*) The equivalent conductivity of a solution is the product of the specific conductivity and the volume of the solution, measured in c.c., which contains 1 gm.-equivalent of the solute.

It is clear that for a large number of substances, for example, sodium chloride, potassium chloride, sodium nitrate, the molecular conductivity and equivalent conductivity are identical. In other cases, the equivalent conductivity and molecular conductivity are related, by definitions (*b*) and (*c*), in the same way as the equivalent weight and molecular weight of the compound.

Example 95. A solution containing 2 gm. of anhydrous barium chloride in 400 c.c. of water has a specific conductivity 0·0058 ohm^{-1}. What is the molecular conductivity of this solution?

The molecular weight of barium chloride ($BaCl_2$) is 208.

Volume of the solution containing 208 gm.

$$=\frac{400}{2}\times 208 \text{ c.c.} = 41{,}600 \text{ c.c.}$$

∴ Molecular conductivity of the solution

$$=0{\cdot}0058\times 41600 \text{ ohm}^{-1}\text{ c.c.} = 241 \text{ ohm}^{-1}\text{ c.c.}$$

The equivalent conductivity (since barium is a divalent metal) $=\frac{241}{2}$ ohm^{-1} c.c.

3. Calculation of apparent degree of dissociation by conductivity methods

The apparent percentage dissociation, x, of an electrolyte in a solution of stated dilution is given by the relationship :

$$\frac{x}{100}=\frac{\text{molecular conductivity at the stated dilution}}{\text{molecular conductivity at infinite dilution}}$$

$$=\frac{\text{the equivalent conductivity at the stated dilution}}{\text{the equivalent conductivity at infinite dilution}} \quad (101)$$

This relation assumes the truth of the Arrhenius theory of partial dissociation ; it is obtained by assigning a constant velocity (under unit potential gradient) to an ion, the increase in molecular conductivity with dilution being attributed solely to an increase in the *number* of ions.

The theory of complete dissociation correlates the increase in conductivity to a greater mobility of the ions. The ratio :

$$\frac{\text{molecular conductivity at a given dilution}}{\text{molecular conductivity at infinite dilution}}$$

$$=\text{the conductance ratio}=f_c.$$

According to the Arrhenius theory :

$$f_c=\frac{\alpha}{100} \text{ where } \alpha=\text{the percentage dissociation.}$$

The Debye-Hückel equation (derived on the assumption of complete dissociation) is :

$$1-f_c=\sqrt{\frac{4\pi e^2}{\epsilon kT}}\left[\frac{e^2}{6\epsilon kT}\cdot w_1+bw_2\right]\sqrt{nc},$$

where symbols have the same significance as on p. 123, w_1 and w_2 being factors depending upon the valencies of the ions and b is the mean diameter of the ions.

The methods of obtaining the molecular and equivalent conductivities of strong and weak electrolytes are discussed on p. 187.

Example 96. The molecular conductivity of acetic acid at infinite dilution is 387 ohm^{-1}. The specific conductivity of acetic acid at a dilution of $N/50$ is 0·00033 ohm^{-1} at the same temperature. What is the percentage dissociation of acetic acid in $N/50$ solution?

The molecular conductivity of acetic acid in $N/50$ solution (the same as the equivalent conductivity since the equivalent of acetic acid = its molecular weight)

$$=0{\cdot}00033 \times 50{,}000 \text{ ohm}^{-1} = 16{\cdot}5 \text{ ohm}^{-1}.$$

$$\therefore \frac{x}{100} = \frac{16{\cdot}5}{387},$$

where x = percentage dissociation in $N/50$ solution.

$$\therefore \mathbf{x = 4{\cdot}3 \text{ per cent.}}$$

When the percentage dissociation at one dilution has been calculated from conductivity data, the percentage dissociation at another dilution can be obtained approximately by applying the dilution law (p. 159) for weak electrolytes.

Example 97. The specific conductivity of a weak monobasic acid in decinormal solution is $0{\cdot}00092$ ohm^{-1}. The molecular conductivity at infinite dilution for the same acid is 370 ohm^{-1}. What are (*a*) the approximate percentage dissociation, (*b*) the approximate specific conductivity, of $N/50$ solution of the acid?

The percentage dissociation, x, in decinormal solution is given by the equation :

$$\frac{x}{100} = \frac{0{\cdot}00092 \times 10{,}000}{370}.$$

$$\therefore \mathbf{x = 2{\cdot}5 \text{ per cent.}}$$

If x_1 = the percentage dissociation in $N/50$ solution, then :

$$\frac{x_1}{2{\cdot}5} \doteqdot \frac{\sqrt{50}}{\sqrt{10}} \text{ (see p. 159).}$$

$$\therefore \mathbf{x_1 = 5{\cdot}85 \text{ per cent.}}$$

$\therefore$ Molecular conductivity of $N/50$ solution

$$= 370 \times \frac{5{\cdot}85}{100} \doteqdot 11{\cdot}6 \text{ ohm}^{-1}.$$

$\therefore$ Specific conductivity of $N/50$ solution

$$\doteqdot \frac{11{\cdot}6}{50{,}000} \doteqdot 0{\cdot}00023 \text{ ohm}^{-1}.$$

4. Relation between molecular conductivity and absolute mobilities of ions

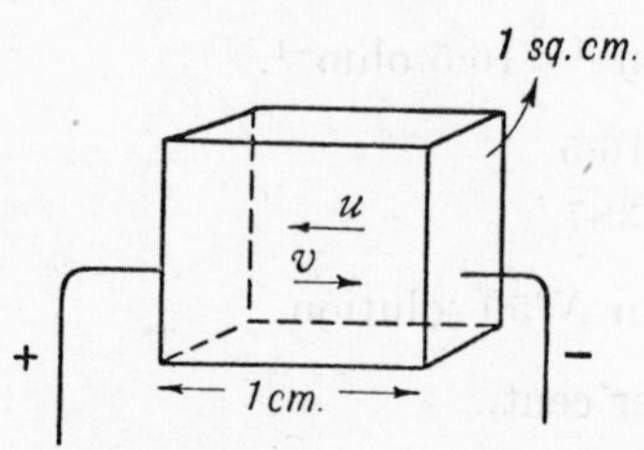

Fig. 16. Relation between molecular conductivity and absolute mobility.

In Fig. 16 assume that a potential difference of 1 volt is maintained between electrodes 1 cm. square and 1 cm. apart. Let c = current which passes through the electrolyte between the electrodes.

Then

$$c=\frac{E}{R}=\frac{1}{R}$$ (since E = electromotive force = 1 volt).

But $\frac{1}{R}=\sigma$ where σ = specific conductivity.

Assume that the solution contains n gm.-equivalents of solute per c.c.

Then $$\Lambda=\sigma\times\frac{1}{n}=c\times\frac{1}{n}.$$

$$\therefore\ c=\Lambda n.$$

Let U = absolute mobility of the anion,

and V = " " " " cation.

Then since the potential gradient in the unit cell of Fig. 16 is 1 volt per cm., U and V are the velocities with which the ions are moving in the cell.

Assume complete dissociation of the solute. Then since there are n gm.-equivalents per c.c., there must be n gm.-ion of each ion.

In 1 second, therefore, nU gm.-equivalents of one ion move in one direction and nV gm.-equivalents of the other ion move in the opposite direction.

$\therefore$ Total current carried $=n\phi(U+V)$ where ϕ = number of coulombs per gm.-equivalent.

$$\therefore\ n\phi(U+V)=\Lambda n.$$

$$\therefore\ (U+V)\phi=\Lambda. \qquad \text{......................(102)}$$

This equation has been derived for an electrolyte giving rise to a univalent anion and a univalent cation. For an electrolyte containing a n-valent anion or cation, the equation is:

$$n(U+V)\phi = \Lambda.$$

Example 98. The molecular conductivity of $N/100$ KCl at 18° is 122. The absolute mobilities of the potassium ion and the chlorine ion are $6{\cdot}68 \times 10^{-4}$ cm. per sec. and 6·82 cm. per sec. respectively. Deduce the apparent degree of dissociation of potassium chloride in $N/100$ solution.

From equation (102):

Molecular conductivity at infinite dilution

$$= (U+V)\phi$$
$$= (6{\cdot}68 \times 10^{-4} + 6{\cdot}82 \times 10^{-4}) \times 96{,}540$$
$$= 130{\cdot}3.$$

$\therefore$ As on p. 184:

$$\frac{\alpha}{100} = \frac{122}{130{\cdot}3},$$

where α = percentage dissociation.

$$\therefore \alpha = 93{\cdot}6.$$

* 5. Calculation of equivalent conductivity at infinite dilution

The equivalent conductivity of solutions of strong electrolytes can be obtained approximately by direct measurement. Accurate values, however, can only be obtained by extrapolation of a suitable curve giving the relation between Λ and concentration. The following equations are representative of many that have been used for this purpose.

$$\Lambda = \Lambda_\infty - A\sqrt{c}. \quad \text{(103)}$$

$$\Lambda = \Lambda_\infty - A_1\sqrt[3]{c}. \quad \text{(104)}$$

$$\Lambda^{-1} = \Lambda_\infty^{-1} + A_2(c\Lambda)^n. \quad \text{(105)}$$

$$\Lambda = \Lambda_0 - (A_3\Lambda + A_4)\sqrt{c}, \quad \text{(106)}$$

where A_1, A_2, A_3 and A_4 are constants, c = the concentration and n = the value obtained by plotting (105) and taking the value which best gives a straight line (n is usually about 0·5). Equation (106) has a theoretical basis in that it can be derived from the modern theory of the complete dissociation of strong electrolytes.

* **Example 99.** From the following values for the equivalent conductivities of sodium chloride at 18°, calculate Λ_∞. Use the equation : $\Lambda = \Lambda_\infty - A\sqrt{c}$.

c (gm.equivalent per litre) -	0·001	0·002	0·01	0·05
Λ - - -	106·3	105·3	101·7	95·5

Since Λ_∞ is constant for a given substance at a fixed temperature, the graph obtained by plotting Λ against $\sqrt{c}$ should

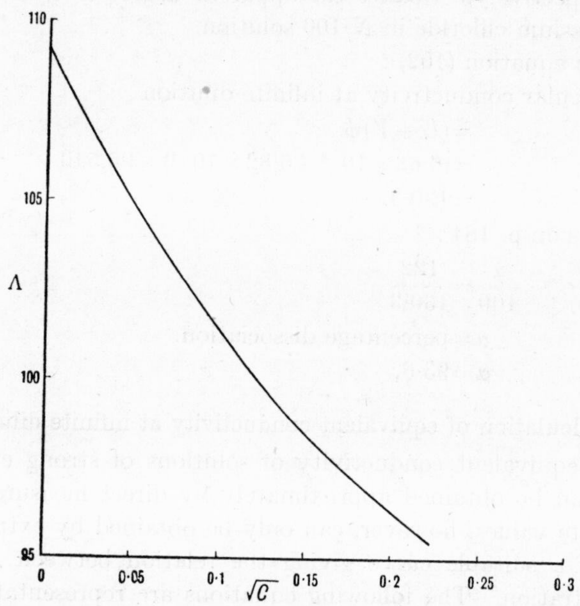

FIG. 17. Determination of equivalent conductivity at infinite dilution.

be a straight line. Extrapolation of the graph to $\sqrt{c} = 0$, that is $c = 0$, should then give Λ_∞. The values of Λ and the corresponding values of $\sqrt{c}$ are :

$\sqrt{c}$ - - -	0·0316	0·0447	0·1	0·224
Λ - - -	106·3	105·3	101·7	95·5

Inspection of Fig. 17 shows that the points most nearly on a straight line are those in very dilute solution. At higher concentrations the equation :

$$\Lambda = \Lambda_\infty - \sqrt[3]{c}$$

more closely holds.

The extrapolated value from the graph of Fig. 17 is

$$\Lambda_\infty = 108{\cdot}8.$$

6. Transport numbers

The transport number (n) of an ion is defined by the equation:

$$n = \frac{\text{fraction of the current carried by that ion}}{\text{total current carried by a compound containing that ion}}.$$

Thus, the transport number of the silver ion in silver nitrate solution at 18° is 0·58.† Therefore, if c is the total current carried at any instant by a solution of silver nitrate, then the current carried by the silver ions in that solution is $0{\cdot}58c$.

Obviously, if the transport numbers of the silver ion and the nitrate ion in silver nitrate solution are denoted by n_{Ag^+} and $n_{NO_3^-}$ respectively, then :

$$n_{Ag^+} + n_{NO_3^-} = 1, \quad \text{......................(107)}$$

and the transport number of the nitrate ion in silver nitrate solution at 18° is 0·42.

For electrolytes dissociating into ions carrying equal but opposite charges, for example, KCl, KNO_3, $MgSO_4$, then

$$\frac{n_a}{n_c} = \frac{V_a}{V_c}, \quad \text{............................(108)}$$

where n_a and n_c are the transport numbers of the anion and cation respectively and V_a and V_c are the corresponding absolute mobilities (p. 186) of these ions.

When an electrolysis is conducted between electrodes which are unaffected by the products of the electrolysis, for example, a solution of copper sulphate between platinum electrodes, the following relation holds :

$$\frac{\text{Transport number of the anion}}{\text{Transport number of the cation}} = \frac{\text{velocity of the anion}}{\text{velocity of the cation}} = \frac{\text{fall of concentration of solute round the cathode}}{\text{fall of concentration of solute round the anode}}. \quad (109)$$

† Transport numbers of ions vary with change of temperature ; with increasing temperature they tend to become more nearly equal.

Example 100. During the electrolysis of silver nitrate solution between platinum electrodes, the fall of concentration of silver ion in the anode chamber was 1·06 gm. per unit volume, while the corresponding fall in the cathode compartment was 0·81. What are the transport numbers of the silver ion and the nitrate ion respectively?

The fall of concentration round the anode is clearly proportional to the velocity of the ions leaving the anode compartment to travel to the cathode, that is, to the velocity of silver ions. Similarly, the more rapidly the nitrate ions leave the vicinity of the cathode and travel towards the anode, the more rapidly will silver ions leave the solution to be deposited on the cathode, that is, the fall of concentration of silver ion round the anode is proportional to the velocity of the nitrate ions.

$$\therefore \frac{\text{Fall of concentration round anode}}{\text{Fall of concentration round cathode}} = \frac{\text{velocity of the silver ion}}{\text{velocity of the nitrate ion}}$$

$$= \frac{\text{transport number of the silver ion } (n_{Ag^+})}{\text{transport number of the nitrate ion } (n_{NO_3^-})}$$

$$\therefore \frac{n_{Ag^+}}{n_{NO_3^-}} = \frac{1{\cdot}06}{0{\cdot}81}.$$

But $$n_{Ag^+} + n_{NO_3^-} = 1.$$

From which $n_{Ag^+} = 0{\cdot}57$ and $n_{NO_3^-} = 0{\cdot}43$.

When the electrolysis is conducted between electrodes which are attacked by the liberated ions a different relationship is obtained. An example is the electrolysis of silver nitrate solution between silver electrodes. Here, the movement of the silver ions from the anode compartment towards the cathode does not involve any fall of concentration of silver in the anode compartment, since the liberated nitrate ions attack the anode to send an equivalent amount of silver ion into solution. When, however, the nitrate ions enter the anode chamber they will, similarly, dissolve an equivalent amount of silver from the silver anode.

∴ Increase in concentration of silver ion in anode compartment = decrease of concentration of silver ion in cathode compartment ∝ velocity of the nitrate ion.

Also increase in weight of cathode = decrease in weight of anode ∝ (velocity of the nitrate ion + velocity of the silver ion).

Therefore, if w_1 = increase of weight of silver ion in anode chamber (or decrease in cathode chamber) and w_2 = total weight of silver deposited on the cathode (or in a separate voltameter in series), then

$$\frac{w_1}{w_2}=\frac{n_{NO_3^-}}{n_{NO_3^-}+n_{Ag^+}}=\mathbf{n}_{NO_3^-}, \quad \text{.................(110)}$$

where $n_{NO_3^-}$ and n_{Ag^+} are the transport numbers of the nitrate ion and silver ion respectively.

Example 101. A solution of silver nitrate of which 100 gm. contained 8·855 gm. of $AgNO_3$ was electrolysed in a suitable transport apparatus between silver electrodes. After electrolysis it was found that the increase in weight of the cathode was 0·8399 gm., and the anode solution which weighed 116·15 gm. contained 10·909 gm. of $AgNO_3$. What are the transport numbers of Ag^+ and NO_3^- in silver nitrate?

After electrolysis :

(116·15 − 10·909) gm. of water contain 10·909 gm. of $AgNO_3$ that is, 105·241 gm. of water contain 10·909 gm. of $AgNO_3$.

But before electrolysis :

(100 − 8·855) gm. of water contained 8·855 gm. of $AgNO_3$.

∴ 105·241 gm. of water would have contained

$$\left(\frac{8\cdot855}{100-8\cdot855}\right)\times 105\cdot241 \text{ gm. of } AgNO_3$$

$$=10\cdot2143 \text{ gm.}$$

∴ Increase of $AgNO_3$ in the anode compartment

$$=10\cdot909-10\cdot2143=0\cdot6947 \text{ gm.}$$

∴ Increase in Ag^+ in anode compartment

$$=0\cdot6947\times\frac{107\cdot9}{169\cdot9}=0\cdot4412 \text{ gm.}$$

∴ Transport number of NO_3^- in $AgNO_3$

$$=\frac{0\cdot4412}{0\cdot8399}=\mathbf{0\cdot525},$$

and transport number of Ag^+ in $AgNO_3$

$$=(1-0\cdot525)=\mathbf{0\cdot475}.$$

* Since ions appear to be heavily hydrated and, consequently, will carry some of the solvent with them during migration, the "true" transport number of an ion will be obtained by using a reference substance, usually raffinose, assumed to remain unchanged by the movement of the ions.

* **Example 102.** A solution consisting of 232·56 gm. of water, 7·862 gm. of raffinose and 11·615 gm. of lithium chloride was electrolysed in a transport apparatus with changeable electrodes. After electrolysis, the anode solution which weighed 110·52 gm. contained 4·0758 gm. of raffinose and 6·3081 gm. of lithium chloride. In a silver voltameter in series with the same circuit, 1·0832 gm. of silver was deposited. Calculate the true transport numbers of Li^+ and Cl^-.

After electrolysis :

4·0758 gm. of raffinose are in solution with 6·3081 gm. of lithium chloride.

Before electrolysis :

4·0758 gm. of raffinose were associated with $\frac{11\cdot615}{7\cdot862}\times4\cdot075$ gm. of lithium chloride = 6.022 gm.

∴ Increase of lithium chloride in anode (with reference to raffinose) = (6·3081 − 6·022) gm. = 0·286 gm.

But 1·0832 gm. of silver is equivalent to $1\cdot0832\times\frac{42\cdot40}{107\cdot9}$ gm. of lithium chloride = 0·4256 gm.

∴ Transport number of Cl^- in LiCl

$$=\frac{0\cdot286}{0\cdot4256}=\mathbf{0\cdot672},$$

and transport number of Li^+ in LiCl = **0·328.**

7. Mobilities of ions and Kohlrausch's law

The mobility of an ion (not to be confused with the **absolute** mobility or velocity) is that proportion of the equivalent or molecular conductivity at infinite dilution which is due to the presence of that ion.

$$\therefore \text{Mobility of an ion} = \Lambda_\infty \times n,$$

where Λ_∞ = the molecular conductivity or equivalent conductivity at infinite dilution of an electrolyte containing that ion and n = the transport number of that ion for a given electrolyte. Thus, for silver nitrate the transport number of the silver ion is 0·58 and the molecular conductivity at infinite dilution is 116 ohm^{-1}.

$\therefore$ The mobility of the silver ion, denoted by l_{Ag^+}, is given by:

$$l_{Ag^+} = 116 \times 0{\cdot}58 = 67{\cdot}1.$$

The mobility of an ion, unlike its transport number, does not vary with the nature of the salt containing that ion. For any silver salt, for example, the following relation always holds:

$$l_{Ag^+} = \Lambda_\infty \times n = 67{\cdot}1,$$

where Λ_∞ = the molecular or equivalent conductivity at infinite dilution of a solution of a silver salt and n = the transport number of the silver ion in that salt. The figures for silver acetate may be taken as illustrative:

l_{Ag^+}	=	120·1	×	0·558	=	67·1
		(molecular conductivity at infinite dilution of silver acetate)		(transport number of the silver ion in silver acetate)		

Kohlrausch's law of **independent ionic mobilities** can be expressed by the equation:

$$\Lambda_\infty = l_a + l_c, \quad \text{.........................(111)}$$

where Λ_∞ = the molecular conductivity at infinite dilution of any electrolyte, l_a = the mobility of the anion derived from that electrolyte, and l_c = the mobility of the cation of the same electrolyte.

Example 103. The molecular conductivity of potassium chloride at infinite dilution is 130. The transport number of the chlorine ion in potassium chloride at the same temperature is 0·505. What is the mobility of the potassium ion?

Mobility of the potassium ion

=molecular conductivity of potassium chloride at infinite dilutions × the transport number of potassium ion in potassium chloride solution.

But the transport number of potassium ion in potassium chloride

=1 – the transport number of the chlorine ion in potassium chloride

$=1-0{\cdot}505=0{\cdot}495.$

∴ Mobility of the potassium ion

$$=130\times 0{\cdot}495=64{\cdot}3.$$

Example 104. The transport number (migration ratio) of the sodium ion in sodium nitrate solution is 0·371, and the molecular conductivity of the salt at infinite dilution is 105·3. What is the absolute mobility of the sodium ion?

As in Example 103 :

$$\text{mobility of the sodium ion}=105{\cdot}3\times 0{\cdot}371.$$

∴ Absolute mobility of the sodium ion

$$=\frac{105{\cdot}3\times 0{\cdot}371}{96{,}540}=4{\cdot}05\times 10^{-4}\text{ cm./sec.}$$

Example 105. The molecular conductivity at infinite dilution of sodium chloride is 109 and the transport number of the sodium ion in the same salt is 0·396. The molecular conductivity at infinite dilution for potassium nitrate is 126, and the transport number of the nitrate ion in this salt is 0·497. Calculate the molecular conductivity at infinite dilution of sodium nitrate.

Using the same notation as above :

$$_{\infty}\Lambda_{NaNO_3}=l_{Na^+}+l_{NO_3^-}.$$

But $$l_{Na^+}=109\times 0{\cdot}396=43{\cdot}3,$$

and $$l_{NO_3^-}=126\times 0{\cdot}497=62{\cdot}6.$$

∴ Molecular conductivity of sodium nitrate at infinite dilution $={}_{\infty}\Lambda_{NaNO_3}=43{\cdot}3+62{\cdot}6$

$$=105{\cdot}9.$$

The method of the foregoing example provides a means of obtaining Λ_∞ for weak electrolytes whose specific conductivity at "infinite" dilution cannot be measured directly.

Example 106. The molecular conductivity of hydrochloric acid at infinite dilution is 377 ohm^{-1} and of sodium acetate 87·5 ohm^{-1}. The transport number of the hydrogen ion in hydrochloric acid is 0·841 and of the acetate ion in sodium acetate 0·484. Calculate the molecular conductivity of acetic acid at infinite dilution, and hence deduce the percentage dissociation of acetic acid in $N/10$ solution at the same temperature, given that the specific conductivity of $N/10$ acetic acid is $1{\cdot}15\times10^{-3}$ ohm^{-1}.

With the usual notation:

$$l_{H^+}=377\times0{\cdot}841=317,$$

$$l_{CH_3COO^-}=87{\cdot}5\times0{\cdot}484=42{\cdot}3.$$

$$\therefore\ {}_\infty\Lambda_{CH_3COOH}=l_{H^+}+l_{CH_3COO^-}$$

$$=317+42{\cdot}3 \doteq \mathbf{359}.$$

The molecular conductivity of $N/10$ acetic acid

$$=1{\cdot}15\times10^{-3}\times10{,}000\ \text{ohm}^{-1}=11{\cdot}5.$$

∴ Percentage dissociation of acetic acid in $N/10$ solution

$$=\frac{11{\cdot}5}{359}\times100=3{\cdot}2.$$

* **Example 107.** The equivalent conductivities, degrees of dissociation and anionic transport numbers of $N/100$ silver nitrate and $N/100$ sodium chlorate are:

	Λ	α	n_α
Silver nitrate - -	124·1	0·90	0·52
Sodium chlorate - -	106·4	0·95	0·45

Calculate the equivalent conductivity of silver chlorate in $N/100$ solution, in which its degree of dissociation is 0·95. (Assume that the "classical" or Arrhenius theory of electrolytic dissociation applies in this case.)

(Manchester Hons. Chem.)

Let ${}_\infty\Lambda_{AgNO_3}$ and ${}_\infty\Lambda_{NaClO_3}$ denote the equivalent conductivities at infinite dilution of silver nitrate and sodium chlorate respectively.

Let l_{Ag^+}, $l_{NO_3^-}$, l_{Na^+} and $l_{ClO_3^-}$ denote the mobilities of the ions indicated by the subscripts.

Then $\Lambda_1 = {}_{\infty}\Lambda_{AgNO_3} \times 0{\cdot}90 = (l_{Ag^+} + l_{NO_3^-}) \times 0{\cdot}90$ where $\Lambda_1 =$ the equivalent conductivity of silver nitrate in $N/100$ solution.

But $\qquad \Lambda_1 = 124{\cdot}1 \text{ ohm}^{-1}.$

$$\therefore\ {}_{\infty}\Lambda_{AgNO_3} = \frac{124{\cdot}1}{0{\cdot}90} = 137{\cdot}9 \text{ ohm}^{-1}.$$

Also, since the transport number of the nitrate ion in silver nitrate is 0·52, the transport number of the silver ion in the same salt $= 1 - 0{\cdot}52 = 0{\cdot}48$.

$$\therefore\ l_{Ag^+} = 137{\cdot}9 \times 0{\cdot}48 = 66{\cdot}2 \text{ ohm}^{-1}.$$

Similarly :

$${}_{\infty}\Lambda_{NaClO_3} = \frac{\Lambda_2}{0{\cdot}95} = \frac{106{\cdot}4}{0{\cdot}95} = 112{\cdot}1 \text{ ohm}^{-1},$$

where $\Lambda_2 =$ the equivalent conductivity of sodium chlorate in $N/100$ solution.

But, since the transport number of the chlorate ion in sodium chlorate is 0·45,

$$\therefore\ l_{ClO_3^-} = 112{\cdot}1 \times 0{\cdot}45 = 50{\cdot}4 \text{ ohm}^{-1}.$$

$$\therefore\ {}_{\infty}\Lambda_{AgClO_3} = l_{Ag^+} + l_{NO_3^-} = 66{\cdot}2 + 50{\cdot}4$$
$$= 116{\cdot}2 \text{ ohm}^{-1},$$

where ${}_{\infty}\Lambda_{AgClO_3} =$ the equivalent conductivity of silver chlorate at infinite dilution. But, since silver chlorate is dissociated to the degree 0·95 in $N/100$ solution, its equivalent conductivity (denoted by Λ_3) at this dilution is given by the equation :

$$\Lambda_3 = {}_{\infty}\Lambda_{AgClO_3} \times 0{\cdot}95 = 116{\cdot}2 \times 0{\cdot}95 \text{ ohm}^{-1}$$
$$= 110{\cdot}4 \text{ ohm}^{-1}.$$

8. Determination of the solubility of sparingly soluble substances

For all solutions of electrolytes the following equation is, by definition of equivalent conductivity, correct :

$$\sigma \times V = \Lambda_V,$$

where $\sigma =$ the specific conductivity of the solution,
$V =$ the volume in c.c. containing 1 gm.-equivalent of the solute,
and $\Lambda_V =$ the equivalent conductivity of the solution at a dilution of 1 gm.-equivalent in V c.c.

When the solution is very dilute, as in the case of sparingly soluble substances, complete dissociation of the solute can usually be assumed, and for the equivalent conductivity, Λ_V, we can write the equivalent conductivity at infinite dilution, Λ_∞. But Λ_∞ can, by Kohlrausch's law, be equated to the sum of the mobilities of the ions.

$$\therefore\ \sigma \times V = \Lambda_V = \Lambda_\infty = l_a + l_c. \quad \ldots\ldots\ldots\ldots\ldots(112)$$

Example 108. The mobilities of the silver ion and the chlorine ion are 56·5 and 68·0 respectively at 20°. A saturated solution of silver chloride in water at 20° has a specific conductivity of $1{\cdot}37 \times 10^{-6}$ ohm^{-1} (allowance having been made for the conductivity of the water in which the solution is made). Calculate the solubility of silver chloride in water at 20°, expressing the result in (*a*) gm.-molecules per litre, (*b*) gm. of the salt per 100 c.c. of solution.

$$\Lambda_\infty = l_a + l_c = 68{\cdot}0 + 56{\cdot}5 = 124{\cdot}5 \text{ ohm}^{-1}.$$

Then if V = the volume in c.c. of the solution containing 1 gm.-molecule, that is, 143·5 gm. of silver chloride :

$$1{\cdot}37 \times 10^{-6} \times V = 124{\cdot}5.$$

$$\therefore\ V = 9{\cdot}09 \times 10^{7} \text{ c.c.}$$

$\therefore$ $9{\cdot}09 \times 10^7$ c.c. contain 1 gm.-molecule of silver chloride.

$$\therefore\ 1000 \text{ c.c. contain } \frac{1000}{9{\cdot}09 \times 10^{7}} \text{ gm.-molecule}$$

$$= \mathbf{1{\cdot}10 \times 10^{-5}} \textbf{ gm.-molecule.}$$

Also $1{\cdot}10 \times 10^{-5}$ gm.-molecule of silver chloride

$$= 1{\cdot}10 \times 10^{-5} \times 143{\cdot}5 \text{ gm.} = 1{\cdot}58 \times 10^{-3} \text{ gm.}$$

$\therefore$ 1000 c.c. of the saturated solution contain $1{\cdot}58 \times 10^{-3}$ gm.

$\therefore$ 100 c.c. of saturated solution contain **$1{\cdot}58 \times 10^{-4}$ gm.**

The ionic product for water (see p. 167) may be calculated similarly, as in the following example.

Example 109. Assuming that the specific conductivity of pure water is $0{\cdot}50 \times 10^{-7}$ ohm^{-1}, calculate the ionic product for water. The mobilities of the hydrogen ion and the hydroxyl ion are 317 and 180 respectively.

The molecular conductivity of water at infinite dilution may be interpreted as the molecular conductivity of that volume of water which contains 1 gm.-molecule of completely dissociated water. If this volume is V c.c., then :

$$0{\cdot}50 \times 10^{-7} \times V = 317 + 180 = 497.$$

$$\therefore\ V = \frac{497}{0{\cdot}50 \times 10^{-7}} \text{ c.c.} = 994 \times 10^{7} \text{ c.c. or } 994 \times 10^{4} \text{ litres.}$$

$\therefore$ 994×10^4 litres contain 1 gm.-molecule of completely dissociated water and, therefore, contain 1 gm.-ion of hydrogen and 1 gm.-ion of hydroxyl.

$\therefore$ $[H^+] = [OH^-]$ = concentration of each of these ions per litre $= \dfrac{1}{994 \times 10^4}$.

$\therefore$ Ionic product for water $= [H^+] \times [OH^-]$

$$= [H^+]^2 = [OH^-]^2 = \left[\frac{1}{994 \times 10^4}\right]^2 = \mathbf{1{\cdot}01 \times 10^{-14}}.$$

QUESTIONS ON CHAPTER IX

1. A current of 0·11 ampère was passed successively through (*a*) acidulated water, (*b*) silver nitrate solution, (*c*) copper sulphate solution, the electrodes in each case being platinum. After the current had flowed for 8 hours, the volume of the hydrogen liberated in (*a*) occupied 391 c.c., the laboratory temperature and pressure being 15° and 752 mm. respectively. Calculate (i) the electrochemical equivalent of hydrogen, (ii) the weights of silver and copper respectively deposited in (*b*) and (*c*). [Cu = 63·6 ; Ag = 107·9 ; aqueous vapour tension of dilute sulphuric acid at 15° = 13 mm. approx.]

2. Calculate the weight of water which must be decomposed electrolytically to give sufficient hydrogen at 15° and 760 mm. to fill a balloon of capacity one million litres. (1st M.B., Man.)

3. During the electrolysis of the nitrate of a metal in aqueous solution between platinum electrodes, 0·5613 gm. of the metal was deposited in the same time that 103·6 c.c. of oxygen was collected at the anode. The laboratory temperature and pressure were 18° and 746 mm. respectively. What is the chemical equivalent of the metal? [Aqueous vapour tension of the solution at 18° = 14·8 mm.]

4. Calculate (*a*) the weight of copper sulphate which must be electrolysed between platinum electrodes in aqueous solution to give 500 litres of oxygen measured at *N.T.P.*, (*b*) the volume of hydrogen measured at *N.T.P.* which would be obtained from the electrolysis of 500 c.c. of normal hydrochloric acid.

5. An electric current is passed through (*a*) a solution of silver nitrate, (*b*) a solution of 10 gm. of copper sulphate crystals, $CuSO_4 . 5H_2O$, in 500 c.c. of water, platinum electrodes being used in each case. After 30 minutes it was found that 1·307 gm. of silver had been deposited. What was the concentration of copper, expressed as gm. of copper ion per litre, in the copper sulphate solution after electrolysis?

6. An $N/50$ solution of a weak acid has a specific resistance of $2{\cdot}160 \times 10^3$ ohms at 18°. What is the equivalent conductivity of this acid in $N/50$ solution at 18°?

7. A weak monobasic acid has a molecular weight 60. A solution of the acid containing 1·36 gm. of the acid in 500 c.c. has an equivalent conductivity 12·6 ohm^{-1} at 18°. What are (*a*) the specific conductivity, (*b*) the specific resistance of the solution at this temperature?

8. A monobasic acid has an equivalent conductivity of 376 ohm^{-1} at infinite dilution. An $N/15$ solution of the acid is 2 per cent dissociated. What value would you expect for the specific resistance of this solution? What would be the approximate percentage dissociation in an $N/50$ solution of this acid?

9. The molecular conductivity at infinite dilution of a weak monobasic acid is 368 ohm^{-1} at 18°. The specific resistance of the same acid in $N/20$ solution is $1{\cdot}26 \times 10^3$ ohms at the same temperature. Calculate (*a*) the percentage dissociation of the acid in $N/20$ solution, (*b*) the approximate percentage dissociation of the acid in $N/100$ solution, both at 18°.

10. An $N/10$ KCl solution has an apparent dissociation of 91·2 per cent at 15°. The molecular conductivity of potassium chloride at the same temperature is 134·8 ohm^{-1}. What are (*a*) the specific conductivity of $N/10$ KCl, (*b*) the boiling point of $N/10$ KCl (assuming that the percentage ionisation at 100° is the same as at 15°).

11. An aqueous solution containing 0·351 gm. of a binary electrolyte (molecular weight, 84·5) in 47 gm. of water has an equivalent conductivity of 112. The equivalent conductivity at infinite dilution is 130. Calculate the freezing point of the solution [molecular depression for water is 1·85° per 1000 gm.]. (1st M.B., London.)

12. A solution of a weak monobasic acid contains 1·5 gm. of the acid per litre, the molecular weight of the acid being 74. What is the osmotic pressure of this solution at 15°, the equivalent conductivity of the solution at this temperature being 18·5 ohm^{-1} and the equivalent conductivity at infinite dilution being 382 ohm^{-1}?

13. The molecular conductivity of acetic acid at infinite dilution is found to be 387 reciprocal ohms. At the same temperature but at a dilution of 1 gm.-mol. in 1000 litres it is 55 reciprocal ohms. What is the percentage dissociation of $0{\cdot}1N$ acetic acid? (C.U.O.S.)

14. A normal solution of potassium chloride has a molecular conductivity 102 ohm^{-1}. The molecular conductivity of potassium chloride is 135 at infinite dilution. Calculate the percentage dissociation of potassium chloride in this solution and the freezing point of the solution.

15. A decinormal solution of potassium nitrate boils at 100·096°. The molecular conductivity of potassium nitrate at infinite dilution is 131 ohm^{-1}. What value would you expect for the specific conductivity of decinormal potassium nitrate?

16. A decinormal solution of a weak monobasic acid has an equivalent conductivity of 14·5 ohm^{-1}. The molecular conductivity of the acid at infinite dilution is 368 ohm^{-1}. Calculate the approximate percentage dissociation of the acid in $N/50$ solution.

17. During the electrolysis of copper sulphate solution between platinum electrodes the fall of concentration round the anode was 0·29 gm. of copper sulphate per 100 c.c., the corresponding fall of concentration round the cathode being 0·24 gm. Calculate the transport numbers of the copper ion and sulphate ion respectively.

18. The molecular conductivity at infinite dilution of a monobasic acid is 387 ohm^{-1}. The transport number of the hydrogen ion in a solution of this acid is 0·83. What is the mobility of the anion?

19. The absolute mobility of the hydrogen ion at 18° is $3{\cdot}24 \times 10^{-3}$ cm. per sec. Given that the transport number of the chlorine ion in hydrochloric acid is 0·176 at 18°, calculate the absolute mobility of the chlorine ion at the same temperature.

20. The specific conductivity of $N/10$ silver nitrate solution at 18° is $1{\cdot}16 \times 10^{-2}$ ohm^{-1}. Assuming that the dissociation of the solute is complete at this dilution, calculate the mobilities of the silver ion and the nitrate ion, given that the transport number of the silver ion in silver nitrate solution at 18° is 0·467.

21. The transport number of the potassium ion in $N/200$ potassium chloride solution at 18° is 0·505. The absolute mobility of the potassium ion in the same solution is $6{\cdot}52 \times 10^{-4}$ cm. per sec. What is the absolute mobility of the chlorine ion?

22. The molecular conductivity at infinite dilution at 15° for potassium chloride is 130 ohm^{-1}. The transport number of the chlorine ion in potassium chloride at 18° being 0·505, what are the mobilities of the potassium ion and chlorine ion respectively at the same temperature?

23. The molecular conductivity of sodium propionate at infinite dilution is 83·5 ohm^{-1}, and the transport number of the sodium ion in sodium propionate is 0·536. The molecular conductivity at infinite dilution for hydrochloric acid is 398 ohm^{-1}, and the transport number of the chlorine ion in hydrochloric acid is 0·159.

Assuming all measurement to refer to the same temperature, calculate the molecular conductivity at infinite dilution for propionic acid at the same temperature.

24. During the electrolysis of copper sulphate between platinum electrodes, the loss of copper in the anode compartment was 0·183 gm. In a silver voltameter, placed in series with the electrolytic cell, 0·961 gm. of silver was deposited. Calculate the transport number of the copper ion in copper sulphate.

25. The specific conductivity of a decinormal solution of a weak monobasic acid is 0·00132 ohm^{-1}. Calculate approximately the specific conductivity of the acid in $N/50$ solution.

26. 2·56 gm. of a weak monobasic acid, of molecular weight 74, was dissolved in water and made up to 500 c.c. Calculate the molecular conductivity of this solution, given that the molecular conductivity of the acid at infinite dilution is 367 ohm^{-1} and that of an $N/50$ solution of the acid is 10·3 ohm^{-1}.

27. The specific conductivity of acetic acid in $N/20$ solution at 18° is $6{\cdot}70 \times 10^{-4}$ ohm^{-1}. Taking the mobilities of the hydrogen ion and the acetate ion to be 317 and 42·1 respectively, calculate the percentage dissociation of acetic acid in $N/20$ solution at 18°.

28. Propionic acid is dissociated to the extent of 4·8 per cent in $N/50$ solution. The molecular conductivity of propionic acid is 355 ohm^{-1} at infinite dilution. What is the specific conductivity of $N/50$ propionic acid?

29. The absolute mobility of the potassium ion is $6{\cdot}52 \times 10^{-4}$ cm. per sec. and of the chlorine ion $6{\cdot}6 \times 10^{-4}$ cm. per sec. The molecular conductivity of potassium chloride at infinite dilution is 130 ohm^{-1}. Calculate the mobilities of the potassium ion and chlorine ion respectively, all measurements being taken at the same temperature.

30. The specific conductivity of a weak monobasic acid was found to be $1{\cdot}34 \times 10^{-3}$ ohm^{-1} in $N/10$ solution at 20°. Given that the mobility of the hydrogen ion is 317 and that of the acidic ion is 53, calculate the percentage dissociation of the acid in $N/10$ solution at 20°.

31. The molecular conductivity of potassium chloride at infinite dilution is 134·8 ohm^{-1}, that of sodium chloride at infinite dilution, 113 ohm^{-1}, and that of potassium bromide at infinite dilution is 137 ohm^{-1}. Calculate the molecular conductivity at infinite dilution of sodium bromide.

32. The hydrogen ion concentration of an $N/20$ solution of a weak monobasic acid is $1{\cdot}27 \times 10^{-4}$ gm.-ion per litre. Calculate the equivalent conductivity of this solution, given that the molecular conductivity of the acid at infinite dilution is 384 ohm^{-1}.

33. The molecular conductivity of a weak monobasic acid at infinite dilution is 386 ohm^{-1} at 18°. At the same temperature the dissociation constant of the acid is $1{\cdot}56 \times 10^{-5}$. Calculate approximately the specific conductivity of the acid in *N*/10 solution at 18°.

34. The specific conductivity of a weak monobasic acid in *N*/10 solution at 18° is 0·00093 ohm^{-1}. What value for the specific conductivity of *N*/20 solution of the acid at the same temperature would be expected?

35. The specific conductivity of *N*/10 acetic acid is 0·0012 ohm^{-1} at 18°, and it is dissociated to the degree of 3·1 per cent at this dilution. If the transport number of the acetate ion in acetic acid at 18° is 0·16, what is the mobility of the acetate ion at this temperature?

36. The dissociation of water increases with rise of temperature. At 50°, the specific resistance of pure water is $8{\cdot}5 \times 10^6$ ohms. Calculate, for water at 50°, the hydrogen ion concentration and the ionic product ($l_{H^+} = 317$; $l_{OH^-} = 170$).

37. Calculate the *p*H of a solution of a weak monobasic acid of decinormal concentration at 15° given that its molecular conductivity at this temperature and dilution is 11·2 ohm^{-1} and that its molecular conductivity at infinite dilution is 367 ohm^{-1}.

38. The *p*H of a decinormal solution of a monobasic acid is 2·6. The molecular conductivity of the acid at infinite dilution and at the same temperature is 372 ohm^{-1}. Calculate the specific resistance of the decinormal solution.

39. The absolute mobility at 18° of the chlorine ion is $6{\cdot}6 \times 10^{-4}$ cm. per sec. The transport number of the hydrogen ion in hydrochloric acid is 0·83. The specific conductivity of *N*/100 HCl is 0·00395 ohm^{-1}. Assuming complete dissociation in *N*/100 HCl, calculate the absolute mobility of the hydrogen ion at 18°.

40. The specific conductivity of a saturated solution of silver bromide at 18° is $0{\cdot}055 \times 10^{-6}$ ohm^{-1}, the specific conductivity of water having been deducted. The mobilities of the silver ion and the bromine ion at this temperature are 56·5 and 67·8 respectively. What is the solubility of silver bromide at 18° (gm. per 100 c.c. solution)? What is the solubility product of silver bromide at this temperature?

41. The mobility of the hydrogen ion at 18° is 317 and of the acetate ion 53. What value would you expect for the specific conductivity of *N*/50 acetic acid, assuming 4·2 per cent dissociation of the acid at this dilution?

42. Calculate (*a*) the solubility (gm. per 100 c.c.), (*b*) the solubility product, at 18°, of lead sulphate given that the specific conductivity of a saturated solution of lead sulphate at this temperature is $1{\cdot}65 \times 10^{-5}$ ohm^{-1} and that the mobilities of the lead ion (Pb^{++}) and sulphate ion (SO_4^{--}) are 120 and 136 respectively.

43. The molecular conductivity at infinite dilution of a weak monobasic acid is 386 ohm^{-1}, and in decinormal solution the molecular conductivity is 12·8 ohm^{-1}. What is the pH of the solution?

44. The specific conductivity of a weak monobasic acid in $N/10$ solution is $9{\cdot}2 \times 10^{-5}$ ohm^{-1}. Given that the molecular conductivity of the acid at infinite dilution is 360 ohm^{-1}, calculate the approximate hydrogen ion concentration in an $N/20$ solution of the acid.

45. During the electrolysis of a solution of copper sulphate between copper electrodes, the increase in the amount of copper sulphate (measured as $CuSO_4$) in the anode compartment was 0·385 gm., and the corresponding increase in the weight of the cathode was 0·592 gm. Calculate the transport numbers of the copper ion and sulphate ion respectively.

46. A solution of copper sulphate was electrolysed between copper electrodes and the loss of copper ion from the cathode compartment was 0·105 gm. In a silver voltameter in series with the same circuit, 0·535 gm. of silver was deposited. What are the transport numbers of the copper ion and the sulphate ion respectively?

47. In the electrolysis of a solution of hydrochloric acid between cadmium electrodes the following results were obtained: gain in chlorine round the cathode, 0·00665 gm.; silver deposited in a voltameter in series with the cell, 0·1190 gm. Find the transport numbers of the hydrogen and chlorine ions. (C.U.O.S.)

* **48.** The equivalent conductivity of sodium fluoride in $N/10$ solution, at which dilution the salt is 92 per cent dissociated, is 83·5 ohm^{-1}. If the transport number of the sodium ion in sodium fluoride is 0·45, what are the absolute mobilities of the sodium ion and fluorine ion respectively?

* **49.** The equivalent conductivities of solutions of potassium hydroxide are given below. Plot Λ against $\sqrt{c}$ and hence obtain Λ_∞. Deduce the apparent degree of dissociation in a solution containing 2 gm. of potassium hydroxide in 10,000 c.c.

c (equiv. per litre)	0·001	0·002	0·01	0·05
Λ - - -	234	233	228	218

* **50.** From the following data calculate (a) the absolute mobility of the potassium ion in $N/10$ potassium chloride solution, (b) the molecular conductivity of potassium chloride at infinite dilution.

	Λ	n_a	α
$N/10$ KNO_3 - -	95·3	0·48	0·79
$N/10$ $NaNO_3$ - -	93·0	0·58	0·84
$N/10$ NaCl - -	92·6	0·61	0·81

where Λ = the equivalent conductivity in $N/10$ solution, n_a = transport number of the anion, α = apparent degree of dissociation. The absolute mobility of the chlorine ion = $6{\cdot}6 \times 10^{-4}$ cm. per sec.

*** 51.** Calculate the true transport number of the sodium ion in sodium chloride solution from the following data. A solution of sodium chloride of which 200 gm. contained initially 11·635 gm. of sodium chloride and 12·072 gm. of raffinose was electrolysed between changeable electrodes. After electrolysis it was found that the total solution in the anode compartment contained 4·9710 gm. of sodium chloride and 5·8406 gm. of raffinose. 3·425 gm. of silver was deposited in the same time in a silver voltameter in series with the cell.

*** 52.** A solution of magnesium iodide was electrolysed between a silver chloride cathode and a platinum anode. It was found that the iodine formed in the anode compartment required 156·3 c.c. of $N/5$ sodium thiosulphate for complete reduction. Given that the transport numbers of magnesium ion and iodide ion in magnesium iodide are 0·409 and 0·591 respectively, calculate the loss of weight of magnesium iodide in the cathode compartment.

*** 53.** Tables of data give the following values for ion conductances (mobilities) at infinite dilution in water at 25°: $H^+ = 350$; $Ag^+ = 61{\cdot}9$; $NO_3^- = 71{\cdot}4$; $CH_3COO^- = 40{\cdot}9$; $Cl^- = 76{\cdot}3$ ohms^{-1} cm.^{2} Outline the principles underlying the experimental determination of these data. At 25° the specific conductance of AgCl in saturated aqueous solution, after allowing for that of water, is $1{\cdot}8 \times 10^{-6}$ ohms^{-1} cm.$^{-1}$ From the above information calculate (*a*) the solubility of AgCl at 25°, and (*b*) the transport number of Ag^+ in very dilute $AgNO_3$ solution. (London B.Sc. Special.)

*** 54.** At a concentration of 0·005 gm.-equivalents per litre the transport number of the cadmium ion in cadmium iodide is approximately 0·44. A solution of cadmium iodide containing 13·463 per cent of the solute was electrolysed in a suitable transport apparatus, and it was found after the electrolysis that the anode solution weighing 130·63 gm. contained 17·681 gm. of cadmium iodide. The silver deposited in a silver voltameter in series weighed 3·082 gm. Show that these results are explained on the assumption that a solution of cadmium iodide behaves according to the equation:

$$2CdI_2 \rightleftharpoons Cd_2I_4 \rightleftharpoons Cd^{++} + CdI_4^{--},$$

and that the tendency to complex ion formation increases with concentration. What explanation would you give of an experiment similar to the one mentioned which gave a negative value for the transport number of the cadmium ion?

CHAPTER X

VOLUMETRIC ANALYSIS (1)

1. Acid-alkali titrations

It is assumed that the student is acquainted with the methods of deriving the equivalents of the following compounds when they are used in acid-alkali titrations.

Compound	Molecular formula	Molecular weight	Equivalent
Hydrochloric acid - -	HCl	36·5	36·5
Nitric acid - -	HNO_3	63	63
Sulphuric acid - -	H_2SO_4	98	49
Oxalic acid			
(anhydrous) - -	$C_2O_4H_2$	90	45
(crystals) - -	$C_2O_4H_2 . 2H_2O$	126	63
Orthophosphoric acid	H_3PO_4	98	
(with methyl orange)			98
(with phenol-phthalein) -			49
Boric acid (in presence of glycerol or mannitol and with phenolphthalein) -	H_3BO_3	62	62
Sodium hydroxide -	$NaOH$	40	40
Potassium hydroxide	KOH	56	56
Barium hydroxide -	$Ba(OH)_2$	171	85·5
Ammonium hydroxide (as ammonia) -	NH_3	17	17
Sodium carbonate			
(anhydrous) - -	Na_2CO_3	106	
(with phenol-phthalein) -			106
(with cold litmus) -			106
(with hot litmus) -			53
(with methyl orange)			53
Sodium bicarbonate -	$NaHCO_3$	84	
(with methyl orange)			84

The student should also confirm the equivalents of the following substances when they are used in precipitation titrations:

silver nitrate (170); potassium thiocyanate (97); ammonium thiocyanate (76).

The following worked examples are illustrative of the methods used in acid-alkali and precipitation titrations.

Example 110. 8·000 gm. of a mixture of anhydrous sodium carbonate and sodium bicarbonate was dissolved in water and made up to 1000 c.c. In separate experiments 25 c.c. of this solution required for neutralisation (*a*) 32·51 c.c. of $N/10$ HCl using methyl orange as indicator, (*b*) 11·80 c.c. of $N/10$ HCl using phenolphthalein as indicator. Use these readings separately to obtain two independent values for the percentage of sodium carbonate in the mixture.

When methyl orange is used as indicator, both the carbonate and the bicarbonate are converted into sodium chloride :

$$Na_2CO_3 + 2HCl = 2NaCl + H_2O + CO_2,$$

$$NaHCO_3 + HCl = NaCl + H_2O + CO_2.$$

Assume that there are x gm. of sodium carbonate in the mixture and, therefore, $(8 - x)$ gm. of sodium bicarbonate.

Then the volume of normal acid required to neutralise 8 gm. of the mixture is obtained by filling in the appropriate weights and volumes, as shown in the following equations :

$$\underset{106}{Na_2CO_3} + \underset{2 \times 36\cdot5}{2HCl} = 2NaCl + H_2O + CO_2.$$

$\therefore$ 106 gm. of anhydrous sodium carbonate require 2000 c.c. N HCl.

$\therefore$ x gm. of anhydrous sodium carbonate would require $\frac{2000}{106} \times x$ c.c. N HCl.

$$\underset{84}{NaHCO_3} + \underset{36\cdot5}{HCl} = NaCl + CO_2 + H_2O.$$

$\therefore$ 84 gm. sodium bicarbonate require 1000 c.c. N HCl.

$\therefore$ $(8 - x)$ gm. sodium bicarbonate would require

$$\frac{1000}{84} \times (8 - x) \text{ c.c. of } N \text{ HCl.}$$

∴ Total volume of normal acid required to neutralise 8 gm. of the mixture (methyl orange indicator)

$$=\left[\left(\frac{2000}{106}\times x\right)+\frac{1000}{84}(8-x)\right] \text{ c.c.}$$

But since 25 c.c. of the solution require 32·51 c.c. of $N/10$ HCl:

∴ 1000 c.c. of the solution would require

$\frac{32\cdot51}{25}\times1000$ c.c. $N/10$ HCl or $\frac{3\cdot251}{25}\times1000$ c.c. of normal acid.

$$\therefore \left(\frac{2000}{106}\times x\right)+\left[\frac{1000}{84}(8-x)\right]=\frac{3\cdot251}{25}\times1000.$$

$$\therefore x=5\cdot00,$$

and percentage $Na_2CO_3=\frac{5}{8}\times100=62\cdot5$.

With phenolphthalein as indicator the only action is the conversion of the sodium carbonate to the bicarbonate :

$$\underset{106}{Na_2CO_3}+\underset{36\cdot5}{HCl}=NaCl+NaHCO_3.$$

∴ Since 25 c.c. of the solution require 11·80 c.c. of $N/10$ HCl, the concentration of the sodium carbonate $=\frac{11\cdot80}{25}\times\frac{1}{10}N$.

But N Na_2CO_3 contains (when phenolphthalein is used as indicator) 106 gm. per litre.

∴ No. of gm. of Na_2CO_3 in 1 litre of the solution

$$=\frac{11\cdot80}{25}\times10\cdot6 \text{ gm.}=5\cdot00 \text{ gm.}$$

The first part of the question can also be solved by the following method.

Since the solution contains x gm. of Na_2CO_3 per litre, it is $\frac{x}{53}N$ with respect to sodium carbonate. Similarly, it is $\frac{(8-x)}{84}N$ with respect to sodium bicarbonate.

∴ Its total normality as an alkali (methyl orange indicator)

$$=\frac{x}{53}+\frac{(8-x)}{84}.$$

But since 25 c.c. of the solution require

$$32{\cdot}51 \text{ c.c., } N/10\,\text{HCl} \equiv 3{\cdot}251 \text{ c.c. } N\,\text{HCl}.$$

$$\therefore \text{ Normality of the solution} = \frac{3{\cdot}251}{25}.$$

$$\therefore \frac{x}{53} + \frac{(8-x)}{84} = \frac{3{\cdot}251}{25}$$

and $\mathbf{x = 5{\cdot}00.}$

When the total weight of solute is unknown, as in the following example, the weights of the two dissolved substances can often be obtained by titration with different indicators.

Example 111. A solution contains sodium hydroxide and sodium carbonate. 25 c.c. of this solution required (*a*) 25·13 c.c. of 0·0972 *N* HCl for neutralisation when phenolphthalein was used as indicator, (*b*) 35·10 c.c. of 0·0972 *N* HCl when methyl orange was used. Calculate the number of gm. of sodium hydroxide and sodium carbonate per litre of the solution.

With phenolphthalein as indicator, the reactions are :

$$\underset{x \text{ c.c.}}{NaOH + HCl} = NaCl + H_2O$$

$$\underset{y \text{ c.c.}}{Na_2CO_3 + HCl} = NaCl + NaHCO_3$$

Assume that in the first titration, x c.c. of HCl are required to neutralise the sodium hydroxide in 25 c.c. of the solution and that y c.c. of HCl are similarly required to convert the sodium carbonate into sodium bicarbonate.

With methyl orange as indicator :

$$\underset{x}{NaOH + HCl} = NaCl + H_2O,$$

$$\underset{2y}{Na_2CO_3 + 2HCl} = 2NaCl + H_2O + CO_2.$$

From equations, it is seen that the sodium hydroxide still requires x c.c. of HCl, but the sodium carbonate now reacts with $2y$ c.c. of HCl.

$$\therefore \text{ 1st reading} = (x+y) \text{ c.c.}$$

$$\text{2nd reading} = (x+2y) \text{ c.c.}$$

$\therefore$ Difference of two readings $= y$ c.c.

$$= (35{\cdot}10 - 25{\cdot}13) \text{ c.c.} = 9{\cdot}97 \text{ c.c.}$$

$$\therefore\ x \text{ c.c.} = 15{\cdot}06 \text{ c.c.}$$

But $9{\cdot}97$ c.c. of $0{\cdot}097\ N$ HCl $\equiv 9{\cdot}97 \times 0{\cdot}097$ c.c. N HCl

$$= 0{\cdot}9672 \text{ c.c. } N \text{ HCl},$$

and $15{\cdot}06$ c.c. of $0{\cdot}097\ N$ HCl

$$= 15{\cdot}06 \times 0{\cdot}097 \text{ c.c. } N \text{ HCl}$$

$$= 1{\cdot}461 \text{ c.c. } N \text{ HCl}.$$

$\therefore$ Normality of the solution with respect to NaOH $= \dfrac{1{\cdot}461}{25} N$.

$\therefore$ No. of gm. of NaOH per litre $= \dfrac{1{\cdot}461}{25} \times 40$

$$= 2{\cdot}34 \text{ gm.}$$

Also, normality of the solution with respect to Na_2CO_3 (phenolphthalein indicator) $= \dfrac{0{\cdot}9672}{25} N$.

$\therefore$ No. of gm. of Na_2CO_3 per litre $= \dfrac{0{\cdot}9672}{25} \times 106$

$$= 4{\cdot}10 \text{ gm.}$$

Calculations on precipitation reactions can often be treated in the same manner as that used in Example 110.

Example 112. $7{\cdot}36$ gm. of a mixture of potassium chloride and potassium iodide was dissolved in water and made up to 1000 c.c. 25 c.c. of this solution required, for exact precipitation, $16{\cdot}91$ c.c. of $N/10$ silver nitrate. What is the percentage of potassium chloride in the mixture?

The equations for the reactions are :

$$\underset{74{\cdot}5}{KCl} + \underset{170}{AgNO_3} = AgCl + KNO_3$$

$$\underset{166}{KI} + \underset{170}{AgNO_3} = AgI + KNO_3$$

Let weight of KCl in $7{\cdot}36$ gm. of the mixture $= x$ gm.

$\therefore$ $74{\cdot}5$ gm. of KCl require 1000 c.c. N $AgNO_3$.

$\therefore$ x gm. of KCl require $\dfrac{1000}{74{\cdot}5} \times x\ N$ c.c. $AgNO_3$.

Similarly, weight of KI $=(7{\cdot}36-x)$ gm. and will require

$$\frac{1000}{166}\times(7{\cdot}36-x) \text{ c.c. } N \text{ AgNO}_3.$$

$\therefore$ Total volume of N $AgNO_3$ to precipitate 1 litre of the solution

$$=\left(\frac{1000}{74{\cdot}5}\times x\right)+\frac{100}{166}\times(7{\cdot}36-x) \text{ c.c.}$$

But since 25 c.c. of the solution require 16·91 c.c. of $N/10$ $AgNO_3$:

$\therefore$ 1000 c.c. of the solution would require

$$\frac{16{\cdot}91}{25}\times 1000 \text{ c.c. } N/10 \text{ AgNO}_3 \text{ or } \frac{1{\cdot}691}{25}\times 1000 \text{ c.c. } N \text{ AgNO}_3.$$

$$\therefore \left(\frac{1000}{74{\cdot}5}\times x\right)+\frac{100}{166}\times(7{\cdot}36-x)=\frac{1{\cdot}691}{25}\times 1000.$$

$$\therefore x=3{\cdot}15 \text{ gm.}$$

and percentage KCl $=\frac{3{\cdot}51}{7{\cdot}36}\times 100=42{\cdot}8$.

As in Example 110, the following quicker method may be used.

The solution is $\frac{x}{74{\cdot}5}$ N with respect to KCl,

and solution is $\frac{7{\cdot}36-x}{166}$ N with respect to KI.

$$\therefore \text{Total normality}=\left(\frac{x}{74{\cdot}5}\right)+\frac{(7{\cdot}36-x)}{166}.$$

$$\therefore \left(\frac{x}{74{\cdot}5}\right)+\frac{(7{\cdot}36-x)}{166}=\frac{1{\cdot}691}{25}.$$

$$\therefore x=3{\cdot}15 \text{ gm.}$$

The following examples are illustrative of the method of working when both volumetric and gravimetric data are provided or when the calculation involves reaction between gases and the standard acid or alkali.

Example 113. 50 c.c. of a solution of barium hydroxide was run into a bottle of capacity 2560 c.c., which was then quickly stoppered and well shaken. It was found that the residual barium hydroxide required 58·4 c.c. of $N/50$ oxalic acid (phenolphthalein indicator). In a separate titration 50 c.c. of the barium hydroxide solution required 63·2 c.c. of $N/50$ oxalic acid for neutralisation.

What value for the percentage by volume of carbon dioxide in air is given by these results?

This calculation is an example of Pettenkoffer's method for the estimation of CO_2 in air.

The reaction between carbon dioxide and barium hydroxide is :

$$Ba(OH)_2 + CO_2 = BaCO_3 + H_2O.$$

Since the equivalent of $Ba(OH)_2 = \frac{1}{2}$ molecular weight :

$$\therefore\ 2000 \text{ c.c. } N\ Ba(OH)_2 \equiv 22{,}400 \text{ c.c. of } CO_2 \text{ at } N.T.P.$$

But amount of barium hydroxide which reacts with the CO_2 in the bottle is equivalent to $(63{\cdot}2 - 58{\cdot}4)$ c.c. $= 4{\cdot}8$ c.c. of $N/50\ Ba(OH)_2$.

$\therefore$ Since 2000 c.c. $N\ Ba(OH)_2 \equiv 22{,}400$ c.c. CO_2,

$$4{\cdot}8 \text{ c.c. } N/50\ Ba(OH)_2 \equiv \frac{22{,}400}{2000} \times \frac{4{\cdot}8}{50} \text{ c.c. } CO_2$$

$$= 1{\cdot}075 \text{ c.c.}$$

But volume of air in the bottle

$$= (2560 - 50) \text{ c.c.} = 2510 \text{ c.c.}$$

$\therefore$ Percentage by volume of CO_2 in air (ignoring temperature correction)

$$= \frac{1{\cdot}075}{2510} \times 100 = \mathbf{0{\cdot}043\ per\ cent.}$$

Example 114. 10 gm. of a mixture of sodium acid oxalate, C_2O_4HNa, and sodium oxalate, $C_2O_4Na_2$, was heated to a constant weight and gave 6·120 gm. of sodium carbonate. If another 10 gm. of the same mixture were dissolved in water and made up to 1000 c.c. and 25 c.c. of this solution were titrated against $N/10$ NaOH with phenolphthalein as indicator, what volume of the sodium hydroxide solution should be required?

The action of heat on the mixture is given by :

$$\underset{224}{2C_2O_4HNa} \rightarrow \underset{106}{Na_2CO_3}$$

$$\underset{134}{C_2O_4Na_2} \rightarrow \underset{106}{Na_2CO_3}$$

∴ If x gm. = weight of C_2O_4HNa in 10 gm. of the mixture, then:

$$x \times \frac{106}{224} + (10 - x) \times \frac{106}{134} = 6{\cdot}12.$$

From which $x = $ **5·63 gm.**

The equivalent of C_2O_4HNa as an acid = 112.

∴ If 10 gm. of the mixture is contained in 1 litre, normality of the solution as an acid $= \frac{5{\cdot}63}{112}$.

∴ 25 c.c. of the solution require 25 c.c. of $\frac{5{\cdot}63}{112}$. N NaOH

$$= 25 \times \frac{5{\cdot}63}{112} \text{ c.c. } N \text{ NaOH}$$

$$= \frac{25 \times 5{\cdot}63 \times 10}{112} \text{ c.c. of } N/10 \text{ NaOH}$$

$$= \mathbf{12{\cdot}57 \text{ c.c.}}$$

Example 115. Calculate the composition of a mixture of potassium chloride, ammonium sulphate and ammonium chloride which gave the following results:

(*a*) 5·000 gm. of the mixture, heated to a constant weight, gave a residue weighing 1·632 gm. (*b*) 5·000 gm. of the mixture, dissolved in water and made up to 1000 c.c., gave a solution of which 25 c.c. required for complete precipitation of the chlorine ion 10·75 c.c. $N/10$ $AgNO_3$. (*c*) 5·000 gm. of the mixture was dissolved in water and made up to 1000 c.c. 25 c.c. of this solution was heated with an excess of sodium hydroxide and the liberated ammonia was absorbed in 50 c.c. $N/10$ HCl, which was found, at the completion of the experiment, to require 36·3 c.c. $N/10$ NaOH.

Weight of KCl = weight of residue = **1·632 gm.**

When 5·000 gm. of the mixture is made up to 1000 c.c. its normality with respect to potassium chloride is $\frac{1{\cdot}632}{74{\cdot}5}$.

∴ Volume of $N/10$ $AgNO_3$ required to precipitate the chlorine from the potassium chloride contained in 25 c.c. of the solution

$$= 25 \times \frac{1{\cdot}632}{74{\cdot}5} \times 10 \text{ c.c.} = 5{\cdot}464 \text{ c.c.}$$

∴ Volume of $N/10$ $AgNO_3$ required to precipitate the chlorine from the ammonium chloride in 25 c.c. of the solution $=(10{\cdot}75-5{\cdot}46)$ c.c. $=5{\cdot}29$ c.c.

∴ Since the equivalent of NH_4Cl in this titration = its molecular weight $=53{\cdot}5$: weight of ammonium chloride per litre

$$=\frac{5{\cdot}29}{25}\times 5{\cdot}35 \text{ gm.} = \mathbf{1{\cdot}132 \text{ gm.}}$$

The weight of ammonium sulphate can be obtained by difference or by using the result of the third estimation.

By difference, $(NH_4)_2SO_4=(5-1{\cdot}632-1{\cdot}132)$ gm.

$$=2{\cdot}236 \text{ gm.}$$

By the third estimation :

25 c.c. of the solution gave with excess sodium hydroxide sufficient ammonia to neutralise $(50-36{\cdot}3)$ c.c. $=13{\cdot}7$ c.c. $N/10$ HCl.

But
$$\underset{53\cdot5}{NH_4Cl}\equiv NH_3\equiv HCl$$

$$\underset{132}{(NH_4)_2SO_4}\equiv 2NH_3\equiv 2HCl,$$

so that the equivalents of NH_4Cl and $(NH_4)_2SO_4$ in this reaction are 53·5 and 66 respectively.

But since 1 litre of the solution contains 1·132 gm. NH_4Cl, the ammonia from the NH_4Cl in 25 c.c. of the solution is sufficient to neutralise

$$25\times\frac{1{\cdot}132}{5{\cdot}35} \text{ c.c. of } N/10 \text{ HCl} = 5{\cdot}29 \text{ c.c.}$$

∴ $(13{\cdot}70-5{\cdot}29)$ c.c. of $N/10$ HCl is neutralised by the ammonia from the ammonium sulphate in 25 c.c. of the solution.

∴ Normality of the solution with respect to ammonium sulphate

$$=\frac{8{\cdot}41}{25}\times\frac{1}{10}.$$

∴ Weight of ammonium sulphate in 5 gm. of the mixture

$$=\frac{8{\cdot}41}{25}\times 6{\cdot}6 \text{ gm.} = \mathbf{2{\cdot}22 \text{ gm.}}$$

QUESTIONS ON CHAPTER X

1. Calculate the weights of materials required to make the stated volumes of the following standard solutions when they are used in acid-alkali titrations :

(*a*) 400 c.c. of $N/10$ oxalic acid solution from oxalic acid crystals, $C_2O_4H_2 . 2H_2O$.

(*b*) 250 c.c. of $0{\cdot}09N$ sodium bicarbonate solution from anhydrous sodium bicarbonate.

(*c*) 2 litres of $N/50$ baryta from barium hydroxide, $Ba(OH)_2 . 8H_2O$.

(*d*) 500 c.c. of $0{\cdot}08N$ solution of potassium quadroxalate from the crystalline salt, $C_2O_4H_2 . C_2O_4KH . 2H_2O$.

2. What are the normalities of the solutions made by dissolving the following weights of substances in water and adding water to make them up to the volumes stated :

(*a*) 1·25 gm. of anhydrous sodium carbonate up to 300 c.c.

(*b*) 16·32 gm. of oxalic acid crystals, $C_2O_4H_2 . 2H_2O$, up to 2 litres.

(*c*) 1·36 gm. of sodium bicarbonate up to 250 c.c.

(*d*) 10 gm. of silver nitrate crystals up to 600 c.c.

3. Calculate the normality of the solution obtained by dissolving 500 c.c. of hydrogen chloride in 660 c.c. of water, the gas being measured at 20° and 750 mm. pressure. (Assume no change in volume during the solution of the gas.)

4. 25 c.c. of a solution of oxalic acid required 29 c.c. of 0·098 normal sodium hydroxide for complete neutralisation. What is the number of grams of anhydrous oxalic acid per litre of the solution? What volume of exactly decinormal oxalic acid solution could be made from 500 c.c. of this solution?

5. 25 c.c. of a solution of a tribasic acid of molecular weight 210 required 23·6 c.c. of decinormal sodium hydroxide solution for neutralisation, and formed the trisodium salt of the acid. What is the concentration of the acid in gm. per litre?

6. 5 gm. of a double sulphate of iron and ammonia was boiled with an excess of sodium hydroxide solution and the liberated ammonia was passed into 50 c.c. of normal sulphuric acid. The excess of acid was found to require 24·5 c.c. of normal sodium hydroxide for neutralisation. Calculate the percentage of ammonia (expressed as NH_3) in the double salt.

7. What is the concentration of a solution of sodium carbonate (expressed as gm. of anhydrous sodium carbonate per litre), 25 c.c. of which required 18·3 c.c. of $0{\cdot}12N$ sulphuric acid for neutralisation, phenolphthalein being used as indicator?

8. Calculate (*a*) the number of gm. of anhydrous sodium carbonate, (*b*) the number of gm. of sodium bicarbonate, per litre of a solution 25 c.c. of which required for neutralisation 11·8 c.c. of $N/10$

hydrochloric acid when phenolphthalein was used as indicator and 31·0 c.c. of $N/10$ hydrochloric acid when methyl orange was used as indicator.

9. Sodium sesquicarbonate has the formula,

$$Na_2CO_3 \,.\, NaHCO_3 \,.\, 2H_2O.$$

Calculate its equivalent as an alkali when it is titrated against hydrochloric acid in the presence of (*a*) phenolphthalein, (*b*) methyl orange, as indicator. Hence calculate the number of gm. of the salt per litre of a solution, 25 c.c. of which required 28·3 c.c. of $0{\cdot}11N$ hydrochloric acid for neutralisation, methyl orange being used as indicator.

10. What is the concentration of a solution of orthophosphoric acid (gm. H_3PO_4 per litre), 25 c.c. of which required 18·8 c.c. of N sodium hydroxide for neutralisation in the presence of phenolphthalein as indicator?

11. Calculate the number of gm. (*a*) of hydrochloric acid, (*b*) of potassium chloride in 1 litre of a solution, 25 c.c. of which required 21·9 c.c. of $N/10$ sodium hydroxide for neutralisation and a further 25 c.c. after the addition of an excess of powdered chalk, required 45·3 c.c. of $N/10$ silver nitrate for the complete precipitation of the chlorine ion.

12. Calculate the number of gm. of borax, $Na_2B_4O_7 \,.\, 10H_2O$, per litre of a solution of which 25 c.c. required 15·6 c.c. of $N/10$ hydrochloric acid for neutralisation, methyl orange being used as indicator. In aqueous solution, borax hydrolyses according to the equation:

$$Na_2B_4O_7 + 7H_2O \rightleftharpoons 2NaOH + 4H_3BO_3.$$

The liberated boric acid is a weak acid and is without effect on methyl orange.

13. 6 gm. of a mixture of ammonium sulphate and ammonium chloride was made up to 1000 c.c. with water. 25 c.c. of this solution was boiled with 50 c.c. of $N/10$ sodium hydroxide until no more ammonia was evolved and it was then found that the excess of sodium hydroxide required for neutralisation 24·3 c.c. of $N/10$ hydrochloric acid. What was the percentage of ammonium chloride in the mixture?

14. 10 gm. of a mixture of potassium chloride and potassium iodide were made up to 1000 c.c. with water. 25 c.c. of this solution required 27·75 c.c. of $N/10$ silver nitrate for complete precipitation. What was the percentage of potassium chloride in the mixture?

15. 7·4 gm. of a mixture of Na_2CO_3 and $NaHCO_3$ were made up to a litre with water. 20 c.c. of the resulting solution required 20 c.c. $N/10$ hydrochloric acid for neutralisation, methyl orange being used as indicator. Calculate the percentage of Na_2CO_3 in the mixture. (O. and C.)

16. When the salt, $KNaC_4H_4O_6 . 4H_2O$ (molecular weight 282), is ignited, there is a residue of sodium carbonate and potassium carbonate. A gram of this salt gave a residue which required 63·8 c.c. of $N/10$ hydrochloric acid for neutralisation, methyl orange being used as indicator. Calculate the percentage purity of the salt.

(O. and C. Subsid.)

17. 0·4609 gm. of moist specimen of sodium nitrate was heated with an excess of caustic soda and about 3 gm. of Devarda's alloy, whereby the nitrate was quantitatively reduced to ammonia. The ammonia was boiled off and absorbed in 80 c.c. of $N/10$ hydrochloric acid. The excess of hydrochloric acid was finally titrated and required 31·65 c.c. of 0·098N sodium hydroxide solution. What was the percentage of sodium nitrate in the specimen?

18. 2 litres of air, measured at *N.T.P.*, were shaken with 50 c.c. of $N/50$ barium hydroxide, the carbon dioxide in the air being converted quantitatively into barium carbonate. The residual barium hydroxide was titrated against $N/50$ oxalic acid of which 33·2 c.c. were required for neutralisation, phenolphthalein being used as indicator. Calculate the percentage by volume of carbon dioxide in the sample of air.

19. 5·832 gm. of a mixture of anhydrous sodium carbonate and sodium bicarbonate was dissolved in water and made up to 1 litre. 25 c.c. of this solution required for neutralisation 8·1 c.c. of 0·109N HCl, phenolphthalein being used as indicator. When methyl orange was the indicator, 25 c.c. of the solution required 23·9 c.c. of $N/10$ HCl for neutralisation. Calculate by two independent methods the percentage of sodium carbonate in the mixture.

20. 2 gm. of a mixture of hydrated sodium carbonate,

$$Na_2CO_3 . 10H_2O,$$

and sodium bicarbonate was dissolved in water and made up to 250 c.c. 25 c.c. of this solution was titrated, using methyl orange as indicator, and 22·5 c.c. of 0·087 N HCl were required for neutralisation. Calculate the percentage of sodium bicarbonate in the mixture.

21. 0·454 gm. of a mixture of ammonium sulphate and sodium sulphate gave 0·773 gm. of barium sulphate on treatment with barium chloride. When 0·454 gm. of the mixture is boiled with 40 c.c. of 0·1N sodium hydroxide until no more ammonia is evolved, how many c.c. of 0·1N hydrochloric acid will be required to neutralise the excess of sodium hydroxide? (C.U.O.S.)

22. 8·601 gm. of a mixture (A) of sodium chloride, potassium chloride and ammonium chloride was heated until no further change in weight occurred. The solid residue, weighing 7·561 gm., was dissolved in water and the solution made up to a litre. 25 c.c. of this solution were found to be equivalent to 15·11 c.c. of 0·2N silver nitrate solution. Calculate the percentage of Na, K, N, H and Cl by weight in the mixture. (Inter. B.Sc., London.)

23. 0·7085 gm. of a mixture (*A*) of anhydrous sodium carbonate and anhydrous sodium sulphate was dissolved in water, and the solution rendered neutral by adding a dilute solution (*B*) of hydrochloric acid, of which 30·30 c.c. were required. 0·4416 gm. of the mixture (*A*) was dissolved in hot water, the solution acidified with nitric acid and barium chloride added until no further precipitation occurred. The precipitate, after being washed and dried, weighed 0·3961 gm. Calculate (*a*) the number of gm. of HCl in one litre of the solution (*B*), and (*b*) the number of c.c. of moist hydrogen which would be obtained if 100 c.c. of the acid (*B*) were treated with metallic zinc and the hydrogen evolved were collected over water at 17° and 740 mm. pressure. The vapour pressure of water at 17° is 14 mm. (Inter. B.Sc., London.)

24. A mixture of barium hydroxide, barium carbonate and anhydrous sodium carbonate was analysed as follows :

(*a*) 0·87 gm. of the mixture was dissolved in 25 c.c. *N* hydrochloric acid and made up to 250 c.c. with water (solution *A*).

(*b*) On titrating solution *A* with *N*/10 sodium hydroxide (methyl orange indicator) it was found that 25 c.c. of *A* required 13·0 c.c. *N*/10 sodium hydroxide.

(*c*) To 25 c.c. of *A* (warmed to 70° to prevent bicarbonate formation) 50 c.c. of *N*/10 sodium carbonate were added to precipitate all the barium as carbonate. After cooling and adding phenolphthalein it was found that 15·5 c.c. of *N*/10 hydrochloric acid were required to discharge the colour of the indicator, that is, to reach the point at which the excess of sodium carbonate had been converted into the bicarbonate.

Calculate the weights of the three constituents present in 0·87 gm. of the mixture. (N.U.J.B.)

25. 25 c.c. of a solution containing hydrochloric acid and orthophosphoric acid required 18·6 c.c. of decinormal sodium hydroxide for neutralisation using methyl orange as indicator, and 23·7 c.c. of the same alkali using phenolphthalein. What are the weights of hydrochloric acid and phosphoric acid per litre of the solution? What weight of sodium hydroxide would be required to convert the acid in 1 litre of the solution into sodium chloride and trisodium phosphate?

26. A sample of boric acid, H_3BO_3, contains borax,

$$Na_2B_4O_7 . 10H_2O,$$

as an impurity. A quantity of the sample was dissolved in water and made up to 1000 c.c. 25 c.c. of this solution was found to require 0·88 c.c. of *N*/10 HCl for neutralisation (methyl orange indicator). To a further 25 c.c. of the solution was added 0·88 c.c. of *N*/10 HCl and a few c.c. of glycerol. The resulting solution required 27·3 c.c. of *N*/10 NaOH for neutralisation, using phenolphthalein as indicator. What is the percentage of boric acid in the sample?

27. A moist specimen of sodium hydroxide contains sodium carbonate and sodium bicarbonate as impurities. A quantity of the specimen was dissolved in water and made up to 1000 c.c. 25 c.c. of this solution required 22·02 c.c. of $N/10$ HCl for neutralisation using phenolphthalein as indicator, and 22·76 c.c. of $N/10$ HCl using methyl orange as indicator. When 25 c.c. of the solution was evaporated to dryness and heated to a constant weight (whereby all the sodium bicarbonate was converted into sodium carbonate) and the residue was dissolved in water, it was found to require 22·34 c.c. of $N/10$ HCl for neutralisation using phenolphthalein as indicator. Calculate the weights of anhydrous sodium carbonate and sodium bicarbonate associated with 10 gm. of sodium hydroxide in the moist specimen.

CHAPTER XI

VOLUMETRIC ANALYSIS (2)

1. Equivalents of oxidising and reducing agents

Compound	Molecular formula	Molecular weight	Equivalent
Potassium permanganate (double molecule) -	$K_2Mn_2O_8$	316	
(acid solution) -			31·6
(alkaline solution)			52·7 (316/6)
(very strongly alkaline solution)			158 (316/2)
Potassium dichromate	$K_2Cr_2O_7$	294	
(acid solution) -			49
Potassium chromate	K_2CrO_4	194	
(acid solution) -			64·7
Hydrogen peroxide -	H_2O_2	34	17
Iodine - - -	I_2	254	127
Copper sulphate			
(crystals) -	$CuSO_4 . 5H_2O$	249	249
(anhydrous) - -	$CuSO_4$	159	159
Titanous chloride -	$TiCl_3$	154·5	154·5
Ferric sulphate -	$Fe_2(SO_4)_3$	400	400
Ferrous ammonium sulphate - - -	$FeSO_4 . (NH_4)_2SO_4 6H_2O$	392	392
Oxalic acid			
(anhydrous) - -	$C_2O_4H_2$	90	45
(crystals) - -	$C_2O_4H_2 . 2H_2O$	126	63
Sodium thiosulphate			
(anhydrous) - -	$Na_2S_2O_3$	158	158
(crystals) - -	$Na_2S_2O_3 . 5H_2O$	248	248
Sodium sulphite			
(anhydrous) - -	Na_2SO_3	126	63
Stannous chloride			
(anhydrous) - -	$SnCl_2$	190	95
Sodium arsenite (as arsenic trioxide)	As_2O_3	198	49·5

It is assumed that the student is acquainted with the methods of calculating the equivalents of the above compounds when they are used in oxidation-reduction titrations. These methods are fully discussed in the standard text-books on volumetric analysis.

2. Oxidation-reduction titrations and change of valency

Problems involving oxidation and reduction are often solved expeditiously by employing the following generalisation :

1 litre of a normal solution of any oxidising agent will increase the electropositive valency of *one gram-atom* of an element by unity (assuming that such a change is possible under the conditions of the experiment).

Conversely, 1 litre of a normal solution of a reducing agent lowers the electropositive valency of 1 gram-atom of an element by unity.

This follows from the fact that 1 litre of a normal solution of any oxidising agent contains a weight of oxidising material just sufficient to oxidise 1 gm. of hydrogen and is equivalent, therefore, to half a gram-atom of oxygen, that is, 8 gm.

When an oxidising agent increases the valency of an element by 2, then one litre of a normal solution of that oxidising agent reacts with half a gram-atom of the element ; if it increases the valency by 3, then only $\frac{1}{3}$ of a gram-atom is oxidised. This is shown by the following equations, which represent reactions in which metals are assumed to be dissolving in an acid in the presence of an oxidising agent :

$$Na + HCl = Na^{+} + Cl^{-} + H.$$

∴ 23 gm. of sodium liberates 1 gm. of hydrogen, which requires 8 gm. of oxygen to convert it into water.

∴ In the oxidation $Na \rightarrow Na^{+}$, that is, an increase in the valency of 1 gram-atom of sodium from $0 \rightarrow 1$, exactly 1 litre of a normal solution of an oxidising agent would be reduced.

$$Mg + 2HCl = Mg^{++} + 2Cl^{-} + 2H.$$

Here, the valency of the magnesium increases from $0 \rightarrow 2$, and for each gram-atom of magnesium oxidised 2 gm. of hydrogen are liberated. To convert 24 gm. of magnesium, therefore, into magnesium ion ($Mg \rightarrow Mg^{++}$) sufficient hydrogen must be released to reduce 2 litres of a normal solution of any oxidising agent :

$$Fe + 3HCl \rightleftharpoons Fe^{+++} + 3Cl^{-} + 3H.$$

The atomic weight of iron is 56, so that for the change $Fe \rightarrow Fe^{+++}$ in which 56 gm. of iron are oxidised to the ferric state, 3 litres of a normal solution of an oxidising agent are required.

Similarly, in the oxidation or reduction of salts, the valency of the metal changes and 1 litre of a normal solution of an oxidising agent or a reducing agent produces a valency change equivalent to *unity per gram-atom*:

$$FeCl_2 + HCl = FeCl_3 + H,$$

or $$Fe^{++} + 2Cl^- + HCl = Fe^{+++} + 3Cl^- + H$$

$$(Fe^{++} \rightarrow Fe^{+++})$$

$$SnCl_2 + 2HCl = SnCl_4 + 2H,$$

or $$\dagger\ Sn^{++} + 2Cl^- + 2HCl = Sn^{++++} + 4Cl^- + 2H$$

$$(Sn^{++} \rightarrow Sn^{++++}).$$

A general proof of these relationships can be obtained as follows:

The process of mutual oxidation and reduction consists in the transfer of electrons as shown in the equation:

$$\underset{\text{(reducing agent)}}{R} + \underset{\text{(oxidising agent)}}{O} = \underset{\text{(oxidised form of reducing agent)}}{(R - xe)} + \underset{\text{(reduced form of oxidising agent)}}{(O + xe)},$$

where e denotes an electron.

Let M = the molecular weight of O.

Then $\frac{M}{x}$ = the equivalent of O since $H - e = H^+$, that is, one electron is removed when 1 atom of hydrogen is oxidised.

An atom or an ion of an element can be denoted in general by $E^{a(+)}$, that is, it carries a positive charges where a is positive, zero, or negative. The oxidation of the element in any reaction is given, therefore, by the equation:

$$E^{a(+)} - xe = E^{(a-x)(+)}.$$

† Stannic chloride behaves mainly as though it were a covalent compound. Provided, however, the number of electrons involved in the oxidation is known, it is immaterial whether or not the reactants and products are covalent or electrovalent.

But since the equivalent of the oxidising agent $=M/x$, then M/x gm. of the oxidising agent oxidise 1 gm. atom or 1 gm.-ion of E according to the equation :

$$E^{a(+)} - e = E^{(a-1)(+)},$$

that is, it increases the positive valency of 1 gm.-atom of E by unity.

Example 116. 0·100 gm. of a polyvalent metal of atomic weight 51·0 reacted with dilute sulphuric acid to give 43·9 c.c. of hydrogen at *S.T.P.* The solution, in this lower state of oxidation, was found to require 58·8 c.c. of $N/10$ permanganate for complete oxidation. What are the valencies of the metal? [H = 1·008.] (O. and C.)

Assume that the metal exerts a valency x in its lower state of oxidation and valency, y, in its higher state of oxidation.

The lower valency, x, is obtained as follows :

Since H = 1·008, the gram-molecular-volume can be taken as 22,400 c.c., and 1·008 gm. of hydrogen occupies 11,200 c.c. at *N.T.P.*

∴ Equivalent of the metal in the formation of its lower sulphate

$$= \frac{0{\cdot}100}{43{\cdot}9} \times 11{,}200$$

$$= \mathbf{25{\cdot}51} \ (\text{H} = 1{\cdot}008).$$

∴ Since the atomic weight of the metal = 51·0,

$$x = \frac{51{\cdot}0}{25{\cdot}51} = 2.$$

To determine y, we can calculate the number of c.c. of normal permanganate required to change the valency of 51·0 gm., that is, 1 gram-atom, of the metal from valency x to valency y.

0·100 gm. of the metal requires 58·8 c.c. of $N/10$ permanganate.

∴ 51·0 gm. of the metal requires $\frac{5{\cdot}88}{0{\cdot}100} \times 51$ c.c. of N permanganate = 3000 c.c. (approximately).

∴ The increase in valency = 3.

$$\therefore \ \mathbf{x = 2 \text{ and } y = 5}.$$

Example 117. Metallic tin in the presence of hydrochloric acid is oxidised by potassium dichromate to stannic chloride. What volume of decinormal dichromate solution would theoretically be reduced by 1 gram of tin? [Sn = 118·7.]

(O. and C.)

The valency change is :

$$\underset{118 \cdot 7}{Sn} \rightarrow Sn^{++++}.$$

∴ 4 litres of N $K_2Cr_2O_7$ will be required to oxidise 118·7 gm. of tin.

$$\therefore \text{ 1 gm. of tin will reduce } \frac{4000}{118 \cdot 7} \text{ c.c. of } N\ K_2Cr_2O_7$$

$$= 33 \cdot 7 \text{ c.c. of } N\ K_2Cr_2O_7$$

$$= 337 \text{ c.c. of } N/10\ K_2Cr_2O_7.$$

This result may be confirmed by using the equation for the reaction :

$$2K_2Cr_2O_7 + 3Sn + 28HCl = 4KCl + 3SnCl_4 + 4CrCl_3 + 14H_2O.$$

Since the equivalent of potassium dichromate

$$= \frac{\text{molecular weight}}{6},$$

∴ 2 gram-molecular weights of potassium dichromate make 12,000 c.c. of N $K_2Cr_2O_7$.

∴ From equation :

$$3 \times 118 \cdot 7 \text{ gm. of tin reduce 12,000 c.c. } N\ K_2Cr_2O_7.$$

$$\therefore \text{ 1 gm. of tin will reduce } \frac{12{,}000}{3 \times 118 \cdot 7} \text{ c.c. } N\ K_2Cr_2O_7$$

$$= 337 \text{ c.c. of } N/10\ K_2Cr_2O_7.$$

QUESTIONS ON CHAPTER XI

1. Calculate the weights of the following materials which are required to make the stated volumes of standard solutions when they are used in oxidation-reduction titrations under the usual experimental conditions :

(*a*) 500 c.c. of $0 \cdot 11N$ potassium dichromate from fused potassium dichromate.

(*b*) 100 c.c. of 0·12*N* ferrous iron solution from ferrous ammonium sulphate crystals, $FeSO_4 . (NH_4)_2SO_4 . 6H_2O$.

(*c*) 200 c.c. of 0·1*N* sodium arsenite solution from pure arsenious oxide, As_2O_3.

(*d*) 750 c.c. of 0·082*N* sodium thiosulphate from sodium thiosulphate crystals, $Na_2S_2O_3 . 5H_2O$.

(*e*) 250 c.c. of 0·05*N* iodine solution from pure resublimed iodine.

(*f*) 600 c.c. of 0·098*N* potassium chromate from potassium chromate crystals, K_2CrO_4.

2. What are the normalities (as oxidising or reducing agents) of the following solutions made by separately dissolving the given weights of substances in water, and adding water to make the solutions up to the stated volumes?

(*a*) 1 gm. of potassium permanganate crystals, $KMnO_4$ to 250 c.c. (dilute sulphuric acid titration).

(*b*) 2·5 gm. of oxalic acid crystals, $C_2O_4H_2 . 2H_2O$, up to 1000 c.c.

(*c*) 1·42 gm. of potassium iodate crystals, KIO_3, to 450 c.c.

(*d*) 5 gm. of fused potassium dichromate, $K_2Cr_2O_7$, up to 500 c.c.

(*e*) 2 gm. of potassium chromate, K_2CrO_4, up to 150 c.c.

(*f*) 10 gm. of pure crystalline ferrous sulphate, $FeSO_4 . 7H_2O$, up to 500 c.c.

3. 25 c.c. of a dilute sulphuric acid solution of ferrous ammonium sulphate required for complete oxidation 18·6 c.c. of 0·096*N* potassium permanganate. What is the concentration of the ferrous solution expressed as (*a*) gm. of ferrous iron per litre, (*b*) gm. of $FeSO_4 . (NH_4)_2SO_4 . 6H_2O$ per litre?

4. One c.c. of a solution of potassium permanganate is equivalent to 0·0048 gm. of iron. What is the concentration of this solution expressed in terms of available oxygen per litre? Assuming that metallic iron reduces permanganate quantitatively in the presence of dilute sulphuric acid, calculate the volume of the above solution of permanganate which is reduced by 1 gm. of iron.

(O. and C. Subsid.)

5. What is the percentage of copper in a cupric salt which gave the following results? 6 gm. of the salt was dissolved in water and made up to 250 c.c. 25 c.c. of this solution, after the addition of an excess of potassium iodide, required 22·3 c.c. of *N*/10 sodium thiosulphate to react with the liberated iodine. What volume of sodium thiosulphate containing 20 gm. of sodium thiosulphate crystals per litre would similarly be required?

6. 5 gm. of a mixture of anhydrous oxalic acid and anhydrous sodium oxalate containing 73 per cent of oxalic acid was dissolved in water and made up to 800 c.c. Calculate (*a*) the volume of 0·17 *N* sodium hydroxide required to neutralise 25 c.c. of this solution, and (*b*) the volume of 0·11*N* potassium permanganate required for the complete oxidation of 25 c.c. of this solution in the presence of an excess of dilute sulphuric acid.

7. 25 c.c. of a mixture of sulphuric and oxalic acids in solution required 32·5 c.c. of $N/10$ NaOH for neutralisation, using phenolphthalein as indicator. A second sample of 25 c.c. when titrated at 60° in the presence of excess dilute sulphuric acid required 17·5 c.c. of $N/10$ $KMnO_4$. Calculate the concentrations of sulphuric acid and of oxalic acid ($H_2C_2O_4 . 2H_2O$) as grams per litre of solution. (N.U.J.B.)

8. 2·026 gm. of crushed haematite was digested with concentrated hydrochloric acid until no more of the ore would dissolve. The solution was then diluted to 250 c.c. with water. 25 c.c. of this solution, after reduction with zinc, required 21·6 c.c. of $N/10$ potassium dichromate for complete oxidation. Calculate the percentage of iron in the ore, expressing the result as a percentage of ferric oxide, Fe_2O_3.

9. 25 c.c. portions of a solution containing 7·3 gm. per litre of potassium quadroxalate, $KHC_2O_4 . H_2C_2O_4 . 2H_2O$, were titrated under the usual experimental conditions with (*a*) decinormal sodium hydroxide, (*b*) decinormal permanganate. What volumes of these standard solutions were required? (O. and C.)

10. 25 c.c. of a solution of hydrogen peroxide was diluted with water to a total volume of 1000 c.c. 25 c.c. of this solution was titrated with 0·0972N potassium permanganate in the presence of dilute sulphuric acid, the volume of permanganate required being 18·7 c.c. Calculate the concentration of the original hydrogen peroxide, expressing the result as (*a*) gm. of H_2O_2 per litre, (*b*) a "volume" solution.

11. Calculate the volume of oxygen at 18° and 743 mm. liberated when an excess of acidified permanganate is added to 50 c.c. of hydrogen peroxide containing 4·5 gm. per litre. (1st M.B., London.)

12. Calculate the solubility of copper sulphate crystals,

$$CuSO_4 . 5H_2O,$$

at 15° from the following data: 5·092 gm. of a saturated solution of the salt was diluted to 100 c.c. 25 c.c. of this solution, treated with an excess of potassium iodide, liberated sufficient iodine to oxidise 14·00 c.c. of 0·092N sodium thiosulphate. Express the solubility as gm. $CuSO_4 . 5H_2O$ per 100 gm. of water.

13. Calculate the volume of a decinormal solution of potassium permanganate required for the complete oxidation of one gm. of ferrous oxalate (FeC_2O_4). (H.S.C., London.)

14. A mixture of ferrous sulphate and ferric sulphate in solution required 17·6 c.c. of $N/10$ potassium permanganate for the complete oxidation of 20 c.c. of the solution. A further 20 c.c., after complete reduction with zinc, required 29·8 c.c. of $N/10$ permanganate. Calculate the percentage composition of the mixture, assuming both salts to be anhydrous.

15. What volume of a decinormal solution of sodium thiosulphate would be required to decolorise 10 c.c. of a solution of 3 gm. of iodine in an excess of an aqueous solution of potassium iodide, and what volume would be required similarly to decolorise 10 c.c. of the same solution to which 0·499 gm. of copper sulphate, $CuSO_4 . 5H_2O$, had been added? (Inter. B.Sc., London.)

16. What volumes of a decinormal solution of potassium dichromate would the two solutions respectively obtained by dissolving 0·327 gm. of metallic zinc and 0·224 gm. of metallic iron in excess of a solution of ferric sulphate in dilute sulphuric acid, reduce? Give equations representing the reactions and the weight of potassium dichromate reduced in each case. (Inter. B.Sc., London.)

17. A given volume of a solution of ferric sulphate when reduced by zinc required 30 c.c. of $N/10$ permanganate for titration. When the same volume of the same solution of ferric sulphate was reduced by another metal, 45 c.c. of $N/10$ permanganate were required. What can you say about this metal? (O. and C.)

18. Calculate the volumes of 0·12N potassium dichromate required for the oxidation of (*a*) 2 gm. of tin to stannic chloride, (*b*) 2 gm. of zinc to zinc chloride, both reactions taking place in hydrochloric acid solution. Hence calculate the volume of 1·1N potassium dichromate required for the complete oxidation of 20 gm. of an alloy of tin and zinc containing 53 per cent of zinc.

19. 0·813 gm. of a metal was dissolved in an excess of dilute sulphuric acid and the resulting solution was diluted to exactly 250 c.c. 25 c.c. of this solution reduced 13·48 c.c. of 0·108N potassium permanganate. The specific heat of the metal is 0·119. What is the accurate atomic weight of the metal?

20. 2 gm. of potassium dichromate were heated with excess of concentrated hydrochloric acid and the gaseous product passed into an excess of a solution of potassium iodide. What volume of a decinormal solution of sodium sulphite would be required to decolorise the potassium iodide solution? (Inter. B.Sc., London.)

21. Calculate the number of grams per litre of calcium chloride in a solution which gave the following results. To 50 c.c. of the solution was added an excess of ammonium oxalate and the precipitated calcium oxalate was filtered off and washed. It was then dissolved in dilute sulphuric acid, and the resulting solution required 23·3 c.c. of 0·52N potassium permanganate for complete oxidation.

22. 50 c.c. of a solution containing 40 gm. of ferrous sulphate crystals ($FeSO_4 . 7H_2O$) per litre, 25 c.c. of a solution of potassium permanganate containing 2·5 gm. per litre and 25 c.c. of a solution of potassium dichromate containing 3 gm. per litre were mixed in the presence of an excess of dilute sulphuric acid. What volume of 0·11N potassium permanganate would be required to complete the oxidation of the ferrous salt?

23. 25 c.c. of a solution of ferric alum,

$$Fe_2(SO_4)_3 \cdot (NH_4)_2SO_4 \cdot 24H_2O,$$

containing 50 gm. per litre, was boiled with an excess of thin iron wire whereby all the ferric sulphate was reduced according to the equation:

$$Fe + Fe_2(SO_4)_3 = 3FeSO_4.$$

The excess of iron was removed by filtering and dilute sulphuric acid was added to the filtrate. What volume of 0·1072*N* potassium permanganate will be required to oxidise the resulting solution? What volume of the same solution of potassium permanganate will be required if the reduction is effected with metallic copper?

24. 25 c.c. of a solution of ferrous sulphate, $FeSO_4 \cdot 7H_2O$, was treated with 50 c.c. of 0·11*N* potassium permanganate which was an excess, and the residual potassium permanganate was found to oxidise 10 c.c. of an oxalic acid solution containing 6 gm. of oxalic acid crystals, $C_2O_4H_2 \cdot 2H_2O$, per litre. What was the concentration of the ferrous sulphate solution expressed as gm. of the hydrated salt per litre?

25. A sample of bleaching powder contains 28·6 per cent of available chlorine. 10 gm. of the sample is made up to 1000 c.c. with water. What volume of 0·103 normal sodium arsenite solution will be required for the titration of 25 c.c. of the bleaching powder solution?

26. 500 c.c. of a mixture of oxygen and ozone at *N.T.P.* are allowed to react with an acidified solution of potassium iodide. The iodine liberated reacts with 37·6 c.c. of decinormal sodium thiosulphate solution. Calculate the percentage by weight of ozone in the gas. (H.S.C., London.)

27. Equal volumes of a solution containing a compound of an element which can exist in different states of valency were found to reduce 10 c.c. of 0·09*N* iodine solution, 18 c.c. of 0·1*N* ferric sulphate solution and 25 c.c. of 0·108*N* potassium permanganate solution respectively. The last of these oxidises the element to the pentavalent state. What do you deduce from these results? (O. and C.)

28. Calculate the atomic weight of an element, *X*, from the following data. The element forms two oxides of the formulae X_2O_3 and X_2O_5 respectively. When 0·200 gm. of the lower oxide is dissolved in sulphuric acid and titrated against a solution of potassium permanganate containing exactly 5 gm. per litre, it is found that 42·97 c.c. of the permanganate solution are required to oxidise the element completely to its higher oxide.

29. 0·3 gm. of bleaching powder treated with acetic acid and potassium iodide liberated iodine equivalent to 24 c.c. of *N*/10 sodium thiosulphate solution. The same weight of bleaching powder treated with warm hydrochloric acid and potassium iodide liberated iodine equivalent to 25 c.c. of $N/10$ sodium thiosulphate solution. What evidence do these results give of the composition of bleaching powder? (C.U.O.S.)

30. 4 gm. of potassium acid iodate, $KIO_3 \cdot HIO_3$, was dissolved in water and made up to 1000 c.c. 25 c.c. of this solution was mixed with an excess of potassium iodide and titrated with $N/10$ sodium arsenite. Calculate the volume of the arsenite solution required. Another 25 c.c. of the original solution was mixed with an excess of potassium iodide and strongly acidified with dilute sulphuric acid. What volume of 0·096N sodium thiosulphate will be required to react completely with the liberated iodine?

31. After qualitative analysis had shown that an aqueous solution contained only a mixture of the chloride and iodide of a certain metal, 25·0 c.c. of the solution were titrated with $N/10$ silver nitrate solution, requiring 42·0 c.c. of the nitrate solution for the process. The mixed silver halides, after filtering, washing and drying, were found to weigh 0·6950 gm. A second 25·0 c.c. portion of the solution was evaporated to dryness with concentrated sulphuric acid, giving 0·4368 gm. of the anhydrous metal sulphate. Calculate (*a*) the relative proportion by weight of chloride and iodide in the mixture, (*b*) the equivalent weight of the metal. (N.U.J.B. Schol.)

CHAPTER XII

DETERMINATION OF NATURE OF REACTION BY VOLUMETRIC METHODS

1. Determination of the nature of a reaction

To determine the nature of a reaction, that is, to find an equation by which the reaction can be represented, reacting weights are converted into gram-atoms or gram-molecules by dividing by the appropriate atomic or molecular weights.

Example 118. 0·108 gm. of finely divided copper was heated with an excess of ferric sulphate solution until the copper had completely dissolved. The solution, after the addition of an excess of dilute sulphuric acid, required 33·7 c.c. of $N/10$ potassium permanganate for complete oxidation. Find the equation which represents the reaction between metallic copper and ferric sulphate solution.

Since 1000 c.c. of N potassium permanganate will oxidise 56 gm. of ferrous iron :

$\therefore$ 33·7 c.c. of $N/10$ $KMnO_4$ will oxidise

$$\frac{56 \times 33{\cdot}7}{10{,}000} = 0{\cdot}1887 \text{ gm. of ferrous iron.}$$

When, therefore, 0·108 gm. of copper dissolves (presumably to form copper sulphate), 0·1887 gm. of ferrous iron is formed by the reduction of ferric iron.

Dividing these weights by the corresponding atomic weights : 0·108/63·5 gm.-atoms of copper react with ferric sulphate to give 0·1887/56 gm.-atoms of ferrous iron, that is, 0·00170 gm.-atoms of copper produce by reduction 0·00336 gm.-atoms of ferrous iron.

$$\therefore \frac{\text{Number of copper atoms}}{\text{Number of ferrous iron atoms}} = \frac{1}{2}.$$

$\therefore$ Cu + ferric sulphate = copper sulphate + $2FeSO_4$.

$\therefore$ The most probable equation is :

$$Cu + Fe_2(SO_4)_3 = CuSO_4 + 2FeSO_4,$$

or

$$Cu + 2Fe^{+++} = Cu^{++} + 2Fe^{++}.$$

Example 119. When a solution of potassium iodate is heated with excess of oxalic acid, iodine is produced and the following data show the quantitative relationships experimentally obtained :

Wt. of iodate (gm.)	Wt. of iodine (gm.)
0·283	0·168
0·486	0·292
0·601	0·357
0·994	0·589

What conclusions do you draw from these data, and how would you proceed to obtain further information to interpret the reaction fully? (N.U.J.B.)

It is assumed first that the reaction taking place is independent of the concentrations of the reacting substances. This can be checked by dividing the weights of iodine by the corresponding weights of iodate :

$$0{\cdot}283/0{\cdot}168 = 1{\cdot}683$$
$$0{\cdot}486/0{\cdot}292 = 1{\cdot}664$$
$$0{\cdot}601/0{\cdot}357 = 1{\cdot}684$$
$$0{\cdot}994/0{\cdot}589 = 1{\cdot}693$$

These ratios are constant within the limits of experimental error. It is sufficient, therefore, to take any pair of corresponding weights to determine the nature of the reaction. Taking the first pair and dividing the weight of the iodate by its molecular weight ($KIO_3 = 214$) and the weight of iodine by its atomic weight ($I = 127$), then :

0·283/214 gm.-molecules of potassium iodate react with oxalic acid to give $\frac{0{\cdot}168}{127}$ gm.-atoms of iodine.

∴ 0·001322 gm.-molecules of potassium iodate liberate 0·001322 gm.-atoms of iodine.

∴ 1 gm.-molecule of potassium iodate liberates 1 gm.-atom of iodine.

∴ $2KIO_3$ + oxalic acid = I_2 + other products.

Since potassium iodate is an oxidising agent, we assume that the reaction involves the following stages :

$$2KIO_3 + C_2O_4H_2 = 2HIO_3 + C_2O_4K_2 \quad \ldots\ldots\ldots\ldots(a)$$
$$HIO_3 + 3C_2O_4H_2 = HI + 6CO_2 + 3H_2O \quad \ldots\ldots\ldots\ldots(b)$$
$$HIO_3 + 5HI = 3I_2 + 3H_2O. \quad \ldots\ldots\ldots\ldots(c)$$

Multiplying (*a*) by 3, (*b*) by 5, and adding (*c*) so as to eliminate HI :

$$6KIO_3 + 3C_2O_4H_2 = 6HIO_3 + 3C_2O_4K_2$$
$$5HIO_3 + 15C_2O_4H_2 = 5HI + 30CO_2 + 15H_2O$$
$$HIO_3 + 5HI = 3I_2 + 3H_2O$$

$$6KIO_3 + 18C_2O_4H_2 + 6HIO_3 + 5HI = 6HIO_3 + 5HI + 3C_2O_4K_2 + 30CO_2 + 18H_2O + 3I_2.$$

$$\therefore\ 6KIO_3 + 18C_2O_4H_2 = 3C_2O_4K_2 + 30CO_2 + 18H_2O + 3I_2.$$

$$\therefore\ 2KIO_3 + 6C_2O_4H_2 = C_2O_4K_2 + 10CO_2 + 6H_2O + I_2.$$

In examples similar to the foregoing, very small decimal quantities may be avoided by the following method of working :

Using the figures as in the previous example :

0·283 gm. of potassium iodate gave 0·168 gm. of iodine.

∴ 214 gm. of potassium iodate, that is, one gram-molecule of potassium iodate, would give $\frac{0{\cdot}168}{0{\cdot}283} \times 214 = 127{\cdot}2$ gm. of iodine = one gram-atom of iodine.

2. Determination of the formulae of double salts and acid salts

The method of working is similar to that used in determining the order of a reaction.

Example 120. From the following data calculate the formula of the hydrated potassium acid oxalate, *A*, whose composition can be represented by the formula :

$$xC_2O_4H_2 \,.\, yC_2O_4K_2 \,.\, zH_2O.$$

10 gm. of *A* was dissolved in water and made up to 1 litre. 25 c.c. of this solution required in separate experiments and under the usual laboratory conditions :

(1) 29·5 c.c. of $N/10$ NaOH ; (2) 39·4 c.c. of $N/10$ $KMnO_4$.

The normality of the solution with respect to free oxalic acid $= \frac{29{\cdot}5}{25} \times \frac{1}{10}$.

∴ No. of gm. of free oxalic acid per litre

$$= \frac{29{\cdot}5}{25} \times 4{\cdot}5 = 5{\cdot}31 \text{ gm.}$$

The normality of the solution with respect to the total oxalate radical $= \frac{39\cdot4}{25} \times \frac{1}{10}$.

∴ No. of gm. of oxalic acid which includes the free oxalic acid of the salt + the oxalic acid derived from the potassium oxalate

$$= \frac{39\cdot4}{25} \times 4\cdot5 \text{ gm.} = \mathbf{7\cdot092 \text{ gm.}}$$

∴ No. of gm. of oxalic acid derived from the potassium oxalate

$$= (7\cdot092 - 5\cdot31) \text{ gm.} \doteq \mathbf{1\cdot78 \text{ gm.}}$$

But the molecular weights of potassium oxalate ($C_2O_4K_2$) and oxalic acid ($C_2O_4H_2$) are 166 and 90 respectively.

∴ Weight of potassium oxalate $= 1\cdot78 \times \frac{166}{90} = \mathbf{3\cdot28 \text{ gm.}}$

Since there were 10 gm. of the hydrated salt per litre,

∴ Weight of water of crystallisation

$$= (10 - 5\cdot31 - 3\cdot28) \text{ gm.} = \mathbf{1\cdot41 \text{ gm.}}$$

Dividing the weights of oxalic acid, potassium oxalate and water by the corresponding molecular weights :

$$\frac{5\cdot31}{90} = 0\cdot0590\ ; \quad \frac{3\cdot28}{166} = 0\cdot0197\ ; \quad \frac{1\cdot41}{18} = 0\cdot07814.$$

∴ Molecular ratios are $C_2O_4H_2 : C_2O_4K_2 : H_2O :: 3 : 1 : 4$.

∴ Formula of the salt is $\mathbf{C_2O_4K_2 . 3C_2O_4H_2 . 4H_2O}$.

QUESTIONS ON CHAPTER XII

1. 0·400 gm. of powdered silver was boiled with an excess of a solution of ferric sulphate and when the reaction was complete it was found that the solution reduced 37·05 c.c. of $N/10$ potassium permanganate. Find an equation to represent the reaction.

2. A double salt of sodium carbonate and sodium bicarbonate can be represented by the formula, $Na_2CO_3 . xNaHCO_3 . yH_2O$. Determine x and y from the following titrations. 10 gm. of the salt was made up to 1000 c.c. 25 c.c. of this solution required 11·0 c.c. of $N/10$ HCl using phenolphthalein, and 33·1 c.c. using methyl orange.

3. From the following data calculate the formula of a hydrated potassium acid oxalate, A, whose composition can be represented by the formula, $xC_2O_4K_2 . yC_2O_4H_2 . zH_2O$.

(*a*) 10 gm. of A was dissolved in water and made up to 1 litre. 25 c.c. of this solution required 29·5 c.c. of $N/10$ sodium hydroxide for neutralisation.

(*b*) 10 gm. of *A* was strongly heated to a constant weight and the resulting residue of potassium carbonate was dissolved in water and made up to 1 litre. 25 c.c. of this solution was titrated against $N/10$ hydrochloric acid using methyl orange as indicator, and 9·8 c.c. of the acid were required for neutralisation.

4. A solution of ammonium metavanadate, NH_4VO_3, in dilute sulphuric acid may be regarded as a solution of vanadium pentoxide, V_2O_5. The solution is easily reduced by sulphur dioxide or metallic zinc, and the solution obtained can be re-oxidised quantitatively by potassium permanganate to V_2O_5. Alternatively, the oxide can be reduced by potassium iodide and the amount of reduction determined by estimating the liberated iodine. Use the following results to determine the formula of the oxide formed by reduction in each case:

(*a*) 25 c.c. of a solution containing 5 gm. of V_2O_5 per litre was reduced with sulphur dioxide and required 13·7 c.c. of $N/10$ potassium permanganate.

(*b*) 25 c.c. of the same solution reduced with zinc required 27·7 c.c. of $N/10$ potassium permanganate.

(*c*) 25 c.c. of the same solution reduced with potassium iodide liberated iodine equivalent to 13·7 c.c. of $N/10$ sodium thiosulphate. [$V = 51{\cdot}0$.]

5. A deep red liquid dissolves in water to form a mixture of chromic acid and hydrochloric acid. 0·150 gm. of the liquid so treated oxidised 29·0 c.c. of $N/10$ ferrous sulphate solution. On precipitating as silver chloride the chlorine ions formed at the same time 0·278 gm. of silver chloride was obtained. Find the empirical formula of the liquid. (O. and C.)

6. When zinc sulphate solution is added to a boiling solution of potassium ferrocyanide, a white precipitate is formed. In an experiment 25 c.c. of potassium ferrocyanide solution, containing 30 gm. of the crystals, $K_4Fe(CN)_6 \cdot 3H_2O$ per litre, required for complete precipitation 31·1 c.c. of a solution containing 24 gm. of the crystals, $ZnSO_4 \cdot 7H_2O$, per litre. What conclusion can be drawn from this result?

7. When ammonium persulphate, $(NH_4)_2S_2O_8$, is boiled with water, in the presence of silver ion as a catalyst, it is converted quantitatively into an acid solution containing hydrogen peroxide. Varying amounts of ammonium persulphate were boiled with water (excess), and the resulting acid solution was titrated against decinormal sodium hydroxide with the following results:

Weight of $(NH_4)_2S_2O_8$	Volume of $N/10$ NaOH
0·208 gm.	18·0 c.c.
0·373 gm.	32·3 c.c.
0·620 gm.	55·2 c.c.

Deduce an equation for the reaction.

8. 50 c.c. of concentrated hydrochloric acid was added to 25 c.c. of a solution of potassium iodide containing 12 gm. KI per litre. A solution of potassium iodate, containing 8 gm. per litre, was then run in slowly until the iodine first formed had entirely disappeared, the volume of the iodate solution required being found to be 24·1 c.c. Suggest an equation to represent the reaction which takes place.

9. A solution was made to contain 35 gm. of ferric ammonium alum, $Fe_2(SO_4)_3 . (NH_4)_2SO_4 . 24H_2O$ and 12 gm. of copper sulphate crystals, $CuSO_4 . 5H_2O$, per litre of dilute sulphuric acid. To 25 c.c. of this solution was added an excess of potassium iodide whereby the copper sulphate reacted according to the equation :

$$2CuSO_4 + 4KI = 2Cu_2I_2 + 2K_2SO_4 + I_2.$$

On titrating this solution with $N/10$ sodium thiosulphate 30·2 c.c. were required. Assuming that the ammonium sulphate is unchanged throughout the reaction, deduce an equation to represent the action between ferric sulphate and potassium iodide in acid solution.

10. Obtain an equation for the reaction between ferrous sulphate and potassium persulphate, $K_2S_2O_8$, given that 50 c.c. of $N/10$ ferrous sulphate solution heated with an excess of potassium persulphate gave a solution from which, on the addition of an excess of barium chloride, a precipitate of barium sulphate weighing 2·35 gm. was obtained.

11. A salt of potassium was heated and found to evolve oxygen, water vapour and iodine. The residue, mixed with an aqueous solution of the original salt, liberated iodine. 1·25 gm. of the salt was dissolved in water and made up to 250 c.c. 25 c.c. of this solution was treated with an excess of potassium iodide and the iodine formed oxidised 3·2 c.c. of $N/10$ sodium arsenite solution. Another 25 c.c. of the solution was strongly acidified, treated with an excess of potassium iodide and the residual acid was neutralised ; the iodine liberated then oxidised 38·4 c.c. of $N/10$ sodium arsenite. Deduce the composition of the salt.

12. Sodium hyponitrite has the molecular formula $Na_2N_2O_2$. A solution of sodium hyponitrite containing 1 gm. of the anhydrous salt per litre is titrated against $N/10$ potassium permanganate solution (3·16 gm. per litre), and the following readings were obtained :

(*a*) 25 c.c. of the hyponitrite solution in alkaline solution required 15·4 c.c. of $N/10$ potassium permanganate.

(*b*) 25 c.c. of the hyponitrite solution in sulphuric acid solution required 18·9 c.c. of $N/10$ potassium permanganate.

Obtain an equation for each reaction.

13. Potassium permanganate is said to convert sodium thiosulphate into sulphate in alkaline solution. Do the following figures confirm this statement?

10 c.c. of a solution of sodium thiosulphate, containing 1·58 gm. of the anhydrous salt per litre, were added to 50 c.c. of an alkaline solution of potassium permanganate containing 3·16 gm. of the salt per litre. The liquid turned green and a brown precipitate was also observed. On adding dilute sulphuric acid the liquid again became pink. 50 c.c. of $N/10$ oxalic acid were then added, and on warming the liquid it became colourless and clear. This solution was found to decolorise 8 c.c. of $N/10$ permanganate solution. Explain the reactions involved. (O.H.C.)

14. Potassium percarbonate reacts with cold dilute sulphuric acid and gives hydrogen peroxide as one of the products. When 0·2 gm. of the percarbonate was allowed to react in this way, the hydrogen peroxide formed required 21·3 c.c. of decinormal potassium permanganate for complete reaction. Deduce an equation for the reaction.

15. Hydroxylamine, NH_2OH, is oxidised in boiling sulphuric acid solution, an oxide of nitrogen being among the products. 25 c.c. of a solution containing 2 gm. of hydroxylamine a litre was boiled with an excess of ferric sulphate and dilute sulphuric acid and the resulting solution required 30·3 c.c. of decinormal potassium permanganate for the oxidation of the ferrous sulphate. Obtain an equation for the reaction.

16. 0·400 gm. of pure iron wire was dissolved in an excess of hydrochloric acid in the absence of air and was then heated with 0·200 gm. of potassium nitrate. When the reaction was complete the residual ferrous chloride required 12·0 c.c. of $N/10$ potassium dichromate for oxidation. What is the equation for the reaction between potassium nitrate and ferrous chloride in the presence of an excess of hydrochloric acid?

17. Obtain an equation for the reaction between aqueous sodium thiosulphate and chlorine, using the following data:

100 c.c. of a solution of sodium thiosulphate containing 20 gm. of the hydrated salt per litre was treated with an excess of chlorine until the reaction was complete. In three separate experiments on 25 c.c. lots of the resulting solution the following results were obtained: (*a*) 25 c.c. of the solution required 20·1 c.c. N. NaOH for neutralisation, (*b*) 25 c.c. solution required 16·1 c.c. N. $AgNO_3$ for the complete precipitation of the chlorine ion, (*c*) 25 c.c. of the solution treated with an excess of barium chloride solution gave a precipitate of barium sulphate weighing 0·939 gm.

MISCELLANEOUS QUESTIONS ON CHAPTERS I–XII

Inorganic and Physical

1. (*a*) 0·5 gm. of the carbonate of a metal gave, on treatment with an excess of dilute sulphuric acid, 0·6798 gm. of the anhydrous metallic sulphate. What is the equivalent of the metal?

(*b*) What is the freezing point of a 5 per cent aqueous solution of urea, $CO(NH_2)_2$?

(*c*) What is the molecular weight of a gas of which 100 c.c. diffuse in the same time, under comparable conditions of temperature and pressure, as 80 c.c. of oxygen?

2. Calculate the molecular weight of a substance from the following results obtained by Victor Meyer's method:

Weight of substance taken	= 0·220 gm.
Volume of air displaced	= 45 c.c.
Temperature of the room	= 20°
Pressure	= 755 mm.
Pressure of aqueous vapour at 20°	= 17·4 mm.

(O. and C. Elem. Sci.)

3. What is the normality of each of the solutions prepared by the following methods respectively?

(*a*) 0·56 gm. of potassium permanganate was dissolved in 123 c.c. of water.

(*b*) 72 c.c. of ammonia gas, measured at 17° and 744 mm., was dissolved in water to make the total volume of the solution 100 c.c.

(*c*) 10 gm. of potassium chlorate was heated to a constant weight and the residue was made up to 500 c.c. with water.

4. What is the oxidising power in gm. of oxygen per litre of the solution obtained by dissolving 2 gm. of potassium permanganate in 500 c.c. of very dilute sulphuric acid and adding 500 c.c. of 0·12*N* potassium dichromate, assuming that the final volume of the mixed solutions is exactly 1000 c.c.?

5. The oxide of an element contains 42·86 per cent of oxygen. 1 litre of the hydride of the element weighs 1·34 gm. at *N.T.P.* What is the probable atomic weight of the element?

6. What is the molecular weight of a substance of which 0·372 gm. dissolved in 100 c.c. of water exerts an osmotic pressure of 1130 mm. at 18°?

7. What volume of *N*/10 potassium permanganate solution would be required for the complete oxidation respectively of (*a*) 1 gm. of hydrated ferrous ammonium sulphate, (*b*) 1 gm. of anhydrous ferrous oxalate?

8. How many gm. of hydrogen peroxide are contained in 1 litre of 10 volume hydrogen peroxide? (1st M.B., London.)

9. A solution containing 0·4281 gm. of a compound, *M*, in 61·33 gm. of water freezes at a temperature 0·362° lower than that at which water freezes. What is the molecular weight of *M*?

10. Calculate the percentage dissociation of nitrogen peroxide at the temperature at which it has a vapour density of 36·5.

11. A metal forms an alum with ammonium sulphate. On ignition 3·104 gm. of the alum left 0·589 gm. of the oxide. Calculate the atomic weight of the metal. (C.U.O.S.)

12. Four compounds of an element contain respectively 72·7 per cent, 50·0 per cent, 36·4 per cent and 66·7 per cent of the element. 1 litre of each of these compounds in the form of a vapour at *N.T.P.* weigh respectively 1·438 gm., 2·091 gm., 1·438 gm. and 2·353 gm. Deduce the probable atomic weight of the element.

13. 25 c.c. of a solution containing 4·3 gm. per litre of oxalic acid crystals, $C_2O_4H_2 . 2H_2O$, was completely oxidised by 23·2 c.c. of a solution of potassium permanganate. It was also found that 28·2 c.c. of this permanganate solution was required to oxidise 25 c.c. of a ferrous iron solution. What is the number of gm. of ferrous iron per litre of the solution?

14. 2 gm. of pure ammonium chloride was heated with an excess of slaked lime and the resulting ammonia gas was dissolved in 250 c.c. of water. If 25 c.c. of this solution is titrated against deci-normal sulphuric acid, what volume of the acid would theoretically be required for neutralisation?

15. 0·529 gm. of the chloride of a metal, dissolved in water and treated with an excess of silver nitrate solution, gave 1·297 gm. of silver chloride. If the metal dissolves in dilute sulphuric acid, in the presence of ammonium sulphate, to form an alum, what is its accurate atomic weight?

16. The air in a room is at 15° and 765 mm. pressure ; it contains 0·04 per cent of carbon dioxide. Calculate the weight of the precipitate formed by passing 100 litres of this air through an excess of a solution of barium hydroxide. (1st M.B., London.)

17. What volume of 0·11*N* potassium permanganate solution would react exactly in dilute sulphuric acid solution, with 5 c.c. of a 3-volume solution of hydrogen peroxide?

18. 12·5 c.c. of a gaseous hydrocarbon was exploded with an excess of oxygen and the products were cooled to the original room temperature and pressure, a contraction of 25 c.c. being observed. On treatment with aqueous potash, a further contraction of 25 c.c. took place. Deduce the molecular formula of the hydrocarbon.

19. 2·462 gm. of a mixture of potassium nitrate and sodium nitrate was heated to a constant weight which was found to be 2·031 gm. What is the percentage of potassium nitrate in the mixture?

20. An organic liquid, *A*, and water are immiscible. When the two liquids are distilled together, they boil at 99° and the distillate contains 12 per cent by weight of *A*. Assuming that the vapour pressure of water at 99° is 734 mm. and that the barometric height is 760 mm., calculate the molecular weight of *A*.

21. 20 c.c. of a solution containing sodium and ferrous sulphates yielded 0·64 gm. of barium sulphate when treated with an excess of barium chloride. 40 c.c. of the same solution, after acidifying with sulphuric acid, were found to decolorise 31·4 c.c. of decinormal potassium permanganate. Calculate the weights of anhydrous sulphates present in 1 litre of the solution. (1st M.B., London.)

22. The following table gives the melting points of mercury-thallium mixtures. Plot a melting point-composition curve and make what deductions you can from it.

Thallium (Tl) per cent	Melting point
0	−39
5	−54
10	−63
15	−22
20	− 8
25	4
30	13
35	11
40	23
45	36
50	54
60	105
70	149
80	193
90	246
100	301

23. What information can be obtained from the following observations?

(*a*) A $\frac{1}{10}$ molar solution of glucose in water freezes at −0·19°; a $\frac{1}{10}$ molar solution of sodium chloride freezes at −0·36°.

(*b*) The vapour density of nitrogen peroxide (referred to hydrogen = 1) is 38·3 at 27° and 24·3 at 100°.

24. 1·536 gm. of a mixture of ammonium chloride and ammonium sulphate was heated with an excess of sodium hydroxide solution and the resulting ammonia was passed beneath the surface of 100 c.c. of $N/2$ hydrochloric acid. When the action was complete, the residual hydrochloric acid was titrated against 1·138N sodium hydroxide, of which 19·71 c.c. were required. In another experiment, 2·016 gm. of the mixture was dissolved in water and treated with an excess of barium chloride solution, the precipitated barium sulphate, when collected and dried, being found to weigh 0·755 gm. From each of these results, calculate the percentage of ammonium chloride in the mixture.

25. 10 c.c. of a saturated solution of potassium permanganate at 15° were diluted to 200 c.c. 25 c.c. of this solution were found to be equivalent to 21·25 c.c. of decinormal oxalic acid. Calculate the solubility in gm. per 100 c.c. of potassium permanganate at 15°. (1st M.B., London.)

26. The absorption coefficients at 15° of three gases, *A*, *B* and *C*, are 0·035, 0·018 and 0·021 respectively. A mixture of these gases is at a total pressure of 800 mm. and contains 40 per cent by volume of *A* and 25 per cent by volume of *B*. What is the composition of the gas absorbed by water on exposure to the mixture of gases at 15°?

27. Calculate the concentration of a solution of glucose, $C_6H_{12}O_6$, expressed in gm. per 100 c.c. of solution, which at 15° is isotonic with a 5 per cent solution of cane sugar, $C_{12}H_{22}O_{11}$, maintained at 50°.

28. 25 c.c. of a solution of potassium permanganate containing 2 gm. per litre is mixed with 25 c.c. of a solution containing 2 gm. of ferrous iron per litre and the mixed solutions were made up to 100 c.c. If 25 c.c. of this solution were then titrated against a solution of ferrous ammonium sulphate, $FeSO_4 . (NH_4)_2SO_4 . 6H_2O$, containing 10 gm. of the crystalline salt in 1 litre of dilute sulphuric acid, what volume of the latter solution would be required?

29. What changes in weight, represented as percentage losses or gains of the original substance, would take place if, in two separate experiments, the salt, $Na_2CO_3 . NaHCO_3 . 2H_2O$, (*a*) were heated to a constant weight, (*b*) were treated with sulphuric acid and then heated to a constant weight? What volume of carbon dioxide, collected over water at 27° and 790 mm., would be formed if 1·750 gm. of the original salt were heated to a dull red heat?

[Vapour pressure of water = 26·5 mm. at 27°.]

(Inter. B.Sc., London.)

30. 0·3061 gm. of a liquid compound containing only sulphur oxygen and chlorine, was allowed to react with water and the resulting solution required 18·2 c.c. of $N/2$ sodium hydroxide for neutralisation. In a separate experiment 0·2813 gm. of the compound was similarly decomposed by water and after the addition of an excess of barium chloride, a precipitate of barium sulphate weighing 0·4856 gm. was obtained. Deduce the formula of the original liquid compound and write an equation for its reaction with water.

31. Calculate the molecular weight of a gas, 100 c.c. of which diffuses in the same time and under the same conditions as 76·2 c.c. of chlorine.

32. Deduce the percentage of manganese dioxide in a specimen of pyrolusite which gave the following analytical results: 0·2018 gm. of the powdered ore was heated with 50 c.c. of $N/10$ oxalic acid in the presence of an excess of dilute sulphuric acid. When no further action took place, the residual oxalic acid required 8·35 c.c. of $0·096N$ potassium permanganate for the complete oxidation of the oxalic acid.

33. The partition coefficient of an organic compound, A, between water and ether, the compound being more soluble in ether, is 1 : 5. Compare the weights of A removed from 100 c.c. of its aqueous solution containing 10 gm. of A after (a) one extraction with 60 c.c. of ether, (b) three successive extractions with 20 c.c. lots of ether.

34. A compound is known which contains 87·5 per cent of nitrogen and 12·5 per cent of hydrogen. The normal sulphate of the compound contains 24·61 per cent of sulphur. Give the structural formula of the compound. (Inter. B.Sc., London.)

35. When 100 c.c. of ozonised oxygen was shaken with oil of turpentine, a contraction of 8·2 c.c. was observed. 100 c.c. of the same specimen of the gas was allowed to diffuse and the time taken was noted. In the same time, 102·0 c.c. of oxygen was found to diffuse under the same conditions. Deduce (a) the vapour density of the sample of ozonised oxygen, (b) the molecular weight of ozone.

36. What is the osmotic pressure of a 2 per cent solution of sodium chloride at 27°, assuming that the salt is 92 per cent dissociated at the temperature and dilution of the solution?

37. In an experiment to determine the percentage of chromium in a chromium salt, 1·508 gm. of the salt was dissolved in water and made up to 100 c.c. 25 c.c. of this solution was heated with an excess of sodium peroxide, the excess being then destroyed by boiling. To the solution of sodium chromate so obtained was added an excess of dilute sulphuric acid and of potassium iodide. The liberated iodine was titrated against $N/10$ sodium thiosulphate, the volume of thiosulphate required being 28·32 c.c. Deduce the percentage of chromium in the salt.

38. 50 c.c. of a mixture of carbon monoxide, carbon dioxide and hydrogen was exploded with 20 c.c. of oxygen. The volume, measured at the original room temperature and pressure, was 37 c.c., and after treatment with sodium hydroxide solution 3 c.c. Calculate the composition of the original mixture. (N.U.J.B.)

39. A decinormal solution of potassium chloride was found to exert an osmotic pressure of 4·44 atmospheres at 17°. Calculate (a) the apparent molecular weight, (b) the amount of ionisation of the dissolved salt. (1st M.B., London.)

40. 1 litre of nitrogen peroxide, measured at 27° and 742 mm., weighs 3·04 gm. Determine the percentage dissociation of the gas at this temperature and pressure.

41. Determine the weight of carbon dioxide which dissolves in 1 litre of water (a) when pure carbon dioxide at $N.T.P.$ is bubbled through water, (b) when a mixture of 3 volumes of carbon dioxide and 1 volume of hydrogen at $N.T.P.$ is bubbled through water. [Absorption coefficient for carbon dioxide at 0° = 1·713.] (C.U.O.S.)

42. Potassium persulphate is decomposed by boiling in aqueous solution, the reaction being catalysed by silver ion. In an experiment 0·5 gm. of potassium persulphate, $K_2S_2O_8$, was dissolved in water, a few drops of silver nitrate solution were added and the mixture was boiled until the reaction was complete, oxygen being evolved. The residual solution required 18·3 c.c. of $N/5$ sodium hydroxide for neutralisation. Construct an equation to show the probable course of the reaction.

43. In a determination of the percentage of carbon dioxide in air, 50 c.c. of 0·018N barium hydroxide was run into a bottle of total capacity 2100 c.c. The bottle was quickly stoppered and well shaken to ensure that all the carbon dioxide had reacted with barium hydroxide. The residual alkali was then rapidly titrated against $N/50$ oxalic acid (phenolphthalein indicator), and it was found that 40·05 c.c. of the acid were required. Deduce the percentage volume of carbon dioxide in the specimen of air used, given that the temperature was 15° and the pressure 760 mm.

44. 10 c.c. of a solution of disodium hydrogen phosphate were treated with ammonium chloride, a solution of ammonia and a solution of magnesium chloride. The precipitate was collected, washed and dried and heated to a constant weight when 0·214 gm. of magnesium pyrophosphate were obtained. Explain the reactions involved, and calculate the concentration of the original solution of disodium hydrogen phosphate in grams per litre.

(1st M.B., London)

45. Show that if the osmotic pressure of two solutions are of equal value, their vapour pressure must be identical. The vapour pressure of pure ether is 442 mm. and that of a solution of 12·2 gm. of an organic compound dissolved in 100 gm. of ether is 410 mm. at the same temperature. What is the molecular weight of the dissolved substance? (C.U.O.S.)

46. 0·203 gm. of a mixture of potassium nitrate and potassium sulphate was dissolved in a small quantity of water and allowed to react with an excess of concentrated sulphuric acid and metallic mercury. The liberated nitric oxide measured 18·6 c.c. at 16° and 748 mm. pressure. What is the percentage of potassium sulphate in the mixture?

47. Determine the probable formula of an acid salt which is an oxidising agent from the following data: its equivalent as an acid is 390, as an oxidising agent 32·5. It contains 10 per cent of potassium and 65 per cent of iodine. (O. and C.)

48. A mixture of 20 c.c. of nitric oxide and 60 c.c. of oxygen was exposed to water until the gas phase was free from oxides of nitrogen and the solution was free from nitrous acid. The volume of the gas remaining was 45 c.c. To what extent do these data establish the composition of nitric acid. (C.H.L.)

49. When iodic acid (HIO_3) is allowed to react with an aqueous solution of sulphur dioxide, sulphuric acid and iodine are formed. In an experiment 0·2 gm. of iodic acid was allowed to react with an excess of an aqueous solution of sulphur dioxide ; the iodine formed and the excess of sulphur dioxide were removed by heating and the sulphuric acid so obtained required 56·8 c.c. of $N/10$ sodium hydroxide for neutralisation. Determine the equation which represents the reaction.

50. If one gm.-molecule of ethyl alcohol and 1 gm.-molecule of acetic acid are mixed and allowed to reach equilibrium at 25°, the equilibrium mixture contains $\frac{2}{3}$ of a gm.-molecule of ethyl acetate. Calculate the number of gm.-molecules of acetic acid which must be allowed to react with one gm.-molecule of ethyl alcohol in order that the equilibrium mixture shall contain 0·9 gm.-molecule of ethyl acetate at 25°.

51. 10 gm. of a mixture of anhydrous sodium sulphate and potassium sulphate was made up to 1000 c.c. of aqueous solution. 100 c.c. of this solution treated with an excess of barium chloride solution gave 1·436 gm. of barium sulphate. Calculate the percentage of sodium sulphate in the mixture.

52. The distribution coefficient C_B/C_w for aniline between benzene and water is 10·0 at 25°. After 0·0273 gm.-mol. of aniline hydrochloride had been shaken with 1000 ml. of water and 500 ml. of benzene at 25° until equilibrium had been established, 0·00165 gm.-mol. of aniline was found in the benzene layer. Calculate the hydrolysis constant of aniline hydrochloride. (C.U.O.S.)

53. What is the dissociation constant of a weak monobasic acid at the temperature at which it is 2 per cent dissociated in $N/30$ solution?

54. 127 c.c. of a certain gas diffused in the same time as 100 c.c. of chlorine under the same conditions. Calculate the molecular weight of the gas. (O. and C.)

55. Calculate the osmotic pressure of (*a*) a fiftieth molar solution of sodium chloride at 0°, (*b*) the solution obtained by mixing exactly equal volumes of fiftieth molar sodium chloride and fiftieth molar silver nitrate, the resulting solution being brought to 30°. [Assume complete dissociation of all soluble salts and no change of volume on mixing.]

56. What explanation can you give of the following facts?

(*a*) When mercuric oxide is dissolved in excess of potassium iodide solution an alkaline liquid results. 0·27 gm. of HgO yield thus a solution which needs 25 c.c. $N/10$ hydrochloric acid.

(*b*) A solution of hydrogen peroxide with 30 gm. per litre is described as " 10 volume ". When such a solution is added to an aqueous solution of potassium ferricyanide 200 c.c. of oxygen are evolved. (O.U.O.S.)

57. The following table gives the melting points of mixtures of phosphorus and sulphur. What conclusions can you draw from these data?

S, per cent	Melting point	S, per cent	Melting point
0	40	54	140
10	20	58	200
18	0	59	240
20	−8	59·5	260
23	0	60	270
30	20	61	280
35	40	62	296
37	44	65	280
38	60	67	260
39	80	69	256
41	100	70·5	260
42	120	71·5	272
43	140	73	260
43·7	155	75	244
45	140	77	260
46	120	79	280
47	100	80	292
48	80	82	300
49	60	86	320
50	52	90	300
50·5	60	92	280
51	80	95	262
52	100	97	171
53	120	100	113

58. What deductions can you make from the following data? 1·072 gm. of the anhydrous chloride of a metal gave, on treatment with an excess of concentrated sulphuric acid, 1·208 gm. of the anhydrous metallic sulphate. A solution of the metallic chloride containing 4·56 gm. in 62·3 c.c. of water boiled at 100·54°. The specific heat of the metal is 0·05.

59. The osmotic pressure of an aqueous solution of a non-electrolyte is 18·8 atmospheres at 15°. What is the freezing point of this solution? What will be its vapour pressure at 100°?

60. What is the normality (*a*) as an alkali, (*b*) as a reducing agent, of the solution obtained by mixing 100 c.c. of 0·108 *N* sodium hydroxide with 50 c.c. of a solution of oxalic acid containing 20 gm. of anhydrous oxalic acid per litre?

61. 25 c.c. of a mixed solution of sodium carbonate and sodium bicarbonate required 9·45 c.c. of decinormal acid using phenol-

phthalein as indicator, but 23·40 c.c. using methyl orange. What were the concentrations of the two salts? (Durham Ent. Schol.)

62. A slow stream of dry air was passed in succession through two series of bulbs containing respectively (*a*) a solution of 10 gm. of an organic compound in 100 gm. of water, (*b*) pure water. The bulbs and their contents were weighed separately at the beginning of the experiment and again after a suitable interval of time. It was found that the loss of weight in the first series of bulbs was 2·086 gm. and the corresponding loss of weight in the second series was 0·069 gm. Calculate the approximate molecular weight of the organic compound.

63. Calculate the *p*H of (*a*) *N*/1000 hydrochloric acid, (*b*) *N*/1000 sodium hydroxide, assuming these solutions to be completely ionised. What are the hydrogen ion concentrations in solutions which have *p*H values of 2·5 and 4·30 respectively?

(1st M.B., London.)

64. Calculate the heat of formation of liquid carbonyl chloride from its elements, using the following data:

$$COCl_{2(liq.)} + H_2O = 2HCl_{(aq.)} + CO_{2(aq.)} + 57{,}970 \text{ cal.}$$

$$H_2 + Cl_2 = 2HCl_{(aq.)} + 78{,}600 \text{ cal.}$$

$$H_2 + \tfrac{1}{2}O_2 = H_2O_{(liq.)} + 68{,}360 \text{ cal.}$$

$$C + O_2 = CO_{2(aq.)} + 102{,}850 \text{ cal.}$$

[aq. = in dilute aqueous solution.]

65. Calculate the molecular weight of a non-electrolyte, 5·63 gm. of which, dissolved in 48·3 gm. of water, exerted a vapour pressure of 16·782 mm. at 20°. Assume that the vapour pressure of pure water is 17·390 mm. at 20° and that the vapour pressure of the pure solute at 20° can be neglected.

66. The specific conductivity of a decinormal solution of sodium chloride at 18° is $9{\cdot}25 \times 10^{-3}$ reciprocal ohms, whilst the equivalent conductivity at infinite dilution is 110·3 reciprocal ohms. Calculate the degree of ionisation of sodium chloride in decinormal solution.

(1st M.B., London.)

67. Varying amounts of an organic compound, *C*, were shaken in four separate experiments with equal volumes of water and benzene so that equilibrium was reached in each case. The concentration of *C* in the water and the benzene were determined with the following results:

Concentration of *C* in water (gm. per litre)	Concentration of *C* in benzene (gm. per litre)
5·36	3·50
7·28	6·52
9·07	10·3
12·64	19·6

What conclusions can be drawn from these data?

68. What is (*a*) the hydrogen ion concentration, (*b*) the *p*H of the solution obtained by adding 100 c.c. of 0·1 *N* sodium hydroxide to 400 c.c. of 0·1 *N* hydrochloric acid, assuming complete dissociation? What is the concentration of hydroxyl ion in the mixed solutions, assuming that the ionic product for water is 10^{-14}?

69. Calculate the osmotic pressure at 15°, the vapour pressure at 100° and the boiling point at 760 mm. pressure of the solution obtained by dissolving 5·63 gm. of urea (CON_2H_4) in 68·7 c.c. of water.

70. The heat of combustion of graphite is 94·3 kilocalories and that of carbon monoxide is 67·4 kilocalories. When the following dissociations take place in the gaseous phase :

$$O_2 \rightarrow 2O$$
$$CO \rightarrow C + O,$$

the heats absorbed are respectively 117·4 kilocalories and 230·6 kilocalories. What is the heat of sublimation of carbon? (C.U.O.S.)

71. 0·6687 gm. of a pure compound (a volatile liquid) was shaken with water, in which it decomposed and dissolved, forming an acid solution. This was divided into three equal parts ; one was titrated with 0·2400 *N* alkali, of which 27·50 c.c. were needed to neutralise it ; the second, on being mixed with aqueous silver nitrate, yielded 0·4732 gm. of silver chloride ; the third, on being mixed with aqueous barium nitrate, yielded 0·3852 gm. of barium sulphate. What was the compound? (Durham Ent. Schol.)

72. 25 c.c. of a solution of a weak organic acid, at a dilution at which the dissociation can be ignored, required for neutralisation 21·7 c.c. of *N* sodium hydroxide. A solution of the acid of the same dilution froze at $-1·62°$. What is the molecular weight of the acid?

73. Assuming that the molecule of potassium chlorate contains six equivalents of oxygen of atomic weight 16·00, calculate the combining weight of chlorine from the following data :

2·45 gm. of potassium chlorate gave, on ignition, 1·49 gm. of potassium chloride. 0·745 gm. of potassium chloride gave, on precipitation with silver nitrate, 1·435 gm. of silver chloride.

0·432 gm. of pure silver when ignited in a stream of chlorine gave 0·574 gm. of silver chloride. (N.U.J.B.)

74. 5·32 gm. of potassium hydrogen oxalate containing water of crystallisation was dissolved in water and made up to 1 litre. 25 c.c. of this solution required for neutralisation 18·3 c.c. of 0·086 *N* alkali. A further 25 c.c. of this solution required 28·7 c.c. of 0·073 *N* potassium permanganate when titrated in dilute sulphuric acid solution. Deduce the formula of the hydrated salt.

75. It is desired to prepare a solution of *p*H 3·5 by adding the requisite amount of 0·0005 *N* sodium hydroxide to 100 c.c. of 0·001 *N* hydrochloric acid. What volume of sodium hydroxide solution would be required assuming complete dissociation of the acid and the alkali?

76. The following table gives the melting points of mixtures of naphthylamine ($C_{10}H_7NH_2$) and phenol (C_6H_5OH). Plot a melting point-composition curve and make what deductions you can from it.

Naphthylamine per cent	Melting point	Naphthylamine per cent	Melting point
10	34	55	27
15	32·5	60	28
20	27	65	27
25	22	70	26
30	17	75	25
35	16	80	26
40	21	85	33
45	24	90	37
50	25	100	48

77. 0·6536 gm. of mineral yields 0·1502 gm. of mixed sodium and potassium chlorides which, on treatment with sulphuric acid, are converted into 0·1811 gm. of the mixed sulphate. Calculate the percentage of sodium and potassium in the mineral.

(Durham Ent. Schol.)

78. The velocity (V) of sound in a gas is given by the equation :

$$V=\sqrt{\frac{P\gamma}{d}},$$

where P = the pressure on the gas (dynes per sq. cm.), γ = the ratio of the specific heats of the gas at constant pressure and at constant volume, and d = the density of the gas (gm. per c.c.). It is found that 1 litre of a gaseous element, measured at 18° and 740 mm., weighs 1·629 gm. The velocity of sound in this gas at 0° and 760 mm. pressure is found to be $3{\cdot}074 \times 10^4$ cm. per sec. What is the atomic weight of the element?

79. A metallic chloride, X, containing 26·2 per cent of chlorine, boiled at 303° and its vapour density at this temperature was 140 ; at 600° the vapour density was 138. When 1 gm. of X was dissolved in 100 gm. of water, the freezing point of the solution was −0·056° ; a similar solution of potassium chloride froze at −0·446°. What conclusions about X can you draw from these data? (C.U.O.S.)

80. 10 c.c. of a saturated aqueous solution of hydrogen sulphide was allowed to react completely with an excess of a solution of iodine, and the resulting solution of hydriodic acid was found to require 28·6 c.c. of $N/10$ sodium hydroxide for neutralisation. Deduce the solubility of hydrogen sulphide at the temperature of the experiment.

81. In atomic weight determination (*a*) 1·0000 gm. of silver gave 1·1485 gm. of Ag_2S, (*b*) 1·4450 gm. of Ag_2SO_4 gave 1·0000 gm. of silver. Calculate the atomic weights of silver and sulphur, assuming the above formulae. [O = 16·0000.] (O. and C.)

82. The heats of combustion of methane and hydrogen are 212,000 cal. and 68,400 cal. respectively. What is the percentage composition by volume of a mixture of methane and hydrogen, 22·4 c.c. of which, measured at *N.T.P.*, gave on complete combustion 78·1 cal.?

83. An element, *X*, forms two volatile chlorides. The first contains 22·55 per cent of *X* and has a vapour density of 69 at 300°; the second contains 14·87 per cent of *X* and has a vapour density of 52 at 300°. Comment on these data and make what deductions you can concerning the atomic weight of *X*. (C.U.O.S.)

84. An inorganic compound, *X*, which contained magnesium, gave a yellow precipitate when dissolved in nitric acid and treated with an excess of ammonium molybdate. 1 gm. of *X* when boiled with soda gave 0·0694 gm. of ammonia. 1 gm. of *X* when heated to a dull red heat gave a residue, *Y*, of 0·4531 gm. *Y* was found to be identical with a compound obtained by heating disodium hydrogen phosphate and treating an aqueous solution of the product with magnesium sulphate. Deduce the probable formula of the compound *X* and explain the above reactions. (C.U.O.S.)

85. 1 gm. approximately of an alloy of zinc and magnesium was dissolved in dilute sulphuric acid and gave 3·384 gm. of the mixed anhydrous sulphates. This residue of mixed sulphates was converted into the corresponding oxides and the weight of the mixed oxides so obtained was 1·397 gm. What is the percentage composition of the alloy?

86. 25 c.c. of a normal solution of ammonia and 25 c.c. of a copper sulphate solution containing a tenth of a gram-molecule of the salt per litre were mixed and shaken vigorously with 75 c.c. of chloroform. When equilibrium had been established, 50 c.c. of the chloroform layer was removed and titrated against 0·08*N* HCl, of which 6·8 c.c. were required. What conclusions respecting the composition of the complex ion formed between copper and ammonia can you draw from these data? [The partition coefficient of ammonia between chloroform and water is 1 : 26, the ammonia being more soluble in water.]

87. The vapour density of iodine at 1000° and 760 mm. pressure is 87·0. Calculate the percentage dissociation at this temperature and use it to calculate the vapour density of iodine at 1000° under a pressure of 380 mm.

88. The solubility product of lead sulphide is $4{\cdot}0 \times 10^{-28}$ at 15°. Compare the concentrations of lead ion remaining in solution of a lead salt after complete saturation with hydrogen sulphide (*a*) if the solution is in *N*/100 HCl, (*b*) if the solution is in *N* HCl, the

normality of a saturated aqueous solution of hydrogen sulphide being approximately 0·1. [The dissociation constant of hydrogen sulphide for complete dissociation into $2H^+$ and S^{--} is $1 \cdot 1 \times 10^{-22}$.]

89. 1·362 gm. of the hydrated sulphate of a metal was heated at 120° to a constant weight and gave 0·8079 gm. of the anhydrous sulphate. The vapour density of the chloride of the metal is about 40 and 1·086 gm. of this chloride gave 0·3403 gm. of the corresponding oxide. The specific heat of the metal at ordinary temperatures is 0·4 approximately. Deduce (*a*) the accurate atomic weight of the metal, (*b*) the formula for its hydrated sulphate.

90. A mixture of hydrogen, carbon monoxide and methane is sparked with 150 c.c. of oxygen. The contraction (measured after cooling) is 217·5 c.c. On adding caustic potash a further contraction of 75 c.c. takes place. The addition of pyrogallol removes the 7·5 c.c. which still remain. Find the volume and composition of the original mixture. (Durham Ent. Schol.)

91. 6·081 gm. of a mixture of sodium cyanide and potassium cyanide was dissolved in water and made up to 1000 c.c. To 25 c.c. of this solution $N/10$ silver nitrate solution was added until a faint but permanent turbidity was obtained. The volume of silver nitrate solution required was 14·05 c.c. Calculate the percentage of sodium cyanide in the mixture.

92. The equivalent conductivity of a weak monobasic acid is 376 mhos at 18°. A decinormal solution of the acid is ionised to the extent of 3·2 per cent. Calculate (*a*) the percentage dissociation in $N/20$ solution, (*b*) the specific conductivity of a normal solution of the acid.

93. 73·2 gm. of the chlorate $MClO_3$ yield on ignition 34·4 gm. of the chloride MCl. 118·7 gm. of silver combine exactly with the chlorine in 46·6 gm. of this chloride. From these data calculate the atomic weight of silver, assuming that the atomic weight of oxygen is 16·00. (N.U.J.B.)

94. Show that for a weak acid the concentration of hydrogen ions in solution is proportional to the square root of the dissociation constant. Express on the pH scale the concentration of hydrogen ions in a $N/10$ solution of an acid which has a dissociation constant of $1 \cdot 8 \times 10^{-5}$. (C.U.O.S.)

95. One litre of hydrogen iodide originally at *N.T.P.* was maintained at 300° and at atmospheric pressure until equilibrium was reached, and was then suddenly " chilled " to room temperature. The contents of the flask after being dissolved in aqueous potassium iodide were found to oxidise 37·5 c.c. of $N/10$ sodium thiosulphate solution. A similar experiment was performed at 500° when 50 c.c. of $N/10$ sodium thiosulphate were oxidised. Calculate (*a*) the degree of dissociation of hydrogen iodide at 300° and 500° respectively, (*b*) the vapour density of the gas at these temperatures.

96. (*a*) 25 c.c. of an aqueous solution of an oxyacid of bromine containing 10 gm. per litre required 19·38 c.c. of *N*/10 sodium hydroxide for neutralisation. Only one sodium salt of the acid is known.

(*b*) 50 c.c. of the same acid solution was treated with an excess of sulphur dioxide and the resulting solution, after treatment with an excess of barium chloride solution, gave 2·712 gm. of barium sulphate. Deduce the formula of the acid and the nature of the reaction between the acid and sulphur dioxide in aqueous solution.

97. What is the *p*H of the solution obtained by mixing 100 c.c. of 0·001*N* HCl and 50 c.c. of 0·003*N* NaOH, assuming complete dissociation?

98. The dissociation constant of a weak monobasic acid is $1{\cdot}53 \times 10^{-5}$ at 20°. Calculate the values of the following at 20°: (*a*) the concentration of hydrogen ion in *N*/20 aqueous solution, (*b*) the concentration of hydrogen ion in *N*/50 aqueous solution, (*c*) the *p*H of *N*/50 aqueous solution.

99. A compound containing sulphur, chlorine and oxygen only had a vapour density of approximately 105. When 0·532 gm. of the compound was allowed to react with water it gave an acid solution containing sulphuric acid; this solution required 14·8 c.c. of *N* NaOH for neutralisation. The neutralised solution was treated with an excess of silver nitrate solution and the resulting precipitate of silver chloride was found to weigh 0·710 gm. What is the probable molecular formula of the compound? Construct an equation to show its reaction with water.

100. In the following experiment to measure the vapour pressure of ether ($C_4H_{10}O$), 10 c.c. of the liquid, having a density 0·725, was admitted to a clean vessel of capacity 2·5 litres which was kept at a uniform temperature of 10°. When the liquid had ceased to evaporate, there remained 5·8 c.c. of liquid. Deduce the vapour pressure of ether at 10°. (Durham Ent. Schol.)

101. The solubility of silver bromide is 6×10^{-7} gm.-molecules per litre at 18°. What weight of silver bromide will be precipitated when 0·119 gm. of potassium bromide is added to one litre of a saturated solution of silver bromide at 18°?

102. 10 gm. of hydrated ferrous oxalate was dissolved in dilute sulphuric acid and diluted to 1000 c.c. 25 c.c. of this solution, titrated at room temperature, required 18·4 c.c. of a solution of potassium permanganate containing 2·5 gm. of potassium permanganate per litre. For titration at 80°, 25 c.c. of the oxalate solution required 43·8 c.c. of *N*/10 potassium permanganate solution. Deduce the empirical formula of the sample of hydrated ferrous oxalate.

103. Molecular volume, measured under suitable conditions, may be assumed to be an additive property. The following are the molecular volumes of four hydrocarbons:

$$CH_4 = 73 ; \quad C_2H_6 = 112 ; \quad C_2H_4 = 101 ; \quad C_3H_8 = 151.$$

A hydrocarbon, the molecular formula of which is C_3H_6, is found to have a "molecular volume" of 140. Upon the basis of the above facts, which of the formulae $CH_3CH{=}CH_2$ or CH_2 (bonded to both carbons of) $CH_2 - CH_2$ (a three-membered ring) do you consider better represents the molecule? (C.U.O.S.)

104. The partition coefficient of an organic compound between chloroform and water is 4 : 1, the substance being more soluble in chloroform. Compare the fractions of the compound extracted from 200 c.c. of its aqueous solution by (*a*) four successive extractions with 50 c.c. lots of chloroform, (*b*) ten successive extractions with 20 c.c. lots of chloroform.

105. The molecular conductivity of a weak monobasic acid is 8·5 ohm^{-1} c.c. in $N/10$ solution. What is the approximate specific resistance of $N/50$ solution of this acid?

106. What conclusions respecting the composition of an oxy-acid can be drawn from the following facts: the volume of an oxidising agent which oxidises a given amount of its sodium salt to sulphate is three times that of another oxidising agent which oxidises it to sulphite. (C.U.O.S.)

107. 2·000 gm. of a mixture of ammonium chloride, ammonium sulphate and sodium chloride was heated with an excess of sodium hydroxide solution and the resulting ammonia was absorbed in 50 c.c. of normal hydrochloric acid. 28·4 c.c. of normal sodium hydroxide were required for the neutralisation of the residual acid. In another experiment, 0·483 gm. of the mixture was dissolved in water and treated with an excess of silver nitrate solution, the precipitated silver chloride being found to weigh 0·850 gm. What is the percentage composition of the mixture?

108. 6 gm. of the oxide of a metal was dissolved in dilute sulphuric acid and made up to 1000 c.c. 25 c.c. lots of this solution were reduced by different reducing agents, the excess of the reducing agent being then removed. The reduced solutions were then titrated separately against $N/10$ potassium permanganate with the following results: (*a*) 25 c.c. of solution after reduction with sulphur dioxide required 16·5 c.c. of $N/10$ $KMnO_4$, (*b*) 25 c.c. of the solution after reduction with magnesium required 33·1 c.c. of $N/10$ $KMnO_4$, (*c*) 25 c.c. of the solution after reduction with zinc required 66·0 c.c. of $N/10$ $KMnO_4$. What deductions concerning the valency and the probable atomic weight of the element can be made from these data?

109. 9·86 c.c. of a gas were mixed with oxygen so as to give a total volume of 104·5 c.c. After explosion the total volume was unchanged. Aqueous potassium hydroxide removed carbon dioxide and left 74·92 c.c. of pure oxygen. Assign a molecular formula to the gas. (C.U.O.S.)

110. The solubility products of ferric hydroxide and manganous hydroxide are $1{\cdot}0 \times 10^{-36}$ and $1{\cdot}5 \times 10^{-14}$ respectively at 18°. The dissociation constant of ammonium hydroxide is $1{\cdot}8 \times 10^{-5}$ at the same temperature. Calculate (*a*) the concentration of ferric ion, (*b*) the concentration of manganous ion which can exist in normal ammonium hydroxide which is also of molar concentration with respect to ammonium chloride. Assume complete dissociation of the ammonium chloride.

111. 80 c.c. of oxygen effuses through a pin-hole orifice in 15 seconds. Under the same conditions of temperature and pressure 80 c.c. of a mixture of carbon dioxide and carbon monoxide effuses in 26·0 seconds. What is the percentage of carbon dioxide in the mixture?

112. The carbide of a certain metal is decomposed by water, yielding a gas of which: (*a*) 1 litre at *S.T.P.* weighs 0·405 gm., (*b*) 20 c.c., exploded with 50 c.c. of oxygen in a eudiometer, left, on cooling, a residue of 35 c.c., of which 10 c.c. were absorbed by alkaline pyrogallol. [All volumes are given as reduced to *S.T.P.* Weight of one litre of oxygen = 1·44 gm.] Show what conclusions can be drawn about the gas. If the metallic carbide contains 6·78 per cent of carbon, what is the equivalent of the metal? (O.U.O.S.)

113. An element forms two hydrides, *A* and *B*, containing 2·3 per cent and 12·5 per cent respectively of hydrogen. The two hydrides can themselves combine to form a salt containing 6·7 per cent of hydrogen. One litre of the element in the form of a gas at *N.T.P.* weighs 1·26 gm. The specific heat of the gaseous element is 0·24 at constant pressure, and 0·17 at constant volume. What deductions can you make from these data?

114. The dissociation constant of ammonium hydroxide is $1{\cdot}8 \times 10^{-5}$ at 18°. What is (*a*) the hydroxyl concentration, (*b*) the *p*H of 0·05*N* ammonium hydroxide at 18°?

115. A saturated solution of lead chloride contains 0·872 gm. of the salt in 100 c.c. of its aqueous solution at 12°. Assuming complete dissociation of the salt, calculate the solubility product for lead chloride at this temperature. What would be the concentration of lead ion in gm.-ion per litre in *N*/100 hydrochloric acid saturated with lead chloride at 12°?

116. It was found that 2 gm. of the oxide of a hexavalent element united with 0·1725 gm. of normal ammonium orthophosphate to give a complex compound, there being no other reaction products. One gram of this compound reacted with 0·4902 gm. of sodium hydroxide to form water, disodium hydrogen orthophosphate and the normal sodium and ammonium salts of the acid most simply derived from the oxide. Suggest an empirical formula for the compound. [$NaOH = 40{\cdot}00$; $(NH_4)_3PO_4 = 149{\cdot}0$.] (C.U.O.S.)

117. The conductances of the hydrogen ion and of the acetate ion are 315 and 35 mhos respectively. The specific conductivity of a solution of acetic acid containing 0·001 gm.-equivalent per litre is 41×10^{-6} mhos. What is the degree of dissociation of the acetic acid in this solution? (C.U.O.S.)

118. In an experiment to determine the reaction which takes place between ammonia and formaldehyde, 50 c.c. of a normal solution of ammonium chloride was added to 20 c.c. of a solution of formaldehyde containing 8·52 gm. of formaldehyde per litre. 40 c.c. of normal sodium hydroxide solution was then added and the mixture was allowed to stand. On titration with normal hydrochloric acid, the mixture was found to require 36·0 c.c. for neutralisation. In a separate experiment, a mixture of 50 c.c. of normal ammonium chloride and 40 c.c. of normal sodium hydroxide was found to require 39·95 c.c. of normal hydrochloric acid, using the same indicator. What deductions can you make from these results?

119. When pure ammonia is maintained at 600° and a pressure of 2 atmospheres, it dissociates to give a gas containing 5 per cent of ammonia by volume. Determine (*a*) the degree of dissociation, (*b*) the equilibrium constant at this temperature (in terms of partial pressures), (*c*) the composition at the same temperature but under a pressure of 20 atmospheres.

120. The equilibrium constant for the reaction :

$$H_2O + CO \rightleftharpoons H_2 + CO_2$$

is 10·8 at 500°, the numerators being the concentrations of hydrogen and carbon dioxide and the concentrations of all gases being expressed in gm.-molecules per litre. Calculate the percentage by volume of carbon dioxide in the mixture of gases obtained by allowing 3·6 gm. of water and 14·0 gm. of carbon monoxide to reach equilibrium at 500°.

121. The specific conductivity of $N/20$ acetic acid at 18° is $4{\cdot}4 \times 10^{-4}$ reciprocal ohms. The mobility of the hydrogen ion is 310 and of the acetate ion, 77, also at 18°. What is the pH of $N/20$ acetic acid? What value do these figures give for the dissociation constant of acetic acid?

122. Calculate the percentage composition of a mixture of potassium chloride, sodium chloride and potassium sulphate from the following data : (*a*) 7·400 gm. of the mixture was dissolved in water and made up to 500 c.c. 25 c.c. of this solution gave 0·3228 gm. of barium sulphate, (*b*) 50 c.c. of the same solution required 39·5 c.c. of $N/10$ silver nitrate for complete precipitation of the chlorine ion.

123. 1 litre of the vapour of iodine at 300° weighs 3·72 gm. and exerts a pressure of 760 mm. Calculate (*a*) the percentage dissociation into iodine atoms at this temperature, (*b*) the equilibrium constant in partial pressures in atmospheres. If the pressure were reduced to 380 mm., temperature remaining constant, what volume would the same mass of iodine occupy?

* **124.** The decomposition of diazo-acetic ester in the presence of hydrogen ion is given by the equation :

$$N_2CH_2COOC_2H_5 + H_2O = HOCH_2COOC_2H_5 + N_2.$$

In the presence of excess of water the reaction is monomolecular. The concentration of an aqueous solution of the ester is such that 50 c.c. on complete decomposition gave 55·1 c.c. of nitrogen at *N.T.P.* Under the same conditions, 50 c.c. of the solution gave 15·6 c.c. of nitrogen in 25 minutes. How long will such a solution take to give 31 c.c. of nitrogen at *N.T.P.*?

* **125.** The dissociation constant of cyanacetic acid, $CH_2CNCOOH$, is $3{\cdot}5 \times 10^{-3}$ at 20°. What is the degree of hydrolysis in $\frac{1}{20}$ molar solution of sodium cyanacetate? What is the *p*H of the solution?

* **126.** The partition coefficient of a substance, *A*, between water and chloroform is 8·5, the substance being more soluble in water. 100 c.c. of chloroform solution of *A* is extracted with successive 50 c.c. quantities of water. What is the minimum number of such extractions which will remove 99 per cent *A* from the chloroform solution?

* **127.** The mean specific heat of liquid benzene between 60° and 80° is 0·45 and of benzene vapour between the same temperatures 0·30. The latent heat of vaporisation of benzene at 80° is 98·0 cal. per gm. What is the latent heat of vaporisation of benzene at 70°?

* **128.** The rate of decomposition of diazo-acetic ester (see question 124) is directly proportional to the hydrogen ion concentration. In two separate experiments 100 c.c. of the solution of diazo-acetic ester gave 25·8 c.c. of nitrogen in 15 minutes when the *p*H of the solution was 3·5 and 38·9 c.c. in 20 minutes from a solution of unknown *p*H. On complete decomposition 100 c.c. of the solution gave 63·8 c.c. of nitrogen. Calculate the velocity constant in each experiment and the *p*H of the second solution.

* **129.** The dissociation constant of ammonium hydroxide in aqueous solution at 25° is $1{\cdot}8 \times 10^{-5}$ and the dissociation constant (ionic product) of water is $0{\cdot}8 \times 10^{-14}$. A solution, $0{\cdot}02N$ with respect to ammonium hydroxide and $0{\cdot}01N$ with respect to a monobasic organic acid, has a hydrogen ion concentration of $1{\cdot}6 \times 10^{-10}$ equivalents/litre. Calculate (*a*) the dissociation constant of the acid, (*b*) the percentage hydrolyses of $0{\cdot}001N$ and $0{\cdot}1N$ solutions of the ammonium salt, (*c*) the percentage hydrolyses of $0{\cdot}001N$ and $0{\cdot}1N$ solutions of the sodium salt. (London B.Sc. Special.)

*** 130.** Two sparingly soluble electrolytes are represented by the formulae AX_1 and AX_2 respectively. Show that when a soluble potassium salt of the formula KX_2 is added to a saturated solution of AX_1, the condition of equilibrium is :

$$\frac{\text{concentration of } X_1^-}{\text{concentration of } X_2^-} = \frac{\text{solubility product of } AX_1}{\text{solubility product of } AX_2}.$$

*** 131.** The dissociation constants of two weak monobasic acids are $1{\cdot}8 \times 10^{-5}$ and $1{\cdot}5 \times 10^{-5}$ respectively. If 500 c.c. each of a normal solution of these acids are mixed, what is the hydrogen ion concentration of the mixture?

*** 132.** A mixture of 2 volumes of hydrogen and 1 volume of oxygen, originally at 100°, is adiabatically compressed until it explodes. Assuming the ignition temperature to be 500°, calculate the final pressure.

*** 133.** The compressibility coefficient of oxygen at 0° is 0·00094 and of hydrogen chloride 0·00748. Calculate the molecular weight of hydrogen chloride. The normal densities of oxygen and hydrogen chloride are 1·4290 and 1·6398 gm. per litre respectively.

*** 134.** The heat of formation of hydrogen iodide (gas) from hydrogen gas and iodine vapour is -420 cal. per mol. at 200°. Calculate the heat of formation at 500° given that the variation of specific heats with temperature are as follows :

$$H_2;\quad C_p = 6{\cdot}50 + 0{\cdot}0009T.$$
$$I_2;\quad C_p = 7{\cdot}4 + 0{\cdot}001T.$$
$$HI;\quad C_p = 6{\cdot}50 + 0{\cdot}001T.$$

Comment on the value you obtain.

*** 135.** The substance X decomposes slowly when dissolved in water. A solution was found to have the following normalities at the times stated after making up :

t (min.) -	0	10	50	100	150
N - -	1·0000	0·9616	0·8235	0·6776	0·5572

Find the order of the reaction and the time at which the decomposition would have amounted to 50 per cent.

(Manchester Hons. Chem.)

*** 136.** The degree of hydrolysis of a salt can be determined by an electrical conductivity method. For the salt of a weak base, which can be written $B\,.\,H\bar{A}$, the following relationship holds :

$$\Lambda_{\text{obs}} = (1 - x)\Lambda_S + x\Lambda_{H\bar{A}},$$

where Λ_{obs} = observed equivalent conductance, Λ_S = equivalent conductance of the unhydrolysed salt and $\Lambda_{H\bar{A}}$ = equivalent conductance of the acid, while x = the degree of hydrolysis. The following results were obtained for aniline hydrochloride at 25° for a dilution of 1 gm.-molecule in 512 litres. $\Lambda_{\text{obs}} = 131{\cdot}8$; $\Lambda_S = 102{\cdot}1$. Assuming complete dissociation of hydrochloric acid ($\Lambda_\infty = 380$), calculate the hydrolysis constant at 25°.

* **137.** What volume of $M/2$ sodium acetate must be added to 200 c.c. of $N/10$ acetic acid in order to produce a buffer solution of $p\text{H} = 5{\cdot}4$?

* **138.** The degrees of dissociation of water vapour and carbon dioxide at 1100° are $7{\cdot}8 \times 10^{-5}$ and $1{\cdot}4 \times 10^{-4}$ respectively. Calculate the values of K_p and K_c for the reactions :

$$2H_2O \rightleftharpoons 2H_2 + O_2,$$
$$2CO_2 \rightleftharpoons 2CO + O_2$$

at 1100°. Hence calculate K_p at 1100° for the water-gas reaction :

$$CO_2 + H_2 \rightleftharpoons H_2O + CO.$$

Calculate also the volume composition of the mixture obtained by allowing 4 volumes of carbon dioxide and 1 volume of hydrogen to reach equilibrium at 1100°.

* **139.** Assuming that the equivalent conductivities (Λ), the percentage of dissociation (α) and the transport numbers of the cations (n) for the following compounds are as shown, calculate the equivalent conductivity at infinite dilution of lithium bromide.

	Λ	α	n
$N/10$ Potassium bromide -	117·0	93	0·49
$N/10$ Lithium chloride -	88·7	90	0·31

* **140.** The specific heat of manganese at various temperatures is given by the equation :

$$C_t = 0{\cdot}03139 + 0{\cdot}0000516 \times T - 9{\cdot}3 \times 10^{-8}T^2,$$

where T = the absolute temperature. Calculate the mean specific heat over the range 0° – 100°.

* **141.** The resistance of a cell filled with potassium chloride solution containing 1·49 gm. per litre and having a specific conductivity of $2{\cdot}768 \times 10^{-3}$ ohm^{-1} is 202·6 ohms. When filled with a solution of sodium thiocyanate in alcohol containing 0·4175 gm. of the salt in 50 c.c. the resistance of the cell is 525·05 ohms. Find the molecular conductivity of the thiocyanate solution.

(London B.Sc. Special.)

* **142.** Given :

$$H_2 + \tfrac{1}{2}O_2 = H_2O, \quad \Delta H_{298} = -\ 64{,}800 \text{ cal.}$$
$$H_2S + 1\tfrac{1}{2}O_2 = H_2O + SO_2, \quad \Delta H_{298} = -136{,}700 \text{ cal.}$$
$$S + \ O_2 = SO_2, \quad \Delta H_{298} = -\ 69{,}000 \text{ cal.}$$
$$H_2 : C_p = \ 6{\cdot}50 + 0{\cdot}0009T,$$
$$H_2S : C_p = 8{\cdot}81 - 0{\cdot}0019T + 0{\cdot}00000222T^2,$$

and that the atomic heat of sulphur varies with the temperature according to the equation, $C_p = 5{\cdot}4 + 0{\cdot}005T$, calculate the heat of formation of hydrogen sulphide at 100°.

*** 143.** The vapour pressure of liquid oxygen is given by the equation:

$$\log_{10} p = 3{\cdot}54595 - \frac{313{\cdot}7}{T} + 1{\cdot}40655 \log_{10} T,$$

where p = the vapour pressure in mm. and T = temperature in °A. What is the boiling point of oxygen under normal pressure?

*** 144.** A substance A is decomposing according to the equation $2A = B + C$, that is, the decomposition is bimolecular. After 20 minutes from the beginning of the reaction it is found that 35·6 per cent of A has decomposed. What should be the percentage decomposition after another 20 minutes?

*** 145.** The dissociation constants of formic acid and acetic acid at 20° are $2{\cdot}14 \times 10^{-4}$ and $1{\cdot}8 \times 10^{-5}$ respectively. What is the pH of the solution obtained by mixing 1 litre of $M/10$ potassium acetate with 1 litre of $N/10$ formic acid? What is the ratio: potassium formate/potassium acetate in the mixture? What would be the effect of diluting the mixture to a total volume of 10 litres?

*** 146.** Deduce Kirchhoff's expression connecting the temperature coefficient of the heat of a reaction with the specific heats of the substances involved. The heat capacity of 1 gm. of saturated steam is 0·4652, that of water being 1·0074, both at 100°. How does the latent heat of vaporisation vary with the temperature?

(Liverpool B.Sc. Hons.)

*** 147.** The solubility product of silver bromide at 18° is $4{\cdot}2 \times 10^{-13}$ and that of silver chloride at the same temperature is $1{\cdot}2 \times 10^{-10}$. What is the concentration of silver chloride which will reduce the solubility of silver bromide to half its normal value?

*** 148.** The transport number of the lithium ion in lithium chloride at 25° is 0·36. An $M/10$ solution of lithium chloride has a molecular conductivity at 18° of 92·5 ohm^{-1} and the apparent degree of dissociation of lithium chloride at this concentration is 89 per cent. Deduce the absolute mobilities of the lithium and chlorine ion respectively.

*** 149.** The dissociation constants of acetic acid and ammonium hydroxide are approximately the same at 18°. Show that the solution obtained by mixing equal volumes of ammonium hydroxide and acetic acid of the same normality has a pH value which is unaffected by further dilution with water.

*** 150.** What is the pH of 0·01M solution of sodium p-toluate? The dissociation constant of p-toluic acid is $4{\cdot}2 \times 10^{-5}$ and the ionic product for water is $1{\cdot}0 \times 10^{-14}$. (London B.Sc. Special.)

*** 151.** Two metals A and B form two intermetallic compounds A_2B and AB_3, melting at 1100° and 600° respectively. Draw a sketch of the phase diagram you would expect and clearly indicate the significance of each section of the diagram. The melting points of A and B are 780° and 232° respectively. No solid solutions are formed and the liquids are miscible in all proportions.

(London B.Sc. Special.)

* 152. Assuming the decomposition of nitrous oxide to be a bimolecular reaction and that in one experiment the pressure (volume constant) of a quantity of nitrous oxide undergoing decomposition increased from 536 mm. to 685 mm. in 15 minutes, calculate the pressure after 30 minutes of a quantity of nitrous oxide decomposing at the same temperature but having an initial pressure of 400 mm.

* 153. The dissociation constant of ammonium hydroxide is $1{\cdot}8 \times 10^{-5}$ and the indicator constant for phenolphthalein (a weak acid) is 10^{-10}. The colour of phenolphthalein becomes perceptible (under the usual conditions) when 10 per cent of the indicator has been converted to its coloured form. Calculate the hydrogen ion concentration of a mixture of 200 c.c. of N NH_4Cl and 50 c.c. of $0{\cdot}1N$ NH_4OH, and hence deduce whether or not a small quantity of phenolphthalein in this solution would show a pink colour.

* 154. Calculate the molecular conductivity of $M/10$ KCl given that the degree of dissociation (apparent) is 0·86, that the transport numbers of K^+ and Cl^- in KCl solution are 0·47 and 0·53 respectively and that the absolute mobilities of these ions are $5{\cdot}5 \times 10^{-4}$ cm./sec. and $6{\cdot}2 \times 10^{-4}$ cm./sec. respectively.

* 155. A current of a few milliamperes was passed through a solution of silver nitrate between silver electrodes. The cathode increased in weight by 0·06588 gm. and the silver ion content of the solution round the anode increased by 0·000321 equivalents. Find the transport number of the silver ion. The atomic weight of silver is 107·9. (London B.Sc. Special.)

* 156. At 40° and at a pressure of 1 atmosphere N_2O_4 is dissociated into NO_2 to the extent of 43 per cent. If 1 gm. of nitrogen peroxide is contained in a flask of 500 c.c. capacity at 40°, what is (*a*) the total pressure in the flask, (*b*) the degree of dissociation?

* 157. For the reaction: $2SO_2 + O_2 \rightleftharpoons 2SO_3$, the variation of the equilibrium constant, K_p, with temperature ($T°$ absolute) is given by the equation: $\log_e K_p = \frac{9888}{T} - 9{\cdot}346$. Determine K_p and K_c at 627°. If 64 gm. of sulphur dioxide and 64 gm. of oxygen are allowed to reach equilibrium at 627° and at 1 atmosphere pressure, what would be the partial pressure of sulphur trioxide in the mixture?

* 158. The iodination of mesityl oxide is catalysed by both acids and bases. The following table gives the values of the velocity constant, K, found for this reaction in a series of buffer solutions containing acetic acid (concentration c_1 mol. per litre) and sodium acetate (concentration c_2 mol. per litre). Calculate the values of the respective catalytic coefficients for the acetic acid molecule and

the acetate ion. Given further that the hydrogen ion concentration in an acetic acid-sodium acetate buffer is given by $(c_1/c_2) \times 1{\cdot}7 \times 10^{-5}$ and that the catalytic coefficients for hydrogen and hydroxyl ions are respectively 0·0147 and 6·5, calculate the velocity constant of the reaction in pure water.

c_1	0·002	0·006	0·005	0·015
c_2	0·02	0·06	0·015	0·045
$K \times 10^6$	0·90	1·19	0·90	1·15

The dissociation constant of water can be taken as 10^{-14}.

(Manchester Hons. Chem.)

*** 159.** Benzoic acid is partly associated in benzene solution and partly dissociated in aqueous solution. Assuming that c_1 = total concentration of benzoic acid in aqueous solution, α_d = the degree of dissociation, k_d = dissociation constant of benzoic acid, c_2 = total concentration (single and double molecules) of benzoic acid in benzene solution, α_a = degree of association and

$$k_a = [(C_6H_5COOH)_2]/[C_6H_5COOH]^2,$$

show that the partition coefficient (K) of benzoic acid between benzene and water is given by the expression :

$$K = \frac{\sqrt{\alpha_a c_2/2k_a}}{\alpha_d{}^2 c_1{}^2/k_d}.$$

*** 160.** Calculate (*a*) the osmotic pressure at 15° of a solution of potassium nitrate which has a vapour pressure of 756·3 mm. at 100°, (*b*) the weight of anhydrous sodium acetate which must be added to 1 litre of $N/10$ acetic acid in order to give a solution of pH = 6 (K_a for acetic acid = $1{\cdot}8 \times 10^{-5}$), (*c*) the molecular weight of ethylene, given that the compressibility coefficients of ethylene and oxygen are 0·0072 and 0·00094 and that the normal densities of these gases are 1·2606 and 1·4290 gm. per litre respectively, (*d*) the time taken for 50 per cent of a gas to decompose if 20 per cent decomposes in 10 minutes and the reaction is of the first order, (*e*) the minimum number of extractions with 50 c.c. lots of ether required to remove 98 per cent of a substance A from 500 c.c. of its aqueous solution if the partition coefficient of A between water and ether is 1 : 5, the substance being more soluble in ether.

CHAPTER XIII

CALCULATIONS IN ORGANIC CHEMISTRY (1)

1. Determination of empirical formula of organic compounds

It is assumed that the student is acquainted with the practical details of estimating the following elements in organic compounds by the methods given below :

Carbon. Oxidation to carbon dioxide (Liebig's method).

Hydrogen. Oxidation to water (Liebig's method).

Nitrogen.

(1) As free nitrogen (Dumas' method).

(2) As ammonia (Kjeldahl's method).

(3) As ammonia by distillation with soda-lime (Will and Varrentrap's method).

Halogens. Conversion to silver halides (Carius' method).

Sulphur. Conversion to barium sulphate (Carius' method).

Oxygen. Always estimated by difference.

Example 121. 0·2036 gm. of an organic compound, containing carbon, hydrogen and oxygen only, gave on complete combustion 0·3895 gm. of carbon dioxide and 0·2390 gm. of water. Calculate the empirical formula of the compound.

Since the molecular weight of carbon dioxide is 44 and the atomic weight of carbon is 12 :

$\therefore$ Weight of carbon $= \frac{12}{44}$ (or $\frac{3}{11}$) $\times$ weight of carbon dioxide

$= \frac{3}{11} \times 0{\cdot}3895$ gm. $= 0{\cdot}1062$ gm.

Similarly :

Weight of hydrogen $= \frac{2}{18}$ (or $\frac{1}{9}$) $\times$ weight of water

$= \frac{1}{9} \times 0{\cdot}2390$ gm. $= 0{\cdot}0266$ gm.

$\therefore$ Weight of oxygen by difference

$= (0{\cdot}2036 - 0{\cdot}1062 - 0{\cdot}0266)$ gm. $= 0{\cdot}0708$ gm.

To find the empirical formula, the weight of the three elements are divided by their respective atomic weights :

		Ratios
Carbon	$=\frac{0\cdot1062}{12}=0\cdot00884$	2
Hydrogen	$=\frac{0\cdot0266}{1}=0\cdot0266$	6
Oxygen	$=\frac{0\cdot0708}{16}=0\cdot00442$	1

∴ Empirical formula of the compound is C_2H_6O.

Example 122. 0·2816 gm. of an organic compound gave by Kjeldahl's method sufficient ammonia to neutralise exactly 18·8 c.c. of $N/2$ sulphuric acid. What is the percentage of nitrogen in the compound?

Since the nitrogen in the compound is converted quantitatively into ammonia, 14 gm. of nitrogen gives 17 gm. of ammonia.

But 17 gm. of ammonia exactly neutralises 1000 c.c. of a normal solution of an acid.

∴ 1000 c.c. of normal acid is exactly equivalent to 14 gm. of nitrogen.

∴ 18·8 c.c. of $N/2$ acid is equivalent to $\frac{14}{1000}\times\frac{18\cdot8}{2}$ gm. of nitrogen $=0\cdot1316$ gm.

∴ Percentage of nitrogen in the compound

$$=\frac{0\cdot1316}{0\cdot2816}\times100=46\cdot7.$$

Example 123. 0·1559 gm. of an organic compound gave by Dumas' method 45·7 c.c. of nitrogen, measured over water, at 14° and at a barometric pressure of 756 mm. Calculate the percentage of nitrogen in the compound.

The volume of the gas at $N.T.P.$ (vapour pressure of water at 14° is 12 mm.)

$$=45\cdot7\times\frac{273}{287}\times\frac{744}{760}\text{ c.c.}=42\cdot6\text{ c.c.}$$

But, since the molecular weight of nitrogen is 28, therefore 22,400 c.c. of nitrogen at $N.T.P.$ weigh 28 gm.

∴ 42·6 c.c. of nitrogen at *N.T.P.* weigh

$$\frac{28}{22,400} \times 42{\cdot}6 \text{ gm.} = 0{\cdot}0532 \text{ gm.}$$

∴ Percentage of nitrogen in the compound

$$= \frac{0{\cdot}0532}{0{\cdot}1559} \times 100 = \mathbf{34{\cdot}1}.$$

Example 124. Calculate (*a*) the percentage of sulphur, (*b*) the percentage of bromine, in an organic compound using the following results: 0·3361 gm. of the compound gave 0·4437 gm. of barium sulphate; 0·2903 gm. of the compound gave 0·3092 gm. of silver bromide.

The molecular weight of barium sulphate, $BaSO_4 = 233$.

∴ Fraction of sulphur in $BaSO_4 = 32/233$.

∴ Weight of sulphur in 0·4437 gm. of barium sulphate

$$= \frac{32}{233} \times 0{\cdot}4437 \text{ gm.}$$

∴ Percentage of sulphur in the compound

$$= \frac{32}{233} \times \frac{0{\cdot}4437}{0{\cdot}3361} \times 100 = \mathbf{18{\cdot}13}.$$

The molecular weight of silver bromide, AgBr, is 188.

∴ Fraction of bromine in AgBr = 80/188.

∴ Weight of bromine in 0·3092 gm. of silver bromide

$$= \frac{80}{188} \times 0{\cdot}3092 \text{ gm.}$$

∴ Percentage of bromine in the compound

$$= \frac{80}{188} \times \frac{0{\cdot}3092}{0{\cdot}2903} \times 100 = \mathbf{45{\cdot}3}.$$

Example 125. Calculate the empirical formula of an organic compound which gave the following results on analysis: 0·2813 gm. gave on complete combustion 0·5586 gm. of carbon dioxide and 0·0977 gm. of water. 0·5107 gm. gave 39·8 c.c. of nitrogen measured at 15° and 754 mm. over water. 0·5003 gm. gave 0·4613 gm. of silver chloride.

$$\text{Percentage of carbon} = \frac{0{\cdot}5586}{0{\cdot}2813} \times \frac{3}{11} \times 100 = \mathbf{54{\cdot}16}.$$

Percentage of hydrogen $= \frac{0{\cdot}0977}{0{\cdot}2813} \times \frac{1}{9} \times 100 = 3{\cdot}86.$

Volume of nitrogen at *N.T.P.*

$$= 39{\cdot}8 \times \frac{273}{288} \times \frac{(754 - 13)}{760} = 36{\cdot}8 \text{ c.c.}$$

Percentage of nitrogen $= \frac{36{\cdot}8}{22400} \times \frac{28}{0{\cdot}5107} \times 100 = 9{\cdot}005.$

Weight of chlorine in 0·4613 gm. of silver chloride

$$= \frac{0{\cdot}4613 \times 35{\cdot}5}{143{\cdot}5} = 0{\cdot}1141 \text{ gm.}$$

Percentage of chlorine $= \frac{0{\cdot}1141}{0{\cdot}5003} \times 100 = 22{\cdot}80.$

Percentage of oxygen (by difference) = 10·13.

Dividing these percentages by the corresponding atomic weights :

		Ratios
C = 54·16/12	= 4·51 - - -	7
H = 3·86/1	= 3·86 - - -	6
N = 9·005/14	= 0·643 - - -	1
Cl = 22·8/35·5	= 0·642 - - -	1
O = 10·13/16	= 0·633 - - -	1

∴ Empirical formula of the compound is $\mathbf{C_7H_6NClO}$.

QUESTIONS ON CHAPTER XIII

1. What is the percentage of carbon in an organic compound 0·2000 gm. of which gave on complete combustion 0·2750 gm. of carbon dioxide?

2. What is the percentage of hydrogen in an organic compound 0·3518 gm. of which gave on complete combustion 0·2021 gm. of water.

3. What is the empirical formula of a compound 0·2801 gm. of which gave on complete combustion 0·9482 gm. of carbon dioxide and 0·1939 gm. of water?

4. What is the empirical formula of a compound containing carbon, hydrogen and oxygen only, of which 0·4080 gm. gave on complete combustion 0·5984 gm. of carbon dioxide and 0·2448 gm. of water?

5. What is the percentage of nitrogen in an organic compound 0·1558 gm. of which gave by Dumas' method 56·3 c.c. of nitrogen collected over water at 16° and at a barometric pressure of 752 mm.?

6. 0·2000 gm. of an organic compound was treated by Kjeldahl's method and the resulting ammonia was passed into 50 c.c. of $N/2\ H_2SO_4$. The residual acid was then found to require 36·6 c.c. of $N/2$ NaOH for neutralisation. What is the percentage of nitrogen in the compound?

7. 0·7105 gm. of naphthalene was burnt in an excess of oxygen and gave 2·442 gm. of carbon dioxide and 0·3996 gm. of water. What is the empirical formula of naphthalene?

8. What is the percentage of sulphur in an organic compound, 0·2000 gm. of which gave 0·3730 gm. of barium sulphate?

9. 0·2118 gm. of an organic compound gave 0·7091 gm. of carbon dioxide and 0·1658 gm. of water. What is the empirical formula of the compound?

10. What volume of nitrogen, measured at 15° and 756 mm., could be obtained from the decomposition of 0·5 gm. of chloroacetamide (empirical formula C_2H_4ONCl)? What weight of silver chloride could be obtained from the chlorine contained in 0·5 gm. of the same compound?

11. When a certain organic compound was heated with soda-lime the nitrogen it contained was liberated quantitatively as ammonia, and it was found that 0·500 gm. gave a quantity of ammonia just sufficient to neutralise 16·9 c.c. of $N/2\ H_2SO_4$. What is the percentage of nitrogen in the compound?

12 What is the empirical formula of a compound of the percentage composition: C = 70·6; H = 13·7; O = 15·7?

13. 0·2059 gm. of an organic compound gave on complete combustion 0·2186 gm. of carbon dioxide and 0·1342 gm. of water. 0·2072 gm. of the same compound gave by Carius' method 0·5887 gm. of silver chloride. What is the empirical formula of the compound?

14. 0·185 gm. of an organic compound gave on combustion 0·440 gm. of carbon dioxide and 0·225 gm. of water; the vapour density of the compound is 37. What is the molecular formula of the compound, and what structural formula might it have? (O. and C.)

15. On combustion, 0·1579 gm. of an organic compound gave 0·2254 gm. of carbon dioxide and 0·0769 gm. of water. The same weight of the original compound on treatment with silver nitrate and nitric acid yielded 0·2450 gm. of silver chloride. The vapour density of the compound was approximately 46. Calculate its molecular formula. (N.U.J.B.)

16. 0·4375 gm. of an organic compound containing carbon, hydrogen and oxygen only gave 0·8415 gm. of carbon dioxide and 0·2952 gm. of water. 0·5782 gm. of the compound displaced in Victor Meyer's method for the determination of vapour density a quantity of air which at 16° and 748 mm. occupied 87·0 c.c. What is the molecular formula of the compound?

17. An organic compound has the following percentage composition: C = 33·8; H = 1·4; N = 19·7; O = 45. 0·317 gm. of it when dissolved in 17·4 gm. of benzene elevated the boiling point of benzene by 0·226°. (The molecular elevation for benzene is 26·7°.) Calculate the molecular formula of the compound and assign a possible constitutional to it. (O. and C.)

18. 0·6872 gm. of an organic compound gave on complete combustion 1·466 gm. of carbon dioxide and 0·4283 gm. of water. A given weight of the compound when heated with nitric acid and silver nitrate gave an equal weight of silver chloride. 0·3178 gm. of the compound gave 26·0 c.c. of nitrogen at 15° and 765 mm. pressure. Deduce the empirical formula of the compound.

19. 0·3101 gm. of an organic compound gave on complete combustion 0·2274 gm. of carbon dioxide and 0·1860 gm. of water. 0·200 gm. of the same compound gave, by Kjeldahl's method, ammonia sufficient to neutralise 13·3 c.c. of $N/2$ hydrochloric acid. What is the empirical formula of the compound?

20. Determine the empirical formula of a compound which gave the following results on analysis: 0·3271 gm. gave 0·4875 gm. of carbon dioxide and 0·2493 gm. of water. 0·2906 gm. gave 60·4 c.c. of nitrogen, collected over aqueous potash, at 745 mm. and 15°.

21. Assign an empirical formula to an organic compound which gave the following results on analysis:

(*a*) 0·200 gm. gave 0·308 gm. of carbon dioxide and 0·054 gm. of water.

(*b*) 0·307 gm. of the compound gave, by Carius' method, 0·289 gm. of silver bromide.

(*c*) 0·330 gm. gave 18·5 c.c. of nitrogen, measured at *N.T.P.*

22. What is the molecular formula of a compound which gave the following analytical results: 0·5061 gm. gave 0·4593 gm. of carbon dioxide and 0·0940 gm. of water. 0·2538 gm. of the same compound gave 0·7500 gm. of silver chloride. 2·83 gm. of the compound dissolved in 52·5 gm. of chloroform raised the boiling point of chloroform by 1·36°.

[Molecular elevation for 100 gm. chloroform = 36·6°.]

23. It is found that the total chlorine in a certain organic compound can be estimated by titration against standard silver nitrate solution. 4 gm. of the compound was dissolved in water and made up to 1000 c.c. and 25 c.c. of this solution required 12·3 c.c. of $N/10$ silver nitrate. In a combustion, 0·500 gm. of the compound gave

0·4424 gm. of water and 0·5405 gm. of carbon dioxide. 0·4065 gm. of the compound on complete decomposition gave 55·8 c.c. of nitrogen measured at *N.T.P.* Deduce the empirical formula of the compound.

24. 0·87 gm. of an organic compound when in the form of a vapour at 100° and 760 mm. occupied 205 c.c. 0·254 gm. of the compound gave on complete combustion 0·1720 gm. of carbon dioxide and 0·0352 gm. of water. 0·200 gm. of the compound gave 0·4416 gm. of silver chloride. Assign a molecular formula to the compound.

25. Determine the empirical formula of an organic compound which gave the following results on analysis :

(*a*) 0·372 gm. gave 0·556 gm. of carbon dioxide and 0·095 gm. of water.

(*b*) 0·426 gm. gave 0·562 gm. of barium sulphate when treated by Carius' method.

(*c*) 0·450 gm. gave 0·366 gm. of silver chloride.

CHAPTER XIV

CALCULATIONS IN ORGANIC CHEMISTRY (2)

1. Molecular weights of organic acids (method of silver salt)

A known weight of the pure silver salt of the organic acid is decomposed by heat to leave a residue of pure silver. If the basicity of the acid is known, the weights of the silver salt and of the silver obtained from it are sufficient for the calculation of the molecular weight of the acid.

If, for example, an organic acid has a basicity, n, one molecule of the acid is represented by the formula H_nX, where X is that part of the molecule other than the replaceable hydrogen. The formula for the silver salt is, therefore, Ag_nX.

When the silver salt is decomposed, the following reaction takes place :

$$Ag_nX \rightarrow nAg.$$

Then, if M is the molecular weight of the silver salt, M gm. of the salt must give $(n \times 108)$ gm. of silver $(Ag = 108)$.

Suppose, in an experiment, that x gm. of silver salt gave a residue of y gm. of silver.

Since M gm. of silver salt give $(108 \times n)$ gm. of silver,

$\therefore$ x gm. of silver salt would give $\dfrac{(108 \times n)}{M} \times x$ gm. of silver.

$$\therefore \quad \frac{(108 \times n)}{M} \times x = y.$$

$$\therefore \quad M = \frac{x}{y} \times (108 \times n).$$

The molecular weight of the acid is then obtained from the relationship :

Molecular weight of acid

$$= \text{molecular weight of silver salt} - 108n + n.$$

If, for example, the molecular weight of the silver salt of a tribasic acid is found to be 420, then :

$$Ag_3X = 420,$$
$$X = 420 - (3 \times 108),$$
$$H_3X = 420 - (3 \times 108) + 3 = \mathbf{99}.$$

Example 126. 0·607 gm. of the silver salt of a tribasic organic acid was completely decomposed by heat and gave 0·370 gm. of silver. Calculate the molecular weight of the silver salt and of the acid.

Since the acid is tribasic, its molecule can be represented by the formula H_3X. The silver salt is, then, Ag_3X. The action of heat on the silver salt is :

$$Ag_3X \rightarrow 3Ag.$$

Denoting the molecular weight of the silver salt by M :

M gm. of silver salt give (3×108) gm. of silver.

$\therefore$ 0·607 gm. of silver salt give $\frac{324}{M} \times 0{\cdot}607$ gm. of silver.

$$\therefore \frac{324}{M} \times 0{\cdot}607 = 0{\cdot}370.$$

From which $M = 531$.

By subtracting three times the atomic weight, that is 324, from the molecular weight of the silver salt, we obtain the " molecular weight " of the radical, X.

$\therefore$ " Molecular weight " of $X = 531 - 324 = 207$.

$\therefore$ Molecular weight of the acid $(H_3X) = 207 + 3 = \mathbf{210}$.

2. Molecular weights of organic bases (method of platinichloride)

Organic bases (assumed to be mono-acid) unite, like ammonia, with chloroplatinic acid, H_2PtCl_6, to give crystalline chloroplatinates (or platinichlorides) ; these are convertible by the action of heat into metallic platinum. The formulae of the platinichlorides are best remembered, for the purposes of calculating molecular weights, by comparing them with ammonium chloroplatinate. Thus :

$$\underset{\text{ammonium chloroplatinate}}{(NH_4)_2PtCl_6} = 2NH_3 \,.\, H_2PtCl_6 \text{ or } (NH_3)_2H_2PtCl_6.$$

If one molecule of ammonia is denoted by B, then the formula for ammonium chloroplatinate is $B_2 \,.\, H_2PtCl_6$.

Similarly, if B' denote one molecule of a mono-acid organic base, the formula of the chloroplatinate of this base can be written $B'_2 \,.\, H_2PtCl_6$. For example, the chloroplatinates of methylamine, CH_3NH_2, and aniline, $C_6H_5NH_2$, have respectively the formulae:

$$(CH_3NH_2)_2H_2PtCl_6 \text{ and } (C_6H_5NH_2)_2H_2PtCl_6.$$

When a platinichloride of a base B is decomposed by heat the reaction is represented:

$$B_2 . H_2PtCl_6 \rightarrow Pt$$
$$M_p \rightarrow 195.$$

If M_p = the molecular weight of the platinichloride, then M_p gm. gives 195 gm. of platinum. If, then, x gm. of the platinichloride are found to give y gm. of platinum, the molecular weight of the platinichloride is given by the equation:

$$M_p = \frac{x}{y} \times 195.$$

But if M_b denote the molecular weight of the base, then:

$$M_p = (2 \times M_b) + (2 \times 1) + (6 \times 35{\cdot}5) + 195.$$

$$\therefore\ M_b = \frac{M_p - 410}{2}.$$

Example 127. 0·352 gm. of the platinichloride of a mono-acid organic base was decomposed and gave 0·137 gm. of platinum. Deduce the molecular weight of the base.

Then, as above:

$$B_2 . H_2PtCl_6 \rightarrow Pt$$
$$M_p \rightarrow 195.$$

$$\therefore\ M_p = \frac{0{\cdot}352}{0{\cdot}137} \times 195 = 500.$$

$$\therefore\ M_b = \frac{500 - 410}{2} = 45.$$

3. Determination of the molecular weight of an organic base (method of titration or precipitation)

The majority of organic bases behave as mono-acid bases, that is, one molecule of the base unites with one equivalent of acid, for example, $B . HCl$, $B_2 . H_2SO_4$, where B represents one molecule of the base. The molecular weight can be determined, therefore, by estimating the percentage of the acid in the salt by a titration or precipitation method.

Example 128. 25 c.c. of an aqueous solution of the hydrochloride of an amine containing 10 gm. of the salt per litre reacted with 26·2 c.c. of a decinormal solution of silver nitrate. Suggest a molecular formula for the amine.

Assume that the formula for the hydrochloride is $B.HCl$ where B represents one molecule of the base. Then the reaction with silver nitrate is :

$$B.HCl + AgNO_3 = B.HNO_3 + AgCl.$$

If M_s = the molecular weight of the salt, then M_s gm. of the salt react exactly with 1 gm.-molecule of silver nitrate and, therefore, with 1000 c.c. of N $AgNO_3$.

But M_s gm. of the salt contain M_b gm. of the base, where M_b = the molecular weight of the base.

$\therefore M_b = M_s - 36{\cdot}5$ (the molecular weight of hydrogen chloride).

Since the solution of the salt contains 10 gm. per litre, 25 c.c. contain 0·25 gm.

26·2 c.c. $N/10$ $AgNO_3$ reacts with 0·25 gm. of the salt.

$$\therefore \text{ 1000 c.c. } N \text{ } AgNO_3 \text{ reacts with } \frac{0{\cdot}25}{2{\cdot}62} \times 1000 \text{ gm. of the salt.}$$

$$= 95{\cdot}4 \text{ gm.}$$

$$\therefore M_b = 95{\cdot}4 - 36{\cdot}5 = 59{\cdot}1.$$

The student may like to show that this value agrees with the following alternative structural formulae :

(1) $CH_3.CH_2.CH_2.NH_2.$

(2) $(CH_3)(CH_3) > CH.NH_2.$

(3) $(C_2H_5)(CH_3) > NH.$

(4) $(CH_3)(CH_3)(CH_3) \to N.$

4. Estimation of methoxy ($-OCH_3$) groups (Zeisel's method)

The compound is heated with constant boiling-point hydriodic acid, the $-OCH_3$ groups being converted into an equivalent amount of volatile methyl iodide :

$$-OCH_3 + HI = -OH + CH_3I.$$

The methyl iodide is carried over by means of a stream of carbon dioxide into alcoholic silver nitrate, an equivalent quantity of silver iodide being precipitated :

$$CH_3I + AgNO_3 = AgI + CH_3NO_3.$$

After washing and drying, the silver iodide is weighed. From the equations it is clear that one gm.-molecule of silver iodide (235 gm.) is produced from each gm.-methoxy group.

Example 129. 0·2063 gm. of an organic compound, of molecular weight 168, gave, by Zeisel's method, 0·8658 gm. of silver iodide. Deduce the number of methoxy groups in one molecule of the compound.

0·2063 gm. of the compound gave 0·8658 gm. of AgI.

∴ 168 gm. of the compound would give

$$\frac{0{\cdot}8658}{0{\cdot}2063} \times 168 \text{ gm. of AgI.}$$

∴ No. of gm.-molecules of AgI (molecular weight = 235)

$$= \frac{0{\cdot}8658}{0{\cdot}2063} \times \frac{168}{235} = 3.$$

∴ No. of methoxy groups = 3.

5. Estimation of hydroxyl groups (method of acetyl derivatives)

The compound is allowed to react with an excess of acetyl chloride, each hydroxyl group being converted into an acetoxy group :

$$-OH + CH_3COCl = -OOCCH_3 + HCl.$$

The acetyl derivative is purified (usually by recrystallisation) and a known weight of it is hydrolysed by boiling with an excess of standard alkali, the excess being estimated by back titration with standard acid. The equivalent of the acetyl derivative can then be calculated and this, together with the known molecular weight of the original compound, suffices to give the number of hydroxyl groups.

Example 130. A compound of molecular weight 124 was fully acetylated. 1 gm. of the acetyl derivative was boiled with 50 c.c. *N* NaOH so that hydrolysis was complete, and the excess of sodium hydroxide was then found to require 36·2 c.c. of N H_2SO_4 for neutralisation. Determine the number of hydroxyl groups in one molecule of the original compound.

The equivalent of the acetyl derivative is the number of gm. of it which will just react with 1000 c.c. of N alkali.

But (50 – 36·2) c.c. N NaOH react with 1 gm. of the acetyl derivative.

∴ 1000 c.c. of N NaOH would react with $\frac{1}{13{\cdot}8} \times 1000$ gm. $= 72{\cdot}5$ gm. of the acetyl derivative.

∴ Equivalent of the acetyl derivative $= 72{\cdot}5$.

The equivalent of the original compound is obtained by replacing $-OOCCH_3$ by $-OH$, that is, by subtracting the "molecular weight" of $-OCCH_3$ and adding 1 for the hydrogen atom.

But $OCCH_3 - H = 43 - 1 = 42$.

∴ The equivalent of the original compound

$$= 72{\cdot}5 - 42{\cdot}0 = 30{\cdot}5.$$

∴ 30·5 gm. of the original compound contain 1 gm. of replaceable hydrogen (in OH).

But the molecular weight is 124.

∴ No. of hydroxyl groups $= \frac{124}{30{\cdot}5} = 4$.

QUESTIONS ON CHAPTER XIV

[Use approximate atomic weights.]

1. 0·1862 gm. of the silver salt of an organic acid gave, on strong heating, 0·1186 gm. of silver. What is the equivalent of the acid?

2. 0·2018 gm. of the silver salt of a dibasic organic acid gave on complete decomposition 0·1073 gm. of silver. What is the molecular weight of the acid?

3. 0·3168 gm. of the platinichloride of a mono-acid base gave 0·1036 gm. of platinum. What is the molecular weight of the base?

4. Calculate (a) the percentage weight of silver in the silver salt of a tribasic acid of molecular weight 210, (b) the percentage of platinum in the platinichloride of a mono-acid base of molecular weight 69.

5. 0·2000 gm. of a dibasic organic acid, when dissolved in water, required 44·4 c.c. of $N/10$ silver nitrate for complete precipitation. What is the molecular weight of the acid?

6. 0·2010 gm. of the sulphate of a di-acid base, dissolved in water and treated with an excess of barium chloride solution, gave 0·2107 gm. of barium sulphate. What is the molecular weight of the base?

7. 2 gm. of the hydrochloride of a mono-acid base was heated with 50 c.c. of *N* NaOH, the organic base being thus liberated and volatilised. The residual sodium hydroxide was then found to require 29·1 c.c. of *N* HCl for complete neutralisation. What is the molecular weight of the base?

8. What is the molecular weight of a mono-acid organic base 0·3317 gm. of the hydrochloride of which gave with an excess of silver nitrate solution a precipitate of silver chloride weighing 0·2984 gm.?

9. When 0·4018 gm. of the silver salt of an organic acid was strongly heated to a constant weight, the residue was found to weigh 0·2854 gm. What weight of cupric oxide would theoretically be obtained by heating 1 gm. of the anhydrous cupric salt of the same acid?

10. An organic acid has the percentage composition: C = 26·7; H = 2·2; O = 71·7. The acid is dibasic and its silver salt contains 71·1 per cent of silver. What is the probable molecular formula of the acid?

11. 0·5018 gm. of the platinichloride of an organic base gave 0·1702 gm. of platinum. If the molecular weight of the base is 165, what is its acidity?

12. What is the number of methoxy groups in one molecule of a compound of molecular weight 138 which treated by Zeisel's method gave the following results? 0·2136 gm. gave 0·7274 gm. of silver iodide.

13. The molecular weight of an organic compound is 168. Treated by Zeisel's method 0·3016 gm. of the compound gave 1·272 gm. of silver iodide. What is the number of methoxy groups in one molecule of the compound?

14. A compound of molecular weight 95 was fully acetylated. 0·500 gm. of the acetyl derivative was hydrolysed by boiling with 50 c.c. of *N* NaOH, and it was found that the residual sodium hydroxide required 41·8 c.c. of *N* HCl for complete neutralisation. What is the number of hydroxyl groups in one molecule of the original compound?

15. What is the molecular weight of a primary aliphatic amine, 0·2000 gm. of which when acted upon by an excess of nitrous acid gave 64·92 c.c. of nitrogen measured at *N.T.P.*? The reaction between the amino-group of the amine and nitrous acid is given by the equation:

$$-NH_2 + HNO_2 = -OH + H_2O + N_2.$$

16. A substance *A* of molecular weight 62 was treated with benzoyl chloride and sodium hydroxide as in Schotten-Baumann's reaction. 1 gm. of the crystalline benzoyl derivative was boiled with 50 c.c. of *N*/2 NaOH, and when hydrolysis was complete the residual sodium hydroxide required 33·7 c.c. of *N*/2 HCl for neutralisation. What is the number of hydroxyl groups per molecule of the compound *A*?

17. Deduce the number of hydroxyl groups in one molecule of an organic compound, *A*, which gave the following results: 0·283 gm. of *A*, when dissolved in 15·2 c.c. of water, lowered the freezing point by 0·285°. The compound *A* was fully acetylated and 1 gm. of the acetyl derivative was boiled with 50 c.c. of *N* NaOH, the residual sodium hydroxide requiring 36·2 c.c. of *N* HCl for the back titration.

18. (*a*) When 1·3 gm. of the sodium salt of an organic acid was ignited to a constant weight, the residue of sodium carbonate was found to neutralise 20·2 c.c. of *N*/2 HCl, methyl orange being used as indicator.

(*b*) The silver salt of the same acid contained 63·2 per cent of silver. Calculate separately from each of these results a value for the equivalent of the acid. If the molecular weight of the acid is 192, what is its basicity?

19. 1 gm. of the anhydrous potassium acid salt of a dibasic organic acid was made up to 100 c.c. with water. 25 c.c. of this solution required for neutralisation 19·35 c.c. of *N*/10 NaOH. What is the probable molecular weight of the organic acid?

20. 1 gm. of the anhydrous cupric salt of a tribasic acid was dissolved in water and treated with 50 c.c. of *N*/2 NaOH, which was an excess. The precipitated cupric hydroxide was removed by filtration and washed thoroughly, the combined filtrate being found to require 27·8 c.c. of *N*/2 HCl for neutralisation. What is the molecular weight of the acid?

21. An organic compound, having the properties of an acid, gives a silver salt containing 56·8 per cent of silver. The empirical formula of the acid is $C_4H_3O_2$. When 1 gm. of the acid is dissolved in 25·6 gm. of benzene, the freezing point is depressed by 1·22°. What structural formulae do these data indicate?

22. An organic acid gives a silver salt containing 59·0 per cent of silver. The acid forms an ethyl ester of molecular weight 104. The ethyl ester can be acetylated, and it is found that 1 gm. of the acetyl derivative requires 13·7 c.c. of normal sodium hydroxide for hydrolysis to the sodium salt of the original acid. Suggest a structural formula for the acid.

23. What structural formula would you assign to a mono-acid organic base which gave the following results? 0·5 gm. of the hydrochloride of the base required 35·0 c.c. of decinormal silver nitrate for complete precipitation of the chlorine ion. The base formed an acetyl derivative. When 0·200 gm. of this acetyl compound was boiled with 50 c.c. of decinormal sodium hydroxide until hydrolysis was complete, the residual sodium hydroxide required 36·5 c.c. of decinormal acid for neutralisation.

CHAPTER XV

CALCULATIONS IN ORGANIC CHEMISTRY (3)

1. Determination of molecular formulae of gases (use of Avogadro's hypothesis)

The methods discussed in Chapter II for the determination of the molecular formulae are widely used in Organic Chemistry, where they are employed mainly to obtain the molecular formulae of hydrocarbon gases.

Example 131. 10 c.c. of gaseous hydrocarbon was mixed with 50 c.c. (excess) of oxygen and exploded, the products being allowed to cool to the original room temperature. The volume of the residual gas was 40 c.c. of which 20 c.c. was absorbed on treatment with aqueous potash. The volume of the residual gas was 20 c.c. and was composed entirely of oxygen. Deduce the molecular formula of the hydrocarbon, assuming all gas volumes to be measured at the same pressure.

The formula of the hydrocarbon can be written C_xH_y, and the reaction on explosion with an excess of oxygen is then given by the equation :

$$C_xH_y + (x + y/4)O_2 = xCO_2 + y/2H_2O.$$

This equation follows from the fact that x atoms of carbon require x molecules of oxygen to form x molecules of carbon dioxide and y atoms of hydrogen (for conversion to water) require $y/2$ atoms of oxygen or $y/4$ molecules of oxygen.

Since 10 c.c. of the hydrocarbon give 20 c.c. of carbon dioxide :

$\therefore$ 1 molecule of the hydrocarbon gives 2 molecules of carbon dioxide.

$$\therefore\ x = 2.$$

Rewriting the equation with substitution for x :

$$C_2H_y + (2 + y/4)O_2 = 2CO_2 + y/2H_2O,$$

y can now be deduced from the observed contraction on explosion.

We have :

1 molecule of the hydrocarbon + $(2+y/4)$ molecules of oxygen give 2 molecules of carbon dioxide and $y/2$ molecules of water.

∴ 10 c.c. of the hydrocarbon + $[(2+y/4)\times 10]$ c.c. of oxygen give only 20 c.c. of carbon dioxide (the volume of water is ignored, since it condenses).

∴ Contraction on explosion

$$=\{10+[(2\times y/4)\times 10]-20\} \text{ c.c.}$$

But the observed contraction on explosion

$$=(60-40) \text{ c.c.} = 20 \text{ c.c.}$$

$$\therefore\ 10+[(2+y/4)\times 10]-20=20.$$

$$\therefore\ (2+y/4)\times 10=30.$$

$$\therefore\ y=4.$$

Formula for the hydrocarbon = $\mathbf{C_2H_4}$.

Alternative method

This method, although much easier than the foregoing, is not so general in its application.

Since the gas is mixed with 50 c.c. of oxygen and 20 c.c. remained after the explosion, only 30 c.c. of oxygen enter into chemical reaction with the hydrocarbon ; also 20 c.c. of carbon dioxide is formed.

∴ 1 molecule of the hydrocarbon requires 3 molecules of oxygen and forms 2 molecules of carbon dioxide.

$$\therefore\ C_xH_y+3O_2=2CO_2+y/2H_2O.$$

$$\therefore\ x=2.$$

$$\therefore\ C_2H_y+3O_2=2CO_2+y/2H_2O.$$

Since 2 molecules of oxygen are required to oxidise 2 atoms of carbon to carbon dioxide, the remaining molecule of oxygen oxidises the hydrogen in 1 molecule of the hydrocarbon to water. But 1 molecule of oxygen (O_2) will oxidise 4 atoms of hydrogen to form water.

∴ Formula for the hydrocarbon is $\mathbf{C_2H_4}$.

It is clear that the second method cannot be used when the volume of the oxygen is not given as in a question which commences " 10 c.c. of a hydrocarbon is exploded with an excess of oxygen ".

2. Analysis of gaseous mixtures

The method of working is indicated by the following example.

Example 132. 25 c.c. of a mixture of hydrogen, methane and carbon dioxide were exploded with 25 c.c. of oxygen and the total volume decreased to 17·5 c.c. On treatment with potash solution, the volume further decreased to 7·5 c.c. Calculate the composition of the mixture by volume. (O. and C.)

Let x = the volume of hydrogen in c.c.,
and y = ,, ,, methane ,,
and z = ,, ,, carbon dioxide ,,

Then the equations for the reaction on explosion are :

$$\underset{x}{H_2} + \underset{x/2}{\tfrac{1}{2}O_2} = \underset{\text{(condensed)}}{H_2O}$$

$$\underset{y}{CH_4} + \underset{2y}{2O_2} = \underset{y}{CO_2} + \underset{\text{(condensed)}}{2H_2O}$$

$$\underset{z}{CO_2} = \underset{z}{CO_2} \text{ (unchanged by the explosion)}$$

But contraction with potash $= 17\cdot5 - 7\cdot5$ c.c. $= 10$ c.c.

$$\therefore\ y + z = 10.$$

But total volume of mixed gases before explosion and before mixing with oxygen $= 25$.

$$\therefore\ x + y + z = 25.$$

$$\therefore\ x = 15 \text{ c.c.} = \text{volume of hydrogen.}$$

$\therefore$ Total amount of oxygen required for the combustion

$$= x/2 + 2y = 7\cdot5 + 2z.$$

But volume of oxygen actually used

$$= 25 - 7\cdot5 = 17\cdot5 \text{ c.c.}$$

$$\therefore\ 7\cdot5 + 2y = 17\cdot5.$$

$$\therefore\ y = 5 \text{ c.c.} = \text{volume of methane.}$$

$\therefore$ **Composition of the gas = 15 c.c. H_2; 5 c.c. CH_4; 5 c.c. CO_2.**

3. Miscellaneous examples

Example 133. A mixture of propane, C_3H_8, with a gaseous hydrocarbon of the olefine series occupied 24 c.c. To burn the mixture completely 114 c.c. of oxygen were required, and after combustion 72 c.c. of carbon dioxide were left. Calculate (*a*) the formula of the olefine, (*b*) the composition of the mixture by volume. All volumes were measured at the same temperature and pressure. (N.U.J.B.)

The general formula for a member of the olefine series is C_nH_{2n}, so that the two equations for complete combustion are :

$$C_3H_8 + 5O_2 = 3CO_2 + 4H_2O$$
$$C_nH_{2n} + (n + n/2)O_2 = nCO_2 + nH_2O$$
or
$$C_nH_{2n} + \tfrac{3}{2}nO_2 = nCO_2 + nH_2O$$

If x = number of c.c. of the olefine, then the volumes of gases taking part in the reaction are given by the equations :

C_3H_8	+	$5O_2$	=	$3CO_2$	+	$4H_2O$
$(24-x)$		$5(24-x)$		$3(24-x)$		(condensed)
C_nH_{2n}	+	$\frac{3}{2}nO_2$	=	nCO_2	+	nH_2O
x		$\frac{3}{2}n \times x$		nx		(condensed)

Since volume of oxygen used is 114 c.c. :

$$\therefore\ 5(24 - x) + \tfrac{3}{2}n \times x = 114. \quad \text{.................. (1)}$$

Since volume of carbon dioxide formed is 72 c.c. :

$$\therefore\ 3(24 - x) + nx = 72. \quad \text{...................... (2)}$$

From equation (2) :

$$nx = 72 - 3(24 - x) = 3x.$$
$$\therefore\ n = 3.$$

$\therefore$ Formula of the olefine = C_3H_6.

Substituting for n in equation (1) :

$$5(24 - x) + (\tfrac{3}{2} \times 3 \times x) = 114.$$

From which $x = 12$.

$\therefore$ The mixture contains 12 c.c. of C_3H_8 and 12 c.c. of C_3H_6.

Example 134. 10 c.c. of an organic compound, gaseous at the temperature of the experiment and containing carbon, hydrogen and oxygen only, was mixed with 100 c.c. of oxygen and exploded under conditions which allowed the water formed to condense ; the volume of the gas after explosion was 90 c.c. On treatment with potash solution, a further contraction of 20 c.c. was observed. Given that the vapour density of the compound is 23, deduce its molecular formula.

The formula for the compound is written $C_xH_yO_z$, and by balancing the amount of oxygen required for complete combustion against the oxygen already in the compound, the equation for the reaction can be written :

$$C_xH_yO_z + (x + y/4 - z/2)O_2 = xCO_2 + y/2H_2O$$
(condensed)

Since 10 c.c. of the gas gave 20 c.c. of carbon dioxide, $x=2$ and the equation can be rewritten:

$$C_2H_yO_z + (2+y/4-z/2)O_2 = 2CO_2 + \underset{\text{(condensed)}}{y/2H_2O}$$

The observed contraction was 20 c.c.

$$\therefore\ 10+[(2+y/4-z/2)\times 10]-20=20.$$

$$\therefore\ y/4-z/2=1.$$

$$\therefore\ y=2z+4.$$

But since the molecular weight of the compound is 46:

$$12x+y+16z=46,$$

by adding the atomic weights.

But $x=2$ and $y=2z+4$, so that by substitution:

$$24+2z+4+16z=46.$$

$$\therefore\ z=1 \text{ and } y=6.$$

$\therefore$ Molecular formula of the compound is $\mathbf{C_2H_6O}$.

Example 135. What is the composition by volume of a mixture of methane, ethylene and acetylene which gave the following results?

18·4 c.c. of the mixed gases was added to 100 c.c. of oxygen and exploded. The contraction after the explosion was found to be 33·2 c.c.

Treatment of the residual gases with potash removed 31·4 c.c. All volumes were measured at the same room temperature and pressure.

Let $x=$ the volume of methane in c.c.

and $y=$ " " ethylene "

and $z=$ " " acetylene "

Then the reactions which take place on explosion and the volumes of gases entering into the equations are as shown in the equations:

$$\underset{x}{CH_4} + \underset{2x}{2O_2} = \underset{x}{CO_2} + \underset{\text{(condensed)}}{2H_2O}$$

$$\underset{y}{C_2H_4} + \underset{3y}{3O_2} = \underset{2y}{2CO_2} + \underset{\text{(condensed)}}{2H_2O}$$

$$\underset{z}{C_2H_2} + \underset{2\frac{1}{2}z}{2\tfrac{1}{2}O_2} = \underset{2z}{2CO_2} + \underset{\text{(condensed)}}{H_2O}$$

The amount of oxygen left = volume of gases before explosion – the contractions on explosion and on treatment with potash

$$= 118{\cdot}4 - 33{\cdot}2 - 31{\cdot}4 = 53{\cdot}8 \text{ c.c.}$$

∴ Amount of oxygen used for combustion

$$= 100 - 53{\cdot}8 = 46{\cdot}2 \text{ c.c.}$$

$$\therefore\ x + y + z = 18{\cdot}4 \text{ (total volume of mixture)},$$

$$2x + 3y + 2\tfrac{1}{2}z = 46{\cdot}2 \text{ (volume of oxygen used)},$$

$$x + 2y + 2z = 31{\cdot}4 \text{ (volume of carbon dioxide)}.$$

From which x = volume of methane = **5·4 c.c.**

y = ,, ethylene = **5·8 c.c.**

z = ,, acetylene = **7·2 c.c.**

QUESTIONS ON CHAPTER XV

1. 15 c.c. of a mixture of ethylene and methane after explosion with oxygen gave 20 c.c. of carbon dioxide. What was the composition of the original mixture? (1st M.B., London.)

2. 10 c.c. of a gaseous hydrocarbon was mixed with 30 c.c. of oxygen and exploded, the resulting mixture being then cooled to the original room temperature and pressure. A contraction of 20 c.c. was observed. After treatment with aqueous potassium hydroxide, the volume further decreased to 10 c.c. and the residual gas was completely absorbed by shaking with alkaline pyrogallol. Deduce the molecular formula of the hydrocarbon.

3. Calculate the number of volumes of oxygen required for the complete combustion of one volume of (*a*) ethane, (*b*) hydrogen. Hence, calculate the percentage composition by volume of a mixture of ethane and hydrogen, 20 c.c. of which required 20 c.c. of oxygen for complete combustion. (O. and C. Subsid.)

4. 5·2 c.c. of a gaseous hydrocarbon was exploded with an excess of oxygen and the products were cooled to room temperature, a contraction of 7·8 c.c. being observed. A further contraction of 10·4 c.c. was noted after treatment with aqueous potash. What is the molecular formula of the hydrocarbon?

5. 10 c.c. of a gaseous hydrocarbon were exploded with 70 c.c. (excess) of oxygen. After explosion the residual gases occupied 50 c.c., and this volume was reduced to 20 c.c. on the addition of potassium hydroxide. From these data identify the hydrocarbon. (All measurements at *N.T.P.*) (N.U.J.B.)

6. A mixture of acetylene (C_2H_2) and ethylene (C_2H_4) was exploded with an excess of oxygen and cooled to room temperature, the total volume of the gases diminishing by 31·5 c.c. A further decrease of 34 c.c. was observed on treatment with potash. Deduce the volume composition of the mixture. What would have been the volume change on explosion if all measurements had been made at a constant temperature of 120°?

7. Calculate the volume of oxygen required for the complete combustion to carbon dioxide and water of 1000 c.c. of a mixture of equal volumes of propane, C_3H_8, and propylene, C_3H_6. Hence, or otherwise, deduce the composition of a mixture of these gases, 400 c.c. of which required 1960 c.c. of oxygen for complete combustion, assuming all measurements to be made at the same temperature and pressure.

8. (*a*) 20 c.c. of a gaseous hydrocarbon were exploded with 120 c.c. of oxygen. A contraction of 60 c.c. was observed, and a further contraction of 60 c.c. took place when an alkali was added. What was the formula of the hydrocarbon? (All volumes at the same room temperature and pressure.)

(*b*) 10 c.c. of a mixture of methane, carbon monoxide and nitrogen were exploded with 20 c.c. of oxygen. The gaseous products, when cool, occupied 20 c.c., of which 8 c.c. were absorbed by alkali and a further 10 c.c. by alkaline pyrogallol. Calculate the composition of the mixture. (O.H.C.)

9. 15·6 c.c. of a gaseous hydrocarbon was exploded with an excess of oxygen and after cooling to the original room temperature and pressure the decrease in volume was found to be 39·0 c.c. A further decrease of 46·8 c.c. took place on treatment with potash. What was the molecular formula of the gas?

10. A volume V c.c. of a gaseous hydrocarbon was exploded with an excess of oxygen. The observed contraction was $2\frac{1}{2}V$, and on treatment with potash a further contraction of $2V$ c.c. occurred. What is the molecular formula of the hydrocarbon?

11. 13·8 c.c. of a mixture of methane, carbon monoxide and nitrogen was exploded with an excess of CO_2-free air and the observed contraction (after cooling to the original room temperature) was 13·4 c.c. The further contraction with potash solution was 11·2 c.c. Calculate the percentage composition of the mixture.

12. Calculate the percentage composition of a mixture of methane, ethylene and acetylene which gave the following results. 15·2 c.c. of the mixture was exploded with an excess of oxygen and the observed contraction (measured at the constant room temperature and pressure) was 26·6 c.c. The further contraction with aqueous potash was also 26·6 c.c.

13. 66 c.c. of a mixture of methane, carbon monoxide and oxygen (in excess) was sparked until there was no further diminution in volume and the resulting mixture then occupied 29 c.c. Treatment with aqueous potash removed 26 c.c. of the gas, and the residual gas was completely absorbed by alkaline pyrogallol. Deduce the percentage composition of the original mixture.

14. When 12·0 c.c. of the vapour of a certain organic compound (vapour density = 15) which contains only carbon, hydrogen and oxygen, were mixed with 100·0 c.c. of oxygen and the mixture sparked, the volume after cooling to the original room temperature was 100 c.c. Admission of aqueous potassium hydroxide removed carbon dioxide and left 88·0 c.c. of oxygen. Deduce the molecular formula of the vapour. (N.U.J.B. Schol.)

15. 20 c.c. of a mixture of methane and a gaseous compound of the acetylene series was mixed with 100 c.c. of oxygen and exploded. The volume of the product after cooling to the original room temperature and pressure was 80 c.c., and on treatment with potash solution a further contraction of 40 c.c. was observed. Calculate (*a*) the molecular formula of the acetylene hydrocarbon, and (*b*) the percentage composition of the mixture.

16. 10 c.c. of a gaseous compound were exploded with 200 c.c. of air; the volume after explosion was 190 c.c., and this was reduced to 170 c.c. by treatment with potash. Two substances agree with the above data. What are they? (All volumes measured at 20° and 750 mm.) (C.U.O.S.)

17. What molecular formula would you assign to a gaseous organic compound containing carbon, hydrogen and oxygen only which gave the following results? 10 c.c. of the gaseous compound was exploded with 20 c.c. of oxygen (excess) and, after allowing to cool to the original room temperature, the volume was found to be 20 c.c., from which 10 c.c. were removed by the action of aqueous potash.

18. 10 c.c. of a gaseous organic compound was exploded with an excess of oxygen and the observed contraction was 15 c.c. Treatment with aqueous potash removed 10 c.c. of the residual gas leaving nothing but oxygen, as shown by complete absorption with alkaline pyrogallol. (All volumes were measured at 50° and 600 mm. pressure.) 1 litre of the compound in the form of a vapour at 100° and 760 mm. weighs 1·05 gm. What is the molecular formula of the compound?

19. What formula would you assign to a gaseous compound containing carbon which behaved as follows? 12·2 c.c. of the gas was exploded with an excess of oxygen, and after cooling it was found that there had been no change in volume. Treatment of the resulting mixture of gases with aqueous potash removed 24·4 c.c. of gas. The residue was then shaken with alkaline pyrogallol and 12·2 c.c. of gas remained unabsorbed.

MISCELLANEOUS QUESTIONS ON CHAPTERS XIII–XV
(Organic)

1. A liquid having the properties of an alcohol gave on oxidation the following figures: 0·700 gm. gave 1·540 gm. of CO_2 and 0·840 gm. of H_2O. What is the formula of the compound?
(O.U.O.S. Elem. Sci.)

2. On combustion 0·2035 of an organic compound containing only carbon, hydrogen and oxygen, gave 0·484 gm. of carbon dioxide and 0·2475 gm. of water. One litre of its vapour was found to weigh as much as 37 litres of hydrogen measured at the same temperature and pressure. Give the constitutional formula of the commonest compound of this composition and molecular weight.
(Inter. B.Sc., Lond.)

3. 20 c.c. of a mixture of ethylene and propane was mixed with 100 c.c. of oxygen and exploded, the products being cooled to the original room temperature and pressure. The volumes of gases (*a*) after explosion, (*b*) after absorption with potash, were 68·6 c.c. and 17·2 c.c. respectively. From each of these results, calculate independently the percentage of ethylene in the mixture.

4. 12 c.c. of a gaseous hydrocarbon was sparked with 50 c.c. of pure oxygen. The residual gas had a volume of 32 c.c., which shrank to 8 c.c. on shaking with caustic potash solution. What is the formula of the hydrocarbon? (Inter. B.Sc., Lond.)

5. An organic liquid contains 12·7 per cent of carbon and 2·1 per cent of hydrogen; 0·306 gm. of the compound gave 0·610 gm. of silver bromide. 0·412 gm. of the vapour of the compound occupied 52·0 c.c. at 15° and 752 mm. pressure. Deduce the molecular formula of the compound.

6. 0·3816 gm. of a compound containing only carbon, hydrogen and oxygen gave 0·8400 gm. of carbon dioxide and 0·4540 gm. of water. 1 gm. of the compound in the form of a vapour occupied 517 c.c. at 100° and 750 mm. pressure. What structural formulae might be assigned to the compound?

7. An organic compound has the molecular formula, $C_6H_6O_5SN$. Calculate (*a*) the weight of carbon dioxide, (*b*) the weight of water, (*c*) the weight of barium sulphate, (*d*) the volume of nitrogen measured over water at 15° and 750 mm. pressure which would be obtained theoretically from 1 gm. of the compound by the usual analytical methods.

8. 0·5106 gm. of an organic compound gave 0·4085 gm. of carbon dioxide and 0·2506 gm. of water. 0·3518 gm. of the same compound gave, by Carius' method, 0·7440 gm. of barium sulphate. What is the empirical formula of the compound?

9. 0·2315 gm. of an organic compound containing only carbon, hydrogen and oxygen gave on combustion 0·3395 gm. of carbon dioxide and 0·1389 gm. of water. Calculate the empirical formula of the compound. Give the structural formulae and names of compounds of this composition containing one and two carbon atoms respectively. (Inter. B.Sc., Lond.)

10. 0·282 gm. of a compound containing carbon, hydrogen and oxygen only, gave on complete combustion 0·620 gm. of carbon dioxide and 0·338 gm. of water. 0·203 gm. of the compound displaced by Victor Meyer's method 80·9 c.c. of air measured over water at 753 mm. and 16°. Calculate the molecular formula of the compound.

11. An organic compound is found to have a vapour density 37 times that of hydrogen and to contain 48·64 per cent of carbon, 8·11 per cent of hydrogen and 43·24 per cent of oxygen. Calculate its molecular formula, and write down the structural formulae of various compounds possessing this molecular formula.

(Inter. B.Sc., Lond.)

12. 0·2316 gm. of an organic substance containing carbon, hydrogen and nitrogen, but no other element, yielded 0·5584 gm. of carbon dioxide and 0·3141 gm. of water on combustion. Its vapour density is found to lie between 35 and 40. Calculate the empirical formula of the substance. What isomers having this formula should exist? (N.U.J.B.)

13. Deduce the empirical formula of an organic compound which gave the following results on analysis :

(*a*) 0·2816 gm. gave on complete oxidation 0·5927 gm. of carbon dioxide and 0·2058 gm. of water.

(*b*) 0·3013 gm. gave 0·2926 gm. of silver chloride.

(*c*) 0·2007 gm. gave 16·5 c.c. of nitrogen collected over water at 15° and at an atmospheric pressure of 756 mm.

14. A mixture of 20 c.c. of a gaseous hydrocarbon and 140 c.c. of oxygen measured at 15° was exploded. After cooling at 15°, the residual gas occupied 100 c.c. ; after treatment with caustic potash solution, there remained 40 c.c. of gas. Find the formula of the hydrocarbon. (O. and C.)

15. 0·2017 gm. of an organic compound gave 0·4512 gm. of carbon dioxide and 0·2769 gm. of water ; 0·1812 gm. of the same compound gave 34·5 c.c. of nitrogen at *N.T.P.* On treatment with nitrous acid the compound evolved nitrogen and formed an alcohol of molecular weight 60. Give the structural formulae of two compounds which would behave in this way.

16. 0·354 gm. of a substance gave on combustion 0·792 gm. of CO_2 and 0·486 gm. of water. The nitrogen in the same weight of the substance occupied 67·2 c.c. at *N.T.P.* Find the molecular formula of the substance. What structural formulae might it have?

(O. and C.)

17. Deduce the composition of a mixture of acetylene, methane and hydrogen which gave the following results: 30 c.c. of the mixture was exploded with 100 c.c. of oxygen and the products were allowed to cool to room temperature, a contraction of 50 c.c. being observed. After treatment with caustic potash solution, the volume further decreased by 30 c.c.

18. On ignition, 6·87 gm. of the silver salt of an organic acid gave a residue of 3·24 gm. of silver. The vapour density of the ethyl ester of the acid was found to be 75 (H = 1). Calculate the molecular weight of the acid and suggest a possible formula for it. (N.U.J.B.)

19. 0·300 gm. of the hydrochloride of an organic base gave 0·450 gm. of silver chloride after treatment with an excess of silver nitrate. What structural formulae can be assigned to the base?

20. On combustion 0·2241 gm. of an organic compound (containing carbon, hydrogen and chlorine only) yielded 0·0815 gm. of water. 0·1520 gm. of the compound, decomposed with nitric acid and silver nitrate, yielded 0·4406 gm. of silver chloride. The vapour density of the compound was found to be about 50. Calculate the empirical and molecular formulae of the compound. Suggest possible structural formulae for it. (Notts. Univ. Ent. Schol.)

21. 10 c.c. of a certain gaseous hydrocarbon were exploded with 100 c.c. of oxygen. The volume after explosion was 85 c.c., and this was reduced to 55 c.c. by treatment with aqueous potassium hydroxide. Find the molecular formula of the gas. All volumes were measured at 15° and 755 mm. (O. and C.)

22. 0·2 gm. of an organic compound yielded 0·489 gm. of carbon dioxide and 0·133 gm. of water. In another experiment 0·2 gm. of the compound yielded 41·5 c.c. of nitrogen measured at 0° and 760 mm. The molecular weight of the compound is 108. Determine the molecular formula of the compound and indicate possible structural formulae for it. (O. and C.)

23. An organic compound contains 69·4 per cent of carbon and 5·8 per cent of hydrogen. When 0·5 gm. of the compound was heated with soda-lime the ammonia evolved was sufficient to neutralise 41·3 c.c. of decinormal sulphuric acid. What structural formula can you assign to the compound?

24. A compound, containing carbon, hydrogen and oxygen only, has a vapour density of 30. On complete combustion 0·301 gm. of the compound gave 0·662 gm. of carbon dioxide and 0·361 gm. of water. Boiled with hydriodic acid the compound gave, among other products, a volatile liquid containing 89·4 per cent of iodine. What structure would you assign to the original compound?

25. An organic liquid has the composition : C = 49·31 per cent ; H = 6·85 per cent ; O = 43·84 per cent. Its vapour density (O = 16) is 73. On treatment with ammonia it gives a white precipitate of empirical formula $CONH_2$. This precipitate when boiled with sodium hydroxide gives off ammonia and leaves a residue which on treatment with hot concentrated sulphuric acid gives off a mixture of carbon monoxide and carbon dioxide. What is the liquid? Give equations for the above reactions? (O. and C.)

26. A compound, of vapour density 29 and having the percentage composition C = 62·1 ; H = 10·4 ; O = 27·5, gave on oxidation an acid containing 48·6 per cent of carbon and on reduction an alcohol containing 60 per cent of carbon. Deduce the structural formula of the original compound.

27. Two compounds were in composition : C = 32·0 per cent, H = 6·7 per cent, N = 18·7 per cent, O = 42·6 per cent. The molecular weight of each compound was 75. One compound, a liquid, when treated with strong reducing agents yielded a primary amine. The other, a solid, when treated with ethyl alcohol containing hydrogen chloride, produced a compound having the formula, $C_4H_9O_2NHCl$. With nitrous acid the latter compound yielded an acid of formula $C_2H_4O_3$. Deduce the constitutional formulae of the two compounds. (O. and C.)

28. A compound, *A*, having the properties of an aldehyde gave C = 62·1 per cent, H = 10·4 per cent, O = 27·5 per cent. Heated with ethyl alcohol it gave a compound, *B*, of the empirical formula, $C_7H_{16}O_2$. What are the structural formulae of the compounds *A* and *B*?

29. A mono-acid base of percentage composition : C = 61·0 ; H = 15·3 ; N = 23·7, forms a hydrochloride, 1 gm. of which requires 104·7 c.c. of *N*/10 silver nitrate for titration. What constitutional formulae are possible for it? How may they be distinguished? (O. and C.)

30. 0·3072 gm. of an organic compound containing carbon, hydrogen and oxygen only, gave on combustion 0·6760 gm. of carbon dioxide and 0·3681 gm. of water. The compound was unaffected by phosphorus trichloride. Heated with hydriodic acid it gave a compound containing 90 per cent of iodine. Deduce the structural formula of the original compound.

31. 0·300 gm. of an organic compound, *A*, gave on combustion 0·2664 gm. of carbon dioxide and 0·1086 gm. of water. An equal weight of the compound treated with nitric acid and silver nitrate gave 0·8690 gm. of silver chloride. When *A* was boiled with potassium hydroxide solution, a volatile liquid, *B*, containing 54·4 per cent of carbon was obtained. Deduce the structural formulae of the compounds, *A* and *B*.

32. A compound of carbon, hydrogen and oxygen gave on analysis C = 59·9 per cent, H = 13·45 per cent, was treated with hydrobromic acid and the volatile product whose vapour density was 61·5 gave the following analytical results :

(*a*) on combustion C = 29·25 per cent, H = 5·74 per cent ;
(*b*) by the Carius method, 0·25 gm. gave 0·382 gm. of silver bromide.

Write down an equation or equations which are in accordance with these facts. (N.U.J.B.)

33. A compound containing 62·1 per cent of carbon, 10·35 per cent of hydrogen and no other element except oxygen gave on oxidation an acid containing 48·6 per cent of carbon and 8·1 per cent of hydrogen. The vapour density of the original compound was 29. Write structural formulae for both compounds. (N.U.J.B.)

34. A compound, *A*, containing carbon, hydrogen and oxygen only, gave C = 54·5 per cent and H = 9·1 per cent. The vapour density of the compound was 22. Treated with hydrogen cyanide, it gave a compound, *B*, containing 19·7 per cent of nitrogen. When *B* was boiled with dilute sulphuric acid it formed a monobasic acid, *C*, of molecular weight 90. What structural formulae can you assign to the compounds *A*, *B* and *C*?

35. On boiling 0·277 gm. of an ester with 50 c.c. of decinormal sodium hydroxide until the reaction was complete, the resulting liquid required 18·5 c.c. of a decinormal solution of hydrochloric acid for neutralisation. If the ester were derived from a monobasic acid and a monohydric alcohol, what would be its molecular weight? (N.U.J.B.)

36. A compound, *A*, containing only carbon, hydrogen and oxygen gave on analysis : C = 58·8 per cent ; H = 9·8 per cent. On treatment with ammonia, the compound gave ethyl alcohol and a compound, *B*, containing 19·2 per cent of nitrogen. When *B* was boiled with caustic soda it gave the sodium salt of a monobasic acid of empirical formula, $C_3H_6O_2$. What are the structural formulae of the compounds *A* and *B*?

37. A certain aliphatic amine, containing only carbon, hydrogen and nitrogen, yielded a hydrochloride which upon combustion gave the following results : (*a*) 0·3240 gm. gave 0·4472 gm. of carbon dioxide and 0·3051 gm. of water, (*b*) 0·5632 gm. gave 66·0 c.c. of nitrogen at *N.T.P.* Suggest possible formulae for the amine. (O. and C.)

38. On treatment with hydroxylamine a colourless volatile liquid, *A*, yielded a crystalline precipitate, *B*, which contained 19·18 per cent of nitrogen. *A* did not reduce Fehling's solution or ammoniacal silver nitrate. Its vapour density is 29. Identify *A* and *B*. (N.U.J.B.)

39. A compound of carbon, hydrogen and oxygen, of vapour density 36 ($O = 16$), forms a white crystalline addition product with sodium bisulphite and gives on oxidation chiefly a mixture of acetic acid and propionic acid. On combustion, 0·100 gm. gave 0·245 gm. of carbon dioxide and 0·100 gm. of water. What is the compound's structural formula? (Staffs. Major Schol.)

40. A compound gave $C = 66{\cdot}4$ per cent; $H = 5{\cdot}5$ per cent; $Cl = 28{\cdot}1$ per cent. On treatment with potash, the compound gave a product having the properties of an alcohol and containing 77·8 per cent of carbon. Assign a structural formula to the original compound.

41. A white crystalline organic compound gave $C = 39{\cdot}4$ per cent; $H = 11{\cdot}5$ per cent; $N = 22{\cdot}9$ per cent; $O = 26{\cdot}2$ per cent; heated with dilute sulphuric acid, the compound gave a volatile product of percentage composition: $C = 54{\cdot}5$ per cent; $O = 36{\cdot}4$ per cent; $H = 9{\cdot}1$ per cent. This latter product reduced an ammoniacal solution of silver oxide. Deduce the structural formulae of both compounds.

42. A compound has the composition: C, 24·24; H, 4·04; Cl, 71·72, and its vapour density ($H = 1$) is 49·5. Give the full structural formulae and names of any compounds which satisfy these data. (N.U.J.B.)

43. 10 c.c. of a gas containing carbon and hydrogen, placed in a eudiometer, exploded on passing a spark, yielding 15 c.c. of gas. 20 c.c. of oxygen were now added and a second explosion resulted on sparking the mixture. From the 25 c.c. of gas in the eudiometer, on cooling, aqueous alkali and aqueous pyrogallol applied in succession extracted 10 c.c. and 5 c.c. respectively. Derive from these results a probable molecular formula for the gas. (C.U.O.S.)

44. An organic compound having the properties of a monohydric alcohol had the percentage composition: $C = 60{\cdot}0$ per cent; $H = 13{\cdot}3$ per cent; $O = 26{\cdot}7$ per cent. Heated with concentrated sulphuric acid, the alcohol gave a hydrocarbon of the percentage composition: $C = 85{\cdot}7$; $H = 14{\cdot}3$. When this hydrocarbon was treated with hydrogen bromide and the resulting product was allowed to react with aqueous potash, an alcohol isomeric with the original compound was obtained. Deduce the structural formulae of the two alcohols and write equations for the reactions involved.

45. An optically active compound had C, 40·4 per cent; H, 7·85 per cent; N, 15·75 per cent and a molecular weight of about 90. It was treated in aqueous solution with hydrochloric acid and sodium nitrite; nitrogen was evolved and an optically active compound, *A*, having C, 40·0; H, 6·67 per cent, was produced. Write structural formulae for the compounds and an equation for the reaction involved. (O. and C.)

46. 10 c.c. of a mixture of propane and a member of the acetylene series, *A*, was mixed with 60 c.c. of oxygen and exploded, the products being then cooled to the original room temperature. The volume of the gas was found to be 44 c.c. Treatment with potash solution removed 30 c.c. of the gas. Deduce the formula of the acetylene, *A*, and the volume composition of the mixture.

47. An organic compound had the following percentage composition: C = 61·3; H = 5·11; N = 10·2; O = 23·4. On reduction it formed an organic base, the hydrochloride of which contained 24·7 per cent of chlorine. Treated with nitrous acid and subsequently with potassium cyanide and copper sulphate, the base gave a compound of the empirical formula C_8H_7N, which after boiling with dilute sulphuric acid gave a monobasic acid. Suggest a formula for the original compound and write equations to represent the above reactions.

48. A monobasic organic acid has the empirical formula CH_2O. Its silver salt consists of C = 18·3 per cent; H = 2·5 per cent; O = 24·3 per cent; Ag = 54·9 per cent. What are the probable molecular formulae of the acid and the silver salt. Give the names and constitutional formulae of two isomeric acids which are in agreement with these data. (Staffs. Major Schol.)

49. A product with the empirical formula CH_3O is acted upon by acetyl chloride and gives a product, *A*, the molecule of which contains 6 carbon atoms. When 0·3 gm. of *A* is hydrolysed, it yields 0·246 gm. of acetic acid. What is the original substance? (C.U.O.S.)

50. A compound (*A*) has the composition, C, 78·5; H, 8·41; N, 13·09 per cent, and a vapour density (H = 1) 53·5. (*A*) is insoluble in water but readily dissolves in dilute hydrochloric acid. When sodium nitrite is added to this acid solution and the mixture is warmed, a gas is evolved and a product, (*B*), C_7H_8O is obtained. (*B*) is soluble in sodium hydroxide solution, but is precipitated when the alkaline solution is saturated with carbon dioxide. If sodium nitrite is added to an ice-cold solution of (*A*) in hydrochloric acid and the resulting solution is treated with cuprous cyanide, a compound, (*C*), C_8H_7N, is obtained. Hydrolysis of (*C*) with hot concentrated sodium hydroxide affords ammonia and the sodium salt of an acid which on distillation with soda-lime yields toluene Identify the compound (*A*) and justify your identification by tracing the reactions described above. (N.U.J.B. Schol.)

51. A compound containing C = 40·4 per cent; H = 7·87 per cent; O = 35·9 per cent; N = 15·7 per cent, was reduced with stannous chloride and gave a compound which was converted into a yellow oil of percentage composition C = 30·5; H = 5·09; O = 40·7; N = 23·7, by the action of nitrous acid. Deduce the structural formula of the original compound.

52. A compound containing carbon, hydrogen, oxygen and chlorine only gave, on analysis, C = 16·3 per cent ; H = 0·7 per cent. 0·320 gm. gave by Carius' method 0·930 gm. of silver chloride. When the compound was boiled with sodium hydroxide it gave two products : (*a*) the sodium salt of a monobasic acid, (*b*) a compound having the percentage composition : C = 10·0 ; H = 0·8 ; Cl = 89·2. The original compound gave the reactions of an aldehyde ; deduce the structural formula of the compound and write an equation for its reaction with sodium hydroxide.

53. 10 c.c. of a gaseous organic compound were exploded with 60 c.c. of oxygen and the resulting volume was 50 c.c. This was reduced to 30 c.c. by treatment with caustic potash solution. All volumes were measured at room temperature. What compounds are indicated by these results? (C.U.O.S.)

54. A liquid compound yielded the following results on analysis: 0·2 gm. gave 0·625 gm. CO_2 and 0·2 gm. H_2O. It combined with bromine to form a compound which contained 74·8 per cent of bromine and on oxidation gave a good yield of monobromacetic acid. What structural formulae do you suggest for the original compound and how do you represent the reactions referred to? (C.U.O.S.)

55. What possible structural formulae can you assign to a compound, *A*, of empirical formula, C_8H_8ClON, which behaved as follows? On hydrolysis *A* was converted into a monobasic acid, of molecular weight 60, and a compound *B* which on treatment with nitrous acid gave a product containing 8·9 per cent of nitrogen and 22·4 per cent of chlorine.

56. A saturated monohydric alcohol formed an acetate (ester) with a vapour density = 58. The alcohol on oxidation gave a monocarboxylic acid. 0·200 gm. of this acid required 22·7 c.c. of *N*/10 NaOH for neutralisation. Calculate the equivalent of the acid. Write the possible formula for the original alcohol and the formulae of other alcohols isomeric with it. State what substances would be produced on oxidising each of these isomeric alcohols.

(Vict. Univ. Manch. Ent. Schol.)

57. A compound, *A*, having the percentage composition : C = 20·0 ; O = 26·7 ; N = 46·7 ; H = 6·6 ; gave on gentle heating a compound of the empirical formula, $C_2O_2N_3H_5$. When *A* was allowed to react with nitrous acid, the sole products were nitrogen, water and carbon dioxide. Deduce the structural formula of *A* and write equations for the reactions involved.

58. A compound, *A*, having the percentage composition : carbon = 49·31, hydrogen, 9·59, oxygen, 21·92, nitrogen, 19·18 was hydrolysed. One of the two products obtained was a volatile liquid, *B*. The percentage composition of *B* was : carbon, 62·07 ; hydrogen,

10·35 ; oxygen, 27·58, and its vapour density was 29. It did not reduce ammoniacal silver oxide solution. What are the compounds? What was the other product of the hydrolysis? (C.U.O.S.)

59. A compound gave C, 27·22 per cent, H, 4·57 per cent. 0·1105 gm. of the substance gave 30·2 c.c. of nitrogen collected over 30 per cent potassium hydroxide solution at 15° and 754 mm. On being boiled with sodium hydroxide solution, the substance evolved ammonia and the residual solution behaved as follows : (*a*) after acidifying with dilute sulphuric acid and warming it decolorised potassium permanganate solution ; (*b*) after acidifying with acetic acid and then adding calcium chloride solution, a white precipitate was formed. Deduce the formula of the original compound and account for the above reactions.

[Vapour pressure of potassium hydroxide solution at 15° = 8·5 mm. 1 c.c. of nitrogen at *N.T.P.* weighs 0·001251 gm.] (C.U.O.S.)

60. 7·8 c.c. of a gaseous organic compound containing carbon, hydrogen and oxygen was exploded with 50 c.c. (excess) of oxygen, and the contraction after explosion was 15·6 c.c. Treatment with potash removed a further 15·6 c.c. of the gas (all volumes measured at the same pressure and constant room temperature). Deduce the molecular formula of the gas, given that 1 litre of the gas at *N.T.P.* weighs 2·04 gm.

61. The hydrochloride of a monacid base contains 37·2 per cent of chlorine. The quaternary ammonium iodide by treating the base with methyl iodide contains 59·1 per cent of iodine. What is the constitution of the base? (C.U.O.S.)

62. A compound, *A*, of empirical formula, C_7H_6O, was heated with acetic anhydride and gave, among other products, acetic acid and a monobasic acid, *B*, of empirical formula $C_9H_8O_2$. Treated with hydroxylamine *A* gave a compound of empirical formula C_7H_7NO. The acid, *B*, gave with bromine a compound, *D*, containing 52 per cent of bromine. Deduce the structural formulae of the compounds *A*, *B*, *C* and *D* and write equations to represent the reactions involved.

63. The ester of a certain acid, containing carbon, hydrogen and oxygen only, with a monohydric alcohol gave C, 59·9 per cent, H, 9·0 per cent, and had a vapour density about 100. When 1·525 gm. were boiled with normal soda, 15·1 c.c. of the soda were neutralised. When the ester was shaken with concentrated aqueous ammonia, a product was obtained which contained 24·1 per cent of nitrogen. The acid obtained from the ester gave an anhydride on heating. Suggest possible formulae for the ester. (C.U.O.S.)

64. 0·360 gm. of an organic compound gave 0·770 gm. of carbon dioxide and 0·236 gm. of water. 0·200 gm. of the same compound gave, by Dumas' method, 54·6 c.c. of nitrogen measured at *N.T.P.* Boiled with hydrochloric acid, the compound gave two products, a

monobasic acid containing 26 per cent of carbon and an amine whose hydrochloride contained 53 per cent of chlorine. What conclusions can you draw concerning the structural formula of the original compound?

65. When tartaric acid is distilled with potassium bisulphate, an acid liquid containing 40·9 per cent of carbon and 4·5 of hydrogen is obtained together with other substances. The molecular weight of the compound is 88 and it reacts with phenylhydrazine. Suggest a constitutional formula for the compound, and state how you would expect it to react with reducing agents. Indicate a possible mechanism for the production of this compound from tartaric acid. (C.U.O.S.)

66. Elucidate the following reactions : an amine, *A*, containing 31·1 per cent of nitrogen was treated with sodium nitrite and dilute hydrochloric acid and gave a product, *B*, containing 38 per cent of nitrogen. When *A* was allowed to react with an excess of acetyl chloride it gave a product, *C*, of which 1 gm. required 11·5 c.c. of normal sodium hydroxide for complete hydrolysis.

67. An organic compound, *A*, containing carbon, hydrogen and oxygen only, gave C = 68·6 per cent and H = 11·4 per cent. The compound did not reduce ammoniacal silver nitrate solution, and on oxidation gave propionic acid as one of the products. Treated with nitrous acid and subsequently with dilute sulphuric acid, *A* was converted into a compound, *B*, of empirical formula C_2H_3O. The action of hydroxylamine on *B* gave two compounds, *C* and *D*, of empirical formulae $C_4H_8O_2N$ and C_2H_4ON, respectively. Deduce the structural formulae of the compounds *A*, *B*, *C* and *D*.

68. When formic acid vapour was passed slowly through a long glass tube maintained at 300° complete decomposition occurred and 21·6 c.c. of a mixture of gases was collected which behaved as follows. On treatment with potash solution the volume decreased to 15·2 c.c. 23 c.c. of oxygen were then added and the mixture exploded. The volume after explosion was 24·2 c.c., and this decreased to 15·4 c.c. on treatment with potash. Discuss these results and give what explanations you can. (C.U.O.S.)

69. A dibasic organic acid gave, on analysis, C = 41·4 per cent ; H = 3·5 per cent ; O = 55·1 per cent. Treated with bromine it formed an addition product containing 58 per cent of bromine. The acid was convertible by the action of heat into a compound of the molecular formula, $C_4H_2O_3$. Write the structural formula of one acid which will behave in this way and give equations for the reactions involved.

70. A compound giving the following results on analysis, C, 15·1 ; H, 2·5 ; N, 17·6 ; Cl, 44·65 per cent reacts with potassium hydroxide to form potassium cyanate and with alcohol to form the compound $C_3H_7O_2N$. What constitutions would you assign to the original compound? (C.U.O.S.)

71. (*a*) Three isomeric organic acids have the following percentage composition: C, 44·0; H, 2·1; O, 16·75; Cl, 37·17. Each gives a silver salt, and on ignition of 2·0 gm. of the salt each of these silver salts yields a product containing 0·725 gm. of silver. On decarboxylation by heating with soda-lime each of the original isomers gives the same dichlorobenzene. What is the orientation of this, and what are the structures of the three isomers?

(*b*) The hydrochloride of a mono-amino-acid of formula

$$NH_2 . C_nH_{2n} . COOH$$

contained 28·3 per cent of chlorine. Give the full structural formulae of all the mono-amino-acids which satisfy these data.

(N.U.J.B. Schol.)

72. A compound *A* dissolves in water giving a solution with an acid reaction. After neutralisation this solution yields with silver nitrate a precipitate containing 65·06 per cent of silver. When *A* is boiled with an ethyl alcoholic solution of sulphuric acid it yields a neutral liquid with a vapour density of approximately 90 from which, after heating with sodium hydroxide and acidification, *A* can be recovered. Suggest a possible formula, or formulae, for *A*. Give your reasons. (C.U.O.S.)

73. Analysis of an aromatic oxygen-containing substance *A* gives the following figures: C, 49·0; H, 3·5; N, 8·2; Cl, 20·7 per cent. Hot aqueous alkali converts it into a halogen-free compound, *B*, for which C = 55·0; H = 4·6; N = 9·1 per cent. Chromic acid mixture oxidises *B* to an acid *C* of the same number of carbon atoms per molecule. When *C* is heated with tin and hydrochloric acid and the product brominated in aqueous alcoholic solution, it yields a substance *D*, for which the following analytical figures were found: C, 22·4; H, 1·1; N, 3·8; Br, 64·1 per cent. Deduce the structures of *A*, *B*, *C* and *D*. (A.R.I.C.)

74. What structure would you assign to a compound which behaved as follows. On analysis it gave C = 55·1; S = 10·5; H = 4·9; N = 13·8 per cent. On reduction with tin and hydrochloric acid it gave two products *A* and *B* of the percentage composition *A*: C, 41·6; H, 4·0; S, 18·5 per cent, and *B*: C, 70·6; H, 8·8; N, 20·6. The substance *A* can be synthesised by heating aniline sulphate.

75. A monobasic acid, *A*, found to contain C, 33·2 per cent, H, 5·0 per cent and Br, 44·2 per cent is converted by boiling aqueous potassium carbonate into an acid, *B*, free from halogen and containing C, 50·8 per cent, H, 8·5 per cent. Hot sulphuric acid acts on *B* to yield an acid, *C*, having C, 60·0 per cent and H, 8·0 per cent. The acid *C* was also produced directly from *A* by the action of alcoholic potassium hydroxide and was reconverted into *A* by the action of hydrogen bromide. Oxidation of *B* in hot acid solution yields methylethylketone and carbon dioxide. Explain these reactions and write formulae for *A*, *B* and *C*. (A.R.I.C.)

76. A substance, *A*, having the properties of a ketone gave C = 38·9 per cent, H = 5·4 per cent, Cl = 38·4 per cent. By the action of zinc *A* was converted into a compound *B* which gave C = 63·2 per cent, H = 8·8 per cent. When *B* was heated under pressure with ammonia it gave a compound *C* of the percentage composition: C = 75·8; H = 9·5; N = 14·7. The compound *C* dissolved in potassium hydroxide to form a potassium derivative. Trace the reactions involved.

77. What structural formula would you assign to a compound, *A*, which gave the following reactions. On vigorous reduction, *A* gave two compounds *B* and *C* of the percentage composition: (*B*) C = 78·5; H, 8·4; N = 13·1; (*C*) C = 77·4; H = 7·5; N = 15·05. The original compound *A* could not be diazotised, but it was converted into an isomeric substance, *D*, capable of diazotisation, by boiling with concentrated hydrochloric acid. When 1 gm. of *D* was allowed to react with nitrous acid at ordinary temperature approximately 110 c.c. of nitrogen measured at *N.T.P.* was obtained.

78. An optically active compound, *A*, gave C = 40 per cent, H = 6·7 per cent. On oxidation there was found among other products a compound, *B*, which had the percentage composition: C = 30·0; H = 3·3. *B* was optically inactive. 2 gm. of the fully acetylated derivative of *A* required 12·7 c.c. of *N* NaOH for complete hydrolysis. Deduce the structural formulae of the compounds *A* and *B*.

79. Elucidate the following reactions. A compound, *A*, of the percentage composition C = 81·5; H = 8·7; O = 9·9, formed a monoxime, *B*, with hydroxylamine. When *B* was treated with phosphorus pentachloride it underwent a Beckmann change and was converted to an isomeric compound *C*. On hydrolysis *C* gave two compounds, *D* and *E*, of the percentage compositions C = 61·0; H = 15·3; N = 23·7, and C = 70·6; H = 5·9, O = 23·5 respectively. The consecutive action of nitrous acid and an oxidising agent converted *D* into acetone. The compound, *E*, on vigorous oxidation gave a compound, *F*, of the formula $C_8H_4O_3$.

80. A compound having the properties of a dibasic acid had the percentage composition C = 40·7; H = 5·1; O = 54·2. When the sodium salt of this acid was heated with benzaldehyde in the presence of acetic anhydride a compound having C = 64·1 per cent and H = 4·8 per cent was obtained and on heating this compound lost carbon dioxide to form a monobasic acid. The latter on reduction gave an acid of the empirical formula C_5H_6O, the acid chloride of which, when heated with aluminium chloride, gave a compound of ketonic properties and having C = 82·2 per cent; H = 6·8 per cent. The ketone on oxidation is converted in phthalic acid. Elucidate these reactions.

81. Distillation of the ketodicarboxylic acid,

$$CO(CH_2CH_2CH_2COOH)_2,$$

yields a substance, $C_9H_{12}O_4$, soluble in aqueous sodium carbonate with effervescence and deposited unchanged from the solution on acidification. This substance gives a violet coloration with ferric chloride. It reacts with hydroxylamine to give a compound $C_9H_{14}O_4N_2$ and with nitrous acid to produce a substance of the composition $C_9H_{13}O_6N$. When the latter is warmed with concentrated sulphuric acid and the mixture poured into cold water, glutaric and succinic acids and ammonia are produced, a Beckmann change having occurred. Give a detailed interpretation of these facts. (F.R.I.C.)

CHAPTER XVI

MAXIMUM WORK OF PHYSICAL CHANGE

1. Maximum work of a physical or chemical change

In the calculation of the work of isothermal expansion given in Chapter VII, it is assumed that the pressure of the expanding gas is, at any instant, only infinitesimally greater than the opposing pressure. For a small increase in volume, ΔV, the work done has been written $p\Delta V$; this will not be true unless the pressure is very nearly balanced by an opposing pressure. In the extreme case of a gas expanding into a vacuum no work would be done. The **maximum** work of expansion will be obtained, therefore, when the pressure of the gas, p, is, at any time, opposed by a pressure $(p-dp)$. This is a **reversible** method of conducting the expansion, since a slight increase of the opposing pressure to $(p+dp)$ would reverse the process. The maximum work of a process is obtained, therefore, when the process is conducted reversibly. The work of expansion of a gas, as calculated on p. 141, is the maximum work theoretically obtainable.

2. Maximum work of isothermal dilution

As in Fig. 18, let p_1 = the vapour pressure of the pure solvent, for example, water, at temperature T°, and let p_2 = the vapour pressure of the same solvent, at temperature T°, over a solution of a non-volatile solute, for example, urea, in this solvent. It is assumed that the quantity of solution is sufficiently large that one gm.-molecule of the pure solvent may be added to the solution without change in the value of p_2. This assumption is clearly justifiable, since the result obtained by the following method would be the same if the transfer involved only a small quantity, dx gm.-molecules of the solvent. The transfer of one gm.-molecule of the solvent from the pure solvent to the solution is then effected reversibly in the following three-stage process.

(1) 1 gm.-molecule of the pure solvent is allowed to vaporise against a constant pressure, $(p_1 - dp_1)$, which is slightly less

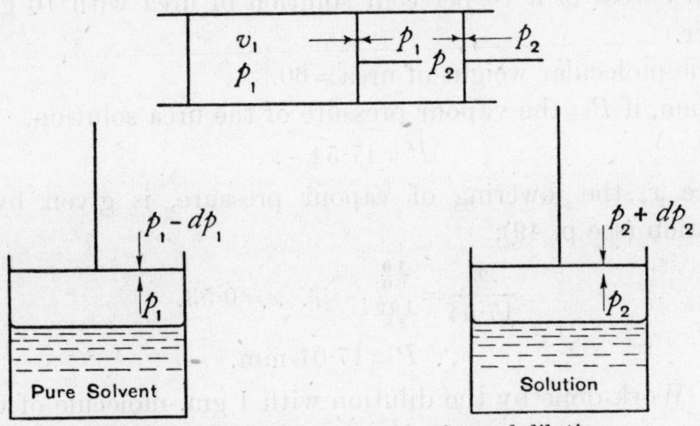

FIG. 18. Maximum work of isothermal dilution.

than the vapour pressure of the pure solvent. If the increase in volume, due to vaporisation, is v_1, then :

$$\text{work done} = \text{maximum work} = (p_1 - dp_1)v_1$$
$$= \mathbf{p_1 v_1} \text{ when } dp_1 \to 0.$$

This work is done *by* the system against the opposing pressure.

(2) The vapour is then allowed to expand isothermally until its volume is v_2 and pressure is p_2 $(p_1 > p_2)$. Then :

$$\text{maximum work done} = \int_{p_1}^{p_2} p\,dv = \mathbf{RT \log_e \frac{p_1}{p_2}},$$

since mass of vapour = 1 gm.-molecule.

This work is done *by* the system against an opposing pressure.

(3) The vapour is now condensed into the solution by means of an applied pressure $= p_2 + dp_2$. Then :

$$\text{work done} = \text{maximum work} = (p_2 + dp_2)v_2$$
$$= \mathbf{p_2 v_2} \text{ when } dp_2 \to 0.$$

This work is done *on* the system by the applied pressure.

∴ Maximum work of the process

$$= p_1 v_1 + RT \log_e \frac{p_1}{p_2} - p_2 v_2.$$

But $\qquad p_1 v_1 = p_2 v_2.$

$$\therefore \text{ Maximum work of the process} = \mathbf{RT \log_e \frac{p_1}{p_2}}. \quad ...(113)$$

Example 136. The vapour pressure of water at 20° is 17·54 mm. Calculate the maximum work of the isothermal dilution of an excess of a 10 per cent solution of urea with 10 gm. of water.

The molecular weight of urea = 60.

Then, if P = the vapour pressure of the urea solution,

$$P = 17{\cdot}54 - x,$$

where x, the lowering of vapour pressure, is given by the equation (see p. 49):

$$\frac{x}{17{\cdot}54} = \frac{\frac{10}{60}}{\frac{100}{18}}. \quad \therefore\ x = 0{\cdot}53.$$

$$\therefore\ P = 17{\cdot}01 \text{ mm.}$$

∴ Work done by the dilution with 1 gm.-molecule of water

$$= RT \log_e \frac{17{\cdot}54}{17{\cdot}01} = 2 \times 293 \times 2{\cdot}303 \times \log_{10} \frac{17{\cdot}54}{17{\cdot}01} \text{ cal.}$$

∴ Work done by dilution with 10 gm. of water

$$= \frac{10}{18} \times 2 \times 293 \times 2{\cdot}303 \times \log_{10} \frac{17{\cdot}54}{17{\cdot}01} \text{ cal.}$$

$$= \mathbf{10{\cdot}1 \text{ cal.}}$$

The same principle can be applied to the calculation of the maximum work of other physical changes, as shown in the following examples.

Example 137. The vapour pressure of ice at − 10° is 1·947 mm., and the vapour pressure of water (supercooled) at the same temperature is 2·144 mm. What is the maximum work of the conversion of 1 gm.-molecule † of water (18 gm.) into ice at this temperature?

The three-stage process is :

(*a*) Allow 1 gm.-molecule of water to vaporise at temperature − 10° against the constant pressure infinitesimally less than 2·144 mm.

(*b*) Allow this volume of vapour to expand reversibly to a pressure = 1·947 mm.

† Although water in the liquid state is highly associated and contains molecular complexes of the type $(H_2O)_n$, the method of derivation of maximum work involves 1 gm.-molecule of water vapour, that is, 18 gm.

(*c*) Condense the vapour on to the ice at a pressure infinitesimally greater than 1·947 mm.

Then the maximum work per gm.-molecule

$$=RT \log_e \frac{2\cdot144}{1\cdot947} = 2 \times 263 \times 2\cdot303 \times \log_{10} \frac{2\cdot144}{1\cdot947} \text{ cal.}$$

$$=50\cdot6 \text{ cal.}$$

Example 138. At 40°, the dissociation pressure of the system: $CuSO_4 . 5H_2O \rightleftharpoons CuSO_4 . 3H_2O + 2H_2O$ is 23·2 mm. At the same temperature the vapour pressure of water is 55·1 mm. Calculate the maximum work of the change:

$$CuSO_4 . 3H_2O + 2H_2O = CuSO_4 . 5H_2O.$$

The system: $CuSO_4 . 3H_2O + 2H_2O \rightleftharpoons CuSO_4 . 5H_2O$ is only in equilibrium at the temperature stated when the pressure of water vapour is 23·2 mm. The addition of water vapour to the system momentarily increases the aqueous vapour pressure; the water vapour is then removed as $CuSO_4 . 5H_2O$ until the original dissociation pressure is reached.

The three-stage process is, therefore:

(*a*) Vaporise 2 gm.-molecules of water at its constant vapour pressure = 55·1 mm.

(*b*) Allow this quantity of vapour to expand isothermally and reversibly to pressure = 23·2 mm. (the dissociation pressure).

(*c*) Condense the two gm.-molecules of water vapour into the system at pressure = 23·2 mm.

Maximum work (per gm.-molecule of $CuSO_4 . 5H_2O$ formed)

$$=2RT \log_e \frac{55\cdot1}{23\cdot2}$$

$$=2 \times 2 \times 313 \times 2\cdot303 \times \log_{10} \frac{55\cdot1}{23\cdot2} \text{ cal.}$$

$$=1080 \text{ cal.}$$

3. The Carnot cycle

The maximum work of a reversible cyclic process is independent of the working substance since this substance is brought finally to its original condition. It is convenient, therefore, to use 1 gm.-molecule of a perfect gas as a working substance, since its behaviour with changes of temperature and pressure is given by the gas equation.

If, as in Fig. 19, the cycle of operations is started at the point A with 1 mol. of a perfect gas at temperature T_1°A and

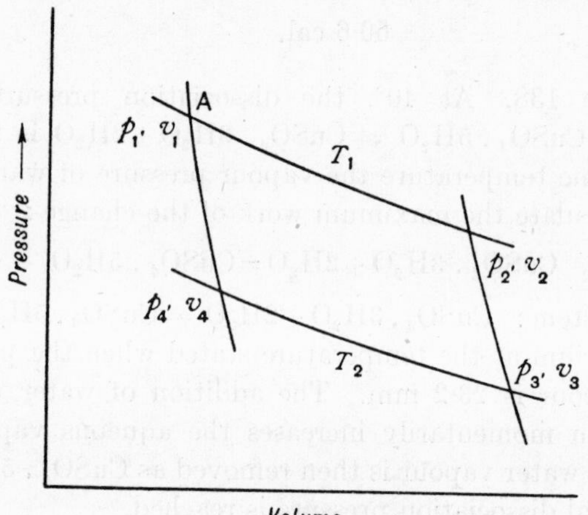

FIG. 19. The Carnot cycle.

pressure p, it occupies a volume v_1 such that $p_1v_1 = RT_1$. It is possible, then, to complete a full cycle of operations so as to bring the working substance back to its original condition at A in the following four stages.

(1) Allow the gas to expand isothermally to the volume v_2 and corresponding pressure, p_2. In this, and subsequent operations, it is assumed that the gas expands or is compressed by means of a frictionless piston, the pressure on which is at all times either infinitesimally smaller (for expansion) or infinitesimally larger (for contraction) than the pressure of the gas. The processes are, therefore, reversible, and any work done by the gas is its maximum work. Since, for isothermal expansion, T_1 remains constant and the internal energy is independent of its volume :

$$\underset{\text{(heat absorbed)}}{q_1} = \underset{\text{(work done)}}{w_1} = RT_1 \log_e \frac{p_1}{p_2}$$

$$= RT_1 \log_e \frac{v_2}{v}.$$

(2) The gas is allowed to expand adiabatically to reach the isothermal at T_2 ($T_1 > T_2$), where the gas has volume v_3 and pressure p_3. No heat is absorbed in the process :

$$\underset{(w_2)}{\text{Work done}} = \frac{R(T_1 - T_2)}{\gamma - 1} \quad \text{(see p. 144).}$$

(3) The gas is compressed isothermally at temperature T_2 to volume v_4 and corresponding pressure p_4, at which point it lies on the adiabatic through A.

$$\therefore \underset{\text{(heat evolved)}}{-q_2} = \underset{\text{(work done on the gas)}}{-w_3} = -RT_2 \log_e \frac{p_4}{p_3}$$

$$= -RT_2 \log_e \frac{v_3}{v_4}.$$

(4) Finally, the gas is compressed along the adiabatic until it reaches its original state at A.

$$\text{Work done on the gas} = -w_4 = -\frac{R(T_1 - T_2)}{\gamma - 1}.$$

Since the work of adiabatic expansion (stage 2) is equal but opposite to the work of adiabatic compression (stage 4) :

$\therefore$ Total work done by the gas $= w_1 - w_3$

$$= RT_1 \log_e \frac{v_2}{v_1} - RT_2 \log \frac{v_3}{v_4}.$$

But for adiabatic expansion from v_2 to v_3 :

$$p_2 v_2^{\gamma} = p_3 v_3^{\gamma}.$$

$$\therefore \frac{RT_1}{v_2} \cdot v_2^{\gamma} = \frac{RT_2}{v_3} \cdot v_3^{\gamma};$$

$$\therefore \frac{v_2}{v_3} = \left(\frac{T_2}{T_1}\right)^{\gamma - 1}.$$

Similarly, for adiabatic compression :

$$\frac{v_1}{v_4} = \left(\frac{T_2}{T_1}\right)^{\gamma - 1};$$

$$\therefore \frac{v_2}{v_3} = \frac{v_1}{v_4} \quad \text{and} \quad \frac{v_2}{v_1} = \frac{v_3}{v_4}.$$

$$\therefore \text{ Total work done} = w_1 - w_3$$

$$= RT_1 \log_e \frac{v_2}{v_1} - RT_2 \log_e \frac{v_3}{v_4}$$

$$= R \log_e \frac{v_2}{v_1}(T_1 - T_2).$$

$$\therefore \frac{\text{Heat absorbed at temperature } T_1}{\text{work done by the gas}} = \frac{q}{w_1 - w_3}$$

$$= \frac{RT_1 \log_e \frac{v_2}{v_1}}{R(T_1 - T_2)\log_e \frac{v_2}{v_1}} = \frac{T_1}{T_1 - T_2}.$$

Putting $w_1 - w_3 = W =$ work done by the gas, we have :

$$\frac{W}{q_1} = \frac{T_1 - T_2}{T_1},$$

or for small differences of temperature between the isothermals :

$$\frac{\Delta W}{\Delta T} = \frac{q}{T}, \quad \text{......................(114)}$$

where q is the heat absorbed at temperature T.

4. Maximum work and free energy

The maximum work of the change of a substance from one state to another is obtained when the change is completely reversible ; it is also dependent solely upon the initial and final states of the system. For any system, therefore, we may assign a property which can be called the maximum work function (denoted by A). Then in passing from one state to another, the maximum work function will alter by a fixed amount ΔA. The maximum work of which such a change is capable can be divided into (*a*) work done by expansion, (*b*) all other work, for example, electrical work. Then if the latter is denoted by W, we shall have for any change at constant pressure and temperature :

$$\underset{\substack{\text{(decrease in}\\\text{work function)}}}{-\Delta A} = W + p\Delta V.$$

The term $p\Delta V$, being the work of expansion, is unavoidably associated with the change and does not represent work which is available for any specific purpose, for example, as electrical work. The term W may, therefore, be regarded as that portion of the maximum work which is the net work of the change; it is usually denoted by ΔF and called the change in free energy.† Corresponding with the maximum work function, we may define a free energy function by F (since $p\Delta V$ depends solely upon the initial and final states of the system).

The term W can be equated, therefore, to $-\Delta F$.

$$\therefore \quad -\Delta A = -\Delta F + p\Delta V,$$

or

$$\Delta A = \Delta F - p\Delta V.$$

Since spontaneous changes are those which are capable of doing work, a system will be in equilibrium when the work of a small change in the system $=0$. These conditions are expressed by the equations:

$$(\Delta A)_{T,v} = 0, \quad \text{..........................(115)}$$

$$(\Delta F)_{T,p} = 0. \quad \text{..........................(116)}$$

5. Change in free energy due to the isothermal reversible expansion of a gas

The change in free energy is related to the maximum work content by the equation:

$$\Delta A = \Delta F - p\Delta V, \quad \text{.....................(116a)}$$

where the pressure is constant. This equation can then be written:

$$\Delta A = \Delta F - \Delta(pV).$$

For a gas expanding isothermally and reversibly:

$$\int \Delta A = -RT \log_e \frac{p_1}{p_2} \quad \text{(see p. 141).}$$

$$\therefore \quad -RT \log_e \frac{p_1}{p_2} = \int_{p_2}^{p_1} \Delta F + \int_{p_2}^{p_1} \Delta(pV).$$

But since the gas is assumed to obey the gas equation

$$\int_{p_2}^{p_1} \Delta(pV) = 0.$$

† The symbol G is also used to denote the free energy function. Then net work $= -\Delta G$.

$$\therefore \int_{p_2}^{p_1} \Delta F = \text{increase in free energy}$$

$$= -RT \log_e \frac{p_1}{p_2}.$$

$$\therefore \text{Decrease in free energy} = +\mathbf{RT} \log_e \frac{\mathbf{p_1}}{\mathbf{p_2}}. \quad \text{......(117)}$$

6. Change of free energy due to the isothermal evaporation of a liquid

A result which is of great importance in the use of free energy equations (cf. p. 345) is the change of free energy associated with the conversion of a liquid into its vapour when the latter is at 1 atmosphere pressure. The process can be considered as taking place in two stages :

Liquid → saturated vapour, pressure, p → vapour at 1 atmosphere pressure

Since the liquid is in equilibrium with its saturated vapour, the net work of the first stage is zero (the only work done is the work of expansion against the constant pressure, p, and is equal to $p\Delta V$). The net work of the second stage

$$= RT \log_e \left(\frac{p}{1}\right) \quad \text{(see p. 141).}$$

$$\therefore \text{Net work of the process} = RT \log_e \left(\frac{p}{1}\right). \quad \text{......(118)}$$

$$= \text{decrease in free energy of the system}$$

$$= -\Delta F.$$

7. The Clapeyron-Clausius equation

The Clapeyron-Clausius equation is usually written in the form :

$$\frac{dP}{dT} = \frac{q}{T(V_b - V_a)},$$

where V_a = the volume of a given mass of the substance in one physical state, V_b = volume occupied by the same mass of the substance in a different physical state, T = the temperature in °A. at which the change from one state to the other takes place at a pressure, P, and q = the latent heat of the change. The equation may be deduced in the following manner.

In Fig. 20, let the curves $ABCD$ and $EFGH$ be the isothermals of a given substance at temperature T and $(T+dT)$ respectively. In the curve $ABCD$, AB is the vapour pressure-volume for the substance in one physical state, BC is the line

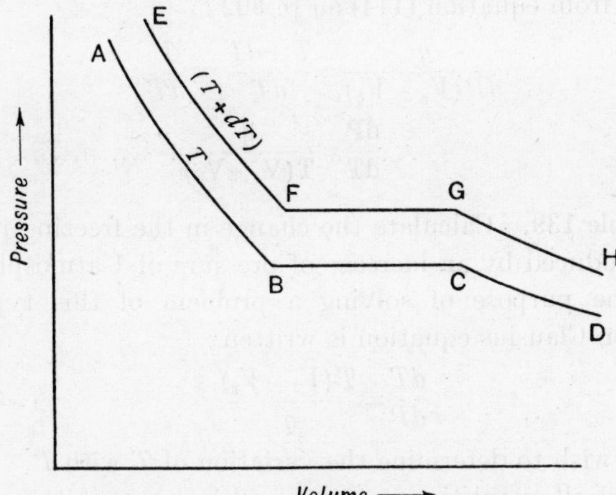

FIG. 20. The Clapeyron-Clausius equation.

of constant pressure corresponding with the change of state, and CD is the vapour pressure-volume curve for the substance in its new physical state, all at temperature, T. EF, FG and GH are the corresponding vapour pressure-volume curves at temperature $(T+dT)$.

The following cycle of operations can then be performed :

(1) Starting with a given mass of the substance at B, allow the temperature to rise to $(T+dT)$ and the pressure to $(P+dP)$ (adiabatic).

(2) Allow the substance to change its state at temperature $(T+dT)$, the volume increasing from V_a to V_b, that is, from B to C (isothermal). Let the heat absorbed be q. This is the latent heat of the change of state.

(3) Decrease the temperature to its original value, the temperature falling to T (adiabatic).

(4) Abstract heat from the system so that the substance reverts to its original physical state at B (isothermal).

Therefore :

Heat absorbed at $(T+dT)=q$.

Work done = area $FGCB \doteq (P+dP)(V_a - V_b) - P(V_a - V_b) = dP(V_a - V_b)$.

Then, from equation (114) on p. 302 :

$$\frac{q}{dP(V_a - V_b)} = \frac{T+dT}{dT} \doteq \frac{T}{dT};$$

$$\therefore \ \frac{\mathrm{dP}}{\mathrm{dT}} = \frac{\mathrm{q}}{\mathrm{T}(\mathrm{V_a} - \mathrm{V_b})}. \quad \text{.................(119)}$$

Example 139. Calculate the change in the freezing point of water produced by an increase of pressure of 1 atmosphere.

For the purpose of solving a problem of this type, the Clapeyron-Clausius equation is written :

$$\frac{dT}{dP} = \frac{T(V_l - V_s)}{q},$$

since we wish to determine the variation of T with P.

Then, if all quantities are expressed in C.G.S. units :

q = latent heat of fusion of 1 gm. of ice at 0°

$= 80$ cal. $= 80 \times 4{\cdot}2 \times 10^7$ ergs.

V_l = volume of 1 gm. of water at 0° = 1·000 c.c.

V_s = volume of 1 gm. of ice at 0° = 1·091 c.c.

T = temperature of fusion of ice at 1 atmosphere pressure

$= 0° = 273°\ A$.

$$\therefore \ \frac{dT}{dP} = \frac{273(1{\cdot}000 - 1{\cdot}091)}{80 \times 4{\cdot}2 \times 10^7} = -7{\cdot}4 \times 10^{-9} \text{ in } ° \text{ per dyne.}$$

To convert the lowering to ° per atmosphere, we note that :

Pressure in dynes per sq. cm. due to 76 cm. of mercury

$= 76 \times 13{\cdot}6 \times 981 \doteq 10^6$.

$$\therefore \ \frac{dT}{dP} = -7{\cdot}4 \times 10^{-9} \times 10^6 = -0{\cdot}0074° \text{ per atmosphere.}$$

The negative value obtained for $\frac{dT}{dP}$ in the foregoing example shows that the melting point of ice is lowered by an increase in pressure. The same result can be obtained qualitatively by the application of Le Chatelier's principle, which may be stated in the following manner : A system, *in equilibrium*, which is subjected to any strain, behaves in such a way as to remove or minimise the effect of that strain. Since the melting of ice is accompanied by a decrease in volume, the effect of increase in pressure can be minimised by melting. Ice, therefore, will tend to melt as the pressure on it is increased. In all examples in which the sign of $\frac{dT}{dP}$ or $\frac{dP}{dT}$ is not clear, Le Chatelier's principle should be applied.

Example 140. The transition point of α-sulphur to β-sulphur is 96·00° at 1 atmosphere pressure. At this temperature the densities of α- and β-sulphur are 2·03 gm. per c.c. and 1·98 gm. per c.c. respectively. The heat absorbed in the change is 77 cal. per gm.-atom. What is the transition temperature at 10 atmospheres pressure?

1 gm. of α-sulphur occupies $\frac{1}{2{\cdot}03}$ c.c. $=0{\cdot}493$ c.c. and 1 gm. of β-sulphur occupies $\frac{1}{1{\cdot}98}$ c.c. $=0{\cdot}505$ c.c. According to Le Chatelier's principle, therefore, an increase of pressure will tend to prevent the change α-sulphur to β-sulphur since this change is accompanied by an increase in volume. The transition temperature, therefore, will be raised by an increase in pressure. Then, as in example 139:

$$\frac{dT}{dP}=\frac{369\,(0{\cdot}505-0{\cdot}493)}{(77/32)\times 4{\cdot}2\times 10^7}\times 10^6 \text{ degree/atmosphere.}$$

$$\doteqdot 0{\cdot}044 \text{ degree/atmosphere.}$$

$\therefore$ Transition temperature at 10 atmospheres pressure

$$=96{\cdot}00+(10\times 0{\cdot}044)=96{\cdot}44°.$$

When the change of state is from solid to gas or from liquid to gas or is the reverse of either of these changes, the Clapeyron-Clausius equation can be modified by means of the gas equation.

If V_l = the volume of 1 gm.-molecule of the substance as a liquid (or solid) and V_g = the volume of 1 gm.-molecule of the same substance as a gas (at the *same temperature and pressure*) and q = the latent heat of vaporisation per gm.-molecule, then:

$$\frac{dP}{dT}=\frac{q}{T\,(V_g-V_l)}\doteqdot\frac{q}{TV_g}, \qquad \ldots\ldots\ldots\ldots(119a)$$

since V_g is very large compared with V_l.

But $V_g = \frac{RT}{P}$, since the mass of substance to which equation (119*a*) refers is 1 gm.-molecule.

$$\therefore \frac{dP}{dT} = \frac{Pq}{RT^2},$$

or

$$\frac{1}{P} \cdot \frac{dP}{dT} = \frac{q}{RT^2}. \quad \text{..........................(120)}$$

Example 141. At what pressure (in mm. of mercury) will water boil at 101°?

In equation (120):

$P = 760$ mm.

q = latent heat of steam at 760 mm. pressure per gm.-molecule $= 536 \times 18 = 9660$ cal.

R = the gas constant = 2 cal. per gm.-molecule per degree.

$T = 100° = 373°$ *A*.

$$\therefore \frac{dP}{dT} = \frac{760 \times 9660}{2 \times 373 \times 373} = 27 \text{ mm. per degree.}$$

∴ Pressure at which water boils at 101° = 760 + 27 = 787 mm.

It should be noted that the foregoing calculations assume that the latent heat, q, is a constant over the range of temperature of the question. On this assumption the Clapeyron-Clausius equation can be integrated as follows.

Since

$$\frac{1}{P} \cdot \frac{dP}{dT} = \frac{q}{RT^2},$$

or

$$\frac{d(\log_e P)}{dT} = \frac{q}{RT^2}; \quad \text{......................(120a)}$$

$$\therefore \int d(\log_e P) = \int \frac{q}{RT^2}\, dT,$$

or

$$\log_e P = -\frac{q}{RT} + K, \quad \text{................(121)}$$

where K = the constant of integration.

Assuming P to have values P_1 and P_2 at temperatures T_1 and T_2 respectively, then:

$$\log_e P_2 - \log_e P_1 = -\frac{q}{R}\left(\frac{1}{T_2} - \frac{1}{T_1}\right)$$

$$= -\frac{q}{R}\left(\frac{T_1 - T_2}{T_1 T_2}\right)$$

$$= \frac{q}{R}\left(\frac{T_2 - T_1}{T_1 T_2}\right).$$

$$\therefore\ q = R \,.\, 2{\cdot}303 \log_{10}\left(\frac{P_2}{P_1}\right)\left(\frac{T_1 T_2}{T_2 - T_1}\right)$$

$$= \mathbf{4{\cdot}606 \log_{10}\left(\frac{P_2}{P_1}\right)\left(\frac{T_1 T_2}{T_2 - T_1}\right)} \ . \ \ldots\ldots\ldots\ldots\ldots(122)$$

Example 142. The dissociation pressure of calcium carbonate at 750° is 68·0 mm. and at 800° it is 168·0 mm. Calculate the heat of dissociation of calcium carbonate over the given range of temperature.

Since the volumes of calcium carbonate and calcium oxide may be neglected, the Clapeyron-Clausius equation can be applied to give the heat of dissociation per gm.-molecule of carbon dioxide formed, that is, per gm.-molecule of calcium carbonate dissociated.

∴ Heat of dissociation per gm.-molecule of calcium carbonate

$$= 4{\cdot}606 \times \log_{10}\left(\frac{168}{68}\right) \times \frac{1023 \times 1073}{1073 - 1023}$$

$$= \mathbf{39{,}770\ cal.}$$ (See also pp. 312. and 346)

Example 143. The dissociation pressure of magnesium sulphate, $MgSO_4 . 7H_2O$, is 35·6 mm. at 35° and 47·2 mm. at 40°, the hydrated salt being in equilibrium with the anhydrous salt. Calculate the heat absorbed in the dissociation :

$$MgSO_4 . 7H_2O \rightleftharpoons MgSO_4 + \underset{\text{(vapour)}}{7H_2O}$$

$$\text{Heat of dissociation} = q = 4{\cdot}606 \times \log_{10}\left(\frac{47{\cdot}2}{35{\cdot}6}\right) \times \left(\frac{313 \times 308}{313 - 308}\right)$$

$$= \mathbf{10{,}880\ cal.}$$

This value is the heat of dissociation per gm.-molecule of water formed. Heat required for the complete dissociation of one gm.-molecule of $MgSO_4 . 7H_2O = 7q =$ **76,160 cal.**

Example 144. The vapour pressure of liquid fluorine expressed in mm. of mercury is reproduced by the equation :

$$\log_{10} p = 7{\cdot}01 - \frac{350{\cdot}6}{T}.$$

Calculate the molar heat of evaporation of fluorine. [$R = 1{\cdot}987$ cal. deg.$^{-1}$per mol.] (London B.Sc. Special.)

The molar heat of evaporation (q) is given by the equation :

$$q = R \log_e \left(\frac{p_1}{p_2}\right)\left(\frac{T_1T_2}{T_1 - T_2}\right)$$

$$= 2{\cdot}303R \log_{10}\left(\frac{p_1}{p_2}\right)\left(\frac{T_1T_2}{T_1 - T_2}\right).$$

But $\qquad \log_{10} p_1 = 7{\cdot}01 - \dfrac{350{\cdot}6}{T_1},$

and $\qquad \log_{10} p_2 = 7{\cdot}01 - \dfrac{350{\cdot}6}{T_2}.$

$$\therefore \log_{10}\frac{p_1}{p_2} = \log_{10} p_1 - \log_{10} p_2$$

$$= \left(7{\cdot}01 - \frac{350{\cdot}6}{T_1}\right) - \left(7{\cdot}01 - \frac{350{\cdot}6}{T_2}\right)$$

$$= 350{\cdot}6\left(\frac{T_1 - T_2}{T_1T_2}\right).$$

$$\therefore q = 2{\cdot}303 \times R \times 350{\cdot}6\left(\frac{T_1 - T_2}{T_1T_2}\right) \times \left(\frac{T_1T_2}{T_1 - T_2}\right)$$

$$= 2{\cdot}303 \times 1{\cdot}987 \times 350{\cdot}6$$

$$= \mathbf{1640\ cal.}$$

Example 145. The vapour pressure of mercury between 250° and 435° is given by the equation :

$$\log_{10} p = 9{\cdot}9073436 - 0{\cdot}6519904 \log_{10} T - \frac{3276{\cdot}628}{T},$$

p being in mm. of mercury. What is the latent heat of evaporation at 300°?

Let $\qquad \log_{10} p = X,$

$$\therefore \log_e p = X \,.\, \log_e 10,$$

$$\therefore \frac{d}{dT}(\log_e p) = \frac{dX}{dT} \times \log_e 10$$

$$= \frac{d}{dT}\left(9{\cdot}9073436 - 0{\cdot}6519904 \log_{10} T - \frac{3276{\cdot}628}{T}\right) \times \log_e 10$$

$$= \left(\frac{3276{\cdot}628}{T^2} \times 2{\cdot}303\right) - \frac{0{\cdot}6519904}{T}$$

$$\left(\text{since } 0{\cdot}6519904 \log_{10} T \times \log_e 10 = 0{\cdot}6519904 \log_e T \quad \text{and} \quad \frac{d}{dT}\log_e T = \frac{1}{T}\right).$$

But $$\frac{d}{dT}\log_e p = \frac{q}{RT^2}.$$

$$\therefore q = \left(\frac{3276{\cdot}628}{T^2} \times 2{\cdot}303 - \frac{0{\cdot}6519904}{T}\right) \times RT^2$$

$$= (3276{\cdot}628 \times 2{\cdot}303 - 0{\cdot}6519904T) \times R.$$

Putting $T = 573$ (degrees absolute)

and $R = 2$,

then $q = 14{,}344$ cal. per gm.-molecule.

∴ Latent heat of evaporation of liquid mercury per gm.

$$= \frac{14344}{200{\cdot}6} \text{ cal.}$$

$$= 71{\cdot}5 \text{ cal.}$$

8. Graphical methods (Clapeyron-Clausius equation)

The Clapeyron-Clausius equation :

$$\frac{d(\log_e P)}{dT} = \frac{q}{RT^2}$$

gives, on integration, the equation :

$$\log_e P = -\frac{q}{RT} + C, \quad \text{.....................(122}a\text{)}$$

where C = a constant.

Comparing equation (122a) with the general equation for a straight line :

$$y = mx + c,$$

we see that if $\log_e P$ is plotted against $\frac{1}{T}$ ($\log_e P$ as ordinates, $\frac{1}{T}$ as abscissae), the resulting graph is a straight line whose

slope $= -\frac{q}{R}$ (q being assumed to be constant).

The method of working is shown in the following example.

Example 146. From the following values for the dissociation pressure of calcium carbonate deduce the heat of reaction at constant pressure at 700° :

Temperature (°C.) -	600	650	700	750	800
Pressure (mm. Hg) -	2·35	8·2	25·3	68·0	168·0

(London B.Sc. Honours.)

Since $$\log_e P = -\frac{q}{RT} + C;$$

$$\therefore \log_{10} P \times \log_e 10 = -\frac{q}{RT} + C.$$

If, therefore, we plot $\log_{10} P$ against $\frac{1}{T}$, the slope of the resulting straight line will equal $-\frac{q}{R} \times \frac{1}{\log_e 10}$. The data required for the construction of the graph are given in the following columns :

$T°$	$T°A$	$\frac{1}{T°A}$	P (mm.)	$\log_{10} P$
600	873	0·001146	2·35	0·3711
650	923	0·001083	8·2	0·9138
700	973	0·001028	25·3	1·4031
750	1023	0·0009781	68·0	1·8325
800	1073	0·0009319	168·0	2·2253

The plot of $\log_{10} P$ against $\frac{1}{T° A}$ is shown in Fig. 21. By measurement, the slope of the line $= -\frac{1{\cdot}8}{0{\cdot}00022}$.

$$\therefore \quad -\frac{q}{R} \times \frac{1}{\log_e 10} = -\frac{1{\cdot}8}{0{\cdot}00022};$$

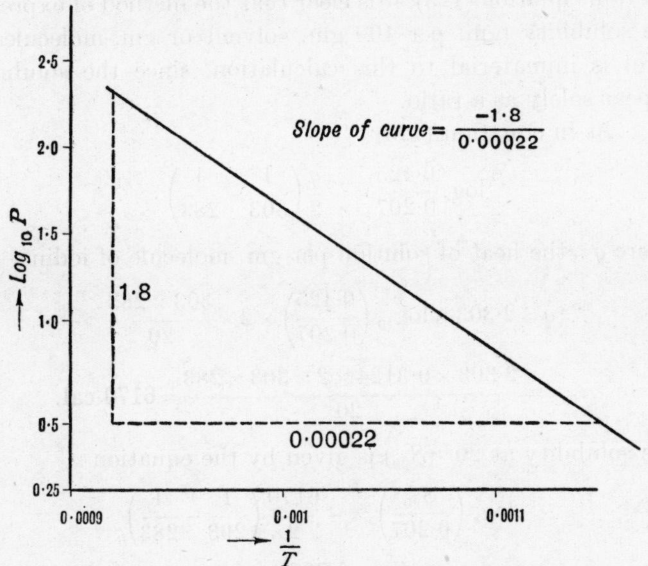

FIG. 21. Graphical application of the Clapeyron-Clausius equation.

$$\therefore\ q=\frac{1{\cdot}8\times 2\times 2{\cdot}303}{0{\cdot}00022}$$

$$=37{,}700 \text{ cal.}$$

9. Calculation of heat of solution

On p. 310 the heat of evaporation has been calculated from the variation of vapour pressure with the temperature. Since, at a given temperature, the solubility of a substance, such as iodine, may be assumed to be proportional to its vapour pressure at that temperature, we can write :

$$\log_e\left(\frac{kS_2}{kS_1}\right)=-\frac{q}{R}\left(\frac{1}{T_2}-\frac{1}{T_1}\right),$$

where S_1 and S_2 are the solubilities at T_1 and T_2 and q = heat of solution per gm.-molecule of the solute.

$$\therefore\ \log_e\left(\frac{S_2}{S_1}\right)=-\frac{q}{R}\left(\frac{1}{T_2}-\frac{1}{T_1}\right). \quad \text{.............(123)}$$

Example 147. The solubility of benzoic acid in water is 0·207 gm. at 10° and 0·425 gm. at 30°. Calculate the mean heat of solution per gm.-molecule and the solubility at 20°.

From equation (123), it is clear that the method of expressing the solubility (gm. per 100 gm. solvent or gm.-molecules per litre) is immaterial to this calculation, since the solubilities appear solely as a ratio.

∴ As in equation (123):

$$\log_e \frac{0{\cdot}425}{0{\cdot}207} = -\frac{q}{2}\left(\frac{1}{303}-\frac{1}{283}\right).$$

where q = the heat of solution per gm.-molecule of iodine.

$$\therefore\ q = 2{\cdot}303 \times \log_{10}\left(\frac{0{\cdot}425}{0{\cdot}207}\right) \times 2 \times \frac{303 \times 283}{20}$$

$$= \frac{2{\cdot}303 \times 0{\cdot}3124 \times 2 \times 303 \times 283}{20} = \mathbf{6170\ cal.}$$

The solubility at 20° (S_{20}) is given by the equation:

$$\log_e\left(\frac{S_{20}}{0{\cdot}207}\right) = -\frac{6170}{2}\left(\frac{1}{293}-\frac{1}{283}\right)$$

$$\therefore\ S_{20} = \mathbf{0{\cdot}296}.$$

10. Trouton's rule

If λ_e = the latent heat of evaporation per gm.-molecule of a liquid and T = the boiling point, then Trouton's rule is given by the equation:

$$\frac{\lambda_e}{T} = \text{a constant} \doteqdot 21. \quad \ldots\ldots\ldots\ldots\ldots\ldots(124)$$

The rule is not valid for substances which are associated, for example, the values for ethyl alcohol and acetic acid are 26·4 and 13·7 respectively.

As an example of the application of the rule, we can use the data of example 144. The boiling point of fluorine is obtained from the equation:

$$\log_{10} 760 = 7{\cdot}01 - \frac{350{\cdot}6}{T},$$

from which $T = 85°\ A$.

$$\therefore\ \frac{\lambda_e}{T} = \frac{1640}{85} \doteqdot 20.$$

It can be assumed, therefore, that fluorine is not associated in the liquid state.

* 11. Integration of the Clapeyron-Clausius equation (general treatment)

For a solid in equilibrium with its saturated vapour:

$$\frac{d \log_e p}{dT} = \frac{\Delta H_e}{RT^2}, \quad \text{......................(124}a\text{)}$$

where H_e = the heat of evaporation of 1 gm.-molecule of the solid at pressure, p, and temperature, T. Since ΔH_e will vary with the temperature, integration of equation (124a) is only possible when the relation between ΔH_e and T is known. The general equation giving this relationship is:

$$\Delta H_e = \Delta H_{e(0)} + \int_0^T \Delta C_p \,.\, dT, \quad \text{................(125)}$$

where $\Delta H_{e(0)}$ = heat of evaporation at $T=0$ and ΔC_p = heat capacity of the vapour − heat capacity of the solid per gm.-molecule.

$$\therefore \quad \frac{d \log_e p}{dT} = \frac{\Delta H_{e(0)}}{RT^2} + \frac{\int_0^T \Delta C_p \, dT}{RT^2}.$$

∴ On integration:

$$\log_e p = -\frac{\Delta H_{e(0)}}{RT} + \int \frac{\int_0^T \Delta C_p \, dT}{RT^2} + i, \quad \text{.......(126)}$$

where i = constant of integration.

On integrating by parts†:

$$\int \frac{\int_0^T \Delta C_p \, dT}{RT^2} = -\frac{\int_0^T \Delta C_p \, dT}{RT} + \int_0^T \frac{\Delta C_p \, dT}{RT};$$

$$\therefore \log_e p = -\frac{\Delta H_{e(0)}}{RT} - \frac{\int_0^T \Delta C_p \, dT}{RT} + \int_0^T \frac{\Delta C_p \, dT}{RT} + i$$

$$= -\frac{\Delta H_e}{RT} + \int_0^T \frac{\Delta C_p \, dT}{RT} + i. \quad \text{.................(127)}$$

from equation (125).

The constant of integration "i" is called the true chemical constant of the substance (cf. p. 407).

† For the method of integration by parts see p. 428.

*** 12. Some important thermodynamical relationships**

The results obtained on p. 302 by means of the Carnot cycle can be expressed by the equation :

$$\frac{Q_1 - Q_2}{Q_1} = \frac{T_1 - T_2}{T_1};$$

$$\therefore \frac{Q_1}{T_1} = \frac{Q_2}{T_2} \quad \text{and} \quad \frac{Q_1}{T_1} - \frac{Q_2}{T_2} = 0.$$

The quantity $\frac{Q_1}{T_1}$ = change of **entropy** at temperature T_1 and is denoted by ΔS_1.

Writing similarly $\frac{Q_2}{T_2} = \Delta S_2$:

$$\Delta S_1 - \Delta S_2 = 0,$$

that is, increase of entropy at temperature T_1 = decrease of entropy at temperature T_2. For a complete reversible cycle, therefore, S (the entropy of the system) remains constant, that is, $\Delta S = 0$. In any natural, that is, spontaneous, process irreversible effects, such as the dissipation of heat due to friction, occur and the work done is not the maximum work. In such a process, therefore :

$$\frac{Q' - Q''}{Q'} < \frac{T_1 - T_2}{T_1},$$

where Q' = heat absorbed at temperature T_1,
and Q'' = heat returned at temperature T_2.

$$\therefore \frac{Q'}{T_1} - \frac{Q''}{T_2} > 0,$$

that is, the entropy of the system increases. Spontaneous processes, therefore, are those which are characterised by an increase in entropy while for a system in equilibrium $\Delta S = 0$.

Equation (73) on p. 140 can now be put into a different form. Since :

$$Q = \Delta U + w + p\Delta V$$

$$= \Delta U - \Delta A;$$

$$\therefore \; -\Delta A = Q - \Delta U \quad \text{and} \quad \Delta A = \Delta U - Q$$

$$= \Delta U - T \cdot \frac{Q}{T} = \Delta U - T\Delta S.$$

Since A, U and S all depend solely upon the state of the system, we can write :

$$\mathrm{A = U - TS.} \qquad \text{.........................(128)}$$

The free energy content, F, can similarly be written (see equation (128)) :

$$\mathrm{F = H - TS.} \qquad \text{.........................(129)}$$

The application of this equation to the calculation of free energy change from thermal data is discussed in Chapter XXI.

Differentiation of equation (128) gives :

$$dA = dU - T\,dS - S\,dT. \qquad \text{..................(130)}$$

But, from equation (75), when the only work done is due to the expansion of the system :

$$dU = dQ - p\,dv;$$

$$\therefore\ dA = dQ - p\,dv - T\,dS - S\,dT. \qquad \text{............(131)}$$

If, now, the volume is kept constant, $p\,dv = 0$, and since $T\,dS = dQ$:

$$dA = -S\,dT;$$

$$\therefore\ \left(\frac{\mathrm{dA}}{\mathrm{dT}}\right)_{\mathrm{v}} = -\mathrm{S}. \qquad \text{............................(132)}$$

Similarly :

$$\left(\frac{\mathrm{dF}}{\mathrm{dT}}\right)_{\mathrm{p}} = -\mathrm{S}. \qquad \text{............................(133)}$$

Also, since $\Delta A = A_1 - A_2$:

$$\left(\frac{\mathrm{d}(\Delta \mathrm{A})}{\mathrm{dT}}\right)_{\mathrm{v}} = -(\mathrm{S_1 - S_2}) = -\Delta \mathrm{S} \qquad \text{..............(134)}$$

and

$$\left(\frac{\mathrm{d}(\Delta \mathrm{F})}{\mathrm{dT}}\right) = -\Delta \mathrm{S}. \qquad \text{..............................(135)}$$

* 13. Calculation of change of entropy

The following examples are illustrative of the methods of calculating entropy changes in physical processes.

Example 148. What are the changes of entropy in the following processes : (*a*) the fusion of 1 gm.-molecule of benzene at its melting point at normal pressure (5·48°), (*b*) the vaporisation of 1 gm.-molecule of water at its normal boiling point, (*c*) the isothermal expansion of 2 gm. of oxygen at 15° from 2 atmospheres pressure to 1 atmosphere pressure?

(*a*) The latent heat of fusion of benzene

$$=30 \text{ cal. per gm.} = 30 \times 78 \text{ cal. per gm.-molecule.}$$

$$\therefore \ \Delta S = \frac{Q}{T} = \frac{30 \times 78}{(273 + 5{\cdot}48)} = \mathbf{8{\cdot}40\ cal./degree.}$$

(*b*) The latent heat of steam $=540$ cal. per gm.

$$\therefore \text{ As in } (a): \ \Delta S = \frac{540 \times 18}{373} = \mathbf{26\ cal./degree.}$$

(*c*) Since U, the internal energy of a gas is independent of its volume (perfect gas):

heat absorbed = maximum work of expansion

$$= \int_{p_2}^{p_1} RT \log_e \frac{p_1}{p_2} \text{ per gm.-molecule.}$$

$\therefore$ Heat absorbed by 2 gm. of oxygen

$$= \frac{R}{16} \cdot T \log_e 2 = 0{\cdot}0087T.$$

$$\therefore \ \Delta S = \mathbf{0{\cdot}0087\ cal.\ per\ degree.}$$

Example 149. The molal heat capacity of a monatomic gas is 5·0 cal. per degree. What is the increase in the entropy of a gm.-molecule of this gas when its temperature is raised by 100° from $-50°$ to 50°?

The value given for the molal heat capacity refers to the gas at constant pressure $= C_p$.

$$\therefore \ \Delta S = \int_{223}^{323} \frac{C_p \cdot dT}{T} = 5{\cdot}0 \log_e \frac{323}{223}$$

$$= \mathbf{1{\cdot}85\ cal.\ per\ degree.}$$

* 14. Standard entropies

The Third Law of Thermodynamics (see Chapter XXI) states that the entropy of a crystalline solid at the absolute zero is itself zero. On this assumption the entropy of a substance at a stated temperature is obtained from the equation:

$$S = \int_0^T \frac{dQ}{T} = \int_0^T \frac{C_p \, dT}{T}.$$

Where the relation between C_p and T is known (as in example 149), S may be obtained by integration. In general, however, the entropy of a substance is more accurately obtained by observations of C_p at various temperatures. If C_p is assumed to be constant over a small temperature range, $T_1 - T_2$, then the increase of entropy is given by:

$$\Delta S = C_p(\log_e T_2 - \log_e T_1).$$

If then C_p is plotted against $\log_e T_1$ (as abscissæ), the increase of entropy between two temperatures is given by the equation:

$$\Sigma \Delta S = \Sigma C_p(\log_e T_2 - \log_e T_1)$$
$$= \text{area under the curve.}$$

That part of the area corresponding with the difference in temperature between the absolute zero and the temperature at which the measurement of C_p first becomes practicable can be obtained by extrapolation or by calculation from the Debye equation for specific heats. Any change of entropy due to a transition point, for example, fusion, must of course be added to the increase of entropy with rising temperature.

A list of entropies of common substances is given on p. 434, and the use of entropies in calculating the free energy of a reaction is discussed in Chapter XXI.

QUESTIONS ON CHAPTER XVI

1. The vapour pressure of water at 35° is 42·00 mm. and that of a dilute solution of sulphuric acid at the same temperature is 38·17 mm. Calculate the maximum work of the dilution of an excess of dilute sulphuric acid with 23·5 gm. of water.

2. The boiling point of ethyl acetate is 77° at 760 mm. pressure and its latent heat of evaporation is 85 cal. per gm. What is its boiling point at 300 mm. pressure (assuming latent heat constant) and at what pressure will it boil at 80°?

3. The vapour pressures of chlorine peroxide at 10° and 11·2° are 732 mm. and 769 mm. respectively. Calculate the latent heat of evaporation per gm.-molecule (ClO_2) of the substance at 10·6°, and assuming that this has the same value at the boiling point, 11°, calculate the Trouton coefficient. What conclusion may be drawn from the value of the latter? (London B.Sc. Special.)

4. The vapour pressure of ethyl alcohol is 24·1 mm. at 10° and 44·0 mm. at 20°. Calculate the mean latent heat of evaporation of ethyl alcohol over this range of temperature.

5. The vapour pressure of ethyl acetate is 72·8 mm. at 20° and its latent heat of evaporation is 7480 cal. per gm.-molecule. What value would you expect for the vapour pressure of ethyl acetate at 30°?

6. The vapour pressure of chloroform varies with the temperature as follows:

$T°$	10°	20°	30°	40°
p (mm.)	100·5	159·6	246·0	366·4

Calculate the mean heat of evaporation of chloroform over this temperature range.

7. The vapour pressures of benzene at various temperatures are as follows:

T (°C.)	0	10	20	30	40
p (mm.)	26·5	45·4	74·6	115	181

Determine the mean heat of evaporation per gm.-molecule of benzene.

8. The latent heat of fusion of bismuth is 2400 cal. per gm.-atom and its melting point at 760 mm. is 269°. If $V_s - V_l = -0{\cdot}707$ c.c. per gm.-atom, what is the melting point of bismuth at a pressure of 100 atmospheres?

9. The solubility of succinic acid in water at 20° is 6·90 and at 40° it is 16·2. Calculate the mean heat of solution and the solubility at 30°. The molecular weight of succinic acid is 118.

10. The vapour pressure of chlorobenzene varies with temperature ($T°\ A$) according to the equation:

$$\log_{10} p = 8{\cdot}189 - \frac{2120}{T}.$$

Calculate the heat of evaporation per gm.-molecule of chlorobenzene. What conclusions concerning the molecular state of liquid chlorobenzene can be drawn from this value? The boiling point of chlorobenzene = 132°.

11. The solubility of iodine in water is 0·00134 gm.-molecule per litre at 25° and 0·00416 gm.-molecule at 60°. Calculate (*a*) the mean heat of solution of iodine in water over the temperature range, (*b*) the solubility of iodine in water at 40°. (London B.Sc. Special.)

12. The vapour pressure of liquid ammonia is given by the equation:

$$\log_{10} p = 8{\cdot}47 - \frac{1340}{T}.$$

Calculate the latent heat of evaporation per mol.

13. When 100 gm. of aluminium is melted the increase in volume is 1·9 c.c. Calculate $\frac{dT}{dP}$ given that the latent heat of fusion per gm.-atom is 2080 cal. and that the melting point of aluminium is 657° at normal pressure.

14. 10 gm. of oxygen originally at 15° and 760 mm. pressure expands isothermally until its pressure has fallen to 100 mm. What is the free energy change?

15. The dissociation pressure of zinc sulphate heptahydrate is 44.0 mm. at 40°. Calculate the maximum work of the change :

$$ZnSO_4 . 7H_2O = ZnSO_4 + 7H_2O.$$

The vapour pressure of water at 40° = 55·13 mm.

16. Derive the Clausius-Clapeyron equation and also derive a simplified form of the equation applicable to liquid-vapour systems remote from the critical temperature. Calculate the latent heat of vaporisation of water from the following data, expressing the result in calories per gram: Temperature = 100°; $dp/dT = 2{\cdot}717$ cm. Hg. per degree; density of water = 0·962 gm. per c c.; density of water vapour = $5{\cdot}973 \times 10^{-4}$ gm. per c.c.; density of mercury = 13·59 gm. per c.c.; 1 calorie = $4{\cdot}185 \times 10^7$ ergs. (A.R.I.C.)

17. The vapour pressure of acetic acid varies with the temperature as follows :

$T°$	20°	30°	40°	50°	60°
p (mm. Hg)	11·7	20·6	34·8	56·6	88·9

Calculate graphically the heat of vaporisation of acetic acid. Does your result conform with Trouton's rule? *B.P.* of acetic acid = 118°

18. The density of chlorobenzene at its boiling point, 132°, is 0·9814 gm./c.c. for the liquid and 0·00359 gm./c.c. for the saturated vapour. If the change of vapour pressure (dp/dT) for this temperature is 20·5 mm. per degree, calculate the heat of evaporation of chlorobenzene at its boiling point. Compare this value with that obtained by assuming the gas laws to be valid, that is, by applying the Clausius-Clapeyron equation. (Liverpool B.Sc. Hons.)

19. Calculate the vapour pressure of a solution of cane sugar (molecular weight = 342) containing 8·56 gm. of cane sugar in 35·3 gm. of water at 25°, given that the vapour pressure of pure water at this temperature is 23·70 mm. Hence calculate the work of isothermal dilution of an excess of this solution with 20 gm. of water.

20. The value of dp/dT (p in mm.) for propyl alcohol is 28·8 at its boiling point, 97°. Calculate (*a*) the latent heat of evaporation per mol. at its boiling point, (*b*) the boiling point at 360 mm. pressure. How far do your results agree with Trouton's rule?

*21. By a process similar to that employed on p. 317, show:

$$\left(\frac{\partial F}{\partial p}\right)_T = V.$$

*22. The melting point of α-sulphur is 115° and its latent heat of fusion is 9 cal. per gm. What is the increase in the entropy of 20 gm. of sulphur when it melts at 115°?

*23. The specific heat of ice = 0·50 cal. per gm. Calculate the total change in entropy when 10 gm. of ice at −20° is converted into water at 20°.

*24. The molecular specific heat at constant pressure of carbon dioxide varies with the absolute temperature according to the equation:

$$C_p = 7{\cdot}0 + 0{\cdot}0071T - 0{\cdot}00000186T^2.$$

Calculate the change of entropy when 50 gm. of carbon dioxide is brought from −10° to 50°.

*25. The boiling point of acetic acid is 118° and its latent heat of evaporation at this temperature is 94 cal. per gm. Calculate the entropy increase when 1 gm.-molecule of acetic acid is vaporised at 118°. How far does your result agree with Trouton's rule? Explain any divergence.

CHAPTER XVII

APPLICATIONS OF THE SECOND LAW OF THERMODYNAMICS TO SOLUTION

1. Relation between vapour pressure, boiling point and latent heat of evaporation

For a non-volatile solute, the relative lowering of vapour pressure is given by the equation :

$$\frac{p_1 - p_2}{p_1} = \frac{n_2}{n_1 + n_2} \doteq \frac{n_2}{n_1} \text{ (for dilute solutions).}$$

But according to equation (120*a*), p. 308, the variation of the vapour pressure of a liquid (in this case the dilute solution) is given by the expression :

$$\frac{d(\log_e p)}{dT} = \frac{\lambda}{RT^2}. \quad \ldots\ldots\ldots\ldots\ldots\ldots\ldots(135a)$$

By integration between the limits p_1 and p_2, we can find the temperature, T_2, at which the vapour pressure of the solution is equal to the vapour pressure of the pure solvent at the temperature, T_1.

Integrating equation (135*a*) between T_1 and T_2 and the corresponding pressures p_1 and p_2 :

$$\therefore \log_e\left(\frac{p_1}{p_2}\right) = \frac{\lambda}{R}\left(\frac{T_2 - T_1}{T_1 T_2}\right).$$

But $\log_e\left(\frac{p_1}{p_2}\right)$ can be written in the form :

$$\log_e\left(1 + \frac{p_1 - p_2}{p_2}\right),$$

and since $\frac{p_1 - p_2}{p_2}$ is small and $p_2 \doteq p_1$:

$$\dagger \log_e\left(1 + \frac{p_1 - p_2}{p_2}\right) \doteq \frac{p_1 - p_2}{p_2} \doteq \frac{p_1 - p_2}{p_1};$$

$$\therefore \frac{\lambda}{R}\left(\frac{T_2 - T_1}{T_1 T_2}\right) \doteq \frac{p_1 - p_2}{p_1} \doteq \frac{n_2}{n_1}.$$

† $\log_e (1+x) = x + x^2 + x^3 + \ldots$ so that if x is small, $\log_e (1+x) \doteq x$, since higher powers of x can be ignored in comparison with x.

Also, since $T_1 \doteq T_2$ and $T_2 - T_1 = \Delta T$,

$$\therefore \frac{\lambda}{R}\left(\frac{T_2 - T_1}{T_1 T_2}\right) \doteq \frac{\lambda}{R} \cdot \frac{\Delta T}{T_1^2}.$$

$\therefore$ Elevation of boiling point $= \Delta T$

$$= \frac{n_2}{n_1} \cdot \frac{RT^2}{\lambda} \text{ ....(136)}$$

But the molecular elevation (by definition) is the theoretical elevation for 1 gm.-molecule of the solute in 100 gm. of the solvent. Therefore, in equation (136), $n_2 = 1$ and $n_1 = 100/M$ where M = the molecular weight of the solvent **in the form of a vapour.**

$\therefore$ Molecular elevation of boiling point

$$= \frac{1}{100/M} \cdot \frac{RT^2}{\lambda} = \frac{1}{100} \cdot \frac{RT^2}{\lambda/M}$$

$$= \frac{1}{100} \cdot \frac{RT^2}{L}, \text{ ....(137)}$$

where L = the latent heat of evaporation **per gm.** of the solvent.

Example 150. A solution of 0·6308 gm. of acetanilide (molecular weight, 135) in 26·35 gm. of ethyl alcohol boiled at a temperature 0·204° higher than pure ethyl alcohol. Calculate the latent heat of evaporation of ethyl alcohol at its boiling point (78°).

The molecular elevation (135 gm. of acetanilide in 100 gm. of ethyl alcohol)

$$= \frac{0{\cdot}204 \times 135 \times 26{\cdot}35}{0{\cdot}6308 \times 100}$$

$$= 11{\cdot}5.$$

$$\therefore 11{\cdot}5 = \frac{1}{100} \cdot \frac{RT^2}{L} \text{ and } L = \frac{RT^2}{100 \times 11{\cdot}5}.$$

$$\therefore L = \frac{2 \times 351 \times 351}{100 \times 11{\cdot}5} = \textbf{214 cal. per gm.}$$

2. Relation between vapour pressure, freezing point and latent heat of fusion

In Fig. 22, the three curves show respectively (1) the variation of the vapour pressure of pure water, (2) the variation of the vapour pressure of an aqueous solution, and (3) the variation of the vapour pressure of ice, all with change of temperature.

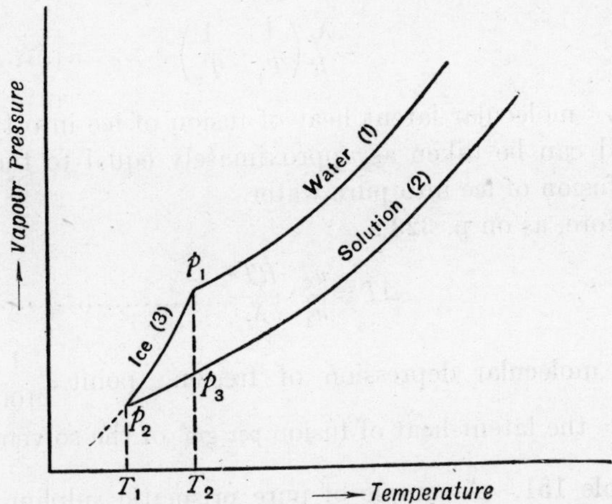

FIG. 22. Relation between vapour pressure, freezing point and latent heat of fusion.

Then, if the pressures and temperatures are as shown in the figure, we can relate p_1, p_2 and p_3 to T_1 and T_2 in the following manner.

The variation of the vapour pressure of ice with temperature is given by the equation :

$$\frac{d(\log_e p)}{dT}=\frac{\lambda}{RT^2},$$

where λ_e = molecular heat of **evaporation** of ice. Integrating between limits p_2 and p_1 :

$$\log_e\left(\frac{p_1}{p_2}\right)=-\frac{\lambda_e}{R}\left(\frac{1}{T_2}-\frac{1}{T_1}\right)$$

$$=\frac{\lambda_e}{R}\left(\frac{1}{T_1}-\frac{1}{T_2}\right). \quad \text{.................(137}a\text{)}$$

Similarly, for the solution :

$$\log_e\left(\frac{p_3}{p_2}\right)=\frac{\lambda}{R}\left(\frac{1}{T_1}-\frac{1}{T_2}\right), \quad \text{................(137}b\text{)}$$

where λ = molecular latent heat of evaporation of water from the solution.

From equations (137*a*) and (137*b*):

$$\log_e \frac{p_1}{p_3} = \frac{\lambda_e - \lambda}{R}\left(\frac{1}{T_1} - \frac{1}{T_2}\right)$$

$$= \frac{\lambda_f}{R}\left(\frac{1}{T_1} - \frac{1}{T_2}\right), \quad \ldots\ldots\ldots\ldots\ldots\ldots(137c)$$

where λ_f = molecular latent heat of fusion of ice into the solution, and can be taken as approximately equal to the latent heat of fusion of ice into pure water.

Therefore, as on p. 323:

$$\Delta T = \frac{n_2}{n_1} \cdot \frac{RT^2}{\lambda_f}, \quad \ldots\ldots\ldots\ldots\ldots\ldots(138)$$

and the molecular depression of freezing point $= \frac{1}{100} \cdot \frac{RT^2}{L}$, where L = the latent heat of fusion per gm. of the solvent.

Example 151. A sample of pure prismatic sulphur melted initially at 119·25°, but in the course of a few minutes the melting point fell to 114·5°. When the sulphur had completely melted at this temperature, the liquid sulphur was plunged into iced water. 3·6 per cent of the resultant solid sulphur was then found to be insoluble in carbon disulphide. Comment on these results, and deduce the molecular formula of the type of sulphur insoluble in carbon disulphide. [S = 32. The latent heat of fusion of sulphur is 9 cal. per gm.] (C.U.O.S.)

Molecular lowering of melting point for sulphur

$$= \frac{1}{100} \cdot \frac{RT^2}{L}$$

$$= \frac{1}{100} \times \frac{2 \times 392 \times 392}{9},$$

(putting 119·25 ≑ 119).

Let M = the molecular weight of the insoluble form of sulphur.

3·6 gm. of insoluble sulphur lower the melting point of 96·4 gm. of sulphur by 4·75°.

∴ Molecular lowering

$$= \frac{4 \cdot 75}{3 \cdot 6} \times \frac{96 \cdot 4}{100} \times M.$$

$$\therefore \frac{4\cdot75}{3\cdot6} \times \frac{96\cdot4}{100} \times M = \frac{1}{100} \times \frac{2 \times 392 \times 392}{9}.$$

$$\therefore M = \frac{2 \times 392 \times 392 \times 3\cdot6}{4\cdot75 \times 96\cdot4 \times 9} = 268.$$

The molecular formula for insoluble sulphur is, therefore, probably S_8.

3. Ideal solubility

The distinction between a solubility curve and a freezing-point curve is merely one of convenience. A freezing-point curve gives the temperature at which the solvent (which is by convention the constituent of the mixture which is in the greater proportion) separates as a solid, while the solubility curve expresses the relation between the temperature and the concentration at which the solute begins to separate from the solution. If, however, a solution contains two solids A and B (neither being in great excess), the temperature at which A separates from the mixture can be used either to define the solubility of A in B or the freezing point of A containing B. Thus, if a mixture of naphthalene and benzene begins to deposit naphthalene at a certain temperature (say 45°) and the mol. fraction of naphthalene is x, then this is the freezing point of naphthalene containing a mol. fraction $(1-x)$ of benzene or the temperature at which naphthalene has a solubility of mol. fraction x in benzene. According to Raoult's law, the vapour pressure (p) of one of the constituents of a mixture (provided the solution behaves ideally) is given by $p = p^0 N$ (see p. 45). Combining this equation with equation (137c) (p. 326):

$$\log_e \frac{p}{p^0} = \log_e N = -\frac{\lambda_f}{R}\left(\frac{1}{T_1} - \frac{1}{T_2}\right). \quad \ldots\ldots\ldots\ldots(139)$$

If, now, the solution is composed of naphthalene and chlorobenzene, T_2 = melting point of pure naphthalene, T_1 = the temperature at which naphthalene begins to crystallise from a solution in which naphthalene has mol. fraction N and λ_f = latent heat of fusion of naphthalene. Therefore, if T_1 is fixed, N is the same **for all solvents** (provided the solution behaves ideally).

Example 152. What is the mol. fraction of naphthalene in a solution from which naphthalene begins to crystallise at 60°? Latent heat of fusion of naphthalene is 4400 cal. per mol. and its melting point is 80°.

$$\therefore \log_e N = -\frac{4400}{2}\left(\frac{1}{333} - \frac{1}{353}\right).$$

$$\therefore N = 0{\cdot}688.$$

4. Relation between osmotic pressure and lowering of vapour pressure

Using the scheme of Fig. 23, the following cycle of operations can be performed.

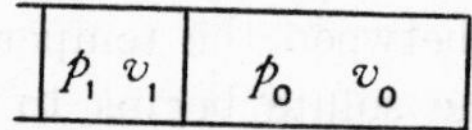

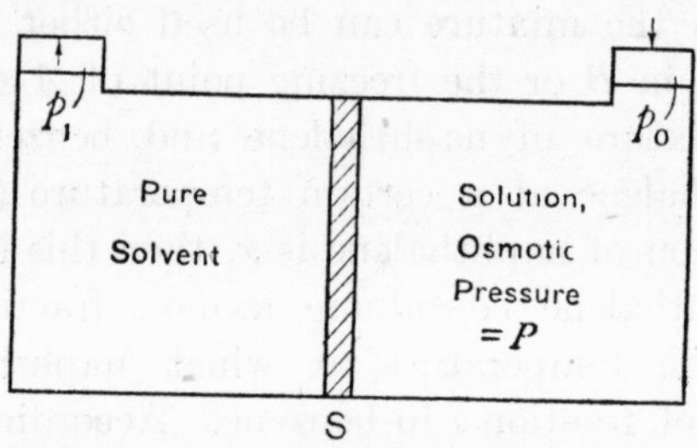

FIG. 23. Relation between osmotic pressure and lowering of vapour pressure.

(1) Vaporise 1 gm.-molecule of the pure solvent at pressure, p_1 (its own vapour pressure).

Work done by the system $= p_1v_1$.

(2) Allow this quantity of vapour to expand reversibly to pressure, p_0.

Work done by the system $= RT \log_e \frac{p_1}{p_0}$.

(3) Condense the 1 gm.-molecule of vapour into the solution at pressure, p_0.

Work done on the system $= p_0v_0$.

(4) Transfer 1 gm. molecule of the solvent from the solution to the compartment containing the pure solvent, by moving the semi-permeable membrane S. Work is done on the system against the opposing osmotic pressure. If this operation is performed simultaneously with (3), the concentration of the solution can be kept constant. Therefore, the osmotic pressure, P, remains constant.

$$\text{Work done on the system} = PV,$$

where V = the volume of the *solution* containing 1 gm.-molecule of the solvent. (More exactly $V = \overline{V}$ = the partial molal volume of the solvent in the solution (see p. 43).)

$\therefore$ Since total work is zero and since, also, $p_0 v_0 = p_1 v_1$:

$$PV = RT \log_e \left(\frac{p_1}{p_0}\right),$$

or

$$\frac{\mathbf{PM}}{\mathbf{d_s}} = \mathbf{RT} \log_e \left(\frac{\mathbf{p_1}}{\mathbf{p_0}}\right) \quad \text{(as on p. 59).} \quad \text{......(139}a\text{)}$$

If $p_1 - p_0$ is small, then as on p. 323,

$$\log_e \left(\frac{p_1}{p_0}\right) \doteq \frac{p_1 - p_0}{p_0} \doteq \frac{p_1 - p_0}{p_1}.$$

$$\therefore RT \left(\frac{p_1 - p_0}{p_1}\right) = \frac{M}{d_s} \times P.$$

$$\therefore \frac{p_1 - p_0}{P} = \frac{M}{d_s} \times \frac{1}{RT} \cdot p_1$$

$$= \frac{M}{d_s} \times \frac{1}{p_1 v_1} \times p_1$$

$$= \frac{M}{d_s} \times \frac{1}{v_1}$$

$$\doteq \rho,$$

where ρ = density of the vapour at a given temperature, T, and pressure, p_1. (This is the approximate relation given on p. 56.)

Example 153. The vapour pressure of water at 16° is 13·624 mm. The vapour pressure of an aqueous solution of glucose at the same temperature is 13·588 mm. What is the osmotic pressure of the glucose solution at 16°?

From equation (139*a*) :

$$P = RT \log_e \left(\frac{p_1}{p_0}\right) \times \frac{d_s}{M}$$

$$= 2{\cdot}303 \times R \times 289 \times \log_{10}\left(\frac{13{\cdot}624}{13{\cdot}588}\right) \times \frac{1}{18}.$$

R has to be expressed in the correct units, and from equation (139*a*) we see that R has the units of $\frac{M}{d_s} \times \frac{P}{T}$.

$\therefore$ If P is expressed in cm. of mercury, R has the units c.c. × cm./per degree.

$$\therefore R = \frac{22{,}400 \times 76}{273}.$$

$$\therefore P = \frac{2{\cdot}303 \times 22{,}400 \times 76 \times 289}{273 \times 18} \log_{10}\left(\frac{13{\cdot}624}{13{\cdot}588}\right)$$

$$= 254 \text{ cm.}$$

Using the approximate relation as on p. 56 :

$$P = \frac{p_1 - p_0}{\rho};$$

$$\mathbf{P} = 263 \text{ cm.}$$

* 5. Activities and activity coefficients

The change of free energy due to the isothermal expansion of a perfect gas is given by the equation :

$$-\Delta F = RT \log_e \frac{p_A}{p_B} \quad \text{(see p. 303).}$$

For any real gas the equation will not be exact ; it can be modified by introducing the **fugacity** (or **escaping tendency**) of the gas which is defined by the equation :

$$F = RT \log_e f + C, \quad \text{......................(140)}$$

where f = the fugacity and C = a constant at a given temperature.

$$\therefore \; -\Delta F = RT \log_e \frac{f_A}{f_B}. \quad \text{..................(141)}$$

For a perfect gas, $f_A/f_B = p_A/p_B$.

If f_B is made to equal the fugacity of the gas at some standard state, then $f_A/f_B = \alpha$, where α is, by definition, the activity of the gas in the state A.

The following examples indicate how the activity of a substance with reference to a standard state can be calculated.

Example 154. An aqueous solution has an aqueous partial pressure of 16·55 mm. at 20°. What is the activity of the water in this solution?

The standard state of a solvent is taken as the pure solvent itself, and the vapour pressure of the pure solvent is the unit of activity.

Vapour pressure of pure water at 20° = 17·54 mm.

∴ Activity of water in the solution

$$=\frac{16{\cdot}55}{17{\cdot}54}=0{\cdot}9436.$$

Example 155. Using the following data of partial pressures of ethyl alcohol in aqueous solution, calculate the activity of ethyl alcohol in an aqueous solution in which the mol. fraction of the alcohol is 0·6.

Partial pressure of ethyl alcohol (mm.)	Mol. fraction of ethyl alcohol
10·51	0·05234
16·6	0·09173
22·25	0·1344
24·85	0·1675
26·75	0·2022
30·70	0·2849
32·15	0·3370
36·65	0·4903
39·42	0·5822
47·33	0·7889
59·01	1

The graph of the vapour pressure plotted against the mol. fraction is shown in Fig. 24.

In order to indicate how the activity of solute is related to its behaviour in very dilute solution, we shall assume that at the lowest dilution Raoult's law is obeyed and that the vapour pressure of the ethyl alcohol at this dilution is proportional to its mol. fraction (see p. 45). The convention adopted is, that over the range of concentration in which Raoult's law is obeyed, the activity of the solute is *equal* to its mol. fraction.

∴ For every dilute solution ($N \rightarrow 0$) :

$$\frac{a}{N} = 1 = \frac{kp}{N}, \quad \text{.......................(142)}$$

since a is proportional to the partial pressure.

At any concentration the activity of the solute is measured by its vapour pressure : $a_c = kp_c$. Eliminating k :

$$a_c = p_c \times \frac{N}{p} \quad \text{or} \quad \frac{a_c}{p_c} = \frac{N}{p}. \quad \text{.................(143)}$$

From the graph we find that $\frac{N}{p} = 0{\cdot}00498$ and p_c when $N = 0{\cdot}6$ is 40·5 mm.

$$\therefore \; a_c = 0{\cdot}00498 \times 40{\cdot}5 = \mathbf{0{\cdot}202}.$$

Alternatively, the activity of the solute in a pure condition ($N = 1$) may be taken as the standard activity ($a = 1$). The activity of the solute at any concentration is then given

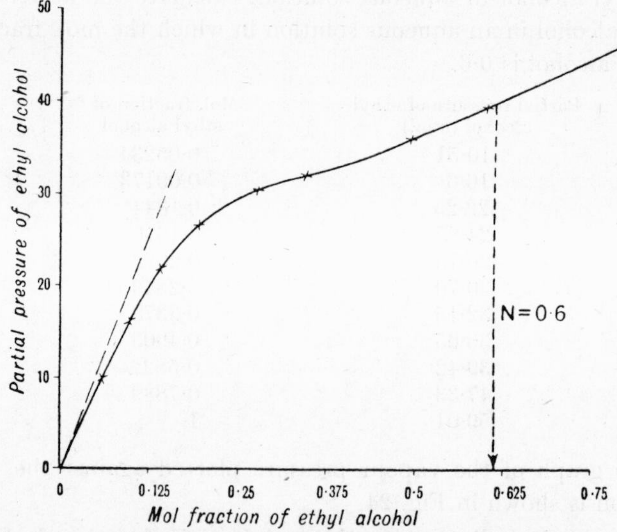

FIG. 24. Partial pressure of ethyl alcohol in aqueous solution.

directly by the ratio of the partial pressure (p_c) to the vapour pressure (p_0) of the pure solute at the same temperature :

$$a_c = p_c / p_0. \quad \text{.............................(144)}$$

The activity of the solute in very dilute solution (where direct measurements of partial pressure may become impracticable) can then be obtained by extrapolation of the activity-mol. fraction curve. The value of the activity of a solute will clearly (from the nature of the graph of Fig. 24) differ according as $\frac{a}{N}=1$, $N\rightarrow 0$ (dilute solution) or $N=1$, $a=1$ (pure solute) is taken as the standard state.

Example 156. The solubility of a liquid, of molecular weight 120, in water at 25° is 0·012 gm., and the liquid does not dissolve any water. What is the activity and the activity coefficient of the liquid in its saturated solution in water at 25°?

Let a_1 = the activity of the pure liquid

and a_2 = the activity of the dissolved liquid.

Then if dn gm.-molecules of the pure liquid are transferred from the pure liquid phase to the solution:

Change in free energy accompanying the transfer

$$=dn\,RT\log_e\frac{a_1}{a_2}.$$

But since the liquid is in equilibrium with its saturated solution, the free energy change of transfer = 0.

$$\therefore\ dn\,RT\log_e\frac{a_1}{a_2}=0$$

and $a_1=a_2=1$ (if the activity of the pure liquid is taken as standard unit activity).

The mol. fraction of the solute

$$=\frac{0{\cdot}012}{120}\Bigg/\left(\frac{0{\cdot}012}{120}+\frac{100}{18}\right)=0{\cdot}000018.$$

By definition the activity coefficient (γ) is given by the equation:

$$\underset{\text{(mol. fraction)}}{N}\times\gamma=\underset{\text{(activity)}}{a}$$

$$\therefore\ \gamma=\frac{a}{N}=\frac{1}{0{\cdot}000018}=5{\cdot}5\times 10^4.$$

QUESTIONS ON CHAPTER XVII

1. The latent heat of fusion of benzene at its melting point at normal pressure (5·48°) is 30 cal. per gm. Calculate the molecular lowering (one gm.-molecule per 100 gm.) of the freezing point for benzene.

2. The osmotic pressure of an aqueous solution of an organic compound is found to be 3·56 atmospheres at 15°. What is the vapour pressure of this solution at 15°?

3. 0·5307 gm. of a compound, *A*, dissolved in 35·61 gm. of benzene lowered the freezing point by 0·358°. Calculate the molecular weight of *A*. The melting point of pure benzene is 5·48° and the latent heat of fusion of benzene = 30 cal. per gm.

4. The vapour pressure of ether at 15° is 357·7 mm.; a solution containing 14·31 gm. of an organic compound in 100 gm. has a vapour pressure at 15° of 347·1 mm. What is the molecular weight of the organic compound?

5. The vapour pressure of a certain aqueous solution of urea is 748·6 mm. at 100°. What is the boiling point of the solution?

6. A solution of nitrobenzene in benzene begins to solidify, that is, to deposit pure benzene, at 0°. What is the solubility of benzene in nitrobenzene at this temperature? [Latent heat of fusion of benzene = 30 cal. per gm. Freezing point of pure benzene = 5·48°.]

7. The latent heat of evaporation of benzene is 93·0 cal. per gm. and its boiling point is 80·0°. Calculate the molecular weight of a substance, *A*, 2·58 gm. of which dissolved in 75·6 gm. of benzene elevated the boiling point of benzene by 0·428°.

8. The addition of 0·1407 gm. of mesitylene (C_9H_{12}) to 11·375 gm. of palmitic acid ($C_{16}H_{32}O_2$) lowered the freezing point of the latter from 62·25° to 61·81°. Find the latent heat of fusion per gm. of palmitic acid. (London B.Sc. Special.)

9. A solution of 3·855 gm. of a non-electrolyte, when dissolved in 60·8 gm. of water, gave a solution which started to freeze at −1·96°. When 4·632 gm. of the same solute was dissolved in 63·7 gm. of benzene, the freezing point of the solution was 2·46°. What deductions can you make from these data? [Latent heat of fusion of ice = 80 cal. per gm. Latent heat of fusion of benzene = 30 cal. per gm. Freezing point of pure benzene = 5·48°.]

10. The vapour pressure of water at 30° is 31·71 mm. and that of an aqueous solution of glucose at the same temperature is 31·35 mm. What is the osmotic pressure of this solution at 15°?

11. 2 gm. of a substance (assumed to be non-volatile and having a molecular weight of 68) was shaken with a mixture of 50 c.c. of benzene and 50 c.c. of water. Assuming the molecular weight of the substance to be the same in both solvents, calculate the parti-

tion coefficient given that the benzene layer started to freeze at 5·07°. [Latent heat of fusion of benzene = 30 cal. per gm. Freezing point of pure benzene = 5·48°.]

12. What is the solubility of *p*-xylene in a liquid of molecular weight 106 at 8·56° if this is the temperature at which *p*-xylene begins to crystallise from a solution of the liquid in *p*-xylene? [Latent heat of fusion of *p*-xylene = 39 cal. per gm. Freezing point of *p*-xylene = 15·0°.]

13. Calculate the solubility of naphthalene ($C_{10}H_8$) in (*a*) mol. fraction (*b*) gm. of naphthalene per 100 gm. of toluene (C_7H_8) at 50°. [Melting point of naphthalene = 80°; latent heat of fusion of naphthalene = 4400 cal. per mol.]

14. Derive by thermodynamic methods an expression for either the osmotic pressure of a solution or the depression of the freezing point of a solvent by a solute, and comment on each step in your derivation. (Birmingham Hons. Chem.)

15. A solution of potassium chloride in water begins to freeze at −0·82°. Calculate the ratio between the weights of ice which would have separated from this solution at −1·52° and −2·94° respectively. The latent heat of fusion of ice is 80·0 cal. per gm. and the percentage dissociation of the salt may be assumed to be constant.

16. The density of a 5 per cent solution of sodium nitrate is 1·0318 gm. per c.c. at 20° and the apparent degree of dissociation is 0·78. What is (*a*) the vapour pressure (*b*) the osmotic pressure of this solution at 20° if the vapour pressure of water at this temperature is 17·54 mm.?

17. Show that two substances, *A* and *B*, having approximately the same latent heat of fusion, will have solubilities in a substance *C* such that (at a fixed temperature) the solubility of *A* is greater than that of *B* if the melting point of *A* is lower than that of *B*.

18. Assuming that benzoic acid (C_6H_5COOH) is associated to the extent of 92 per cent, calculate the freezing point of a solution of benzoic acid in benzene in which the mol. fraction of benzoic acid (calculated from the formula C_6H_5COOH) is 0·056. Use data given in Q. 6. What would be the vapour pressure of this solution at 20° if the vapour pressure of pure benzene at this temperature is 74·63 mm.?

* **19.** A liquid of molecular weight 92 has an activity coefficient of 10,560 in its saturated aqueous solution at 25°. Taking the activity of the pure liquid as unity at 25°, calculate the solubility of the liquid in water in gm. of the liquid per 100 gm. of water.

* **20.** The solubility of chloroform in water at 20° is 0·65 gm. per 100 gm. of water. Calculate the activity coefficient of chloroform in its saturated solution at 20°, taking the activity of pure chloroform = 1 at this temperature.

* 21. Show that the osmotic pressure of a solution, of such concentration (c) that c cannot be taken $\doteq 1$, is given by the equation :

$$P=\frac{1000}{M_s}\left(\rho-c\frac{d\rho}{dc}\right)RT\log_e\frac{p_0}{p},$$

where P = osmotic pressure,
M_s = molecular weight of the solvent,
ρ = the density (gm./c.c.) of the solution,
c = concentration of solute in moles per litre,
p_0 = vapour pressure of the pure solvent at temperature $T°\,A$,
and p = vapour pressure of the solution at $T°\,A$.

[HINT.—Put $P\overline{V}=RT\log_e\frac{p_0}{p}$ (see p. 329). Then if in the solution there are n gm.-molecules of the solvent of molecular weight M_s and 1 gm.-molecule of the solute of molecular weight M, then

$$p=(nM_s+M)/10000V,$$

where V = volume in litres occupied by the solution. Express n in terms of p and hence obtain $\frac{dV}{dn}=\overline{V}$.]

* 22. The partial pressures at 50°, of ethyl iodide over solutions of this substance in carbon tetrachloride are given in the following table in which x denotes the mol. fraction of ethyl iodide in the solution and p, the partial pressure, in mm. :

x - -	0	0·036	0·088	0·197
p - -	0	15	37	79

Calculate the activity on the usual conventional standard of ethyl iodide in a solution of mol. fraction 0·180.

(Manchester Hons. Chem.)

* 23. The following table gives the partial pressures (p_1) of water and the partial pressures (p_2) of methyl alcohol in methyl alcohol-water mixtures at 25° (N_2 = mol. fraction of methyl alcohol). Taking the activities of water and alcohol as unity when each substance is in the pure condition, calculate the activity coefficients of (a) methyl alcohol in infinitely dilute solution, (b) water in a solution in which N_2 = 0·95.

N_2	p_1 (mm.)	p_2 (mm.)	N_2	p_1 (mm.)	p_2 (mm.)
0	23·77	—	—	—	—
0·0202	22·9	3·85	0·0791	21·2	15·1
0·0403	22·3	7·67	0·1145	21·1	21·5
0·0620	22·2	11·76	0·2017	19·5	35·8
0·3975	15·8	59·6	0·8137	5·26	104·6
0·6579	10·5	85·7	1·000	0·0	126·6

CHAPTER XVIII

GIBBS-HELMHOLTZ EQUATION

1. The Gibbs-Helmholtz equation

For a completed reversible cycle (p. 302), the following equations are true whatever the nature of the operations involved :

$$\frac{W}{Q}=\frac{\Delta Q}{Q}=\frac{\Delta T}{T}.$$

But Q = the heat absorbed at the temperature $(T+\Delta T)$, and must be equal to the change of energy and the total work done.

$$\therefore\ Q=\Delta U+\text{total work}.$$

But if p, the pressure, remains constant, then :

$$Q=\Delta U+\text{net work}+p\,\Delta V.$$

Also the net work = *decrease* in free energy $=-\Delta F$.

$$\therefore\ Q=\Delta U-\Delta F+p\,\Delta V=\Delta H-\Delta F.$$

But for a completed cycle in which the **initial and final temperatures are the same** and in which the **pressure remains constant**, there is no final change in volume and the term $\Sigma p\Delta V$ is zero. Therefore, the total work done in the cycle is the **net work**, and this must be equal to the difference of the net work done at temperature $(T+\Delta T)$ and that done at T. Since, also, the net work is numerically equal to the change in free energy, we have, for a completed cycle :

$$\text{Total work done}=\text{net work}=-\frac{\partial}{\partial T}(\Delta F)\times\Delta T.$$

But net work = heat absorbed in the cycle $=\Delta Q$

$$\therefore\ -\frac{\partial}{\partial T}(\Delta F)\times\Delta T=\Delta Q=\frac{Q\times\Delta T}{T};$$

$$\therefore\ -\frac{\partial}{\partial T}(\Delta F)=\frac{1}{T}\times Q=\frac{1}{T}(\Delta H-\Delta F);$$

$$\therefore\ \mathrm{T}\left(\frac{\partial}{\partial \mathrm{T}}(\Delta \mathrm{F})\right)_{\mathrm{P}}=\Delta\mathrm{F}-\Delta\mathrm{H}. \quad\text{..............(145)}$$

For reactions at **constant volume**, $p\Delta V$ is zero and $\Delta H = \Delta U$.

Therefore, the work done $= -\frac{\partial}{\partial T}(\Delta A) \times \Delta T$.

$$\therefore \ \frac{Q}{T} = \left(\frac{\partial Q}{\partial T}\right)_v = -\left(\frac{\partial(\Delta A)}{\partial T}\right)_v.$$

Also $Q = -\Delta A + \Delta H = -\Delta A + \Delta U$ since the volume is constant.

$$\therefore \ -\left(\frac{\partial(\Delta A)}{\partial T}\right)_v = -\frac{\Delta A + \Delta U}{T};$$

$$\therefore \ \mathrm{T}\left(\frac{\partial}{\partial \mathrm{T}}(\Delta \mathrm{A})\right)_v = \Delta\mathrm{A} - \Delta\mathrm{U}. \quad \text{.................(146)}$$

2. The Van't Hoff isotherm

The Van't Hoff Isotherm gives the maximum work which can theoretically be obtained from a gaseous reaction at constant temperature when both the reactants and the products are at suitable arbitrary pressures. The isotherm is most easily derived by considering a particular reaction, the one usually chosen being: $2H_2 + O_2 = 2H_2O$, the water being in the form of steam since the reaction is assumed to be a homogeneous gas reaction.

In Fig. 25, the box containing the equilibrium mixture is provided with semi-permeable membranes, S_{H_2}, S_{O_2} and S_{H_2O},

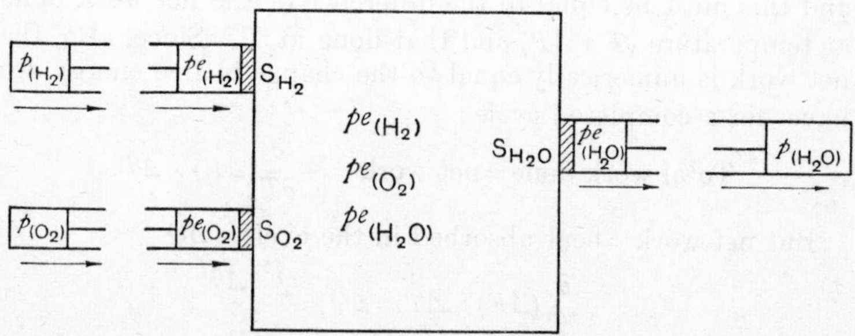

FIG. 25. Use of equilibrium box.

which may be assumed to allow the passage of the gas indicated by the subscripts but are not permeable to the other gases.

The following theoretical operations may be performed:

(*a*) Introduce 2 gm.-molecules of hydrogen and 1 gm.-molecule of oxygen into the equilibrium box and allow them to react.

(*b*) *Simultaneously* withdraw 2 gm.-molecules of steam from the equilibrium box so that at any time during the reaction the partial pressures of the three gases remain unaltered.

The total work done can then be calculated as follows:

(*a*) 2 gm.-molecules of hydrogen, initially at pressure $p_{(H_2)}$, expand to pressure $p_{e(H_2)}$, temperature remaining constant.

$$\therefore \text{ Work done } by \text{ the gas} = 2RT \log_e \frac{p_{(H_2)}}{p_{e(H_2)}}.$$

This quantity of gas is then forced into the equilibrium box against the constant pressure, $p_{e(H_2)}$, by means of the semi-permeable membrane.

Work done *on* the gas $= 2RT$.

Similarly, for 1 gm.-molecule of oxygen:

$$\text{Work done } by \text{ the gas} = RT \log_e \frac{p_{(O_2)}}{p_{e(O_2)}}$$

Work done *on* the gas $= RT$.

$\therefore$ Total work obtained in introducing 2 gm.-molecules of hydrogen and 1 gm.-molecule of oxygen into the equilibrium box:

$$= 2RT \log_e \frac{p_{(H_2)}}{p_{e(H_2)}} + RT \log_e \frac{p_{(O_2)}}{p_{e(O_2)}} - 3RT.$$

(*b*) The withdrawal of 2 gm.-molecules of steam from the equilibrium box similarly involves the following amount of work:

Work done *by* the gas in leaving the equilibrium box $= 2RT$.

Work done *on* the gas when it is compressed from pressure $p_{e(H_2O)}$ to $p_{(H_2O)}$

$$= 2RT \log_e \frac{p_{(H_2O)}}{p_{e(H_2O)}}.$$

$\therefore$ Total work *by* the gas

$$= 2RT - 2RT \log_e \frac{p_{(H_2O)}}{p_{e(H_2O)}}.$$

The conditions in the equilibrium box are now the same as at the beginning of the reaction.

∴ Total work done *by* the reacting gases in the reaction

$$= 2RT \log_e \frac{p_{(H_2)}}{p_{e(H_2)}} + RT \log_e \frac{p_{(O_2)}}{p_{e(O_2)}} - 3RT + 2RT - 2RT \log_e \frac{p_{(H_2O)}}{p_{e(H_2O)}}$$

$$= RT \log_e \frac{p^2_{(H_2)}}{p^2_{e(H_2)}} + RT \log_e \frac{p_{(O_2)}}{p_{e(O_2)}} - RT \log_e \frac{p^2_{(H_2O)}}{p^2_{e(H_2O)}} - RT$$

$$= RT \log_e \frac{p^2_{e(H_2O)}}{p^2_{e(H_2)} \times p_{e(O_2)}} - RT \log_e \frac{p^2_{(H_2O)}}{p^2_{(H_2)} \times p_{(O_2)}} - RT. \quad .....(147)$$

But the first term $= RT \log_e K_p$, and if the reaction is started with oxygen and hydrogen each at 1 atmosphere pressure and the resulting steam is also at 1 atmosphere pressure, then the second term $= RT \log_e 1 = 0$.

∴ Maximum work of the reaction

$$= \mathbf{RT \log_e K_p - RT}. \quad ....(148)$$

Extension of this method to any homogeneous gas reaction gives the general result :

$$\text{Maximum work} = \mathbf{RT \log_e K_p + nRT}. \quad ....(149)$$

where **n** = number of gm.-molecules of products − number of gm.-molecules of reactants.

To obtain the general result, we can consider the homogeneous gaseous reaction represented by the equation :

$$aA + bB + cC + ... = qQ + rR + sS + ...$$

Then work done by the gas when a gm.-molecules of the gas A are brought from pressure p_A to pressure $p_{e(A)}$ and introduced into the equilibrium box

$$= aRT \log_e \frac{p_A}{p_{eA}} - aRT$$

$$= RT \log_e \left(\frac{p_A}{p_{eA}}\right)^a - aRT.$$

For all the reactants, work done by the gas when the appropriate numbers of gm.-molecules of each gas are introduced into the equilibrium box

$$= \Sigma RT \log_e \left(\frac{p_A}{p_{eA}}\right)^a - \Sigma aRT$$

$$= RT \Sigma \log_e \left(\frac{p_A}{p_{eA}}\right)^a - RT \Sigma a.$$

Similarly, work *by* the gas in the removal of the appropriate numbers of gm.-molecules of the products and in bringing them from equilibrium pressures to arbitrary pressures

$$= RT\,\Sigma q - RT\,\Sigma \log_e \left(\frac{p_Q}{p_{eQ}}\right)^q.$$

$\therefore$ Total work of the reaction

$$= RT\,\Sigma \log_e \left(\frac{p_A}{p_{eA}}\right)^a - RT\,\Sigma \log_e \left(\frac{p_Q}{p_{eQ}}\right)^q + RT\,\Sigma q - RT\,\Sigma a$$

$$= RT \log_e \frac{(p_{eQ})^q \times (p_{eR})^r \times (p_{eS})^s \times \dots}{(p_{eA})^a \times (p_{eB})^b \times (p_{eC})^c \times \dots}$$

$$- RT \log_e \frac{(p_Q)^q \times (p_R)^r \times (p_S)^s \times \dots}{(p_A)^a \times (p_B)^b \times (p_C)^c \times \dots} + RT\,(\Sigma q - \Sigma a).$$

From which, if the reactants and products are all at partial pressures of 1 atmosphere, work done

$$= RT \log_e K_p + RT\,(\Sigma q - \Sigma a)$$

$$= RT \log_e K_p + nRT,$$

where n = number of gm.-molecules of the resultants − number of gm.-molecules of reactants. Thus, in the following reactions, n has the value shown.

Reaction	n
$H_2 + Cl_2 = 2HCl$	0
$N_2 + 3H_2 = 2NH_3$	−2
$2NO + O_2 = 2NO_2$	−1
$2Cl_2O = 2Cl_2 + O_2$	+1

The term nRT obviously measures the work obtained as a result of the expansion of the system at constant pressure. But from equation (116*a*), p. 303, the decrease in the free energy of the system

$$= \text{maximum work} - p\Delta V.$$

$\therefore$ Net work of the reaction

$$= \text{decrease in free energy of the system}$$

$$= \mathbf{RT \log_e K_p}. \quad \dots\dots\dots\dots(150)$$

Example 157. Deduce an expression by means of which the maximum work obtainable from a chemical reaction in a gaseous system at constant pressure may be calculated in terms of the equilibrium constant of the reaction. Calculate the maximum work obtainable from the reaction:

$$2CO + O_2 = 2CO_2 \text{ at } 1000°$$

when the reactants are mixed in stoichiometrical proportions and the resultant mixture has a total pressure of 1 atmosphere, being given that the degree of dissociation of carbon dioxide is 0·003 per cent. (London B.Sc. Special.)

From equation (150):

$$\begin{aligned}\text{Maximum work} &= RT \log_e K_p + nRT \\ &= RT \log_e K_p - RT\end{aligned}$$

($n = -1$, since 3 gm.-molecules of gas react to form 2 gm.-molecules).

At equilibrium the partial pressures are those shown in the equation:

$$\underbrace{\underset{0\cdot00003}{2CO} \quad + \quad \underset{0\cdot000015}{O_2} \quad = \quad \underset{1}{2CO_2}}_{\text{atmospheres}}$$

These figures are obtained by noting (*a*) that the fraction (0·003/100) of CO_2 dissociated is so small that it can be ignored in comparison with unity, (*b*) 2 molecules of CO_2 give 2 molecules of CO and 1 molecule of O_2.

$$\therefore\ K_p = \frac{p^2_{(CO_2)}}{p^2_{(CO)} \times p_{(O_2)}} = \frac{1}{(3 \times 10^{-5})^2 \times (1\cdot5 \times 10^{-5})}.$$

$$\begin{aligned}\therefore\ \text{Maximum work} &= 2\cdot303 \times RT \log_{10} K_p - RT \\ &= 2\cdot303 \times 2 \times 1273 \times \log_{10} (7\cdot41 \times 10^{13}) - (2 \times 1273) \\ &\doteqdot 78{,}000 \text{ cal.}\end{aligned}$$

It should be noted that, by definition of maximum work and net work, the maximum work of this reaction is less than the net work which is equal to $RT \log_e K_p = 81{,}200$ cal.

Example 158. The free energy change of the reaction $2Fe + O_2 = 2FeO$ is $\varDelta F = -47{,}000$ cal. per gm.-molecule of FeO at 1000° *A* for oxygen at a pressure equal to 1 atmosphere. Calculate the dissociation pressure of ferrous oxide at this temperature. What is the affinity of the reaction in which ferrous oxide is formed at 1000° *A* from iron and oxygen in air at atmospheric pressure, that is, oxygen at a pressure equal to $\frac{1}{5}$ atmosphere?

As in example 150, the net work of the reaction

$$2Fe + O_2 = 2FeO$$

is given by :

$$\text{Net work} = RT \log_e \frac{[FeO]_e}{[Fe]_e \times p_{e(O_2)}} - RT \log_e \frac{[FeO]}{[Fe] \times p_{(O_2)}},$$

where [ ] denotes active masses and $p_{e(O_2)}$ = the equilibrium (dissociation) pressure of oxygen and $p_{(O_2)}$ = pressure of oxygen in the standard state = 1 atmosphere. Since the active masses of the solids are constant at a fixed temperature :

$$\text{Net work} = RT \log_e \frac{p_{(O_2)}}{p_{e(O_2)}} = RT \log_e \frac{1}{p_{e(O_2)}}.$$

But net work $= -\Delta F = 47{,}000$ cal. per gm.-molecule = 94,000 cal. for the given reaction.

$$\therefore\ RT \log_e \frac{1}{p_{e(O_2)}} = 94{,}000.$$

$$\therefore\ p_{e(O_2)} = 3{\cdot}98 \times 10^{-21} \text{ atmospheres.}$$

The affinity of the reaction :

$$2Fe + \underset{\substack{\text{(gas at}\\ \frac{1}{5}\text{ atmosphere)}}}{O_2} = 2FeO$$

is given by :

$$A = RT \log_e \frac{p_{(O_2)}}{p_{e(O_2)}} = RT \log_e \frac{\frac{1}{5}}{3{\cdot}98 \times 10^{-21}}$$

$$= 90{,}800 \text{ cal.}$$

3. Standard free energy

The method of calculating the change of free energy of a reaction is given in example 157, and it is clear that free energy changes are analogous to changes in heat content in that they represent the differences in the free energies of the reacting substances and the products under the conditions of the experiment. The standard free energy of an element is arbitrarily assumed to be zero when the element is in its stable state at 25° and 1 atmosphere pressure. The standard free energy of a compound (also at 25° and 1 atmosphere pressure) can then be obtained from the calculated free energy change of its formation. Thus :

$$\underbrace{H_2 \quad + \quad \tfrac{1}{2}O_2}_{\substack{\text{each at } 25^\circ \\ \text{and 1 atmosphere} \\ \text{pressure}}} = \underset{\substack{25^\circ \text{ and} \\ \text{1 atmosphere} \\ \text{pressure}}}{H_2O_{\text{liquid}}}\ ; \quad \Delta F_{298} = -56{,}500 \text{ cal.}$$

Since the standard free energies of hydrogen and oxygen are both taken as zero, the standard free energy of water is written :

$$H_2O_{\text{liq.}}\ ; \ \Delta F_{298} = -56{,}500 \text{ cal.}$$

A list of standard free energies is given on p. 433. For the method of obtaining the standard free energies of ions and the use in calculations, the student is referred to p. 380.

Example 159. The standard free energy of silver oxide is -2400 cal. What is the dissociation pressure of silver oxide at 25°?

Let p_e = the dissociation (equilibrium) pressure = pressure of oxygen.

Then the net work of the process = the net work of formation of Ag_2O at equilibrium pressure from silver and oxygen (at 1 atmosphere pressure) = $-\Delta F$.

The equation is :

$$Ag + \tfrac{1}{2}O_2 = Ag_2O,$$

and since the active masses of Ag and Ag_2O are constant at a given temperature, we have (see p. 341) :

$$\text{Net work} = RT \log_e \frac{[Ag_2O]}{[Ag] \times [p_e]^{1/2}} - RT \log_e \frac{[Ag_2O]}{[Ag] \times [1]^{1/2}}$$

$$= RT \log_e \frac{1}{p_e^{1/2}} = \tfrac{1}{2} RT \log_e \frac{1}{p_e}.$$

$$\therefore \text{ Net work} = -\Delta F = 2400 = \tfrac{1}{2} RT \log_e \frac{1}{p_e}.$$

$$\therefore \log_e \frac{1}{p_e} = \frac{2400 \times 2}{2 \times 298}.$$

$$\therefore p_e = 3{\cdot}2 \times 10^{-4} \text{ atmospheres.}$$

Free energy equations can clearly be used to determine whether or not a given physical or chemical change will take place (or is capable of taking place) at a given temperature and pressure since if such a change is to occur it must be attended by a *decrease* in free energy. The standard free energy of liquid chlorine, for example, is 1146 cal., and since this is a positive value the change $Cl_{2(g)} \rightarrow Cl_{2(l)}$ must be accompanied by an *increase* in free energy = 1146 cal. The change does not, therefore, take place at 25° and 1 atmosphere pressure. The equilibrium pressure of the system at 25° can be calculated as follows.

The free energy equation is :

$$\underset{}{Cl_{2(l)}} \rightarrow \underset{\text{(1 atmosphere pressure)}}{Cl_{2(g)}} \qquad \Delta F = -1146 \text{ cal.}$$

Then if p_e = equilibrium pressure = saturated vapour pressure, then (as on p. 141) the net work of the vaporisation $= RT \log_e \frac{p_e}{1}$.

$$\therefore RT \log_e \frac{p_e}{1} = -\Delta F = 1146.$$

$$\therefore p_e = 6{\cdot}84 \text{ atmospheres.}$$

Chlorine gas, at 1 atmosphere pressure and 25°, will, therefore, not change spontaneously into liquid chlorine at the same temperature.

For bromine (liquid at its standard state) the free energy equation is :

$$\underset{755}{Br_{2(g)}} \rightarrow \underset{0}{Br_{2(l)}} \quad \Delta F = -755.$$

Therefore the change $Br_{2(g)} \rightarrow Br_{2(l)}$ is attended by a decrease in free energy and takes place spontaneously. By the same method as was used for liquid chlorine, it can be shown that the equilibrium vapour pressure for bromine is less than 1 atmosphere ($p_e \doteqdot 0{\cdot}28$ atmosphere).

4. The Van 't Hoff isochore

The relation is derived by combining the equation :

$$-\Delta F = RT \log_e K$$

with the Gibbs-Helmholtz equation (see p. 337).

Since $$T\left\{\frac{\partial(\Delta F)}{\partial T}\right\}_p = \Delta F - \Delta H$$

and $$\left\{\frac{\partial(\Delta F)}{\partial T}\right\}_p = -\left\{\frac{\partial}{\partial T}(RT\log_e K_p)\right\}$$

$$= -R\log_e K_p - RT\left\{\frac{\partial}{\partial T}(\log_e K_p)\right\}.$$

Multiplying through by T:

$$T\left\{\frac{\partial(\Delta F)}{\partial T}\right\}_p = -RT\log_e K_p - RT^2\left\{\frac{\partial}{\partial T}(\log_e K_p)\right\}_p$$

$$= \Delta F - \Delta H.$$

But since $$-\Delta F = RT\log_e K_p,$$

$$\therefore\ \Delta H = RT^2\left\{\frac{\partial}{\partial T}(\log_e K_p)\right\}$$

or $$\left\{\frac{\partial}{\partial \mathrm{T}}(\log_e \mathrm{K_p})\right\}_\mathrm{p} = \frac{\Delta \mathrm{H}}{\mathrm{RT}^2}. \quad \text{.................(151)}$$

Equation (151) is the Van't Hoff isochore. If the assumption is made that ΔH remains constant over a temperature range, T_1–T_2, that is, ΔH is independent of T, the equation can be integrated as follows.

Since $$\frac{\Delta H}{RT^2} = -\frac{\partial}{\partial T}\left(\frac{\Delta H}{RT}\right)_p;$$

$$\therefore\ \int\frac{\partial}{\partial T}(\log_e K_p)_p = -\int\frac{\partial}{\partial T}\left(\frac{\Delta H}{RT}\right)_p + C.$$

Integrating between the limits T_1 and T_2 for which the corresponding values of K_p are K_p' and K_p'', we have:

$$\log_e K_p'' - \log_e K_p' = -\frac{\Delta H}{R}\left(\frac{1}{T_2} - \frac{1}{T_1}\right)$$

$$= \frac{\Delta H}{R}\left(\frac{1}{T_1} - \frac{1}{T_2}\right);$$

$$\therefore\ \Delta \mathrm{H} = \mathrm{R}\log_e\left(\frac{\mathrm{K_p}''}{\mathrm{K_p}'}\right) \times \left(\frac{\mathrm{T_1T_2}}{\mathrm{T_2} - \mathrm{T_1}}\right). \quad \text{...........(152)}$$

Example 160. The percentage dissociation of water at 1500° A is $1{\cdot}97 \times 10^{-2}$ and at 1000° A it is 3×10^{-5}. Deduce the heat of the reaction: $2H_2+O_2=2H_2O$ over the given range of temperature and at constant pressure.

The partial pressures of the constituents (assuming that the equilibrium mixture exerts a pressure of 1 atmosphere) are as shown in the equation:

	$2H_2$	+	O_2	=	$2H_2O$.
At 1000° *A*:	(3×10^{-7})		$(1{\cdot}5\times10^{-7})$		1
At 1500° *A*:	$(1{\cdot}97\times10^{-4})$		$(0{\cdot}98\times10^{-4})$		1

(Note 3×10^{-7}, etc., since 3×10^{-5} is the *percentage* dissociation.)

$$K_p(\text{at }1000^\circ A)=\frac{1}{(3\times10^{-7})^2\times(1{\cdot}5\times10^{-7})}=7{\cdot}41\times10^{19}.$$

$$K_p(\text{at }1500^\circ A)=\frac{1}{(1{\cdot}97\times10^{-4})^2\times(0{\cdot}98\times10^{-4})}=2{\cdot}63\times10^{11}.$$

Substituting in equation (152):

$$\Delta H=R\log_e\left(\frac{2{\cdot}63\times10^{11}}{7{\cdot}41\times10^{19}}\right)\times\left(\frac{1000\times1500}{1500-1000}\right)$$

$$=1{\cdot}98\times2{\cdot}303\times\log_{10}\left(\frac{2{\cdot}63\times10^{11}}{7{\cdot}41\times10^{19}}\right)\times\left(\frac{1000\times1500}{1500-1000}\right)$$

$$=-115{,}600.$$

$$\therefore\ \text{Heat of reaction}=-\Delta H=\mathbf{115{,}600\ cal.}$$

When the heat of reaction varies widely with the temperature it can be calculated from its known value at one temperature by means of the Kirchhoff equation (p. 146), or from the known variation of K_p with temperature as in the following example.

Example 161. The equilibrium constant $K_p=\dfrac{(p_{NH_3})^2}{p_{N_2}\times p_{H_2}^3}$ can be shown, by means of the Kirchhoff equation and the Van't Hoff isochore, to vary with the temperature according to the equation:

$$\log_e K_p=\frac{1}{R}\left(\frac{18{,}850}{T}-9{\cdot}92\log_e T-1{\cdot}15\times10^{-3}T\right.$$
$$\left.+1{\cdot}7\times10^{-6}T^2+19{\cdot}72\right).$$

What is the heat of formation of 1 gm.-molecule of ammonia according to the equation :

$$\underset{\text{(1 atmosphere)}}{\tfrac{1}{2}N_2} + \underset{\text{(1 atmosphere)}}{1\tfrac{1}{2}H_2} = \underset{\text{(1 atmosphere)}}{NH_3}$$

at 900° ?

From equation (151), p. 346 :

$$\frac{d(\log_e K_p)}{dT} = \frac{\Delta H}{RT^2}, \text{ when pressure is constant.}$$

But $$\frac{d}{dT}(\log_e K_p) = \frac{d}{dT}\left[\frac{1}{R}\left(\frac{18{,}850}{T} - 9{\cdot}92 \log_e T - 1{\cdot}15 \times 10^{-3}\,T + 1{\cdot}7 \times 10^{-6}\,T^2 + 19{\cdot}72\right)\right]$$

$$= \frac{1}{R}\left(-\frac{18{,}850}{T^2} - \frac{9{\cdot}92}{T} - 1{\cdot}15 \times 10^{-3} + 3{\cdot}4 \times 10^{-6}\,T\right);$$

$$\therefore \frac{\Delta H}{RT^2} = \frac{1}{R}\left(-\frac{18{,}850}{T^2} - \frac{9{\cdot}92}{T} - 1{\cdot}15 \times 10^{-3} + 3{\cdot}4 \times 10^{-6}\,T\right).$$

$$\therefore \Delta H = -18{,}850 - 9{\cdot}92T - 1{\cdot}15 \times 10^{-3}T^2 + 3{\cdot}4 \times 10^{-6}T^3.$$

From which, on substituting $T = 1173$,

$$\Delta H = -27{,}582 \text{ cal.}$$

∴ Heat of reaction per gm.-molecule

$$= -\frac{\Delta H}{2} \doteq 13{,}800 \text{ cal.}$$

5. Relation between K_c and ΔU

The equilibrium constant, K_c, can be introduced into the isochore in the following manner.

Since $$K_c = K_p \times (RT)^{\Sigma n} \quad \text{(p. 97)},$$

$$\therefore \log_e K_c = \log_e K_p + \Sigma n \log_e RT$$

and $$\frac{d}{dT}(\log_e K_c) = \frac{d}{dT}(\log_e K_p) + \frac{d}{dT}(\Sigma n \log_e RT)$$

or $$\frac{d}{dT}(\log_e K_c) = \frac{d}{dT}(\log_e K_p) + \frac{\Sigma n}{T};$$

$$\therefore \frac{d}{dT}(\log_e K_p) = \frac{d}{dT}(\log_e K_c) - \frac{\Sigma n}{T}.$$

But $\Delta H = \Delta U + p\Delta V$, where ΔV = the increase in volume.

$$\therefore \Delta H = \Delta U - RT\Sigma n.$$

$$\therefore \frac{\Delta H}{RT^2} = \frac{\Delta U}{RT^2} - \frac{\Sigma n}{T}.$$

But since
$$\frac{\Delta H}{RT^2} = \frac{d}{dT}(\log_e K_p)$$
$$= \frac{\Delta U}{RT^2} - \frac{\Sigma n}{T}.$$

$$\therefore \frac{\Delta U}{RT^2} = \frac{d}{dT}(\log_e K_c). \quad \text{......................(153)}$$

6. The Arrhenius activation equation

The equilibrium constant, K_p, of a reaction is the ratio of the velocity constants, k_p' and k_p'', of the reverse and direct reactions respectively.

$$K_p = \frac{k_p'}{k_p''}.$$

$$\therefore \log_e K_p = \log_e k_p' - \log_e k_p''.$$

But, since from the Van't Hoff isochore :

$$\frac{d}{dT}(\log_e K_p) = \frac{\Delta H}{RT^2};$$

$$\therefore \frac{d}{dT}(\log_e K_p) = \log_e k_p' - \log_e k_p'' = \frac{\Delta H}{RT^2}.$$

Two quantities, $\Delta H'$ and $\Delta H''$, can, therefore, be defined by the equations :

$$\frac{d}{dT}(\log_e k_p') = \frac{\Delta H'}{RT^2} + C \quad \text{......................(154)}$$

and
$$\frac{d}{dT}(\log_e k_p'') = \frac{\Delta H''}{RT^2} + C, \quad \text{......................(155)}$$

where C is a constant and is independent of the temperature and $\Delta H' - \Delta H'' = \Delta H$. Either of the equations (154) or (155) is the Arrhenius activation equation, the terms $\Delta H'$ and $\Delta H''$ being the **energies of activation** for the reactions to which the velocity constants k_p' and k_p'' respectively refer. It is found experimentally that $C = 0$, so that the equation can be integrated between limits under the same conditions as the isochore, that is, on the assumption that $\Delta H'$ and $\Delta H''$ remain constant.

If the velocity constants refer to concentrations in gm.-molecules per litre, then :

$$\frac{d}{dT}(\log_e k_c') = \frac{\Delta U'}{RT^2}, \quad \text{.....................(156)}$$

and

$$\frac{d}{dT}(\log_e k_c'') = \frac{\Delta U''}{RT^2}. \quad \text{.....................(157)}$$

Example 162. The velocity constant, K_c, for the reaction $H_2 + I_2 \rightarrow 2HI$ is 3·58 at 781° A and 0·172 at 700° A. Calculate the energy of activation.

Integrating equation (156) between temperatures, $T_{(a)}$ and $T_{(b)}$, corresponding with velocity constants, $k_{c(a)}$ and $k_{c(b)}$:

$$\log_e k_{c(a)} - \log_e k_{c(b)} = -\frac{\Delta U}{R}\left(\frac{1}{T_{(a)}} - \frac{1}{T_{(b)}}\right);$$

$$\therefore\ 2{\cdot}303\,(\log_{10} 3{\cdot}58 - \log_{10} 0{\cdot}172) = -\frac{\Delta U}{R}\left(\frac{1}{781} - \frac{1}{700}\right)$$

$$= \frac{\Delta U}{R}\left(\frac{1}{700} - \frac{1}{781}\right);$$

$$\therefore\ \Delta \mathbf{U} = \mathbf{40{,}950\ cal.}$$

7. Graphical method of calculating the energy of activation

The method is essentially the same as that used on p. 312 for obtaining the heat of dissociation of calcium carbonate. The Arrhenius equation can be written :

$$\log_e k_{(c)} = -\frac{\Delta U}{RT} + C_1. \quad \text{.....................(158)}$$

Assuming ΔU constant, then by plotting $\log_e K_{(c)}$ against $\frac{1}{T}$ we can obtain a straight line of slope $= -\frac{\Delta U}{R}$. The units in which $k_{(c)}$ are expressed are immaterial, provided the active mass of the substance is given as mass per unit volume (not partial pressures).

Example 163. The velocity constants for the reaction $2HI = H_2 + I_2$ vary with the absolute temperature as follows :

$T°\ A$ -	666	700	716	781
$k_{(c)}$ -	0·00022	0·00116	0·0025	0·0395

Determine the overall heat of activation per gm-molecule of hydrogen iodide.

As in example 146, we plot $\log_{10} k_c$ against $\frac{1}{T}$ (Fig. 26).

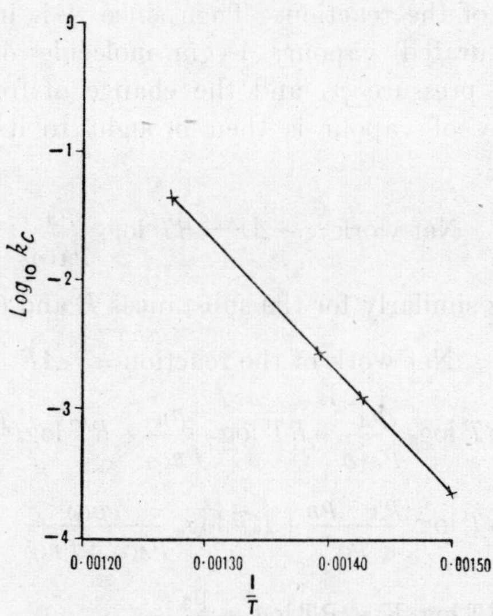

FIG. 26. Graphical method of calculating energy of activation.

Then
$$-Q = \text{slope} \times \log_e 10 \times R$$
$$= -\frac{2{\cdot}70}{0{\cdot}00028} \times 2{\cdot}303 \times 2$$
$$= -44{,}400 \text{ cal.}$$

Heat of activation = **44,400 cal.**

★ 8. Application of the Van 't Hoff isotherm to condensed systems

A condensed system is one in which the constituents are entirely in the solid or liquid state. The calculation of the free energy change accompanying reaction in the solid state is of considerable importance in the use of the Nernst heat theorem (see p. 400). The general expression for the free energy change can be obtained by a consideration of a simple type of reaction such as that represented by the equation :

$$A_{(\text{solid})} + B_{(\text{solid})} = C_{(\text{solid})}$$

The method of the equilibrium box may be adapted to this reaction in the following manner.

Let p_A = saturated vapour pressure of the solid A at the temperature of the reaction. Then since A is in equilibrium with its saturated vapour, 1 gm.-molecule of A can be vaporised at pressure p_A and the change of free energy = 0. This quantity of vapour is then brought to its equilibrium pressure $p_{A(e)}$.

$$\text{Net work} = -\Delta F = RT \log_e \frac{p_A}{p_{A(e)}}.$$

Proceeding similarly for the substances B and C, we have :

$$\text{Net work of the reaction} = -\Delta F$$

$$= RT \log_e \frac{p_A}{p_{A(e)}} + RT \log_e \frac{p_B}{p_{B(e)}} + RT \log_e \frac{p_{C(e)}}{p_C}$$

$$= RT \log_e \frac{p_A \times p_B}{p_C} + RT \log_e \frac{p_{C(e)}}{p_{A(e)} \times p_{B(e)}}$$

$$= \mathbf{RT \log_e K_p - RT \log_e \frac{p_C}{p_A \times p_B}}. \quad \ldots\ldots\ldots\ldots\ldots\ldots(159)$$

★ 9. The Van't Hoff isochore (general treatment)

An equation which is of importance in the treatment of problems involving the Nernst heat theorem is obtained by combining the Van't Hoff isochore with the Kirchhoff equation. For a gaseous reaction :

$$\frac{d \log_e K_p}{dT} = \frac{\Delta H}{RT^2}.$$

Then if, as on p. 148, we write :

$$\frac{d(\Delta H)}{dT} = \Delta C_{p(2)} - \Delta C_{p(1)} = \Delta C_p,$$

where $\Delta C_{p(2)}$ = heat capacity of the products
and $\Delta C_{p(1)}$ = ,, ,, ,, reactants,
we can obtain, exactly as on p. 315 :

$$\mathbf{\log_e K_p = -\frac{\Delta H}{RT} + \int_0^T \frac{\Delta C_p}{RT} \cdot dT + i_x}. \quad \ldots\ldots\ldots(160)$$

* 10. Calculation of free energy from heat of reaction

By direct differentiation it can be shown that the Gibbs-Helmholtz equation :

$$T\frac{d}{dT}(\Delta F)=\Delta F-\Delta H$$

can be written in the form :

$$\frac{d}{dT}(\Delta F/T)=-\frac{\Delta H}{T^2}.$$

$$\therefore\ \frac{\Delta F}{T}=\int-\frac{\Delta H}{T^2}\,dT+C, \quad\text{..............(161)}$$

where C = the integration constant.

But from Kirchhoff's law (p. 146) :

$$\frac{d}{dT}(\Delta H)=\Delta C_p.$$

Writing ΔC_p with empirical constants to give its variation with temperature :

$$\Delta C_p=a+bT+cT^2+\dots.$$

$$\therefore\ \Delta H=aT+\tfrac{1}{2}bT^2+\tfrac{1}{3}cT^3+\dots\ K,$$

where K = value of ΔH when $T=0$ and can be denoted by ΔH_0.

$$\therefore\ \Delta H=\Delta H_0+aT+\tfrac{1}{2}bT^2+\tfrac{1}{3}cT^3+\dots.$$

Substituting for ΔH in equation (161), we have :

$$\frac{\Delta F}{T}=\frac{\Delta H_0}{T}-a\log_e T-\tfrac{1}{2}bT-\tfrac{1}{6}cT^2-\dots+C;$$

$$\therefore\ \mathbf{\Delta F=\Delta H_0-aT\log_e T-\tfrac{1}{2}bT^2-\tfrac{1}{6}cT^3-\dots+CT.} \quad\text{....(162)}$$

Example 164. Calculate the free energy change of the reaction : $N_2+3H_2=2NH_3$ at 600° A from the following data :

$N_2+3H_2=2NH_3$; $\Delta H_{298}=-21{,}900$ cal.

$N_2+3H_2=2NH_3$; $\Delta F_{298}=-7820$ cal.

N_2 ; $C_p=6{\cdot}50+0{\cdot}0010T.$

H_2 ; $C_p=6{\cdot}50+0{\cdot}0009T,$

NH_3 ; $C_p=8{\cdot}04+0{\cdot}0007T+0{\cdot}0000051T^2,$

where T in the specific heat equations is expressed in °A.

For the given reaction :

$$\Delta C_p = 2(8{\cdot}04 + 0{\cdot}0007T + 0{\cdot}0000051T^2)$$
$$- 3(6{\cdot}50 + 0{\cdot}0009T) - (6{\cdot}50 + 0{\cdot}0010T)$$
$$= -9{\cdot}92 - 0{\cdot}0023T + 0{\cdot}0000102T^2.$$

$$\therefore \Delta H = \Delta H_0 - 9{\cdot}92T - 0{\cdot}0023T^2 + 0{\cdot}0000102T^3.$$

Substituting $\Delta H_{293} (T = 293° A)$:

$$-21{,}900 = \Delta H_0 - (9{\cdot}92 \times 293) - (0{\cdot}0023 \times 293^2) + (0{\cdot}0000102 \times 293^3).$$

$$\therefore \Delta H_0 = -19{,}060 \text{ cal.}$$

$$\therefore \Delta F = -19{,}060 - (-9{\cdot}92)T \log_e T - \tfrac{1}{2}(-0{\cdot}0023T^2) - \tfrac{1}{6} \times 0{\cdot}0000102T^3 + CT.$$

But $\Delta F_{298} = -7820$ cal. Substituting this value $(T = 298° A)$:

$$298 \times C = -7820 + 19{,}060 - (9{\cdot}92 \times 298 \times 2{\cdot}303 \times \log_{10} 298) - (\tfrac{1}{2} \times 0{\cdot}0023 \times 298^2) + (\tfrac{1}{6} \times 0{\cdot}0000102 \times 298^3).$$

$$\therefore C = -19{\cdot}0.$$

The **general free energy** equation for this reaction, that is, the equation which gives the change of free energy at any temperature is, therefore :

$$\Delta F = -19{,}060 + 9{\cdot}92T \log_e T + 0{\cdot}00115T^2 - \tfrac{1}{6} \times 0{\cdot}0000102T^3 - 19T.$$

To obtain the free energy change at 600° A we merely substitute $T = 600$.

$$\therefore \Delta F \text{ (at } 600° A) = +7677 \text{ cal.}$$

QUESTIONS ON CHAPTER XVIII

[A table of standard free energies is given on p. 433.]

1. At 1500° water vapour is dissociated to the degree of 0·16 per cent. Calculate (*a*) the maximum work, (*b*) the net work of the reaction $2H_2 + O_2 = 2H_2O$ at 1500°, the reactants and products being measured at the standard state, that is, each at a pressure of 1 atmosphere.

2. At 2200° A hydrogen is dissociated ($H_2 \rightleftharpoons 2H$) to the degree of 0·39 per cent and at 2500° A the degree of dissociation is 1·61 per cent, the pressure being 1 atmosphere in each case. Calculate K_p for the reaction at these two temperatures, and hence deduce the mean heat of dissociation over the given range of temperature.

3. The percentage dissociation of nitrogen tetroxide (N_2O_4) at 26·7° is 20·1 and at 39·8° it is 29·4, the total pressure being 760 mm. in each case. Calculate K_p for the dissociation $N_2O_4 \rightleftharpoons 2NO_2$ at these two temperatures, and hence deduce the heat of dissociation. What value would you expect for the percentage dissociation at 45° and 1 atmosphere pressure, assuming the heat of dissociation to remain constant?

4. In the following table $K_p = \dfrac{(p_{NH_3})^2}{(p_{N_2}) \times (p_{H_2})^3}$, that is, the equilibrium constant in partial pressures for the reaction :

$$N_2 + 3H_2 \rightleftharpoons 2NH_3.$$

Determine graphically the mean change of heat content for this reaction over the given temperature range :

Temperature °*A*	K_p
623	$7{\cdot}07 \times 10^{-4}$
648	$3{\cdot}28 \times 10^{-4}$
673	$1{\cdot}66 \times 10^{-4}$
698	$8{\cdot}64 \times 10^{-5}$
723	$4{\cdot}57 \times 10^{-5}$

5. Given that the dissociation of water vapour at 1400° *A* is 0·00787 per cent and that of carbon dioxide at the same temperature is 0·0146 per cent (both gases being at 1 atmosphere pressure), calculate K_p for the reaction : $H_2 + CO_2 \rightleftharpoons CO + H_2O$. Hence deduce the net work of the reaction : $H_2 + CO_2 = CO_2 + H_2O$ at 1400° *A* and under standard conditions. What is the maximum work of this reaction?

6. At a temperature of 1073° *A* and a total pressure of 2·57 atmospheres the percentage of CO_2 (by volume) in the gas mixture after establishment of the equilibrium $CO_2 + C$ (solid) $\rightleftharpoons 2CO$ is 26·45 per cent. The heat of the reaction $CO_2 + C$ (solid) $\rightarrow 2CO$ at constant pressure and at a temperature of 1123° *A* is −42,000 cal. Calculate the percentage of CO_2 in the equilibrium gas mixture at 1173° *A* and at a total pressure of 5 atmospheres. (Liverpool B.Sc. Hons.)

7. If D_0 = the vapour density corresponding with the molecular formula PCl_5 for phosphorus pentachloride, D_1 = its vapour density at temperature T_1° *A* and D_2 = vapour density at T_2° *A*, show that the heat of dissociation is given by the equation :

$$\Delta H = R\frac{(T_2 - T_1)}{T_2 T_1} \cdot \log_e \frac{(D_0 - D_1)^2/(D_0 - D_2)^2}{(2D_1 - D_0)/(2D_2 - D_0)}.$$

8. The vapour density of iodine is 114·9 at 800° and 102·4 at 900° Calculate ΔU for the dissociation $I_2 \rightleftharpoons 2I$ at 850°.

9. Calculate the dissociation pressure of lead monoxide at 25°.

10. Calculate the free energy change of the reaction :

$$2H_2S + SO_2 = 2H_2O_{(l)} + 3S \text{ at } 25°.$$

11. The standard free energy change of the reaction :

$$2NO_{(g)} + Cl_{2(g)} = 2NOCl_{(g)}$$

is -1810 cal. at 300°. If 2 gm.-molecules of nitric oxide and 1 gm.-molecule of chlorine are brought to equilibrium at 300° and at a total pressure of 1 atmosphere, what are the partial pressures of NO, Cl_2 and NOCl respectively?

12. The equilibrium constant of the reaction :

$$C_{(s)} + CO_{2(g)} \rightleftharpoons 2CO_{(g)}$$

varies with the absolute temperature according to the equation :

$$RT \log_e K_p = -40{,}900 + 4{\cdot}9T \log_e T - 4{\cdot}95 \times 10^{-2}T^2 + 5{\cdot}1 \times 10^{-7}T^3 + 12{\cdot}66T,$$

and that of the reaction :

$$CO_{2(g)} + H_{2(g)} \rightleftharpoons CO_{(g)} + H_2O_{(g)},$$

according to the equation :

$$RT \log_e K_p = -10{,}100 + 1{\cdot}81T \log_e T - 4{\cdot}45 \times 10^{-3}T^2 + 6{\cdot}8 \times 10^{-7}T^3 + 0{\cdot}54T.$$

Calculate the free energy change of the reaction :

$$C_{(s)} + H_2O_{(g)} \rightleftharpoons CO_{(g)} + H_{2(g)}$$

at 1200° *A*.

13. The dissociation pressure of calcium carbonate is 0·07 mm. at 500°. Calculate the free energy change in the formation of calcium carbonate from calcium oxide and dry air, containing 0·04 per cent by volume of carbon dioxide, at 500°.

14. For the reaction : $H_2O_{(g)} + \frac{1}{2}O_2 = H_2O_{2(g)}$, the free energy change varies with the absolute temperature according to the equation :

$$\Delta F = 26{,}210 + 4{\cdot}56T \log_e T - 0{\cdot}00280T^2 + 0{\cdot}00000037T^3 - 13{\cdot}22T.$$

What is the partial pressure of hydrogen peroxide in the equilibrium mixture at 1500° and at a total pressure of 1 atmosphere?

15. The heat of formation of nitric oxide is $-21{,}600$ cal. per gm.-molecule at 25° and $\Delta F_{298} = 20{,}870$ cal. Using the following values for the specific heats of the reacting gases, show that the general free energy equation for the reaction

$$\tfrac{1}{2}N_2 + \tfrac{1}{2}O_2 = NO$$

is

$$\Delta F = 21{,}600 - 2{\cdot}45T.$$

N_2 ; $C_p = 6{\cdot}50 + 0{\cdot}0010T.$

O_2 ; $C_p = 6{\cdot}50 + 0{\cdot}0010T.$

NO ; $C_p = 6{\cdot}50 + 0{\cdot}0010T.$

16. The velocity constants for the decomposition of nitrogen pentoxide are 0·0900 and 0·292 at 55° and 65° respectively. The reaction is monomolecular. Calculate the heat of activation.

17. The decomposition of diethyl ether in the gaseous phase is a monomolecular reaction and the velocity constants (in arbitrary units) vary with the temperature as shown. Calculate the mean energy of activation by a graphical method.

$t°$	450	470	500	520	550
k	$3{\cdot}96 \times 10^{-5}$	$1{\cdot}21 \times 10^{-4}$	$3{\cdot}98 \times 10^{-4}$	$9{\cdot}33 \times 10^{-4}$	$2{\cdot}29 \times 10^{-3}$

18. The standard free energy of mercuric oxide is 9,600 cal. at 200°. Calculate the dissociation pressure at this temperature, and hence determine whether or not mercuric oxide will decompose at 200° in air assumed to contain 20 per cent of oxygen.

19. The standard free energy of silver oxide (Ag_2O) is given by the equation :

$$\Delta F = -7240 - 1{\cdot}0T \log_e T + 21{\cdot}95.$$

If 10 gm. of silver oxide is heated in a previously evacuated flask of 500 c.c. capacity to 400°, what weight of silver oxide will have decomposed when equilibrium is reached? (Ignore the volume of the silver oxide.)

★ **20.** Using the following data, obtain the general free energy equation for the reaction :

$$H_2 + \tfrac{1}{2}O_2 = H_2O_{(g)}.$$

$$\Delta H_{298} = -58{,}100 \text{ cal.} ; \ \Delta F_{298} = -54{,}500 \text{ cal.}$$

$$H_2 ;\ C_p = 6{\cdot}50 + 0{\cdot}0009T.$$

$$O_2 ;\ C_p = 6{\cdot}50 + 0{\cdot}0010T.$$

$$H_2O ;\ C_p = 8{\cdot}81 - 0{\cdot}0019T + 0{\cdot}00000222T^2.$$

Hence calculate ΔF for the reaction at 700° A.

★ **21.** The table below gives the free energies of formation and the heats of formation, both at 298° A, of the compounds named ; the figures given refer to the substances in the states which are stable at 298° A, and under a pressure of 1 atmosphere. Calculate the partial pressure of CO in the system C, CO, CO_2 in equilibrium at 1000° A, under a total pressure of 1 atmosphere. Assume the heats of formation to be independent of the temperature.

Substance	$\Delta F_{298°A}$	$\Delta H_{298°A}$
CO	− 32,500 cal.	− 29,000 cal.
CO_2	− 94,300 cal.	− 97,000 cal.

(Manchester Hons. Chem.)

CHAPTER XIX

CONCENTRATION CELLS

1. Distinction between concentration cell with transport and concentration cell without transport

A concentration cell is obtained when electrodes of the same chemical composition are immersed respectively in two solutions containing an ion with respect to which the electrodes are reversible, the concentration (or activity, see pp. 330 and 377) of the ion being different in the two solutions. Examples of such cells are electrodes of silver in two solutions of silver nitrate of different molality or hydrogen electrodes in solutions having a different hydrogen ion concentration.

The electromotive force of a concentration cell will vary according as the two solutions are, or are not, in contact. Thus, in the simple type of cell shown diagrammatically as follows :

$$\mathrm{Ag} \,\Big|\, \underset{m_1}{\mathrm{AgNO_3}} \,\Big\vdots\, \underset{m_2}{\mathrm{AgNO_3}} \,\Big|\, \mathrm{Ag}$$

the observed *E.M.F.* includes a potential difference between the two liquids. Since this potential difference depends upon the transport number of the silver ion (see p. 366), such a cell is a concentration cell " with transport " (often also called " with transference "). The potential difference due to the liquid junction can be removed (*a*) by the insertion of a concentrated solution of ammonium nitrate between the two solutions :

$$\mathrm{Ag} \,\Big|\, \underset{m_1}{\mathrm{AgNO_3}} \,\Big\vdots\, \underset{\text{solution}}{\mathrm{NH_4NO_3}} \,\Big\vdots\, \underset{m_2}{\mathrm{AgNO_3}} \,\Big|\, \mathrm{Ag}$$

or (*b*) by the insertion of a neutral electrode between the two solutions as in the following hydrogen concentration cell :

$$H_2 \;\Big|\; \underset{m_1}{HCl} \;\Big\vdots\; \underset{\text{solid}}{AgCl} \;\Big|\; \overbrace{Ag\;Ag} \;\Big|\; \underset{\text{solid}}{AgCl} \;\Big\vdots\; \underset{m_2}{HCl} \;\Big|\; H_2$$

Such cells, in which the liquid potential difference is removed, are called concentration cells " without transport " (or " without transference ").

The calculation of the $E.M.F.$ of a cell *without transport* can be effected, therefore, by considering solely the electrode processes and ignoring the liquid potential difference.

2. Concentration cells (without transport)

An expression for the electromotive force of a concentration cell without transport can be obtained by considering the special case shown in Fig. 27.

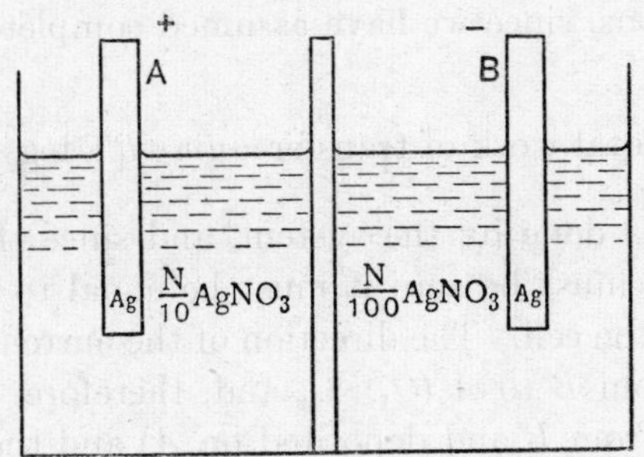

FIG. 27. Concentration cell without transport.

Two silver electrodes are considered to have reached equilibrium with $N/10$ and $N/100$ silver nitrate solutions respectively, and the solutions themselves are assumed to be separated by a partition impervious both to water and the ions formed in the solutions (the liquid potential difference can then be ignored). Assuming complete dissociation of the salt in both solutions, the pressure of silver ions in $N/10$ solution will be greater than in $N/100$ solution ; electrode A will be, therefore, at a higher potential than electrode B.

The following reversible operations can then be considered.

(1) Transfer dm gm.-ion of silver from the electrode A to the solution in contact with it.

(2) Transfer *dm* gm.-ion of silver from the more concentrated solution ($N/10$) to the $N/100$ solution.

(3) Transfer *dm* gm.-ion of silver from $N/100$ solution to the electrode *B*.

Since both electrodes are assumed to be in equilibrium with the solutions in which they are in contact, operations (1) and (3) do not involve any change in free energy, and since, also, the operations may be assumed to occur at constant temperature and volume, no work is done.

∴ Total work done by the system in the transfer of *dm* gm.-ions of silver = work done in (2) $= dm \,.\, RT \log_e \frac{p_1}{p_2}$, where p_1 = " osmotic " pressure of silver ion in the more concentrated solution and p_2 = the corresponding pressure in the weaker solution. But if the solutions are sufficiently dilute, p_1 and p_2 are proportional to the respective concentrations of the silver nitrate solutions, since we have assumed complete dissociation of the solute.

$$\therefore \text{ Total work of transfer} = dm \,.\, RT \log_e \frac{C_1}{C_2}.$$

This work is done by the system, and since the total work of the change must be zero it must be equal to the electrical work done in the cell. The direction of the current through the cell will be from *B* to *A* ($C_1 > C_2$ and, therefore, ions are sent into solution from *B* and deposited on *A*) and the " osmotic " work is done against the current.

Work done by the system in the transfer of *dm* gm.-ions against a potential difference, *E* :

$$= -dm \,.\, nE\phi,$$

where n = the number of positive charges associated with one ion (in this case $n = 1$) and ϕ = number of coulombs per gm.-equivalent = 96,540. (The symbol ϕ is used in this book to denote the faraday, instead of the more usual *F*, to avoid confusion with free energy equations.)

$$\therefore dm \,.\, RT_e \log \frac{C_1}{C_2} - dm \,.\, n \,.\, E\phi = 0.$$

$$\therefore \mathbf{E} = \frac{\mathbf{RT}}{\mathbf{n\varphi}} \cdot \mathbf{\log_e} \frac{\mathbf{C_1}}{\mathbf{C_2}}. \quad \text{.....................(163)}$$

Example 165. Calculate the electromotive force of the cell :

$$\text{Ag} \left| \; N/10\ \text{AgNO}_3 \;\vdots\; N/100\ \text{AgNO}_3 \; \right| \text{Ag}$$

at 18°.

$$RT \log_e \frac{\frac{1}{10}}{\frac{1}{100}} = nE\phi = E\phi, \text{ since } n=1.$$

Since the product, $E\phi$, is expressed in practical units (volt-coulombs), R, the gas constant, must be given in joules/degree.

$\therefore\ R = 1{\cdot}98$ cal. per degree $= 1{\cdot}98 \times 4{\cdot}2$ joules per degree.

$$\therefore\ E = \frac{RT}{\phi} \log_e \frac{\frac{1}{10}}{\frac{1}{100}} = \frac{1{\cdot}98 \times 4{\cdot}2 \times 291 \times 2{\cdot}303 \times \log_{10} 10}{96{,}540}$$

$$= 0{\cdot}0577 \text{ volt.}$$

3. Determination of solubility of sparingly soluble substances (method of concentration cell)

From equation (163), it is clear that if the *E.M.F.* of a concentration cell is observed and the concentration of the metallic ion in contact with one electrode is known, the concentration of the same metallic ion in contact with the other electrode can be deduced.

Example 166. Calculate the solubility of silver chloride in $N/10$ KCl at 18°, given that the *E.M.F.* of the cell :

$$\text{Ag} \left| \begin{array}{l} \text{AgCl} \\ \text{in } N/10\ \text{KCl} \end{array} \;\vdots\; N/10\ \text{AgNO}_3 \; \right| \text{Ag}$$

is 0·447 volt at 18°.

If $c = [\text{Ag}^+]$ in presence of $N/10$ KCl, then :

$$0{\cdot}447 = \frac{RT}{\phi} \log_e \frac{\frac{1}{10}}{c}.$$

$$\therefore\ \log_{10} \left(\frac{1}{10c} \right) = \frac{0{\cdot}447 \times 96{,}540}{1{\cdot}98 \times 4{\cdot}2 \times 291 \times 2{\cdot}303}.$$

From which :

$$c = 1{\cdot}82 \times 10^{-9} \text{ gm.-ion per litre.}$$

$\therefore$ Solubility of AgCl in $N/10$ KCl

$$= 1{\cdot}82 \times 10^{-9} \text{ gm.-molecule per litre.}$$

4. Concentration cells (with transport)

In the treatment of concentration cells given on p. 359, the two solutions were assumed to be separated in such a way that the movement of ions from one solution to the other was prevented, that is, the liquid potential difference was ignored. Where the ions are free to move across the boundary of the two liquids as in Fig. 28, a somewhat different value for the calculated electromotive force is obtained.

Let Fig. 28 represent a concentration cell consisting of silver electrodes immersed in solutions of silver nitrate of concentra-

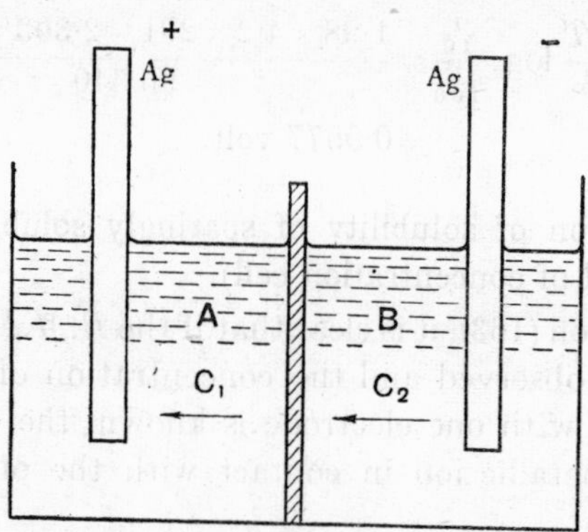

FIG. 28. Concentration cell with transport.

tions c_1 and c_2 molar ($c_1 > c_2$), and let the solutions be separated by a porous partition. Then the direction of the current through the solutions is from right to left.

During the working of the cell, let *dm* gm.-equivalents of silver be transferred from the negative electrode to the positive electrode. Let T_{Ag} and T_{NO_3} be the transport numbers of the silver ion and nitrate respectively. Then during the passage of *dm* equivalents from right to left, *dm* equivalents of silver leave the negative electrode and enter solution *B*, while *dm* equivalents leave solution *A* and are deposited on the positive electrode. But in the passage of *dm* gm.-equivalents of silver, $dm\,\phi$ coulombs of electricity are transferred, and this quantity of electricity is carried by the silver ion and the nitrate ion in the proportion of their transport numbers.

$\therefore$ Decrease of silver ion in solution *A*

$$= dm - T_{Ag}\,dm = dm(1 - T_{Ag}) = dm T_{NO_3};$$

$\therefore dmT_{NO_3}$ gm.-equivalents of silver ion are transferred from solution A to solution B.

$$\therefore \text{ Work done} = dmT_{NO_3} RT \log_e \frac{[NO_3^-]_A}{[NO_3^-]_B}$$

$$= dmT_{NO_3} RT \log_e \frac{c_1}{c_2},$$

assuming complete dissociation.

But at the same time, dmT_{NO_3} gm.-equivalents of nitrate ion leave solution A and enter solution B.

$$\therefore \text{ Work done} = dmT_{NO_3} RT \log_e \frac{[NO_3^-]_A}{[NO_3^-]_B}$$

$$= dmT_{NO_3} RT \log_e \frac{c_1}{c_2}.$$

$$\therefore \text{ Total work done} = 2dmT_{NO_3} RT \log_e \frac{c_1}{c_2}.$$

Equating this work to the electrical work :

$$dmE\phi = 2dmT_{NO_3} RT \log_e \frac{c_1}{c_2}.$$

$$\therefore E = 2T_{NO_3} \cdot \frac{RT}{\varphi} \cdot \log_e \frac{c_1}{c_2}. \quad \text{..................(164)}$$

The above equation has been derived for a cell in which the electrodes are reversible with respect to the cation, that is, the silver ion. We may consider, however, a cell such as that in Fig. 29 in which the electrodes are reversible to the anion.

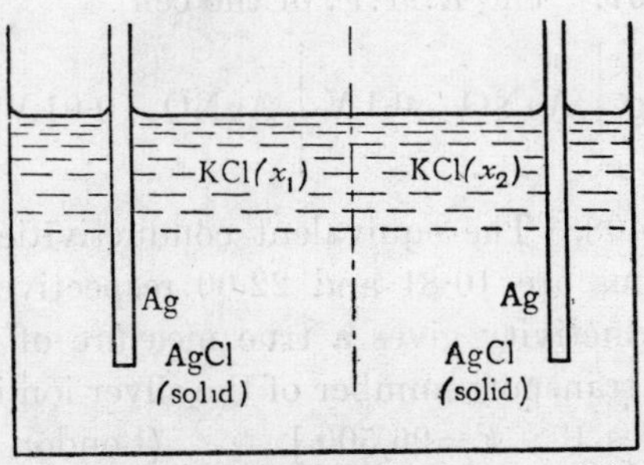

FIG. 29. Concentration cell with electrodes reversible with respect to chlorine ion.

Then if the electrolyte is denoted by B^+A^- where A^- is the anion with respect to which the electrodes are reversible and

$c_1 > c_2$, the polarity of the electrodes is the reverse of that in the cell discussed above.

Then if T_A = transport number of the anion
and T_B = " " " cation,

the passage of *dm* equivalents of the anion involves the following changes of concentration.

Solution (1).

$dm(1 - T_A) = dmT_B$ gm.-equivalents of A^- leave the solution.

Solution (2).

$dm.\ T_B$ gm.-equivalents of B^+ enter the solution from solution (2).

$\therefore$ As on p. 363 :

$$E = \frac{2T_B}{\varphi} . RT \log_e \frac{c_1}{c_2} . \quad \text{.....................(165)}$$

In general, therefore, the *E.M.F.* of a concentration cell with transport is given by the equation :

$$E = 2T_i . \frac{RT}{n\phi} . \log_e \frac{c_1}{c_2},$$

where T_i = the transport number of that ion with respect to which the electrodes are **not** reversible and n = the valency of that ion with respect to which the electrodes **are** reversible.

Example 167. The *E.M.F.* of the cell :

$$\text{Ag} \,\Big|\, AgNO_3 . 0{\cdot}1N \,\Big\vdots\, AgNO_3 . 0{\cdot}01N \,\Big|\, \text{Ag}$$

at 25° is 0·0408. The equivalent conductivities of 0·1*N* and 0·01*N* solutions are 10·81 and 22·00 respectively. Assuming that the conductivity gives a true measure of the ionisation, calculate the transport number of the silver ion in the solution. [R = 8·32 joules/1° ; F = 96,500.] (London B.Sc. Special).

As on p. 362, the electrodes are reversible with respect to the silver ion.

$$\therefore E = 2T_{NO_3} . \frac{RT}{\phi} \log_e \left(\frac{c_1}{c_2}\right).$$

The question, however, does not assume the complete dissociation of the silver nitrate, so that the equation must be written :

$$E = 2T_{\mathrm{NO_3}} \cdot \frac{RT}{\phi} \cdot \log_e \frac{[\mathrm{Ag}^+]_{0\cdot 1}}{[\mathrm{Ag}^+]_{0\cdot 01}} \cdot$$

where $[\mathrm{Ag}^+]_{0\cdot 1N}$ = concentration of Ag^+ in $0\cdot 1N$ $AgNO_3$
and $[\mathrm{Ag}^+]_{0\cdot 01N}$ = ,, ,, ,, $0\cdot 01N$ $AgNO_3$.

But $[\mathrm{Ag}^+]_{0\cdot 1N} = \alpha \times 0\cdot 1$ where α = fraction of silver nitrate dissociated in $0\cdot 1N$ $AgNO_3$, and $[\mathrm{Ag}^+]_{0\cdot 01} = \alpha' \times 0\cdot 01$ where α' = fraction of silver nitrate dissociated in $0\cdot 01N$ $AgNO_3$.

$$\therefore \frac{[\mathrm{Ag}^+]_{0\cdot 1N}}{[\mathrm{Ag}^+]_{0\cdot 01N}} = \frac{\alpha \times 0\cdot 1}{\alpha' \times 0\cdot 01} = \frac{\alpha}{\alpha'} \times \frac{0\cdot 1}{0\cdot 01}$$

$$= \frac{10\cdot 81}{22} \times \frac{0\cdot 1}{0\cdot 01} = \frac{1\cdot 081}{0\cdot 22},$$

assuming that α and α' are proportional to the respective electrical conductivities.

$$\therefore E = 2T_{\mathrm{NO_3}} \cdot \frac{RT}{\phi} \cdot \log_e \left(\frac{1\cdot 081}{0\cdot 22}\right)$$

$$= 2T_{\mathrm{NO_3}} \times \frac{RT}{\phi} \times \log_{10} \left(\frac{1\cdot 081}{0\cdot 22}\right) \times 2\cdot 303.$$

$$\therefore T_{\mathrm{NO_3}} = \frac{0\cdot 0408 \times 96{,}500}{2 \times 8\cdot 32 \times 298 \times \log_{10} \left(\frac{1\cdot 081}{0\cdot 22}\right) \times 2\cdot 303}$$

$$= 0\cdot 494.$$

$\therefore$ Transport number of the silver ion = **0·506**.

5. Potential difference between solutions

Consideration of equations shows that the different values obtained for the *E.M.F.* of a concentration according as the cell is treated as working with or without transport indicate that the former type of cell must develop a potential difference between the two solutions. This potential difference appears to be removed in practice by the introduction of a saturated solution of ammonium nitrate between the two solutions and its value is, as a rule, small. It can, however, be calculated in the following manner.

Let AB (Fig. 30) be the boundary between two solutions of the same electrolyte of different concentrations c_1 and c_2 respectively and let $c_1 > c_2$. Then, by the ordinary process of diffusion, the solute in c_1 will tend to pass into c_2. But assuming the solute in c_1 to be completely dissociated, the diffusion process involves the transfer of ions across the boundary AB. Let V = the velocity of the anion and U = the velocity of the cation. Then if $V > U$, more anions than cations pass across AB and solution (2) becomes negatively charged (solution (1) carrying a corresponding positive charge). The more dilute solution, therefore, takes on the charge of the more rapidly-moving ion.

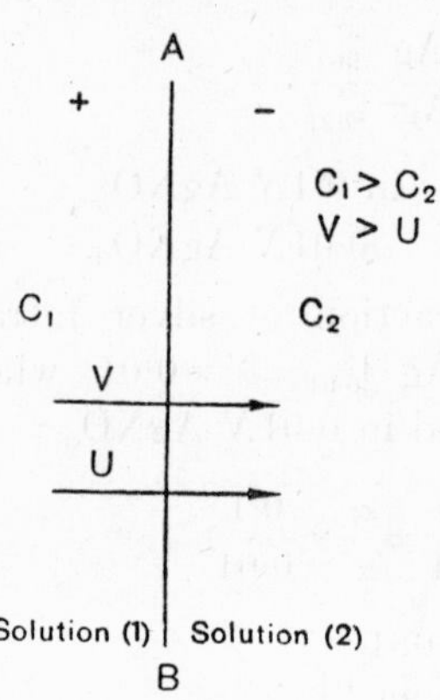

FIG. 30. Potential difference between solutions.

Since the normal velocities of the ions may be taken as proportional to their absolute mobilities (that is, their velocities under an electric field of unit potential gradient), the more dilute solution develops the same charge as the ion with the higher absolute mobility. Since we have assumed $V > U$, solution (2) becomes negatively charged and a potential difference, E_l, is established.

Assume now that when equilibrium is reached at a potential difference, E_l, dm gm.-equivalents of chemical action are produced by the passage of an electric current against this potential difference. Then the electrical work done is $dm \,.\, E_l\phi$. The current is carried by the ions in proportion to their transport numbers and $dm \,.\, V/(U+V)$ gm.-equivalents are transferred from solution (1) to solution (2), while $dm \,.\, U/(U+V)$ gm.-equivalents are transferred from solution (2) to solution (1).

$\therefore$ Osmotic work done

$$= dm\left(\frac{V}{U+V}\right) RT \log_e\left(\frac{c_1}{c_2}\right) + dm\left(\frac{U}{U+V}\right) RT \log_e\left(\frac{c_2}{c_1}\right)$$

$$= dm\left(\frac{V-U}{V+U}\right) RT \log_e\left(\frac{c_1}{c_2}\right).$$

$$\therefore\ dm\,E_l\phi = dm\left(\frac{V-U}{V+U}\right) RT \log_e\left(\frac{c_1}{c_2}\right).$$

$$\therefore\ E_l = \left(\frac{\mathrm{V-U}}{\mathrm{V+U}}\right)\frac{\mathrm{RT}}{\varphi}\cdot \log_e\left(\frac{\mathrm{c}_1}{\mathrm{c}_2}\right). \quad \text{............(166)}$$

The potential difference between solutions of two uni-univalent electrolytes, such as KBr and NaCl, is given by ∴

$$E = \frac{RT}{\phi}\log_e\frac{(l_c + l'_a)}{(l_a + l'_c)}$$

where l represents mobilities

Example 168. Calculate the liquid potential difference between $N/10$ HCl and $N/100$ HCl at 18°, assuming complete dissociation in both solutions.

The sign of the potential difference is as shown since the hydrogen ion has a much greater mobility than the chlorine ion.

−	+
$N/10$ HCl	$N/100$ HCl

Taking the mobilities of the hydrogen ion and chlorine ion respectively as 315 and 65 (since these are proportional to their absolute mobilities), and assuming complete dissociation in both solutions :

$$E = \left(\frac{V \sim U}{V+U}\right)\cdot\frac{RT}{\phi}\cdot\log_e\left(\frac{c_1}{c_2}\right),$$

where $(V \sim U)$ replaces $(V-U)$, since we have already deduced the sign of the potential difference.

$$\therefore\ E = \frac{315-65}{380}\times\frac{291\times 8{\cdot}32}{96{,}540}\times 2{\cdot}303\times\log_{10}10 \ = \mathbf{0{\cdot}038\ volt.}$$

It is apparent that when V and U are very nearly equal the potential difference between two solutions is very small, and can often be ignored.

The expression for the $E.M.F.$ of a concentration cell with transport can be derived by combining equations (163) and (166).

Without transport : $\quad E = \dfrac{RT}{\phi}\cdot\log_e\left(\dfrac{c_1}{c_2}\right).$

Liquid potential difference :

$$E_l=\left(\frac{V-U}{V+U}\right)\cdot\frac{RT}{\phi}\cdot\log_e\left(\frac{c_1}{c_2}\right).$$

With transport (E_T) :

$$E_T=E+E_l$$

$$=\frac{RT}{\phi}\cdot\log_e\left(\frac{c_1}{c_2}\right)+\left(\frac{V-U}{V+U}\right)\cdot\frac{RT}{\phi}\cdot\log_e\left(\frac{c_1}{c_2}\right)$$

$$=\left[1+\frac{V-U}{V+U}\right]\log_e\left(\frac{c_1}{c_2}\right)\cdot\frac{RT}{\phi}$$

$$=\left(\frac{2V}{V+U}\right)\cdot\frac{RT}{\phi}\cdot\log_e\left(\frac{c_1}{c_2}\right)$$

$$=2\mathrm{T_i}\cdot\frac{\mathrm{RT}}{\varphi}\cdot\log_e\left(\frac{\mathrm{c_1}}{\mathrm{c_2}}\right), \quad \text{......................(167)}$$

where, as on p. 364, T_i = the transport number of that ion with respect to which the electrode is **not** reversible.

6. Application of the Gibbs-Helmholtz equation to voltaic cells

For any reaction taking place at constant pressure, the relation between the change of heat content and of free energy is given by the equation :

$$T\left\{\frac{\partial(\Delta F)}{\partial T}\right\}_p=\Delta F-\Delta H.$$

If W denote the net work of the reaction, then since

$$W=-\Delta F,$$

$$T\left\{\frac{\partial(W)}{\partial T}\right\}_p=W+\Delta H. \quad \text{....................(168)}$$

For a galvanic cell, exerting an electromotive force, E, against an equal, or nearly equal, potential difference, any electrical work done by the cell is done reversibly and is, therefore, the maximum net work of the change. If, then, n equivalents of chemical action occur in the cell, the net work done is $nE\phi$, and this must be identified with W in equation (168).

$$\therefore T\left\{\frac{\partial}{\partial T}(nE\phi)\right\}_p=nE\phi+\Delta H,$$

or

$$Tn\phi\left(\frac{\partial E}{\partial T}\right)_p=nE\phi+\Delta H. \quad \text{............(169)}$$

But if q = heat **absorbed** in the working of the cell :

$$q = W + \Delta H ;$$

$$\therefore \mathbf{q} = \mathbf{Tn\varphi} \left(\frac{\partial \mathrm{E}}{\partial \mathrm{T}}\right)_{\mathrm{p}} . \qquad \text{......................(170)}$$

The term $\left(\frac{\partial E}{\partial T}\right)_p$ may be positive, negative or zero, so that the following considerations may arise.

(*a*) $\left(\frac{\partial \mathrm{E}}{\partial \mathrm{T}}\right)_{\mathrm{p}}$ **is positive.**

The *E.M.F.* of the cell increases with rise of temperature.

Also $\qquad \Delta H + nE\phi > 0. \quad \therefore nE\phi > -\Delta H.$

But ΔH = increase in the heat content $= -Q_p$ where Q_p is the heat of the **chemical reaction.**

$$\therefore nE\phi > Q_p.$$

$\therefore$ The electrical energy obtained is greater than the heat of the chemical reaction.

$\therefore$ Heat is *absorbed* in the working of the cell.

(*b*) $\left(\frac{\partial \mathrm{E}}{\partial \mathrm{T}}\right)_{\mathrm{p}}$ **is negative.**

By the converse of (*a*), heat is *evolved* in the working of the cell.

(*c*) $\left(\frac{\partial \mathrm{E}}{\partial \mathrm{T}}\right)_{\mathrm{p}}$ **is zero.**

Then $\qquad nE\phi = -\Delta H = Q_p,$

and the temperature of the cell remains constant.

The same result is obtained for all cells working at the absolute zero, since $\dot{n}\phi T \left(\frac{\partial E}{\partial T}\right)_p$ is zero.

$$\therefore nE\phi = -\Delta H = Q_p \text{ at } 0^\circ K.$$

$\therefore$ At the absolute zero, the heat of the chemical reaction always equals the maximum electrical work.

Example 169. A reversible electric cell of the form :

$$\mathrm{Cu} \;\Big|\; \mathrm{Cu_2O} \;\Big\vdots\; \mathrm{NaOH} \;\Big|\; \mathrm{H_2}$$

has an *E.M.F.* at 18° of 0·461 volt and a temperature coefficient of $-0{\cdot}00066$ volt/degree. Calculate the heat of the reaction :

$$Cu_2O + H_2 \rightarrow 2Cu + H_2O.$$

(London B.Sc. Special.)

Using equation (169) :

$$\text{Heat of the reaction} = -\Delta H.$$

But
$$\Delta H = n\phi T\left(\frac{\partial E}{\partial T}\right)_p - nE\phi$$

$$= \frac{n\phi T\left(\frac{\partial E}{\partial T}\right)_p - nE\phi}{4{\cdot}2}\ \text{cal.},$$

if E and ϕ are expressed in practical units.

$$\therefore\ \Delta H = \frac{2 \times 96{,}540 \times 291 \times (-0{\cdot}00066) - 2 \times 96{,}540 \times 0{\cdot}461}{4{\cdot}2}$$

$$= -30{,}020\ \text{cal.}$$

$$\therefore\ \text{Heat of reaction} = \mathbf{30{,}020\ cal.}$$

Example 170. The following reaction :

$$Ag + HgCl_{(s)} = AgCl_{(s)} + Hg$$

takes place in a galvanic cell. The heat content change is $\Delta H = 1280$ cal. and the *E.M.F.* of the cell at 25° is 0·0455 volts. Calculate (*a*) the change in free energy, (*b*) the temperature coefficient of the cell.

$$\Delta F = -\text{net work} = -nE\phi$$

$$= -1 \times 0{\cdot}0455 \times 96{,}540\ \text{joules}$$

$$= -\frac{1 \times 0{\cdot}0455 \times 96{,}540}{4{\cdot}2}\ \text{cal.}$$

$$= -\mathbf{1046\ cal.}$$

As in example 169 :

$$\Delta H = n\phi T\left(\frac{\partial E}{\partial T}\right)_p + \Delta F\ ;$$

$$\therefore\ \left(\frac{\partial E}{\partial T}\right)_p = \frac{\Delta H - \Delta F}{n\phi T} = \frac{(1280 + 1046) \times 4{\cdot}2}{96{,}540 \times 298},$$

since ΔH and ΔF must be converted from calories to joules.

$$\therefore\ \left(\frac{\partial E}{\partial T}\right)_p = \mathbf{3{\cdot}39 \times 10^{-4}\ volt\ per\ degree.}$$

Example 171. The Weston standard cell is constructed as follows:

Hg	Hg_2SO_4	$CdSO_4$ (saturated solution)	$CdSO_4 . 8/3H_2O$	Cd (12·5 per cent amalgam)

The cell reaction is:

$$\underset{\text{(12·5 per cent amalgam)}}{Cd} + Hg_2SO_4 + 8/3H_2O$$

$$= CdSO_4 . 8/3H_2O + 2Hg.$$

The $E.M.F.$ of the cell is given by

$$E_t = 1{\cdot}0186 - 3{\cdot}8 \times 10^{-5}(t-20) - 6{\cdot}5 \times 10^{-7}(t-20)^2,$$

where t = temperature in °C. Calculate (*a*) the free energy change in the reaction, (*b*) the heat of the reaction at 25°.

$$E_{25} = 1{\cdot}0186 - (3{\cdot}8 \times 10^{-5} \times 5) - 6{\cdot}5 \times 10^{-7} \times 25$$

$$= 1{\cdot}0182 \text{ volt.}$$

Free energy change $\Delta F = -nE\phi = -\dfrac{2 \times 1{\cdot}0182 \times 96{,}540}{4{\cdot}2}$

$$= -46{,}790 \text{ cal.}$$

As on p. 368:

$$\Delta H = Tn\phi\left(\frac{\partial E}{\partial T}\right)_p + \Delta F.$$

But $\left(\dfrac{\partial E}{\partial T}\right)_p = -3{\cdot}8 \times 10^{-5} - 6{\cdot}5 \times 10^{-7}(2t - 40)$

$$\doteq -3{\cdot}9 \times 10^{-5} \text{ (since } t = 25).$$

$$\therefore \Delta H = -\frac{298 \times 2 \times 96{,}540 \times 3{\cdot}9 \times 10^{-5}}{4{\cdot}2} - 46{,}790 \text{ cal.}$$

$$= -47{,}326 \text{ cal.}$$

QUESTIONS ON CHAPTER XIX

[A list of absolute mobilities is given on p. 432]

1. The electromotive force of the cell:

Ag	saturated $AgBrO_3$	⋮	$N/10\ AgNO_3$	Ag

is 0·066 volt at 18°, the potential difference between the solutions having been eliminated. Calculate (*a*) the solubility product of $AgBrO_3$, (*b*) the solubility of $AgBrO_3$ at 18° in gm. per litre.

2. The solubility product of silver iodide at 18° is $1{\cdot}7 \times 10^{-6}$. What should be the *E.M.F.* at 18° of the cell :

Ag	saturated AgI	$N/20$ $AgNO_3$	Ag

if the potential difference between the solutions is ignored?

3. The solubility product for silver chloride is $1{\cdot}2 \times 10^{-10}$ at 18°. Ignoring the potential difference between the two liquids and assuming complete ionisation of the potassium chloride, calculate the *E.M.F.* at 18° of the cell :

Ag	AgCl (saturated in $N/100$ KCl)	$N/10$ $AgNO_3$	Ag

4. Calculate, at 18°, the liquid potential difference between $N/10$ and $N/50$ $AgNO_3$ assuming complete dissociation. (The mobilities of Ag^+ and NO_3^- are 54·0 and 61·6 respectively.)

5. Calculate, at 18°, the *E.M.F.*, (including the potential difference between the liquids) of the cell :

Cu	$M/10$ $CuSO_4$	$M/200$ $CuSO_4$	Cu

assuming complete dissociation in both solutions. (The transport number of the copper ion in copper sulphate = 0·395.)

6. By a method similar to that described on p. 365, obtain an expression (in terms of the mobilities of the ions) for the liquid potential difference between two solutions containing respectively binary electrolytes which give rise to different cations but a common anion.

7. Calculate the *E.M.F.* of the cell (including the liquid potential difference) :

Ag	$N/10$ $AgNO_3$	$N/50$ $AgNO_3$	Ag

Assume that $N/10$ $AgNO_3$ is dissociated to the degree of 89 per cent and that $N/50$ $AgNO_3$ is dissociated to the degree of 95 per cent.

8. Calculate the liquid potential difference between $N/10$ HCl and $N/10$ NaOH, assuming complete dissociation.

9. The *E.M.F.* of the cell:

$$\text{Zn} \left| \begin{array}{c} \text{ZnCl}_2 \\ \text{(solution)} \end{array} \right| \text{Hg}_2\text{Cl}_2 \left| \text{Hg} \right.$$

is 1·0267 volts at 25° and $\frac{dE}{dT} = 9{\cdot}4 \times 10^{-5}$ volt per degree. What is the reaction taking place in the cell and what is the heat of the reaction?

10. The *E.M.F.* of the cell:

$$\text{HgZn} \left| \begin{array}{c} \text{ZnCl}_2 \\ \text{(solution)} \end{array} \right| \text{PbCl}_2 \left| \text{Pb} \right.$$

is 0·500 volt at 20° and its temperature coefficient can be ignored. Calculate the heat of the reaction: $Zn + PbCl_2 = ZnCl_2 + Pb$, at 20°.

11. The cell:

$$\text{Hg Cd (10\%)} \mid \text{CdI}_2 \mid \text{PbI}_2 \mid \text{Hg Pb (10\%)}$$

has an *E.M.F.* given by the equation:

$$E_t = 0{\cdot}09835 + 0{\cdot}000245\,(t - 20).$$

Formulate the cell reaction and calculate the heat of the reaction and the free energy change at 25°. Is heat absorbed or evolved during the working of the cell?

12. The cell:

$$\text{Hg} \quad \begin{array}{c} \text{Cd} \\ \text{(12·5 per} \\ \text{cent)} \end{array} \left| \begin{array}{c} \text{CdCl}_2 \\ \text{(saturated} \\ \text{solution)} \end{array} \right| \begin{array}{c} \text{Hg}_2\text{Cl}_2 \\ \text{(paste)} \end{array} \left| \text{Hg} \right.$$

has an *E.M.F.* of 0·6718 volts at 18° and its temperature coefficient $\left(\frac{dE}{dT}\right)$ is $-7{\cdot}4 \times 10^{-5}$ volts. Calculate (*a*) the heat of the chemical reaction, (*b*) the free energy change in the same reaction, (*c*) the heat evolved or absorbed in the working of the cell, all at 18°.

13. Assuming that the transport number of the chlorine ion in lithium chloride is 0·728, what value would you expect for the *E.M.F.* of the following cell at 18°?

$$\text{Ag, AgCl} \left| \begin{array}{c} \text{LiCl} \\ (N/10 \text{ solution}) \end{array} \right| \begin{array}{c} \text{LiCl} \\ (N/100 \text{ solution}) \end{array} \left| \text{AgCl, Ag} \right.$$

Assume complete dissociation of the lithium chloride in both solutions.

14. The Clark standard cell :

$$\text{Hg} \quad \underset{\text{(10 per cent)}}{\text{Zn}} \;\Big|\; \underset{\text{(saturated)}}{ZnSO_4 \cdot 7H_2O} \;\vdots\; \underset{\text{(paste)}}{Hg_2SO_4} \;\Big|\; \text{Hg}$$

has an electromotive force given by the equation :

$$E_t = 1{\cdot}4328 - 0{\cdot}00119\,(t-15) - 0{\cdot}000007\,(t-15)^2 \text{ volts.}$$

Calculate the heat of the reaction at 25° :

$$Zn + Hg_2SO_4 = ZnSO_4 + 2Hg$$

under the conditions in which it takes place in the cell.

15. The *E.M.F.* of the cell :

$$\text{Ag} \;\Big|\; \underset{\text{(saturated)}}{AgBr} + N/10\ KBr \;\vdots\; KNO_3 \;\vdots\; N/10\ AgNO_3 \;\Big|\; \text{Ag}$$

is 0·647 volts at 18°. Assuming that the potassium nitrate solution removes the liquid potential difference, calculate the solubility of silver bromide in pure water at 18°, expressing your result in gm. AgBr/litre.

16. Calculate the *E.M.F.* at 18° of the following cell :

$$\text{Ag} \;\Big|\; \underset{\text{(saturated)}}{AgBrO_3} + N\ KBrO_3 \;\vdots\; NH_4NO_3 \;\vdots\; N\ AgNO_3 \;\Big|\; \text{Ag}$$

given that the solubility product of $AgBrO_3$ is $6{\cdot}4 \times 10^{-5}$, that $N\,KBrO_3$ is 84 per cent dissociated and that $N\,AgNO_3$ is 70 per cent dissociated.

17. The electromotive force of the cell :

$$\text{Ag, AgCl,} \quad \underset{\text{(3 moles per litre)}}{\text{LiCl,}} \quad Li(Hg)_x - Li(Hg)_x, \quad \underset{\text{(0·3 moles per litre)}}{\text{LiCl,}} \quad \text{AgCl, Ag}$$

is 0·1417 volts and, at the same temperature, the *E.M.F.* of the cell :

$$\text{Ag, AgCl} \;\Big|\; \underset{\text{(3 moles per litre)}}{\text{LiCl}} \;\vdots\; \underset{\text{(0·3 moles per litre)}}{\text{LiCl}} \;\Big|\; \text{AgCl, Ag}$$

is 0·0396 volts. What is the transport number of the lithium ion in lithium chloride ?

18. The heat of formation of solid $PbCl_2$ from lead and chlorine at one atmosphere pressure is 83,000 cal. at 25°. The *E.M.F.* of the cell :

$$\text{Pb} \;\Big|\; PbCl_{2(s)} \;\vdots\; N/10\ KCl \;\Big|\; \underset{\text{(1 atmosphere)}}{Cl_2}$$

is 1·633 volts at the same temperature. What is the *E.M.F.* of the cell at $t°$?

19. Calculate the *E.M.F.* of a concentration cell containing $N/100$ and $N/1000$ thallous nitrate at 25°, given that the activity coefficients (see p. 377) of thallous nitrate in the solutions are respectively 0·92 and 0·98 and that the transport number of the nitrate ion is 0·483. (A.R.I.C.)

CHAPTER XX

STANDARD ELECTRODE POTENTIAL

1. Standard electrode potentials

The significance of the term standard electrode potential is, probably, most easily appreciated by combining a concentration cell with a reference electrode such as a normal calomel electrode† or hydrogen electrode (see p. 378).

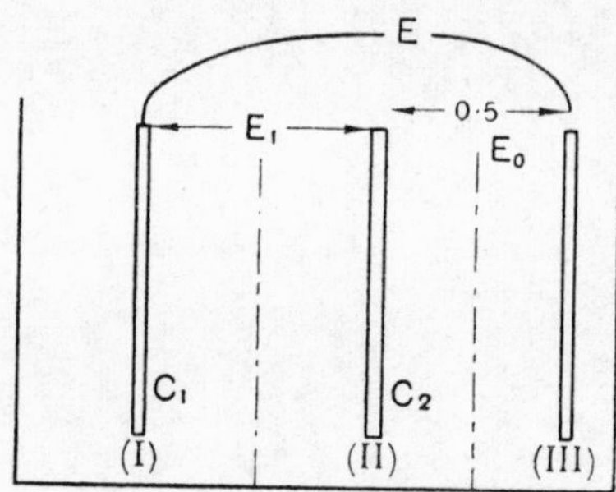

FIG. 31. Significance of standard electrode potential.

Then, as in Fig. 31, if the electrode denoted (iii) is the reference electrode, the observed potential difference between the points (i) and (iii)

$$=E_1+E_0=E.$$

Both E and E_0 include E_x, the contact potential difference between silver and the platinum of the reference electrode.

For convenience in the treatment of the sign of the total *E.M.F.*, assume that $E_0=+0{\cdot}5$ and that the silver electrode (ii) is positive with respect to the reference electrode (iii).

The difference of potential between the two silver electrodes can be obtained from equation (163), p. 360. Assume that the concentrations of the two solutions of silver nitrate are c_2 and c_1 ($c_2>c_1$) and are expressed in gm.-molecules per litre. Then electrode (ii) is positive to electrode (i), the *E.M.F.* of the concentration cell being given by :

$$E_1=\frac{RT}{\phi}\log_e\frac{c_2}{c_1}.$$

† The calomel electrode consists of a platinum wire in contact with mercury over which is a paste of mercurous chloride contained in a solution of potassium chloride. According as the potassium chloride solution is saturated, normal or decinormal, so is the electrode called the saturated, normal or decinormal calomel electrode respectively.

$\therefore$ Observed total *E.M.F.* between electrodes (i) and (iii)

$$= +0{\cdot}5 - \frac{RT}{\phi}\log_e\frac{c_2}{c_1} \quad \text{.........................(170}a\text{)}$$

$$= +0{\cdot}5 - \frac{RT}{\phi}\log_e c_2 + \frac{RT}{\phi}\log_e c_1.$$

$\therefore$ Replacing 0·5 by E_0:

$$E = E_0 - \frac{RT}{\phi}\log_e c_2 + \frac{RT}{\phi}\log_e c_1. \quad \text{..............(170}b\text{)}$$

If $c_2 = 1$, then $\log_e c_2 = 0$.

$$\therefore E = E_0 + \frac{RT}{\phi}\log_e c_1 \quad \text{..................(171)}$$

where E_0 = the standard electrode potential of silver measured against a reference electrode.

2. Standard electrode potentials and activities of ions

The equations of the preceding paragraph have been derived on two assumptions: (1) that the solutions are sufficiently dilute to allow us to take the concentration of the ions as equal to the concentration of the solute, and (2) that the solution pressure or ionic pressure of an ion is proportional to its concentration. These assumptions are only true in very dilute solution.

In general, the solution pressure of an ion is proportional to its activity, which is defined by the equation:

activity of an ion = concentration of that ion × activity coefficient of that ion.

Equation (163) on p. 360 for the *E.M.F.* of a concentration cell without transport then becomes:

$$E = \frac{RT}{\phi}\log_e\frac{\alpha_2}{\alpha_1} = \frac{RT}{\phi}\log_e\frac{\gamma_2 c_2}{\gamma_1 c_1}, \quad \text{............(172)}$$

where α_2 and α_1 are the **activities** of the silver ion in the two solutions, γ_2 and γ_1 are the **activity coefficients** of the silver ion at concentrations c_1 and c_2 respectively. The same equation is obtained if we consider the activity of the solute as a whole. Thus, if α_1 and α_2 represent the activities of silver nitrate in two solutions the osmotic work of transfer is $RT \log_e \frac{\alpha_2}{\alpha_1}$ (see p. 360).

Equation (170*a*) of p. 377 similarly takes the form :

$$E=E_0-\frac{RT}{\phi}\log_e\frac{\gamma_2c_2}{\gamma_1c_1}$$

$$=E_0-\frac{RT}{\phi}\log_e\gamma_2c_2+\frac{RT}{\phi}\log_e\gamma_1c_1. \quad \text{..........(173)}$$

For very dilute solutions we assume that the activity of an ion is the same as its concentration.

∴ If c_1 is small :

$$E=E_0-\frac{RT}{\phi}\log_e\gamma_2c_2+\frac{RT}{\phi}\log_e c_1.$$

If, further, we define the standard electrode potential as the difference of potential between a metal, in a solution containing its ions at unit activity, and a standard reference electrode, then $\gamma_2c_2=1$.

$$\therefore E=E_0+\frac{RT}{\phi}\log_e c_1. \quad \text{..................(174)}$$

Equation (174) becomes more nearly exact as $c_1 \to 0$. If it were correct for all values of c_1, the graph of E against $\log_e c_1$ should be a straight line (since E_0 = a constant). Fig. 32 shows the type of graph obtained. At very small concentrations a straight line is obtained. Extrapolation of this straight line to $c_1=1$, that is, to $\log_e c_1=0$, will give $E=E_0$, that is, the standard electrode potential.

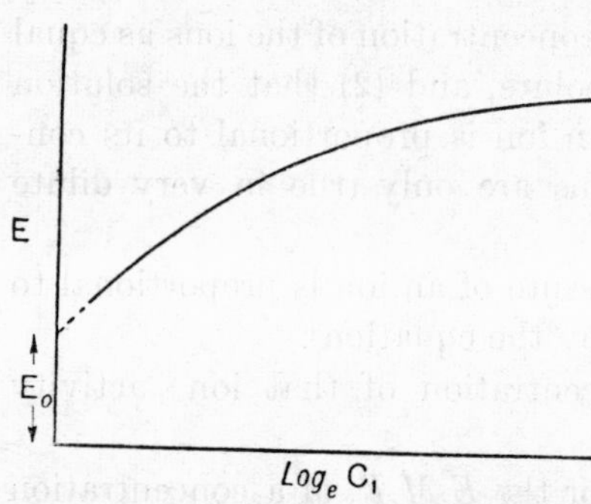

FIG. 32. Graphical method of determining standard electrode potentials.

3. The hydrogen electrode

The hydrogen electrode consists merely of a sheet of platinum, covered with platinum black and arranged (as in Fig. 33) so that the electrode is exposed both to hydrogen gas at a definite pressure and to a solution containing hydrogen ions at a constant concentration.

If two such electrodes are placed in two solutions of different hydrogen ion concentration and the pressure of hydrogen gas is assumed to be the same at each electrode (Fig. 33), the

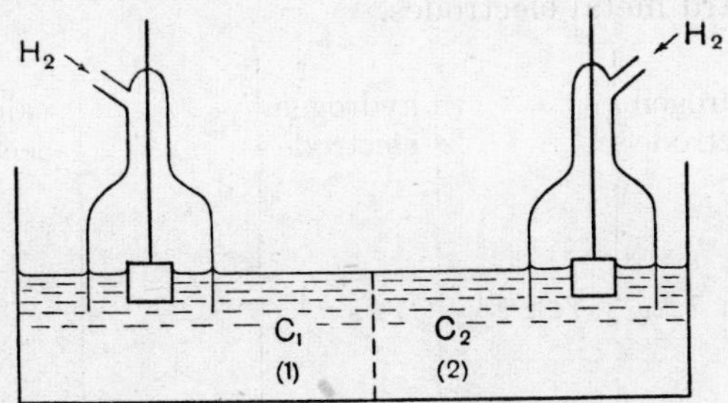

FIG. 33. Hydrogen electrodes forming a concentration cell.

potential difference between the two electrodes can be deduced as follows.

Assume that 1 gm.-molecule of hydrogen gas at pressure P is allowed to enter solution (1) as hydrogen ions. Since the electrode and the solution are in equilibrium the net work of the change is zero. Transfer 2 gm.-equivalents of hydrogen ion from solution (1) to solution (2) ($c_2 > c_1$).

$$\text{Work done on the system} = 2RT \log_e \frac{c_2}{c_1}.$$

Allow 2 gm.-equivalents of hydrogen ion to leave the solution at electrode (ii) as hydrogen gas at pressure P. Net work of the change is zero. Finally transfer 1 gm.-molecule of hydrogen from electrode (ii) to electrode (i). The net work of this change is also zero, since pressure remains constant.

The system is now in its original condition, so that the total net work is nil.

∴ Since electrical work = work done in transferring 2 gm.-equivalents of hydrogen ion from electrode (i) to electrode (ii) $= 2\phi E$.

$$\therefore\ 2\phi E = 2RT \log_e \frac{c_2}{c_1}.$$

$$\therefore\ E = \frac{RT}{\varphi} \log_e \frac{c_2}{c_1}. \quad \ldots\ldots\ldots\ldots\ldots\ldots\ldots(175)$$

As on p. 377, the equation is more accurately written:

$$E = \frac{RT}{\varphi} \log_e \frac{\gamma_2 c_2}{\gamma_1 c_1}. \quad \ldots\ldots\ldots\ldots\ldots\ldots\ldots(176)$$

4. The standard hydrogen electrode

The method of obtaining the value for the potential of a standard hydrogen electrode is similar to that used on p. 376 for standard metal electrodes.

hydrogen electrode	hydrogen electrode	calomel electrode
$\gamma_1 c_1 \doteq c_1$ $\gamma_2 c_2 = 1$	$\gamma_2 c_2 = 1$	

As on p. 378, the observed potential difference between a calomel electrode and a hydrogen electrode is given by the equation:

$$E = E_0 - \frac{RT}{\phi} \log_e \frac{\gamma_2 c_2}{\gamma_1 c_1}.$$

$$= E_0 - \frac{RT}{\phi} \log_e \gamma_2 c_2 + \frac{RT}{\phi} \log_e \gamma_1 c_1.$$

Putting $\gamma_2 c_2 = 1$ and $\gamma_1 \rightarrow 1$ as $c_1 \rightarrow 0$:

$$E = \mathbf{E}_0 + \frac{\mathbf{RT}}{\boldsymbol{\varphi}} \log_e \mathbf{c}_1. \quad \text{......................(177)}$$

The limiting value of E_0 can then be obtained by extrapolation, as explained on p. 378.

5. Standard free energy of an ion

Methods of calculating the *change* of free energy accompanying a physical or chemical process have been discussed on pp. 303 and 341. It is clear that if a value is arbitrarily assigned to a substance in a stated condition, the change of free energy when it undergoes change can be indicated by the relative free energy content of the product. If, for example, the free energy of chlorine gas is taken as zero when the gas is at one atmosphere pressure and at 25°, the fact that the process $Cl_{2(g)} \rightarrow Cl_{2(l)}$ involves an increase in free energy of 1146 cal. can be expressed merely by writing:

$$\underset{\text{(liquid at 25°)}}{Cl_2} \;;\; \Delta F = 1146 \text{ cal.}$$

Examples of the use of standard free energies defined in this way have been given on p. 343.

The standard free energies of ions may be similarly defined. By taking the standard free energy of the hydrogen ion at unit activity as arbitrarily equal to zero, the values for other ions, also at unit activity, can be obtained. The standard free energy of silver ion at unit activity can, for example, be obtained from the measured *E.M.F.* of the cell of Fig. 34. Since both hydrogen gas at unit pressure and hydrogen ion at

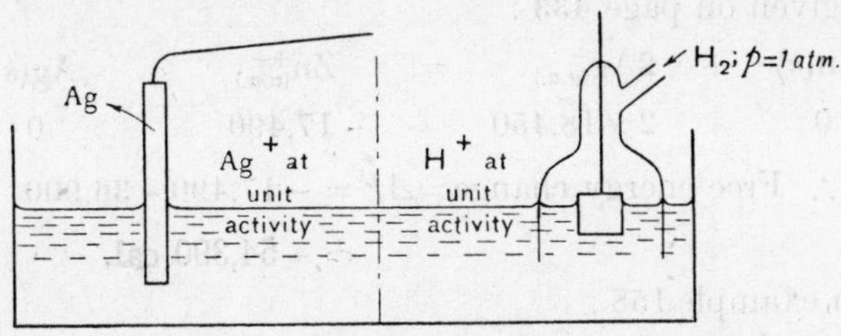

FIG. 34. Measurement of the standard free energy of the silver ion.

unit activity are assumed to have zero free energy and the silver electrode is at its standard state and must also have zero free energy, the sole change of free energy is $Ag \rightarrow Ag^+$ (unit activity), and this can be obtained from the observed *E.M.F.* of the cell.

Example 172. Calculate the ionisation constant (ionic product) for water at 25°.

From the table of standard free energies on p. 433,

$$H_2O_{(liq.)}\,;\ \Delta F_{298} = -56{,}560 \text{ cal.}\,;\ H^+\,;\ \Delta F_{298} = 0\,;\ OH^-\,;$$
$$\Delta F_{298} = -37{,}450.$$

$$\begin{array}{ccccc} H_2O_{(liq.)} & \rightleftharpoons & H^+_{(u.a.)} & + & OH^-_{(u.a.)} \\ -56{,}560 \text{ cal.} & & 0 & & -37{,}450 \text{ cal.} \end{array}$$

$\therefore$ Free energy change in the direction $\rightarrow$ is

$$-37{,}450 + 56{,}560 \text{ cal.} = +19{,}110 \text{ cal.}$$

$\therefore$ As in example 158 :

$$\text{Net work} = RT \log_e \frac{[H^+_e]\,[OH^-_e]}{[H_2O]} - RT \log_e \frac{[H^+_{(u.a.)}]\,[OH^-_{(u.a.)}]}{[H_2O]}$$
$$= RT \log_e [H^+_e][OH^-_e],$$

where subscript " e " denotes equilibrium concentrations.

$$\therefore\ RT\log_e [H_e^+]\times[OH_e^-] = -19{,}110.$$

$$\therefore\ [H_e^+]\times[OH_e^-] \doteqdot 10^{-14}.$$

Example 173. Calculate the free energy change of the reaction: $Zn(s)+2Ag^+ = Zn^{++}+2Ag(s)$, at 25°. What is the concentration of silver ion in the solution obtained when an excess of metallic zinc is placed in $N/10$ $AgNO_3$ and allowed to reach equilibrium?

The free energy change is obtained by substituting the values given on page 433:

$$\begin{array}{ccccccc} Zn(s) & + & 2Ag^+_{(u.a.)} & = & Zn^{++}_{(u.a.)} & + & Ag(s) \\ 0 & + & 2\times 18{,}450 & & -17{,}490 & & 0 \end{array}$$

$$\therefore\ \text{Free energy change} = \Delta F = -17{,}490 - 36{,}900$$

$$= -\mathbf{54{,}390\ cal.}$$

As in example 158:

$$\text{Net work} = RT\log_e \frac{[Ag(s)]\times[Zn_e^{++}]}{[Zn(s)]\times[Ag_e^+]^2}$$

$$-RT\log_e \frac{[Ag(s)]\times[Zn^{++}_{(u.a.)}]}{[Zn(s)]\times[Ag^+_{(u.a.)}]^2}$$

$$= RT\log_e \frac{[Zn_e^{++}]}{[Ag_e^+]^2} = -\Delta F = 54{,}390.$$

$$\therefore\ \frac{[Zn_e^{++}]}{[Ag_e^+]^2} \doteqdot 10^{40}.$$

But from the equation:

$$Zn(s)+2Ag^+ = Zn^{++}+Ag(s),$$

$$[Zn_e^{++}] \doteqdot \frac{M}{20}.$$

$$\therefore\ [Ag_e^+]^2 = \frac{1}{20\times 10^{40}}.$$

$$\therefore\ [Ag_e^+] \doteqdot \mathbf{7\times 10^{-21}\ gm.\text{-}ion\ per\ litre.}$$

Example 174. Calculate the solubility of silver chloride in water at 25°.

The process is represented by the equation:

$$AgCl = Ag^+ + Cl^-.$$

Then :

$$-\Delta F = RT \log_e \frac{[Ag_e^+][Cl_e^-]}{[AgCl_s]} - RT \log_e \frac{[Ag_{u.a.}^+][Cl_{u.a.}^-]}{[AgCl_s]}$$

$$= RT \log_e [Ag_e^+] \times [Cl_e^-],$$

where $[Ag_e^+] \times [Cl_e^-]$ = solubility product of silver ions and chlorine ions in equilibrium with solid silver chloride.

But the standard free energy change is obtained from the equation :

$$\begin{array}{cccccc} AgCl & = & Ag^+ & + & Cl^- & \\ -26{,}187 & & +18{,}448 & & -31{,}367 & \Delta F = +13{,}268. \end{array}$$

$$\therefore \log_{10} [Ag_e^+] \times [Cl_e^-] = -\frac{13{,}268}{2 \times 2{\cdot}303 \times 298}.$$

$$\therefore [Ag_e^+] \times [Cl_e^-] = 2{\cdot}04 \times 10^{-10} \text{ gm.-ions per litre.}$$

$\therefore$ Solubility of silver chloride

$$= \sqrt{2{\cdot}04 \times 10^{-10}} = \mathbf{1{\cdot}43 \times 10^{-5}} \textbf{ gm.-molecules per litre.}$$

Example 175. The cell : $Ag \mid M/_1\ Ag^+ \parallel M/_2\ Cu^{++} \mid Cu$ has an electromotive force of 0·4547 volt at 25°, the silver electrode being the positive pole. Calculate the equilibrium value of the ratio $[Ag^+]/\sqrt{Cu^{++}}$, which is reached when silver nitrate solution is treated with excess of copper.

(Manchester Hons. Chem.)

Since the silver electrode is the positive pole, the cell reaction is :

$$\tfrac{1}{2}Cu + Ag^+ = \tfrac{1}{2}Cu^{++} + Ag.$$

Then, as in example 170 :

Free energy decrease $= -\Delta F = E\phi$ (per gm.-equivalent).

$$\therefore\ -\Delta F = \frac{0{\cdot}4547 \times 96{,}540}{4{\cdot}2} \text{ cal.} = 10{,}460 \text{ cal.}$$

But for the reaction represented by the chemical equation :

$$-\Delta F = RT \log_e \frac{[Cu_e^{++}]^{\frac{1}{2}}}{[Ag_e^+]} = -RT \log_e \frac{[Ag_e^+]}{[Cu_e^{++}]^{\frac{1}{2}}}.$$

$$\therefore\ -RT \log_e \frac{[Ag_e^+]}{[Cu_e^{++}]^{\frac{1}{2}}} = 10{,}460.$$

$$\therefore \log_e \frac{[Ag_e^+]}{\sqrt{[Cu_e^{++}]}} = -\frac{10{,}460}{2 \times 298}.$$

$$\therefore \frac{[Ag_e^+]}{\sqrt{[Cu_e^{++}]}} = 2{\cdot}39 \times 10^{-8}.$$

6. Convention as to sign of electrode potentials

Standard electrode potentials are usually determined by measuring the potential difference between the metal and a suitable calomel electrode, the method of extrapolation described on p. 378 being used. The metallic electrode then has a positive standard potential if it is the positive of the cell in which the other electrode is the calomel electrode. If, for example, the standard electrode potential of a metal has the value $+0{\cdot}5$ volt with reference to the decinormal calomel electrode, then this is the potential difference of the cell: Metal/Metallic ion at unit activity/Calomel electrode, the metal being the positive electrode.

It is customary to express the standard electrode potential of a metal with reference to the standard hydrogen electrode, since hydrogen gas at unit pressure and hydrogen ions at unit activity are both taken as zero in free energy changes. The conversion of standard electrode potentials measured against the decinormal calomel electrode to potentials against the standard hydrogen electrode merely involves a knowledge of the potential of the decinormal calomel electrode against the standard hydrogen electrode. Since the value of the latter is $+0{\cdot}3335$ volt at 25°, the standard electrode potential of a metal (measured against the standard hydrogen electrode and denoted by E°_{H}) is related to its potential against the decinormal calomel electrode (denoted by $E^{\circ}_{C(N/10)}$) by the equation:

$$E^{\circ}_{\mathrm{H}} = E^{\circ}_{C(N/10)} + 0{\cdot}3335.$$

A table of standard electrode potentials is given on p. 432. It will be noticed that those metals at the top of the electrochemical series have negative values for their standard electrode potentials; the more negative is the electrode potential the greater is the tendency of the metal to send positively charged ions into solution. It should be clearly understood the convention used in American textbooks is directly the reverse, an element high in the electro-chemical series having a positive standard electrode potential. The American convention clearly measures the potential of the solution with reference to the metal.

Example 176. The standard electrode potentials of Cu/Cu^{++} and Ni/Ni^{++} are $+0{\cdot}344$ volt and $-0{\cdot}136$ volt. What are the potentials of these electrodes measured against the normal calomel electrode ($E^{\circ}_{H} = +0{\cdot}28$ volt)?

The required potentials are most easily obtained by means of a simple diagram :

Cu	Cu^{++}		H_2		Normal calomel
$+0{\cdot}344$	0	$+0{\cdot}28$

The potential of the electrode Cu/Cu^{++} (unit activity) compared with the normal calomel electrode is clearly

$$+0{\cdot}344 - 0{\cdot}28 = \mathbf{+0{\cdot}064\ volt.}$$

For the standard electrode potential of Ni/Ni^{++},

$$P.D. = -0{\cdot}136 - 0{\cdot}28 = \mathbf{-0{\cdot}416\ volt.}$$

7. Determination of hydrogen ion concentration

The hydrogen ion concentration of a solution can be measured by an electrometric method, an apparatus of the type indicated in Fig. 35 being commonly used.

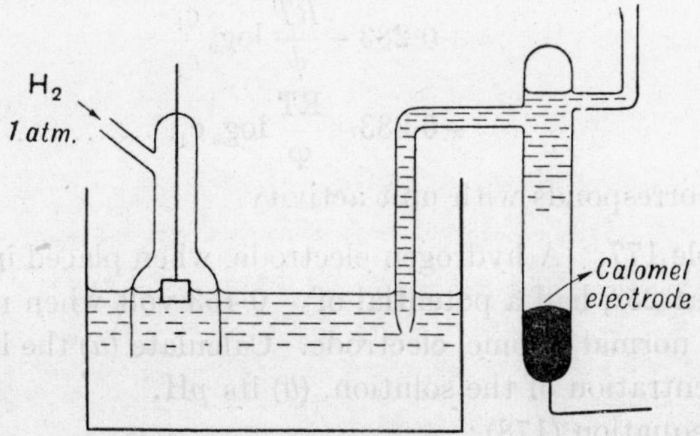

FIG. 35. Measurement of the hydrogen ion concentration of a solution.

The relation of the observed *E.M.F.* to the hydrogen ion concentration is best seen by introducing a standard hydrogen electrode which will not affect the potential difference between the electrodes A and B.

A	C	B
Hydrogen electrode $[H^+]=c_1$	Hydrogen electrode (standard) Unit activity (c_2)	Calomel electrode

The observed *E.M.F.* can then be treated as the algebraic sum of the two potential differences (*a*) between A and C (the electrodes of the hydrogen concentration cell) and (*b*) between C and B (the two standard electrodes). These two potential differences are then evaluated as follows:

(*a*) The potential difference between B and C = potential of the normal calomel electrode referred to the standard hydrogen electrode at unit activity = +0·283 volt (B being the positive pole).

(*b*) The potential of C with regard to A is given by $-\frac{RT}{\phi}\log_e\frac{c_1}{c_2}$ (if $c_1 <$ unit activity, $\log_e\frac{c_1}{c_2}$ is negative, $-RT\log_e\frac{c_1}{c_2}$ is positive and C is at a higher potential than A).

∴ Potential difference between A and B

$$= +0{\cdot}283 - \frac{RT}{\phi}\log_e\frac{c_1}{c_2}$$

$$= +0{\cdot}283 - \frac{RT}{\phi}\log_e c_1. \quad \ldots\ldots\ldots\ldots\ldots\ldots(178)$$

since c_2 corresponds with unit activity.

Example 177. A hydrogen electrode, when placed in an acid solution at 25°, had a potential of −0·453 volt when measured against a normal calomel electrode. Calculate (*a*) the hydrogen ion concentration of the solution, (*b*) its *p*H.

From equation (178):

$$0{\cdot}453 = 0{\cdot}283 - \frac{RT}{\phi}\log_e c_1;$$

$$\therefore\ RT\log_e c_1 = -0{\cdot}170.$$

Then, $\log_{10} c_1 = -\dfrac{0\cdot170 \times 96{,}540}{2 \times 288 \times 2\cdot303 \times 4\cdot2} = -2\cdot95.$

$\therefore\ c_1 = 1\cdot12 \times 10^{-3}$ **gm.-ion per litre.**

$p\mathrm{H} = -\log_{10} c_1$ (see p. 166).

$\therefore\ p\mathrm{H} = \mathbf{2\cdot95}.$

Example 178. The dissociation constant for acetic acid is $1\cdot85 \times 10^{-5}$ at 18°. A decinormal solution of acetic acid is also $M/10$ with respect to sodium acetate. What value for the potential difference between a hydrogen electrode in this solution and the decinormal calomel electrode would you expect, assuming complete dissociation of sodium acetate in $M/10$ solution?

The hydrogen ion concentration is given by the equation:

$$\frac{[\mathrm{H}^+] \times \frac{1}{10}}{\frac{1}{10}} = 1\cdot85 \times 10^{-5} \quad \text{(see p. 160).}$$

$$\therefore\ [\mathrm{H}^+] = 1\cdot85 \times 10^{-5}.$$

The potential difference of the decinormal calomel electrode measured against the standard hydrogen electrode

$$= +0\cdot335 \text{ volt at } 18°.$$

$\therefore$ Calculated $E.M.F.$ (E) is given by the equation:

$$E = 0\cdot335 - \frac{RT}{\phi} \log_e [\mathrm{H}^+]$$

$$= 0\cdot335 - 2\cdot303 \times \frac{RT}{\phi} \log_{10} (1\cdot85 \times 10^{-5})$$

$$= 0\cdot335 + 0\cdot275 = \mathbf{0\cdot610 \text{ volt.}}$$

8. The quinhydrone electrode

Quinhydrone is an equimolecular compound of quinone and hydroquinone of the formula, $C_6H_4O_2 . C_6H_4(OH)_2$. Hydroquinone, itself, acts as a weak acid and dissociates according to the equation:

$$C_6H_4(OH)_2 \rightleftharpoons C_6H_4O_2 + 2H^+ + 2\epsilon$$

where ϵ denotes an electron. Since the dissociation is small, the concentration of quinone is equal to that of the hydroquinone since they are both derived from quinhydrone.

The potential (E) of an electrode placed in the quinhydrone solution is given by the equation :

$$E = E_0 + \frac{RT}{2\phi} \log_e \frac{[C_6H_4O_2] \times [H^+]^2}{[C_6H_4(OH)_2]}$$

$$= \mathbf{E_0 + RT \log_e [H^+]}, \quad \text{.........................(179)}$$

where E_0 is a constant corresponding with the standard state and $[C_6H_4O_2]/[C_6H_4(OH)_2] = 1$, since they are in equimolecular proportions.

9. The oxygen electrode

In the same manner that it is possible to produce a hydrogen electrode, so the tendency of oxygen gas to send ions into solution should lead to a definite potential for the oxygen electrode. If a sheet of platinum is arranged as for the hydrogen electrode but is surrounded by oxygen gas, oxygen ions tend to go into solution to form hydroxyl ions :

$$O^{--} + H_2O \rightleftharpoons 2OH^-.$$

The potential of the oxygen electrode should, therefore, be expressible by the equation :

$$E = E_0 - \frac{RT}{\phi} \log_e [OH^-]. \quad \text{..................(180)}$$

(Note $-\frac{RT}{\phi} \log_e [OH^-]$, since OH^- carries a charge opposite in sign to H^+.)

The results obtained do not, however, conform to this equation, nor does the value of the potential difference agree with the theoretical value obtained from purely chemical data.

10. Oxidation-reduction electrodes (Redox)

An oxidation-reduction electrode consists of a suitably inert metallic electrode placed in a solution of a substance which can exist in two forms of oxidation, both forms being present in the solution. An example is the quinhydrone electrode. Examples of importance involving metallic ions are those represented by the equations :

$$Fe^{+++} + \epsilon = Fe^{++}$$
$$Sn^{++++} + 2\epsilon = Sn^{++}$$

where ϵ denotes an electron. If, for example, an inert electrode, such as platinum, is placed in a solution containing both ferric ions and ferrous ions, the former will tend to take electrons from the platinum electrode while the ferrous ions will act conversely. The potential of the platinum electrode (measured against a standard electrode) can then be obtained by consideration of the scheme shown below.

A	*C*	*B*
	←—— 0·5 ——→	
$Fe^{+++}_{c_1}$ − dm. equiv.	$Fe^{+++}_{c_3}$ + dm. equiv.	hydrogen electrode
$Fe^{++}_{c_2}$ + dm. equiv.	$Fe^{++}_{c_4}$ − dm. equiv.	

Then if we assign an arbitrary value (+0·5 volt) to the potential difference between C and B, then potential difference between A and $B = 0{\cdot}5 +$ potential difference between A and C. Assume that A is positive to C. If now electrons are assumed to leave the positive electrode A, they will reduce the charge on the ferric ions in the region of A, an equal number of electrons leaving the ferrous ions in the region of C and going to the positive pole, C. The net effect is the formation of ferrous ions at the expense of the ferric ions in the region of A and the reverse process at C.

Therefore, as on p. 376:

$$E\phi = RT \log_e \frac{c_4}{c_2} - RT \log_e \frac{c_3}{c_1}$$

$$= RT \log_e \frac{c_1}{c_2} - RT \log_e \frac{c_3}{c_4}.$$

If now $c_3 = c_4 =$ unit activity, then

$$E = \frac{RT}{\phi} \log_e \frac{c_1}{c_2} = RT \log_e \frac{[Fe^{+++}]}{[Fe^{++}]}.$$

The total $E.M.F.$ between A and C, therefore:

$$= 0{\cdot}5 + RT \log_e \frac{[Fe^{+++}]}{[Fe^{++}]},$$

or replacing 0·5 by E_0 :

$$E = E_0 + RT \log_e \frac{[Fe^{+++}]}{[Fe^{++}]} \ldots\ldots\ldots\ldots\ldots\ldots \quad (181)$$

By definition E_0 = the standard oxidation-reduction potential for the system $Fe^{+++} - Fe^{++}$. Where the reaction involves the transfer of two electrons from one ion to another as in the reduction $Sn^{++++} + 2\epsilon = Sn^{++}$, the potential difference is given by the equation :

$$E = E_0 + \frac{RT}{2\phi} \log_e \frac{[Sn^{++++}]}{[Sn^{++}]}.$$

Example 179. The *E.M.F.* of the cell :

+ Ag	$AgNO_3$ unit activity	$Fe(NO_3)_2$ $Fe(NO_3)_3$ both at unit activity	Pt −

is 0·0528 volt at 25°. Calculate the equilibrium constant of the reaction $Fe^{+++} + Ag \rightleftharpoons Ag^+ + Fe^{++}$ at 25°.

Let E_{Ag} = the potential of the silver electrode and E_{Pt} = the potential of the platinum electrode when the two electrodes are placed in the equilibrium mixture. Then, for equilibrium, $E_{Ag} = E_{Pt}$.

But
$$E_{Ag} = E_{Ag(O)} + \frac{RT}{\phi} \log_e [Ag^+],$$

and
$$E_{Pt} = E_{Pt(O)} + \frac{RT}{\phi} \log_e \frac{[Fe^{+++}]}{[Fe^{++}]},$$

where $E_{Ag(O)}$ = standard electrode potential for $Ag - Ag^+$ and $E_{Pt(O)}$ = standard electrode potential for $Fe^{+++} - Fe^{++}$, and square brackets denote equilibrium concentrations.

$$\therefore E_{Ag(O)} + \frac{RT}{\phi} \log_e [Ag^+] = E_{Pt(O)} + \frac{RT}{\phi} \log_e \frac{[Fe^{+++}]}{[Fe^{++}]}.$$

$$\therefore E_{Ag(O)} - E_{Pt(O)} = \frac{RT}{\phi} \log_e \frac{[Fe^{+++}]}{[Fe^{++}]} - \frac{RT}{\phi} \log_e [Ag^+]$$

$$= \frac{RT}{\phi} \log_e \frac{[Fe^{+++}]}{[Fe^{++}] \times [Ag^+]}$$

$$= \frac{RT}{\phi} \log_e \frac{1}{K}.$$

But $$E_{Ag(O)} - E_{Pt(O)} = 0{\cdot}0528.$$

$$\therefore \frac{RT}{\phi} \log_e \frac{1}{K} = 0{\cdot}0528.$$

$$\therefore \mathbf{K} = 0{\cdot}128.$$

Provided the sign of the potential difference is carefully noted we can write directly :

$$nE\phi = RT \log_e K,$$

since both sides represent the net work of the reaction from standard conditions to equilibrium. In the reaction :

$$Ag + Fe^{+++} = Ag^{+} + Fe^{++},$$

the silver electrode would become negatively charged and the platinum would be the positive electrode.

$$\therefore -0{\cdot}0528 = \frac{RT}{\phi} \log_e K.$$

$$\therefore \mathbf{K} = 0{\cdot}128.$$

The *E.M.F.* of an oxidation-reduction cell when it is not at the standard state can be obtained by equating the electrical work to the net work. As an example we can take the reaction :

$$2Fe^{+++} + Sn^{++} \rightleftharpoons 2Fe^{++} + Sn^{++++}.$$

Then, as in Chap. XVIII :

$$\text{net work} = RT \log_e K - RT \log_e \frac{[Fe^{++}]^2 \times [Sn^{++++}]}{[Fe^{+++}]^2 \times [Sn^{++}]},$$

where K = the equilibrium constant and square brackets denote the concentrations of the ions in the cell

Pt	Sn^{++} Sn^{++++}	Fe^{+++} Fe^{++}	Pt

$\therefore$ Since the reaction involves the transfer of 2 faradays :

$$2E\phi = RT \log_e K - RT \log \frac{[Fe^{++}]^2 \times [Sn^{++++}]}{[Fe^{+++}]^2 \times [Sn^{++}]}.$$

The same result can be obtained by considering the potential of each electrode separately.

The potential difference with reference to the standard electrode potentials is obtained as follows:

For Sn^{++++}/Sn^{++}:

$$E_{Sn} = E_{Sn(O)} + \frac{RT}{2\phi}\log_e\frac{[Sn^{++++}]}{[Sn^{++}]}.$$

For Fe^{+++}/Fe^{++}:

$$E_{Fe} = E_{Fe(O)} + \frac{RT}{\phi}\log_e\frac{[Fe^{+++}]}{[Fe^{++}]}.$$

$$\therefore \text{ Potential difference} = E_{Sn} - E_{Fe}$$

$$= E_{Sn(O)} - E_{Fe(O)} + \frac{RT}{2\phi}\log_e\frac{[Sn^{++++}]}{[Sn^{++}]} - \frac{RT}{\phi}\log_e\frac{[Fe^{+++}]}{[Fe^{++}]}$$

$$= E_{Sn(O)} - E_{Fe(O)} + \frac{RT}{2\phi}\log_e\frac{[Sn^{++++}]\times[Fe^{++}]^2}{[Sn^{++}]\times[Fe^{+++}]^2}.$$

For oxidation-reduction reactions in general, the electrode potential of an inert electrode is given by the equation:

$$E = E_0 + \frac{RT}{n\phi}\log_e\frac{[\mathbf{Ox}]}{[\mathbf{Red}]}, \quad \text{..................(182)}$$

where n = the number of electrons involved in the change from one ion to the other and [**Ox**] and [**Red**] are the active masses of that ion in the oxidised and reduced state respectively. The following examples are of importance:

(*a*) **Reduction of permanganate ions in acid solution**

The reduction of the permanganate ion in acid solution is represented by the equation:

$$MnO_4^- + 8H^+ + 5\epsilon = Mn^{++} + 4H_2O.$$

The reaction may be assumed to take place in two stages:

$$MnO_4^- + 8H^+ = Mn^{7+} + 4H_2O,$$

$$Mn^{7+} + 5\epsilon = Mn^{++}.$$

$$\therefore E = E_0 + \frac{RT}{5\phi}\log_e\frac{[Mn^{7+}]}{[Mn^{++}]}.$$

But from equation (182):

$$E = E_0 + \frac{RT}{5\phi}\log_e\frac{[MnO_4^-]\times[H^+]^8}{[Mn^{++}]\times[H_2O]^4}$$

$$= E_k + \frac{RT}{5\phi}\log_e\frac{[MnO_4^-]\times[H^+]^8}{[Mn^{++}]}, \quad \text{..........(183)}$$

since $[H_2O] \doteqdot$ constant

(*b*) **Reduction of chromate and dichromate ions in acid solution**

The equation is:

$$CrO_4^{--} + 8H^+ + 3\epsilon = Cr^{+++} + 4H_2O.$$

$$\therefore E = E_k + \frac{RT}{3\phi} \log_e \frac{[CrO_4^{--}] \times [H^+]^8}{[Cr^{+++}]}.$$

For potassium dichromate the equation is:

$$Cr_2O_7^{--} + 14H^+ + 6\epsilon = 2Cr^{+++} + 7H_2O.$$

$$\therefore E = E_k + \frac{RT}{6\phi} \log_e \frac{[Cr_2O_7^{--}] \times [H^+]^{14}}{[Cr^{+++}]^2} \quad \text{.........(184)}$$

11. Electrodeposition of metals

The minimum voltage required for the electrodeposition of a metal by the electrolysis of solutions of its salts is equal to that developed by the metal when it is in equilibrium with the metallic ions in solution. The standard electrode potential for the system Zn/Zn^{++} is, for example, $-0{\cdot}762$ volt when measured against the standard hydrogen electrode; this measures the tendency of zinc ions to go into solution. If, therefore, the electrode is subject to an applied potential difference, as measured against the standard hydrogen electrode, the tendency of the zinc ions to go into solution is exactly balanced by the attraction of zinc ions to the negative electrode and deposition of zinc begins.

The potential difference required for electrodeposition clearly depends upon the concentration of the solution surrounding the electrode. If, for example, it is required to deposit zinc from $M/10$ solution at 25°, the temperature at which the standard electrode potential is measured, the potential difference is given by the equation:

$$E = E_0 + \frac{RT}{2\phi} \log_e \frac{1}{10}$$

$$= -0{\cdot}762 - 0{\cdot}029 = \mathbf{-0{\cdot}791\ volt.}$$

From the equation:

$$E = E_0 + \frac{RT}{2\phi} \log_e [Zn^{++}]$$

it is clear that $E - E_0 = -0{\cdot}058/2$, when $[Zn] = \frac{1}{10}$, that is, for a decrease of zinc ion concentration from 1 to $\frac{1}{10}$, the potential is reduced by 0·058/2. In general, when the concentration of an ion of valency n is reduced $\frac{1}{10}$ of its original value, the potential of the electrode is decreased by 0·058/n volt.

Example 180. The standard electrode potentials of Bi/Bi^{+++} and Cu/Cu^{++} are 0·226 volt and 0·344 volt respectively. If a mixture of the salts of these two metals are electrolysed, to what value can the concentration of cupric ion be reduced before the deposition of bismuth commences?

Let $[Cu^{++}]$ = the required concentration of cupric ion.

Then $$E = E_0 + \frac{RT}{2\phi} \log_e [Cu^{++}]$$

$$= 0{\cdot}344 + 0{\cdot}029 \log_{10} [Cu^{++}].$$

$$\therefore\ 0{\cdot}226 = 0{\cdot}344 + 0{\cdot}029 \log_{10} [Cu^{++}].$$

$$\therefore\ [Cu^{++}] = \mathbf{10^{-4}\ gm.\text{-}ion\ per\ litre.}$$

12. Hydrogen overvoltage

The potential of the hydrogen electrode is taken arbitrarily as zero. If, therefore, a metal is immersed in acid solution, of unit activity with regard to hydrogen ion, evolution of hydrogen from the metal should commence when its potential, measured against the standard hydrogen electrode, is very slightly >0 volt. For platinised platinum this result is confirmed by experiment. For other metallic electrodes it is found that the potential of the electrode has to be reduced to a certain negative value; this " hydrogen overvoltage " has different values according to the chemical nature of the metallic electrode (see p. 432). Until this potential is attained, therefore, no hydrogen will be liberated from the metal.

Example 181. The standard electrode potential $E°$ of zinc is $-0{\cdot}762$ volt, and its hydrogen overvoltage is 0·746 volt. Calculate the maximum permissible final acidity of a solution of zinc ions if the concentration of zinc is to be reduced to 10^{-6} gm.-ions/litre by electrodeposition without the evolution of hydrogen at the cathode. (Manchester Hons. Chem.)

For $[Zn^{++}] = 10^{-6}$:

$$E = E^\circ + \frac{RT}{2\phi} \log_e 10^{-6} = E^\circ + 0{\cdot}029 \times \log_{10} 10^{-6}$$

$$= -0{\cdot}762 - 0{\cdot}174 = -0{\cdot}936 \text{ volt.}$$

Let $[H^+]$ = maximum final acidity.

$$-0{\cdot}936 = -0{\cdot}746 + \frac{RT}{\phi} \log_e [H^+]$$

$$= -0{\cdot}746 + 0{\cdot}058 \log_{10} [H^+].$$

$\therefore$ $[H^+] = 5{\cdot}75 \times 10^{-3}$ **gm.-ions per litre.**

QUESTIONS ON CHAPTER XX

[Use the data given on p. 432.]

1. What is the standard electrode potential Zn/Zn^{++} measured against the decinormal calomel electrode?

2. Calculate the hydrogen ion concentration and the *p*H of a solution given that a hydrogen electrode immersed in this solution had a potential $-0{\cdot}416$ volt with respect to the normal calomel electrode at 18°.

3. The standard electrode potentials of Cu/Cu^{++} and Zn/Zn^{++} with reference to the standard hydrogen electrode are $+0{\cdot}344$ volt and $-0{\cdot}762$ volt at 25°. Ignoring the inter-solution potential difference, calculate the *E.M.F.* of the cell:

Cu	$CuSO_4$	$ZnSO_4$	Zn
	$M/10$	$M/100$	

Assume that the activities of the ions are equal to the actual concentrations of the ions and that both solutes are completely dissociated.

4. The standard electrode potential Cd/Cd^{++} measured against the standard hydrogen electrode is $-0{\cdot}402$ volt at 25°. What is the potential of a cadmium electrode in $M/10$ $CdCl_2$ when measured against the saturated calomel electrode?

5. The standard electrode potential Cu/Cu^{++} is $0{\cdot}345$ volt and Ag/Ag^+ is $0{\cdot}799$ volt. Calculate the concentration of silver ion at equilibrium when metallic copper is placed in $N/10$ silver nitrate solution.

6. Given that the standard free energy of formation of liquid water from its elements at 25° is $-56{,}560$ cal. per mol. and that the dissociation constant of water into its ions is 10^{-14} at the same temperature, calculate the standard potential of the oxygen-hydroxyl ion electrode at 25°. (Manchester Hons. Chem.)

7. Calculate the potential difference between the electrodes of the cell :

$$\begin{array}{c|c:c|c} Pt & H_2 & H_2 & Pt \\ & \text{(1 atmosphere)} & (\frac{1}{100}\text{ atmosphere}) & \\ A & [H^+]=1 & [H^+]=\frac{1}{100} & B \end{array}$$

Which of the electrodes A and B is the positive?

8. Calculate the free energy change of the reaction :

$$KBr + AgNO_3 = \downarrow AgBr + KNO_3.$$

Deduce also the solubility of silver bromide in $N/10$ KBr, assuming complete dissociation of the potassium bromide.

9. The cell :

$$Sb,\ Sb_2O_3 \mid \text{buffer solution of } pH8 \mid H_2,\ Pt$$

has an *E.M.F.* of 0·144 volt at 25°, the antimony electrode being the positive pole. What is the "standard potential" of the Sb, Sb_2O_3 electrode? (Manchester Hons. Chem.)

10. At 25° the standard redox potentials of the electrodes

$$Pt \mid Ce^{4+}, Ce^{3+} \text{ and } Pt \mid Fe^{3+}, Fe^{2+}$$

are 1·45 and 0·75 volts respectively. What inference may be drawn from these data? (A.R.I.C.)

11. Calculate the *E.M.F.* of the cell at 25° :

$$\begin{array}{c|c:c|c} Pt & & & Pt \\ H_2 & N/10\ HCl & N\ KOH & H_2 \\ \text{(1 atmosphere)} & & & \text{(1 atmosphere)} \end{array}$$

assuming that $N/10$ HCl is 92 per cent dissociated and N KOH is 78 per cent dissociated. Ignore the liquid *P.D.*

12. The *E.M.F.* of the cell :

$$\begin{array}{c|c|c} & & Pt \\ Hg & HgO_{(s)},\ N/10\ NaOH & H_2 \\ & & \text{(1 atmosphere)} \end{array}$$

is 0·929 volts at 25°. Calculate the dissociation pressure of mercuric oxide at 25°. The *E.M.F.* of oxy-hydrogen cell under standard conditions at 25° is 1·23 volts.

13. The standard free energies of $HCN_{(aq.)}$ and CN^- are 27,520 cal. and 39,370 cal. respectively at 25°. Calculate the dissociation

constant of hydrocyanic acid and hence deduce the degree of hydrolysis in $N/10$ KCN solution.

14. Calculate the *E.M.F.* of the cell :

$$\mathrm{Pb} \,\Big|\, \mathrm{PbO_{(s)}},\ N/10\ \mathrm{NaOH} \,\Big|\, \begin{matrix}\mathrm{Pt}\\ \mathrm{O_2}\\ \text{(1 atmosphere)}\end{matrix}$$

given that the standard free energy of PbO is $-41,000$ cal. at 25°. What is the dissociation pressure of PbO at this temperature?

15. Given that the *E.M.F.* at 25° of the cell :

$$\mathrm{Cu} \,\Big|\, \mathrm{CuO_{(s)}},\ N\ \mathrm{NaOH} \,\Big|\, \begin{matrix}\mathrm{Pt}\\ \mathrm{H_2}\\ \text{(1 atmosphere)}\end{matrix}$$

is 0·470 volt and that the standard free energy of water (liquid) is $-56,560$ cal., calculate the standard free energy of $\mathrm{CuO_{(s)}}$ at 25°.

16. Calculate the *E.M.F.* of the following cell at 25°, ignoring the liquid potential difference and assuming complete dissociation :

$$\begin{matrix}\mathrm{Pt}\\ \mathrm{O_2}\\ \text{(400 mm.)}\end{matrix} \,\Big|\, N\ \mathrm{KOH} \,\vdots\, N\ \mathrm{HCl} \,\Big|\, \begin{matrix}\mathrm{Pt}\\ \mathrm{H_2}\\ \text{(600 mm.)}\end{matrix}$$

17. The standard electrodes potentials $\mathrm{Sn/Sn^{++}}$ and $\mathrm{Pb/Pb^{++}}$ are $-0·136$ volt and $-0·122$ volt respectively at 25°. What is the value of $[\mathrm{Sn^{++}}]/[\mathrm{Pb^{++}}]$ when equilibrium is established in the reaction :

$$\mathrm{Sn_{(s)} + Pb(ClO_4)_2 = Sn(ClO_4)_2 + Pb_{(s)}} \text{ at } 25°?$$

18. Using the data of free energies given on p. 433, calculate (*a*) the solubility of silver bromide in water at 25°, (*b*) the ionic product for water (K_w) at 25°, (*c*) the vapour pressure of pure liquid hydrogen peroxide at 25°.

19. Calculate the percentage hydrolysis of aluminium chloride at 25° in a solution containing 1 gm.-molecule in 32 litres given that the *E.M.F.* of the cell :

$$\begin{matrix}\mathrm{Pt}\\ \mathrm{H_2}\\ \text{(1 atmosphere)}\end{matrix} \,\Big|\, \begin{matrix}\mathrm{AlCl_3},\\ (M/32)\end{matrix}\ \mathrm{NH_4NO_3},\ \begin{matrix}\mathrm{Hg_2Cl_2}\\ \text{(normal)}\end{matrix} \,\Big|\, \mathrm{Hg}$$

is 0·4567 volts and that the potential of the normal calomel electrode against the hydrogen electrode is $+0{\cdot}2822$ volts. Calculate also the degree of hydrolysis in $M/16$ solution and hence deduce the *E.M.F.* of the cell :

$$\underset{(1\ \text{atmosphere})}{\text{Pt}} \left| \underset{(M/16)}{AlCl_3,}\ NH_4NO_3,\ \underset{(\text{normal})}{Hg_2Cl_2} \right| Hg$$

20. The *E.M.F.* of the cell :

$$\begin{array}{c}\text{Pt}\\ H_2\\ (1\ \text{atmosphere})\end{array} \left| N/10\ HCl \ \vdots\ N/10\ KOH \right| \begin{array}{c}\text{Pt}\\ H_2\\ (1\ \text{atmosphere})\end{array}$$

is 0·700 volt at 25°. Assuming that the percentage dissociation of $N/10$ HCl is 86·3 and that of $N/10$ KOH is 85·1, calculate K_w (the ionic product for water) at 25°.

21. At 25°, the *E.M.F.* of the cell :

$$Hg,\ HgCl \mid KCl \mid AgCl,\ Ag$$

is 0·0455 volts and the temperature coefficient is 0·000336 volts per degree. Find ΔF, ΔH and ΔS for the reaction occurring when the cell operates. (London B.Sc. Special.)

22. The standard potentials of the Ag, Ag_2O/OH^- and the O_2/OH^- electrodes are respectively $+0{\cdot}344$ volt and $+0{\cdot}400$ volt at 25°. For the formation of Ag_2O, $\Delta H = -7000$ cal./mol., and may be assumed independent of the temperature. Calculate the temperature at which silver oxide will begin to decompose in air (20 per cent oxygen by volume). (Manchester Hons. Chem.)

23. The *E.M.F.* of the cell :

$$Hg \mid Hg_2Cl_2 \text{ in } N\ KCl \mid HgO \text{ in } N\ NaOH \mid Hg$$

is 1·504 volts at 20°, and the *E.M.F.* of the cell:

$$Hg \mid HgO \text{ in } N\ NaOH \mid \text{Red } PbO \text{ in } N\ NaOH \mid Pb$$

is 0·6760 volts. What is the concentration of lead ion in the system : red PbO in N NaOH ?

24. The standard potentials of the iodine-iodide and arsenate-arsenite electrodes are $+0{\cdot}536$ and $+0{\cdot}574$ volts respectively. Calculate an equilibrium constant for the reaction which occurs between sodium arsenite and iodine and discuss its analytical application. (London B.Sc. Special.)

25. A solution molar in respect to both nickel ion (Ni^{++}) and cupric ion (Cu^{++}) is electrolysed. The standard electrode potentials, Ni/Ni^{++} and Cu/Cu^{++} are respectively $-0{\cdot}23$ and $+0{\cdot}344$. At what concentration of cupric ion will nickel commence to deposit ?

26. A solution of cadmium chloride of $p\text{H}=5$ is electrolysed. At what concentration of cadmium ion will the evolution of hydrogen commence? The standard electrode potential of cadmium is $-0{\cdot}401$ volts and its hydrogen overvoltage is 0·48.

27. If $E^{\circ}_{(1)}$ denote the standard electrode potential of the electrode Fe, Fe^{++} and $E^{\circ}_{(2)}$ denote the standard potential of the electrode Fe, $\frac{Fe^{++}}{Fe^{+++}}$, show that the standard electrode potential Fe,Fe^{+++} (denoted by $E^{\circ}_{(3)}$) is given by the equation:

$$E^{\circ}_{(3)}=\frac{2E^{\circ}_{(1)}+E^{\circ}_{(2)}}{3}.$$

28. The standard electrode potential of Sn, Sn^{++} is $-0{\cdot}136$ volts and that of the electrode Sn, $\frac{Sn^{++}}{Sn^{++++}}$ is $-0{\cdot}15$ volts. Calculate the standard potential of the electrode Sn, Sn^{++++}.

CHAPTER XXI

THE THIRD LAW OF THERMODYNAMICS

1. Nernst's heat theorem

The relation between the change of free energy and the change of heat content is given by the Gibbs-Helmholtz equation, namely :

$$\Delta F - \Delta H = T\left(\frac{d(\Delta F)}{dT}\right)_p \text{ ....(185)}$$

It is clear that ΔH can be calculated, provided ΔF and $\frac{d(\Delta F)}{dT}$ are both known. Examples of this type of calculation are given on pp. 368–371 for voltaic cells. The reverse process of calculating ΔF from ΔH is not possible without making certain assumptions which form the basis of the Nernst Heat Theorem. It is obviously of importance to have a method of calculating ΔF from the observed values of ΔH, since it then becomes possible to state the conditions under which $\Delta F = 0$, that is, the conditions of equilibrium.

By suitable transposition of equation (185), we obtain :

$$\frac{d}{dT}\left(\frac{\Delta F}{T}\right) = -\frac{\Delta H}{T^2},$$

which on integration gives :

$$\frac{\Delta F}{T} = a - \int_0^T \frac{\Delta H}{T^2} \cdot dT, \text{ ....(186)}$$

where a = the integration constant.

The variation of ΔH with temperature can be written :

$$\Delta H = \Delta H_0 + \alpha T + \beta T^2 + \gamma T^3 + \dots, \text{ ....(187)}$$

where ΔH_0 = the value of ΔH when $T = 0°\ A$.

$$\therefore \frac{\Delta H}{T^2} = \frac{\Delta H_0}{T^2} + \frac{\alpha}{T} + \beta + \gamma T + \dots \text{ ....(188)}$$

$$\therefore \int_0^T \frac{\Delta H}{T^2} \cdot dT = -\frac{\Delta H_0}{T} + \alpha \log T + \beta T + \tfrac{1}{2}\gamma T^2 + \dots \text{ ......(189)}$$

$$\therefore\ \frac{\Delta F}{T} = a + \frac{\Delta H_0}{T} - \alpha \log T - \beta T - \tfrac{1}{2}\gamma T^2 + \dots,$$

or
$$\Delta F = aT + \Delta H_0 - \alpha T \log T - \beta T^2 - \tfrac{1}{2}\gamma T^3 + \dots \quad (190)$$

The principle of the Nernst Heat Theorem is now introduced to provide a solution to this equation.

From equation (185) it is clear that when $T = 0$, $T\left(\frac{d(\Delta F)}{dT}\right) = 0$, provided $\frac{d(\Delta F)}{dT}$ remains finite. At temperature $T = 0$, therefore, $\Delta F = \Delta H$. The Nernst theorem assumes that the curves ΔF against T and ΔH against T not only coincide at $T = 0$, but approach each other asymptotically as $T \to 0$ (see Fig. 36).

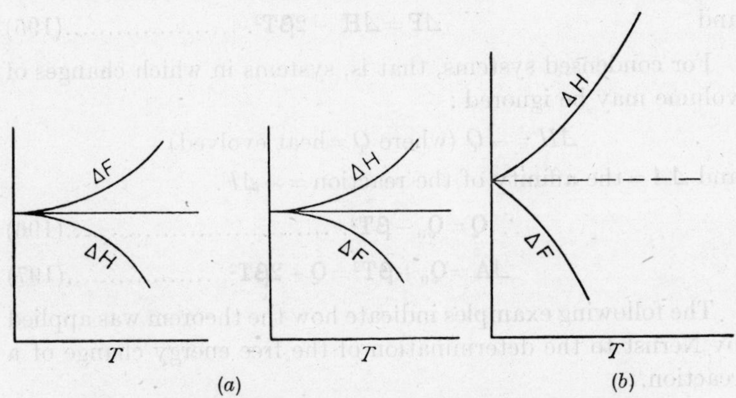

Fig. 36. Free energy and heat content curves approaching asymptotically as in (*a*) and not intersecting as in (*b*).

In the immediate region of the absolute zero, therefore, it is correct to write:

$$\frac{d(\Delta H)}{dT} = \frac{d(\Delta F)}{dT} = 0.$$

But, from equation (190):

$$\frac{d(\Delta F)}{dT} = a - \alpha(1 + \log_e T) - 2\beta T - \tfrac{3}{2}\gamma T^2 + \dots$$

(since $\Delta H_0 =$ a constant).

Also from equation (187):

$$\frac{d(\Delta H)}{dT} = \alpha + 2\beta T + 3\gamma T^2 + \dots.$$

$\therefore$ For $T \to 0$:

$$a - \alpha(1 + \log_e T) - 2\beta T - \tfrac{3}{2}\gamma T^2 + \ldots$$

$$= \alpha + 2\beta T + 3\gamma T^2 + \ldots = 0.$$

$$\therefore a = 0 \text{ and } \alpha = 0.$$

$$\therefore \Delta H = \Delta H_0 + \beta T^2 + \gamma T^3 + \ldots, \quad \ldots\ldots\ldots\ldots\ldots\ldots(191)$$

and $$\Delta F = \Delta H_0 - \beta T^2 - \tfrac{1}{2}\gamma T^3 + \ldots \quad \ldots\ldots\ldots\ldots\ldots\ldots(192)$$

It is sufficient in most problems to ignore the coefficient γ and all powers of x higher than 2.

$$\therefore \mathbf{\Delta H = \Delta H_0 + \beta T^2}, \quad \ldots\ldots\ldots\ldots\ldots\ldots(193)$$

$$\mathbf{\Delta F = \Delta H_0 - \beta T^2}, \quad \ldots\ldots\ldots\ldots\ldots\ldots(194)$$

and $$\mathbf{\Delta F = \Delta H - 2\beta T^2}. \quad \ldots\ldots\ldots\ldots\ldots\ldots(195)$$

For condensed systems, that is, systems in which changes of volume may be ignored:

$$\Delta H = -Q \text{ (where } Q = \text{heat evolved)}$$

and ΔA = the affinity of the reaction $= -\Delta F$.

$$\therefore \mathbf{Q = Q_0 - \beta T^2}, \quad \ldots\ldots\ldots\ldots\ldots\ldots(196)$$

$$\mathbf{\Delta A = Q_0 + \beta T^2 = Q + 2\beta T^2}. \quad \ldots\ldots\ldots\ldots\ldots\ldots(197)$$

The following examples indicate how the theorem was applied by Nernst to the determination of the free energy change of a reaction.

Example 182. Calculate the transition temperature of the system: $S_\alpha \to S_\beta$ given that the heat of transformation at 50° is $-2{\cdot}77$ cal. per gm. and that $\dfrac{dQ}{dT} = 2{\cdot}3 \times 10^{-5}T$ cal. per gm. per degree.

From equation (193):

$$\frac{dQ}{dT} = -2\beta T = +2{\cdot}3 \times 10^{-5}T.$$

$$\therefore \beta = -1{\cdot}15 \times 10^{-5}.$$

$$\therefore \quad -2{\cdot}77 = Q_0 + 1{\cdot}15 \times 10^{-5} \times 323 \times 323.$$

$$\therefore Q_0 = -1{\cdot}57 \text{ cal. per gm.}$$

Let T_x = the transition temperature. Then since the system is in equilibrium at this temperature $\Delta A = -\Delta F = 0$.

$$\therefore\ Q_0 = -\beta T_x^{\,2}.$$

$$\therefore\ 1{\cdot}57 = 1{\cdot}15 \times 10^{-5} \times T_x^{\,2}.$$

$$\therefore\ T_x = \sqrt{\frac{1{\cdot}57}{1{\cdot}15 \times 10^{-5}}} = \mathbf{369^\circ\ A.}$$

Example 183. Calculate the change in free energy per gm. when $S_\beta \rightarrow S_\alpha$ at 0°.

As in example 182 :

$$-\Delta F = \Delta A = 1{\cdot}57 - 1{\cdot}15 \times 10^{-5} \times 273 \times 273$$

$$= +0{\cdot}72 \text{ cal. per gm.}$$

$$\therefore\ \Delta F = \mathbf{-0{\cdot}72\ cal.\ per\ gm.}$$

The following example indicates how the principle may be applied to the calculation of the free energy change in the formation of hydrated salts, for example,

$$CuSO_4 + H_2O = CuSO_4 \,.\, H_2O.$$

Since the specific heat of water varies abnormally with temperature, the free energy change is calculated for the reaction :

$$CuSO_4 + H_2O_{(ice)} = CuSO_4 \,.\, H_2O.$$

Example 184. The heat of hydration of anhydrous copper sulphate to form the monohydrate is 6460 cal. per mol. at 18°, that is :

$$\underset{\text{(anhydrous)}}{CuSO_4} + \underset{\text{(liquid)}}{H_2O} = CuSO_4 \,.\, H_2O + 6460 \text{ cal.}$$

The molecular heat of fusion of ice at 0° is 1440 cal., and its variation with temperature is given by the equation $\frac{d(\lambda_f)}{dT} = 9{\cdot}0$ cal. per mol. The molecular heat of ice (C) can be obtained from the equation : $C = 3{\cdot}0 + 0{\cdot}0223T$ cal. The molecular heat capacity of water of crystallisation in $CuSO_4 \,.\, H_2O$ is 6·60 cal. Calculate the free energy change of the reaction :

$$\underset{\text{(anhydrous)}}{CuSO_4} + \underset{\text{(ice)}}{H_2O} = CuSO_4 \,.\, H_2O$$

at 18°.

We determine first the value of Q in the reaction :

$$CuSO_4 + H_2O_{(ice)} = CuSO_4 \,.\, H_2O + Q$$

at 18°.

Since $CuSO_4 + H_2O_{(liq.)} = CuSO_4 . H_2O + 6460$ cal. at 18° :

$\therefore$ $(6460 - Q)$ = heat content of $H_2O_{(liq.)}$ at 18°

– heat content of $H_2O_{(ice)}$ at 18°

$= \lambda_f$ at $18° = 1440 + (9 \times 18) = 1602$ cal.

$\therefore$ $Q \doteq 4860$ cal. at 18° (denote by Q_{18}).

But since $Q = Q_0 - \beta T^2$ (for any temperature) :

$$\therefore \frac{dQ}{dT} = -2\beta T = C_1 - C_2 \text{ (see Kirchhoff equation),}$$

where C_1 = molecular heat of ice

and C_2 = molecular heat of water of crystallisation

At 9° :

$$\frac{dQ}{dT} = \{3 + (0{\cdot}0223 \times 282)\} - 6{\cdot}60$$

$$= 2{\cdot}69 = -2\beta \times 282.$$

$$\therefore \beta = -\frac{2{\cdot}69}{2 \times 282} = -0{\cdot}00477.$$

But $-\Delta F = \Delta A = Q_{18} + 2\beta T^2$

$$= 4860 - 2 \times 0{\cdot}00477 \times 291 \times 291$$

$$\doteq 4050 \text{ cal.}$$

$$\therefore \Delta F = -4050 \text{ cal.}$$

The Nernst theorem can clearly be applied to the calculation of the *E.M.F.* of a galvanic cell, provided the heat exchange (and its variation with temperature) of the chemical reaction taking place in the cell is known. For if ΔH can be written $\Delta H = \Delta H_0 + \beta T^2$, then, as on p. 402,

$$\Delta F = -nE\phi = \Delta H - 2\beta T^2. \qquad \text{.................(198)}$$

Example 185. Calculate the *E.M.F.* of the cell :

Pb | $PbCl_2$, (solid) $PbCl_2$, (saturated solution) AgCl (saturated solution), AgCl (solid) | Ag, at 20°,

given that the heat of the reaction :

$$Pb + 2AgCl = PbCl_2 + 2Ag$$

varies with the temperature (absolute) according to the equation :

$$Q = 23{,}800 + 0{\cdot}0194T^2.$$

From equations (193) and (194), p. 402 :

$$\beta = -0{\cdot}0194 \text{ and } -\Delta F = nE\phi = A$$
$$= Q_0 + \beta T^2 = 23{,}800 - (0{\cdot}0194 \times 293 \times 293).$$
$$\therefore \frac{2 \times E \times 96{,}540}{4{\cdot}2} = 23{,}800 - (0{\cdot}0194 \times 293 \times 293).$$
$$\therefore E = \frac{(23{,}800 - 1665) \times 4{\cdot}2}{2 \times 96{,}540} = \mathbf{0{\cdot}482 \text{ volt.}}$$

Example 186. Calculate the $E.M.F.$ of the Clark cell :

$$\text{Zn} \mid \underset{\text{(solid)}}{ZnSO_4 \,.\, 7H_2O} \;\vdots\; \underset{\text{(solid)}}{Hg_2SO_4} \mid \text{Hg}$$

at $-7°$, using the following data :

$$\text{Zn} \rightarrow ZnSO_4 \,.\, 7H_2O \;; \quad \Delta H = -252{,}780 \text{ at } 17°.$$
$$2\text{Hg} \rightarrow Hg_2SO_4 \;; \quad \Delta H = 175{,}000 \text{ at } 17°.$$

Molecular latent heat of fusion of ice = 1580 cal. ; molecular heats of the reacting substances (measured at 10°) :

$$\text{Zn} = 6{\cdot}0 \;; \; Hg_2SO_4 = 31{\cdot}0 \;; \; H_2O_{(ice)} = 9{\cdot}1 \;;$$
$$ZnSO_4 \,.\, 7H_2O = 89{\cdot}4 \;; \; \text{Hg} = 6{\cdot}6.$$

The chemical reaction is :

$$\text{Zn} + Hg_2SO_4 + 7H_2O_{(ice)} = ZnSO_4 \,.\, 7H_2O + 2\text{Hg}.$$

As on p. 402 :

$$\frac{dQ}{dT} = -2\beta T = \begin{Bmatrix}\text{Heat content} \\ \text{of reactants}\end{Bmatrix} - \begin{Bmatrix}\text{Heat content} \\ \text{of resultants}\end{Bmatrix}$$
$$= 6{\cdot}0 + 31{\cdot}0 + 63{\cdot}7 - 89{\cdot}4 - 13{\cdot}2 = -1{\cdot}9.$$
$$\therefore \text{Since } T = 283°\,A, \; \beta = \frac{1{\cdot}9}{2 \times 283} = 3{\cdot}4 \times 10^{-3}.$$

The heat of the reaction (Q) at 17° is given by :

Q = (heat evolved in the reaction $\text{Zn} \rightarrow ZnSO_4 \,.\, 7H_2O$)
− (heat absorbed in the reaction $Hg_2SO_4 \rightarrow 2\text{Hg}$)
− (heat absorbed in the conversion of $7H_2O_{(ice)}$ $\rightarrow 7H_2O$ as water of crystallisation)

$$= 252{,}780 - 175{,}000 - 7 \times 1580 = 66{,}720.$$

The heat of the reaction at 17° (Q) can now be written

$$Q = Q_0 - \beta T^2 = Q_0 - 3{\cdot}4 \times 10^{-3} \times (290)^2 = 66{,}720.$$
$$\therefore Q_0 \doteq 67{,}010 \text{ cal.}$$

$\therefore$ At $-7°$:

$$A = Q_0 + \beta T^2 = 67{,}010 - 3{\cdot}4 \times 10^{-3} \times (266)^2$$
$$= 67{,}246 \text{ cal.}$$

$$\therefore \frac{2 \times 96{,}540 \times E}{4{\cdot}2} = 67{,}246.$$

$$\therefore \text{E} = 1{\cdot}463 \text{ volts.}$$

2. Application of the Nernst heat theorem to gaseous reactions

Although the assumptions of the Nernst heat theorem are probably only true for crystalline solids (see p. 412), the following treatment indicates how the theorem can be applied to gaseous reactions. The following relationships have already been derived.

(1) Change of free energy for reactions between solids according to the equation:

$$A_{\text{(solid)}} + B_{\text{(solid)}} = C_{\text{(solid)}}$$

$$-\Delta F = RT \log_e K_p - RT \log_e \frac{p_C}{p_A \times p_B} \quad \text{(p. 351).}$$

(2) Relation between equilibrium constant for gaseous reactions (K_p) and change of heat content:

$$\log_e K_p = -\frac{\Delta H}{RT} + \int_0^T \frac{\Delta C_p \, dT}{RT} + i_x \quad \text{(p. 352).}$$

(3) Relation between saturated vapour pressure and heat of evaporation (sublimation):

$$\log_e p = -\frac{\Delta H}{RT} + \int_0^T \frac{\Delta C_p \, dT}{RT} + i \quad \text{(p. 127).}$$

(4) Relation between change of free energy and heat content:

$$-\Delta F = -\Delta H + T \int_0^T \frac{\Delta C_p \, dT}{T} + i_0 T \quad \text{(p. 353).}$$

If, now, the values of $\log_e K_p$ and $\log_e p$ are substituted in equation (1), we obtain with appropriate subscripts:

$$-\Delta F = RT\left(-\frac{\Delta H}{RT} + \int_0^T \frac{\Delta C_p \, dT}{RT} + i_x\right)$$
$$-RT\left(-\frac{\Delta H_C}{RT} + \int_0^T \frac{\Delta C_{p(C)} \, dT}{RT} + i_C\right)$$

$$+RT\left(-\frac{\Delta H_A}{RT}+\int_0^T \frac{\Delta C_{p(A)}\,dT}{RT}+i_A\right)$$

$$+RT\left(-\frac{\Delta H_B}{RT}+\int_0^T \frac{\Delta C_{p(B)}\,dT}{RT}+i_B\right)$$

$$=-\Delta H+\Delta H_C-\Delta H_A-\Delta H_B$$

$$+T\int_0^T \frac{(\Delta C_p-\Delta C_{p(C)}+\Delta C_{p(A)}+\Delta C_{p(B)})}{T}\,dT$$

$$+RT\,(i_x-i_C+i_A+i_B)$$

$$=-\Delta H_{(r)}+T\int_0^T \frac{\Delta C_{p(s)}\,dT}{T}-RT\,(i_C-i_A-i_B-i_x), \quad \ldots(199)$$

where $\Delta H_{(r)}=\Delta H-\Delta H_C+\Delta H_A+\Delta H_B$
= heat of reaction in gaseous phase
− difference in the heat of evaporation of product (C) and reactants (A and B)
= heat of reaction in the solid phase,

and $\Delta C_{p(s)}=\Delta C_p-\Delta C_{p(C)}+\Delta C_{p(A)}+\Delta C_{p(B)}$
= heat capacity of solid C
− (sum of heat capacities of solids A and B).

Inspection of equation (4) shows that the constant of integration, i_0, has the dimensions of H/T and is, therefore, an entropy term. Also since $-\Delta F=-\Delta H+T\Delta S$, the constant

$$i_0=\Delta S_{t=0}=0 \quad \text{(by the heat theorem).}$$

∴ By comparing equations (160) and (199):

$$-RT\,(i_C-i_A-i_B-i_x)=i_0 T=0.$$

$$\therefore\ R\,(i_C-i_A-i_B-i_x)=i_0=0.$$

$$\therefore\ i_x R=R\,(i_C-i_A-i_B)$$

and $$\mathbf{i_x=i_C-(i_A+i_B)}. \quad \ldots\ldots\ldots\ldots(200)$$

Therefore, i_x = the integration constant of equation (2), which gives the conditions of equilibrium for the reaction in the gaseous phase = the algebraic sum of the integration constants for a series of equations like (3), which give the relationship between the vapour pressures of the separate solid phases and the change of temperature. The constants i_A, i_B and i_C are called the **true chemical constants** of the substances to which they refer.

By considering a general gaseous reaction of the type :

$$aA + bB + \ldots = rR + sS + \ldots ,$$

it is easy to show by substitution in equations (2) and (3) that the general form of equation (3) becomes :

$$\log_e \mathrm{K_p} = -\frac{\Delta \mathrm{H}}{\mathrm{RT}} + \int_0^{\mathrm{T}} \frac{\Delta \mathrm{C_p}\, \mathrm{dT}}{\mathrm{RT}} + \Sigma \mathrm{ni}, \quad \ldots\ldots\ldots\ldots(201)$$

where $\Sigma ni = (ri_r + si_s + \ldots) - (ai_A + bi_B + \ldots)$.

The determination of the true chemical constant of a substance from equation (3) by direct observation of ΔC_p and p clearly presents practical difficulties, so that the following approximations are made.

(1) The Clapeyron-Clausius equation gives :

$$\frac{dp}{dT} = \frac{\Delta H_s}{(V_g - V_s)T},$$

where ΔH_s = heat of evaporation (sublimation),
V_g = volume in the gas phase,
and V_s = volume in the solid phase.

The equation cannot be integrated with accuracy unless (*a*) the deviation from the gas law over wide pressure can be corrected, and (*b*) the variation of ΔH_s with temperature is known. The first of these errors is corrected by use of an empirical equation, namely :

$$p(V_g - V_s) = RT\left(1 - \frac{p}{p_c}\right), \quad \ldots\ldots\ldots\ldots\ldots(202)$$

where p_c = the critical pressure of the vapour phase.

Substituting for $(V_g - V_s)$ in the Clapeyron-Clausius equation :

$$\frac{1}{p} \cdot \frac{dp}{dT} = \frac{\Delta H_s}{RT^2\left(1 - \dfrac{p}{p_c}\right)}.$$

$$\therefore \frac{\mathrm{d}(\log_e \mathrm{p})}{\mathrm{dT}} = \frac{\Delta \mathrm{H_s}}{\mathrm{RT^2}\left(1 - \dfrac{\mathrm{p}}{\mathrm{p_c}}\right)}. \quad \ldots\ldots\ldots\ldots\ldots(203)$$

The variation of ΔH_s with temperature is also obtained from an empirical equation :

$$\Delta \mathrm{H_s} = (\Delta \mathrm{H_{s(0)}} + \mathrm{aT} + \mathrm{bT^2})\left(1 - \frac{\mathrm{p}}{\mathrm{p_c}}\right). \quad \ldots\ldots\ldots\ldots(204)$$

$$\therefore \frac{d(\log_e p)}{dT} = \frac{\Delta H_{s(0)} + aT + bT^2}{RT^2}$$

$$= \frac{\Delta H_{s(0)}}{RT^2} + \frac{a}{RT} + \frac{b}{R}.$$

$$\therefore \log_e p = -\frac{\Delta H_{s(0)}}{RT} + \frac{a \log_e T}{R} + \frac{bT}{R} + C. \quad \text{......(205)}$$

The constant C is called the "conventional chemical constant"; it would clearly be identical with i of equation (3) p. 406 but for the approximations which have been introduced in calculating $\log_e p$ and ΔH_s.

Equation (205) can be put in the form in which it is more often used by noting that $a = 3{\cdot}5$ and that b may often be neglected. By transposing to common logarithms the equation then becomes :

$$\log_{10} p = -\frac{\Delta \mathrm{H}_{s(0)}}{4{\cdot}58\mathrm{T}} + 1{\cdot}75\mathrm{T} + \mathrm{C}. \quad \text{................(206)}$$

The values of C for a number of common substances are given on p. 434 ; it will be seen that they lie mostly between 2 and 4.

The equation relating K_p to the heat content change of a gaseous reaction can now be obtained. The Van't Hoff isochore gives :

$$\frac{d(\log_e K_p)}{dT} = -\frac{\Delta H}{RT^2}.$$

Since $\quad \log_e K_p = \log_e \dfrac{(p_Q{}^q \times p_R{}^r \times p_S{}^s \times \ldots)}{(p_A{}^a \times p_B{}^b \times p_C{}^c \times \ldots)}$

we have : $\log_e K_p = q \log_e p_Q + r \log_e p_R + s \log_e p_S + \ldots$

$$- a \log_e p_A + b \log_e p_B + c \log_e p_C + \ldots .$$

Each of these pressure terms can be expressed by equation (206).

Similarly, ΔH can be separated into the difference of the individual heat capacities (see equation (199)). We can write, therefore :

$$\log_{10} K_p = -\frac{\Delta H_0}{4{\cdot}58T} + 1{\cdot}75\Sigma n \log_{10} T + \Sigma nC,$$

where $\quad \Sigma n = q + r + s + \ldots - a - b - c - \ldots ,$

and $\quad \Sigma nC = qC_Q + rC_R + sC_S - aC_A - bC_B - cC_C.$

The equation is further simplified by replacing ΔH_0 by ΔH where ΔH = change of heat content for a reaction at ordinary temperature.

$$\therefore \log_e K_p = -\frac{\Delta \mathrm{H}}{4{\cdot}58\mathrm{T}} + 1{\cdot}75\Sigma \mathrm{n} \log_{10} \mathrm{T} + \Sigma \mathrm{nC}. \quad \ldots\ldots(207)$$

This equation is the **Nernst approximation formula.** The following miscellaneous examples show how it can be applied both to gaseous and heterogeneous reactions.

Example 187. The heat of dissociation of calcium carbonate is 42,500 cal. ($CaCO_3 = CaO + CO_2 - 42{,}500$ cal.). Find the dissociation pressure of calcium carbonate at 1000° A given that the chemical constant for carbon dioxide is 3·4.

(London B.Sc. Special.)

For the reaction :

$$CaCO_3 = CaO + CO_2,$$

$$K_p = p_{CO_2}; \quad \Sigma n = 1; \quad \Sigma nC = 3{\cdot}4.$$

$$\therefore \log_{10} p_{CO_2} = -\frac{42{,}500}{4{\cdot}58 \times 1000} + 1{\cdot}75 \log_{10} 1000 + 3{\cdot}4.$$

$$\therefore \mathbf{p = 0{\cdot}25 \text{ atmosphere}.}$$

Example 189. The heat absorbed per gm.-molecule in the dissociation of manganese carbonate ($MnCO_3 = MnO + CO_2$) is 23,500 cal. At what temperature will the dissociation pressure of manganese carbonate equal 1 atmosphere?

As in foregoing example :

$$\log_{10} K_p = \log_{10} p_{CO_2}; \quad \Sigma n = 1; \quad \Sigma nC = 3{\cdot}4.$$

But if $\quad p_{CO_2} = 1, \log_{10} p_{CO_2} = 0.$

$$\therefore \log_{10} p_{CO_2} = -\frac{23{,}500}{4{\cdot}58T} + 1{\cdot}75 \log_{10} T + 3{\cdot}4$$

$$= 0.$$

$$\therefore \frac{23{,}500}{4{\cdot}58T} = 1{\cdot}75 \log_{10} T + 3{\cdot}4.$$

The solution to this equation can be obtained graphically as shown in Fig. 37. By trial it is found that T lies between 400° A and 800° A, so that it is only necessary to plot a few values between these temperatures.

From the graph:

$$T = 635^\circ \text{ A.}$$

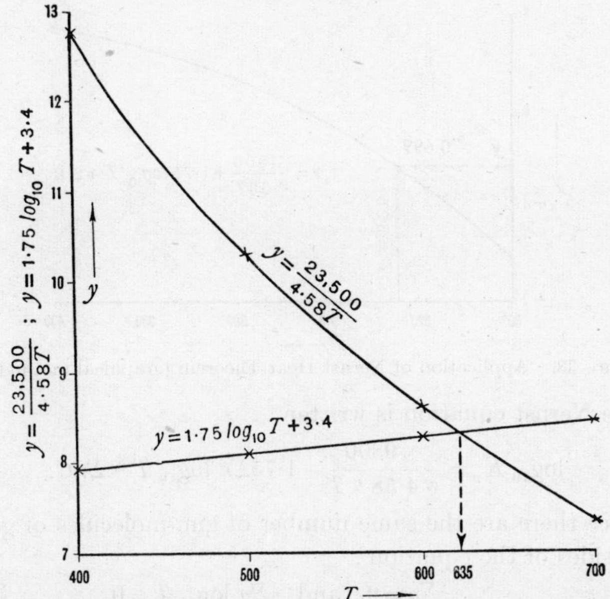

FIG. 37. Application of Nernst Heat Theorem (graphical method).

Example 190. The heat of dissociation of silver oxide is 11,800 cal., that is:

$$2Ag_2O \rightleftharpoons 4Ag + O_2 - 11{,}800 \text{ cal.}$$

At what temperature will silver oxide begin to decompose in air assumed to contain 20 per cent by volume of oxygen?

For silver oxide, $K_p = p_{O_2}$; $\Sigma n = 1$; $\Sigma nC = 2 \cdot 8$.

$$\therefore \log_{10} \frac{1}{5} = -\frac{11{,}800}{4 \cdot 58T} + 1 \cdot 75 \log_{10} T + 2 \cdot 8.$$

$$\therefore -0 \cdot 699 = -\frac{11{,}800}{4 \cdot 58T} + 1 \cdot 75 \log_{10} T + 2 \cdot 8.$$

Solving this equation graphically as in Fig. 38, we find:

Temperature at which decomposition begins $= 325^\circ \text{A} = 52^\circ$.

Example 191. The heat absorbed in the reaction:

$$H_2 + CO_2 = CO + H_2O$$

is 9800 cal. If equilibrium is established at 1200° A, hydrogen and carbon dioxide being initially present in equimolecular proportions, what fraction of carbon monoxide has been formed?

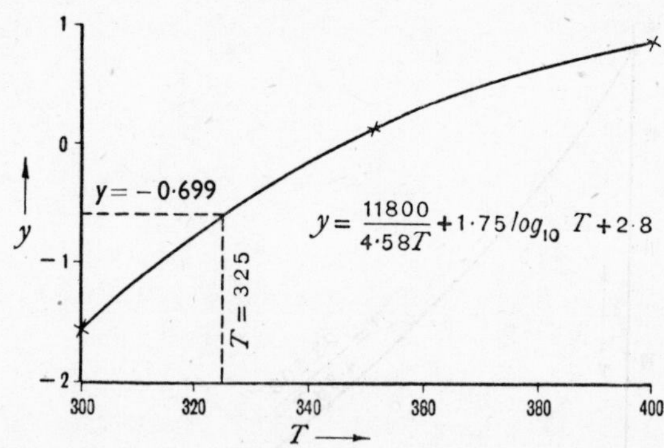

FIG. 38. Application of Nernst Heat Theorem (graphical method).

The Nernst equation is written:

$$\log_{10} K_p = -\frac{9800}{4{\cdot}58 \times T} + 1{\cdot}75\Sigma n \log_{10} T + \Sigma nC.$$

Since there are the same number of gm.-molecules of gas on both sides of the equation:

$$\Sigma n = 0 \quad \text{and} \quad \Sigma n \log_{10} T = 0.$$

Using the chemical constants given on p. 434:

$$\Sigma nC = 3{\cdot}5 + 3{\cdot}6 - 1{\cdot}6 - 3{\cdot}2 = 2{\cdot}3.$$

$$\therefore \log_{10} K_p = -\frac{9800}{4{\cdot}58 \times 1200} + 2{\cdot}3 = 0{\cdot}52.$$

$$\therefore K_p = 3{\cdot}31.$$

$$\therefore K_p = \frac{p_{CO} \times p_{H_2O}}{p_{CO_2} \times p_{H_2}} = \frac{p_{CO}^2}{p_{CO_2}^2} = \frac{x^2}{(1-x)^2} = 3{\cdot}31,$$

where x = fraction of CO_2 converted to CO.

$$\therefore x = 0{\cdot}645.$$

3. Direct application of the third law of thermodynamics to the calculation of free energy change

The assumptions of the Nernst heat theorem are formalised in the Third Law of thermodynamics, which states: the entropies of all crystalline solids at the absolute zero are the same and are, in fact, zero. The change of entropy in a reaction taking place at ordinary temperature can then be obtained by the following method.

We may consider the reaction :

$$A+B=C+D$$

where there is no restriction of physical state on the reacting substances.

Let S_A, S_B, S_C and S_D be the entropies of A, B, C and D respectively at the temperature at which the reaction takes place. Let $S_{0(A)}$, $S_{0(B)}$, etc., represent the entropies at zero. Then, by the Third Law, $\Sigma S_{0(A)}=0$, since each is respectively $=0$. Assume that the reaction occurs at 25°. Then,

S_A = entropy of A at 0° A + increase of entropy in passing from 0° A to 298° A

= standard entropy (see p. 318) of A, since $S_{0(A)}=0$.

But the entropy change in the reaction is given by :

$$\Delta S=S_C+S_D-S_A-S_B$$
$$=\Sigma S,$$

where ΣS = the algebraic sum of the standard entropies of the reacting substances.

If, then, it is possible to measure the standard entropies accurately, the free energy change of a reaction can be obtained directly from the equation :

$$\Delta F=\Delta H-T\Delta S.$$

There is then no necessity to determine the constant of integration of the Gibbs-Helmholtz equation by Nernst's method.

Example 192. The standard molal entropies of hydrogen, nitrogen and ammonia are 31·2, 45·8 and 46·4 cal. degree^{-1} respectively. Calculate the free energy change at 25° of the reaction :

$$3H_2+N_2=2NH_3\ ;\quad \Delta H_{298}=-21{,}340 \text{ cal.}$$
$$\Delta S_{298}=(2\times 46{\cdot}4)-\{45{\cdot}8+(3\times 31{\cdot}2)\}$$
$$=-46{\cdot}6.$$

But $\quad \Delta F_{298}=\Delta H_{298}-T\Delta S_{298}$

$$=(-21{,}340+13{,}887) \text{ cal.}$$
$$\doteq -7{,}450 \text{ cal.}$$

$\therefore\ \Delta F_{298}$ per gm.-molecule of ammonia

$$=-3{,}725 \text{ cal.}$$

When the free energy change of a reaction has been obtained for a given temperature, the free energy change at any other temperature can be calculated by the method outlined on p. 353.

Example 193. Calculate the free energy change at 25° of the following reaction:

$$4HCl_{(g)} + O_{2(g)} = 2Cl_{2(g)} + 2H_2O_{(g)}\,; \quad \Delta H = -27{,}600 \text{ cal.}$$

Calculate also the free energy change of the reaction at 800°.

	Molal entropy at 25°; S_{298}.	Molal specific heats.
$HCl_{(g)}$	44·6	$C_p = 6{\cdot}50 + 0{\cdot}0010T$
$O_{2(g)}$	49·0	$C_p = 6{\cdot}50 + 0{\cdot}0010T$
$H_2O_{(g)}$	45·2	$C_p = 8{\cdot}81 - 0{\cdot}0019T + 0{\cdot}00000222T^2$
$Cl_{2(g)}$	53·3	$C_p = 7{\cdot}4 + 0{\cdot}0010T$

Inserting the molal entropies into the equation:

$$\begin{array}{ccccccc} 4HCl_{(g)} & + & O_{2(g)} & = & 2Cl_{2(g)} & + & 2H_2O_{(g)} \\ (4 \times 44{\cdot}6) & & (49{\cdot}0) & & (2 \times 53{\cdot}3) & & (2 \times 45{\cdot}2) \end{array}$$

we have:

$$\Delta S_{298} = 196{\cdot}2 - 227{\cdot}4 = -31{\cdot}2.$$

$$\therefore\ T\Delta S_{298} = 298 \times -31{\cdot}2 = -9{,}297.$$

But $\Delta F = \Delta H - T\Delta S$.

$$\therefore\ \Delta F_{298} = -27{,}600 + 9{,}297 = \mathbf{-18{,}300\ cal.}$$

The data of molal heat capacities can be used exactly as on p. 353 to give the free energy change at 800°. The value obtained is $\Delta F_{1073} = \mathbf{-18{,}600\ cal.}$

The problems discussed by the use of the Nernst theorem are clearly more easily solved by the direct application of the Third Law, provided that the data of heat capacity, heat of reaction and of the entropies of the reacting substances are available. The free energy change of the reaction at any temperature can be obtained by the methods outlined above. The calculation of electromotive force (as in examples 185 and 186) and of dissociation pressures (as in example 187) is then quickly effected by the methods given in earlier chapters.

QUESTIONS ON CHAPTER XXI

[Tables of chemical constants and standard entropies are given on p. 434].

1. Calculate the transition temperature: grey tin $\rightleftharpoons$ white tin given that the heat of transition is 550 cal. per gm.-atom at 0° and that $\frac{dQ}{dT} = 0{\cdot}0035T$ where Q = heat of transition.

2. The heat of formation of silver iodide is given by

$$Q = 12{,}875 - 0{\cdot}011T^2$$

cal. per gm.-molecule. Calculate the *E.M.F.* of the cell:

$$\text{Ag} \left| \underset{\text{(solid)}}{\text{AgI}} \right| \underset{\text{(solid)}}{I_2},$$

at 17°.

3. Using the data of example 182, calculate the free energy change per gm.-atom of $S_\alpha \rightarrow S_\beta$ at 50°, and hence show that S_α is stable at this temperature.

4. The heat of hydration of magnesium sulphate at 18° is 22,690 cal.

$$MgSO_4 + 7H_2O_{(\text{liq.})} = MgSO_4 . 7H_2O ; \Delta H = -22{,}690.$$

If the heat capacity of all the water of crystallisation in 1 mole of the hydrated salt is 44·6 cal. at 9° and the molecular heat of ice is given by $C = 3{\cdot}0 + 0{\cdot}0223T$ and the variation of the latent heat of fusion of ice with temperature is 9·0 cal. per degree, calculate the affinity of the reaction: $MgSO_4 + 7H_2O = MgSO_4 . 7H_2O$ at 18°.

5. Given that $N_2 + O_2 = 2NO$, $\Delta H = 43{,}200$ cal., calculate the fraction of nitrogen in air which is converted into nitric oxide when equilibrium is established at 1800° *A*.

6. The dissociation pressure of the system:

$$2AgCl . 3NH_3 \rightleftharpoons 2AgCl + 3NH_3$$

is 270 mm. at 48°. Calculate the heat of dissociation.

7. If the heat of decomposition of copper nitrate is 47,600 cal. per mol. (absorbed), calculate (*a*) the dissociation pressure at 200°, (*b*) the temperature at which copper nitrate will decompose in air assumed to contain 20 per cent of oxygen.

8. The percentage dissociation of water vapour is 0·207 at 2000° *A* and 10 atmospheres pressure. Calculate the heat of formation of water.

9. If the dissociation pressure of barium platinichloride:

$$BaPtCl_6 = BaCl_2 + Pt + 2Cl_2$$

is 9·5 mm. at 450°, calculate the heat of decomposition per gm.-molecule of the platinichloride.

10. The heat of dissociation of lead carbonate is 22,580 cal. per gm.-molecule. At what temperature will lead carbonate decompose against a pressure of carbon dioxide equal to 250 mm.?

11. The heat of formation of lead oxide is 50,300 cal. per mole. $Pb + \frac{1}{2}O_2 = PbO$; $\Delta H = -50{,}300$ cal. Calculate the temperature at which lead oxide will begin to dissociate in air.

12. Calculate the *E.M.F.* of the cell :

$$M \;\Big|\; \underset{\text{(solid)}}{MCl_2} \;\Big\vdots\; \underset{\text{(solid)}}{M'Cl_2} \;\Big|\; M',$$

where M and M' are different divalent metals given that the cell reaction is $M + M'Cl_2 = MCl_2 + M'$, that the heat of this reaction is 56,000 cal. at 17° and that the molecular heats have the following values : $M = 6{\cdot}06$; $MCl_2 = 9{\cdot}82$; $M' = 6{\cdot}45$; $M'Cl_2 = 9{\cdot}97$.

13. Calculate the free energy change of the reaction :

$$2C + 3H_2 + \tfrac{1}{2}O_2 = C_2H_5OH$$

at 25°. $\Delta H_{298} = -66{,}300$ cal. S_{298} for ethyl alcohol $= 38{\cdot}4$.

14. Calculate the approximate partial pressure of nitric oxide in air at 2000° *A* given that $\Delta S_{2000} = -7{\cdot}3$ for the reaction $N_2 + O_2 = 2NO$ and that $\Delta H_{2000} = 43{,}200$ cal.

15. The dissociation pressure of calcium carbonate is 56 mm. at 625°. Given :

$$CaCO_3 = CaO + CO_2 - 42{,}500 \text{ cal.},$$

calculate ΔS_{898} for the reaction.

16. Calculate the free energy change of the reaction :

$$2H_{2(g)} + O_{2(g)} = 2H_2O_{(g)}$$

at 1000° given that $\Delta H_{298} = -58{,}100$ cal. per gm.-molecule of water and that the variations of molal heat capacities are given by :

H_2 ; $C_p = 6{\cdot}50 + 0{\cdot}0009T$.
O_2 ; $C_p = 6{\cdot}50 + 0{\cdot}001T$.
$H_2O_{(g)}$; $C_p = 8{\cdot}81 - 0{\cdot}0019T + 0{\cdot}00000222T^2$.

17. The *E.M.F.* of the cell :

$$Pb \;\Big|\; PbCl_2,\ KCl,\ Hg_2Cl_2 \;\Big|\; Hg$$

is 0·536 volt at 25°. Calculate ΔH_{298} for the reaction :

$$Pb + Hg_2Cl_2 = PbCl_2 + 2Hg.$$

18. Calculate the partial pressure of hydrogen in hydrogen sulphide at 1 atmosphere pressure at 1000° :

$H_{2(g)} + \frac{1}{2}S_{2(g)} = H_2S_{(g)}$; $\Delta H_{298} = -19{,}230$ cal.
$S_{2(g)}$; $C_p = 6{\cdot}50 + 0{\cdot}001T$.
$H_{2(g)}$; $C_p = 6{\cdot}50 + 0{\cdot}0009T$.
$H_2S_{(g)}$; $C_p = 8{\cdot}81 - 0{\cdot}0019T + 0{\cdot}00000222T^2$.

Assume $\Delta S_{298} = -8{\cdot}9$.

19. Use the data tabulated below to derive relationships expressing the variation with temperature of (*a*) heat of reaction and (*b*) free energy of reaction :

$$CaS + 3CaSO_4 \rightleftharpoons 4CaO + 4SO_2.$$

Compound	Entropy S_{298} cal. mol^{-1} deg^{-1}	Heat of formation ΔH_{298} cal. mol^{-1}	Heat capacity C_p cal. mol^{-1} deg^{-1}
SO_2	59·2	− 69,300	$11{\cdot}40 + 1{\cdot}414 \times 10^{-3}T - 2{\cdot}045 \times 10^{-5}T^2$
CaO	9·5	− 151,700	$10{\cdot}00 + 4{\cdot}840 \times 10^{-3}T - 1{\cdot}080 \times 10^{-5}T^2$
$CaSO_4$	25·9	− 335,700	$18{\cdot}52 + 21{\cdot}97 \times 10^{-3}T - 1{\cdot}568 \times 10^{-5}T^2$
CaS	13·5	− 113,500	$10{\cdot}00 + 4{\cdot}840 \times 10^{-3}T - 1{\cdot}080 \times 10^{-5}T^2$

What are the values of (*c*) the equilibrium constant and (*d*) the partial pressure of sulphur dioxide at 1273° *A*. (A.R.I.C.)

MISCELLANEOUS QUESTIONS ON CHAPTERS XVI–XXI

1. The melting point of pure benzene at normal pressure is 5·48° and its latent heat of fusion is 30·1 cal. per gm. What is the temperature at which benzene should begin to crystallise from the solution made by dissolving 5·08 gm. of dinitrobenzene, $C_6H_4(NO_2)_2$ in 56·3 gm. of benzene, assuming the solute to behave normally?

2. The transition temperature at 760 mm. pressure of mercuric iodide is 126° :

$$\underset{\substack{\text{red} \\ (\text{density} = 6{\cdot}26 \text{ gm./c.c.})}}{HgI_2} \underset{126^\circ}{\rightleftharpoons} \underset{\substack{\text{yellow} \\ (\text{density} = 6{\cdot}06 \text{ gm./c.c.})}}{HgI_2}$$

the red form being stable at the lower temperature. Calculate the transition temperature at 20 atmospheres pressure. The heat of transition is 6·5 cal. per gm.

3. The dissociation pressure of solid nitrogen pentoxide (N_2O_5) is given by the equation :

$$\log_{10} P\,(\text{mm.}) = \frac{1244}{T} + 34{\cdot}1 \log_{10} T - 85{\cdot}729.$$

What is the mean heat of sublimation per gm.-molecule over the temperature range : −5° to +5°?

4. The reaction between silver and ferric nitrate is given by the equation :

$$Ag + Fe^{+++} \rightleftharpoons Ag^+ + Fe^{++}$$

The equilibrium constant $\left(K=\frac{[Fe^{++}]\times[Ag^{+}]}{[Fe^{+++}]}\right)$ is found to be 0·128 at very low concentrations. Calculate the standard electromotive force of the cell :

$$Ag \mid Ag^{+}_{(u.a.)} \parallel \begin{matrix} Fe^{+++}_{(u.a.)} \\ Fe^{++}_{(u.a.)} \end{matrix} \mid Pt$$

5. (*a*) The equilibrium quantity of NO in air heated to 1604° is 0·42 per cent (volume), and rises to 2·05 per cent (volume) at 2307°. What is the molecular heat of formation of nitric oxide? (Air can be assumed to have the volume composition N_2, 78·1 ; O_2, 21·0 ; A, 0·9.)

(*b*) According to Michaelis, the ionic product of water (K_w) is $0{\cdot}74\times10^{-14}$ at 18° and $1{\cdot}27\times10^{-14}$ at 25°. Calculate the equivalent heat of neutralisation of a strong acid by a strong base in dilute solution. (London B.Sc. Special.)

6. A mixture of hydrogen and oxygen in equivalent proportions at 20° and 760 mm. is exploded in a closed bomb placed in a calorimeter. After the explosion it is found that for each gm. of hydrogen in the bomb 342 gm. of ice must be added to the calorimeter to restore its temperature to 20°. The heat of fusion of ice at 0° is 79·6 cal. The molal heat of vaporisation of water at 100° and constant volume is 9000 cal. and the molal heat capacity of water vapour (at constant volume) is $C_v=8{\cdot}6+0{\cdot}0038t$ (t = temperature in degrees centigrade). Calculate the maximum temperature and pressure attained in the bomb, specifying the assumptions you make. (Liverpool B.Sc. Hons.)

7. Calculate the *E.M.F.* at 25° of the cell :

$$\begin{matrix} Pt \\ H_2 \\ \text{(1 atmosphere)} \end{matrix} \Bigg| \; [H^{+}]=0{\cdot}0026 \; \Bigg\vdots \; N/10 \text{ calomel electrode}$$

assuming the hydrogen ion concentration to be the same as its activity.

8. The solubility of a weak organic acid of molecular weight 136 is 0·12 gm. per 100 gm. of water at 18° and 0·36 gm. per 100 gm. of water at 30°. Calculate the heat of solution per gm.-molecule at 24°.

9. The heat of dissociation of calcium carbonate is 42,000 cal. ($\Delta H=42{,}000$ cal.) The dissociation pressure of calcium carbonate is 170 mm. at 800°. Assuming the heat of dissociation to remain constant, calculate the dissociation pressure at 900°.

10. The vapour pressure of an aqueous solution of urea is 23·50 mm. at 25°. Calculate the osmotic pressure of the solution. What weight of water should have separated from 100 gm. of this solution at −2·5°?

11. The velocity constant for the decomposition of phosphine varies with temperature according to the equation:

$$\log_{10} k = -\frac{18{,}963}{T} + 2\log_{10} T + 12{,}130.$$

Calculate the heat of decomposition at 400°.

12. Give a thermodynamic proof of the formula for the equilibrium constant of the homogeneous gas reaction $A + B \rightleftharpoons C + D$.

At 0° and 87 mm. pressure the density of an equilibrium mixture of NO_2 and N_2O_4 is 0·84 times the density calculated for N_2O_4. Calculate the degree of dissociation at this temperature and pressure, also the degree of dissociation at 0° and 10 mm. pressure.

(London B.Sc. Special.)

13. Given that the vapour pressure of solid benzene at −5° is 3·26 mm., that the latent heat of fusion of benzene is 30 cal. per gm., and that the freezing point of benzene is 5·4°, calculate the vapour pressure of liquid benzene at −5°.

14. The cell:

$$\text{Sb} \mid \text{Sb}_2\text{O}_3 \quad \underset{[\text{H}^+]=10^{-4}}{\text{Solution}}, \quad \underset{\text{KCl}}{\text{Saturated}}, \quad \text{Hg}_2\text{Cl}_2 \mid \text{Hg}$$

has an *E.M.F.* of 0·228 volt. What is the *p*H of a solution which when used in the cell to replace the given acid solution gave an *E.M.F.* of 0·4060 volt?

15. The *E.M.F.* of the cell:

$$\text{Cu} \mid \text{Cu}_2\text{O}, \ N/10 \text{ alkali}, \ \underset{(1\text{ atm.})}{\text{H}_2} \mid \text{Pt}$$

is 0·469 volts at 17° while the *E.M.F.* of the cell:

$$\text{Pt} \mid \underset{(1\text{ atm.})}{\text{O}_2}, \ N/10 \text{ alkali}, \ \underset{(1\text{ atm.})}{\text{H}_2} \mid \text{Pt}$$

is 1·232 volts at the same temperature. Calculate the dissociation pressure of the reaction: $2Cu_2O \rightleftharpoons 4Cu + O_2$ at 17°.

16. Calculate the solubility of silver bromide in water (gm. per 100 c.c.) at 25°. [Data on p. 433.]

17. The change of boiling point with pressure for toluene is given by $dp/dT = 21{\cdot}7$ mm. of mercury per degree. A solution containing 2·56 gm. of a non-volatile solute in 100 gm. of toluene boiled at a temperature 0·327° higher than that of the boiling point of pure toluene. What is the molecular weight of the solute?

18. The *E.M.F.* of the cell:

$$\text{Hg} \mid \text{Hg}_2\text{Cl}_2, \ N\,\text{KCl}, \ \text{NH}_4\text{NO}_3, \ M/16\ \text{NH}_4\text{Cl} \mid \underset{(1\text{ atm.})}{\overset{\text{Pt}}{\text{H}_2}}$$

is 0·5998 volt. Calculate the percentage hydrolysis in $M/16$ NH_4Cl.

19. The latent heat of evaporation of aniline is 104 cal. per gm. Its normal boiling point is 182°. At what pressure will it boil at 175°?

20. The solubility of a liquid of molecular weight 78 is 0·0065 gm. per 100 gm. of water at 25°. What is the activity coefficient of the liquid in the solution if the activity of the pure liquid at the same temperature is taken = 1?

21. The latent heat of fusion of naphthalene is 35 cal. per gm. and its melting point is 80°. Calculate the solubility (gm. per 100 gm.) of naphthalene in benzene at 50°, assuming ideal behaviour.

22. The solubility product of silver bromide is $1{\cdot}2 \times 10^{-7}$ at 30°. Calculate the *E.M.F.* of the cell:

Ag	AgBr (saturated solution), $N/100$ KBr, NH_4NO_3, $N/10$ $AgNO_3$	Ag

at 30°, assuming $N/100$ KBr is 96 per cent dissociated and $N/10$ $AgNO_3$ is 72 per cent dissociated.

23. The change of free energy for the reaction: $CO + \frac{1}{2}O_2 = CO_2$ is given by

$$\Delta F = -67{,}510 + 2{\cdot}75T \log_e T - 0{\cdot}0028T^2 + 0{\cdot}00000031T^3 + 4{\cdot}46T.$$

Calculate the percentage dissociation of carbon dioxide at 1200°.

24. Calculate the equilibrium constant ($K = [Sn^{++}]/[Pb^{++}]$) of the reaction $Sn_{(solid)} + Pb^{++} \rightleftharpoons Sn^{++} + Pb_{(solid)}$, using the data of standard electrode potentials on p. 432.

25. Calculate the total change of entropy when 100 gm. of ice at 0° is converted into water at 100°. (Latent heat of fusion of ice = 80 cal. per gm. Assume the specific heat of water is constant.)

26. Calculate at 18° the *E.M.F.* of the cell:

Pt H_2 (1 atmosphere)	$N/100$ HCl	$N/20$ HCl	Pt H_2 (1 atmosphere)

given that the transport number of the chlorine ion is 0·16.

27. At a temperature of 1023°*A* H_2S is dissociated (according to $2H_2S \rightleftharpoons 2H_2 + S_2$) to the extent of 21·67 per cent, the total pressure being 1 atmosphere; at 1103°*A* the corresponding extent of dissociation is 33·01 per cent. The molecular heats at constant pressure of H_2, S_2 and H_2S are:

$$H_2: \quad C_p = 6{\cdot}50 + 0{\cdot}0009T,$$

$$S_2: \quad C_p = 6{\cdot}50 + 0{\cdot}0010T,$$

$$H_2S: \quad C_p = 8{\cdot}81 - 0{\cdot}0019T + 0{\cdot}00000222T^2.$$

Calculate the heat of the reaction: $H_2S = H_2 + \frac{1}{2}S_2$ at constant pressure, (*a*) at 1063° *A*; (*b*) at 1667° *A*.

(Liverpool B.Sc. Hons.)

28. Show, by differentiation, that the Gibbs-Helmholtz equation can be given in the following form:

$$\frac{d(\Delta F/T)}{d(1/T)} = \Delta H.$$

Using the integrated form of this equation and the data given in Question 27, calculate the free energy change of the reaction

$$H_2S = H_2 + \tfrac{1}{2}S_2; \quad \Delta F_{298} = 17{,}000 \text{ cal.}$$

at 900°. The heat of the reaction at 25° is −19,600 cal.

29. The *E.M.F.* of the cell:

$$Pb \mid \text{fused } PbCl_2 \mid Cl_2$$

is given by the equation: $E = 1{\cdot}263 - [0{\cdot}000679\,(t - 498)]$ volts where t = temperature (°C.). Calculate the heat of formation of lead chloride at 400°.

30. The velocity constant for the decomposition of nitrogen pentoxide varies with temperature according to the equation:

$$\log_e k = -\frac{12{,}443}{T} + 35{\cdot}56.$$

Calculate the energy of activation per gm.-molecule.

31. The equilibrium constant $\left(K_p = \frac{p_{NH_3}}{p_{H_2}^{\frac{3}{2}} \times p_{N_2}^{\frac{1}{2}}}\right)$ for the reaction varies with the absolute temperature according to the equation:

$$\log_{10} K_p = \frac{2068}{T} - 2{\cdot}9278 \log_{10} T + 0{\cdot}0002756T + 5{\cdot}13 \times 10^{-7}T^2 + 3{\cdot}149.$$

Calculate (*a*) the affinity of the reaction (from standard states) at 800°, (*b*) the heat of the reaction at 800°, (*c*) the percentage dissociation of ammonia at 1 atmosphere pressure and at 700°.

32. The dissociation pressures of calcium hydride, CaH_2, at the stated temperatures are:

$T°$ (*A*)	914	943	978	1001	1020
p (mm.)	0·5	1·2	3·0	5·1	8·0

Determine the mean heat of dissociation of calcium hydride. Calculate the dissociation pressure at 1200° *A*, assuming that the heat of dissociation remains constant.

33. The solubility product of silver nitrite is $2{\cdot}0 \times 10^{-4}$ at 25°. What is the free energy change of the reaction:

$$AgNO_{2(solid)} = Ag^+ + NO_2^-,$$

at 25°?

34. From the following data obtain the general free energy equation for the reaction:

$$CO_2 + H_2 = CO + H_2O_{(gas)}.$$

$$CO + \tfrac{1}{2}O_2 = CO_2. \quad \Delta H_{298} = -68{,}300 ; \ \Delta F_{298} = -61{,}750.$$

$$H_2 + \tfrac{1}{2}O_2 = H_2O_{(gas)}. \quad \Delta H_{298} = -58{,}100 ; \ \Delta F_{298} = -56{,}560.$$

$$CO_2 ; \ C_p = 7{\cdot}0 + 0{\cdot}0071T - 0{\cdot}00000186T^2$$

$$H_2 ; \ C_p = 6{\cdot}50 + 0{\cdot}0009T$$

$$CO ; \ C_p = 6{\cdot}50 + 0{\cdot}0010T$$

$$H_2O ; \ C_p = 8{\cdot}81 - 0{\cdot}0019T + 0{\cdot}00000222T^2$$

35. Show that the solubility of ferrous carbonate in carbonic acid (as ferrous bicarbonate) is given by the equation:

$$[Fe(HCO_3)_2] = \sqrt[3]{\frac{K_1K_3}{4K_2}} \cdot \frac{\sqrt[3]{H_2CO_3}}{\alpha},$$

where $K_1 = [H^+] \times [HCO_3^-]/[H_2CO_3]$,

$K_2 = [H^+] \times [CO_3^{--}]/[HCO_3^-]$,

$K_3 =$ the solubility product of $FeCO_3$,

and $\alpha =$ the degree of dissociation of ferrous bicarbonate.

Show also that the equation is in agreement with the following data:

$[H_2CO_3]$ gm.-molecules per litre	$[Fe(HCO_3)_2]$ gm.-molecules per litre	α
0·1868	0·00245	0·912
0·2168	0·00262	0·908
0·3116	0·00304	0·902
0·3294	0·00311	0·900

36. If a mixture of 3 vols. of H_2 and 1 vol. of SO_2 initially at a total pressure of 760·0 mm. and at 1200° absolute be heated at constant temperature and constant volume, the equilibrium

$$3H_2 + SO_2 \rightleftharpoons 2H_2O + H_2S$$

is eventually established and the equilibrium pressure becomes 577·6 mm.

(*a*) Calculate K_p (pressures in atm.) for the equilibrium at 1200° absolute.

(*b*) Calculate the decrease in free energy attending at the same temperature the reaction:

$$3H_2\ (0{\cdot}5\text{ atm.}) + SO_2\ (0{\cdot}5\text{ atm.}) = 2H_2O\ (2\text{ atm.}) + H_2S\ (1{\cdot}0\text{ atm.}).$$

(Liverpool B.Sc. Hons.)

37. The heat of decomposition of silver carbonate is 20,060 cal.:

$$Ag_2CO_3 \rightleftharpoons Ag_2O + CO_2 ; \quad \Delta H = 20{,}060.$$

At what temperature will the dissociation of silver carbonate commence against a pressure of carbon dioxide of $\frac{1}{10}$ of an atmosphere?

38. The velocity constant of a reaction in arbitrary units is 0·0063 at 20° and 0·0192 at 40°. Calculate the overall energy of activation.

39. The *E.M.F.* of the cell:

$$H_2 \left| \overrightarrow{N/32\ C_6H_5NH_3Cl.\ \ NH_4NO_3} \right| \underset{\text{(normal)}}{Hg_2Cl_2},\ Hg$$

is 0·4655 volt at 25°, and the direction of the current through the cell is as shown. Using the values given on p. 432 for the standard electrode potentials, calculate (*a*) the hydrogen ion concentration in $N/32$ aniline hydrochloride, (*b*) the percentage hydrolysis in $N/32$ solution, assuming complete dissociation of the hydrochloric acid.

40. What is the relation between the heat of a reaction and the variation of equilibrium constant with temperature? From what basis can this relation be derived? The vapour of ammonium sulphide is practically completely dissociated into ammonia and hydrogen sulphide at temperatures above 0°. The total pressure set up when excess of solid ammonium sulphide is placed in an evacuated vessel is 150 mm. at 10° and 250 mm. at 25°. Calculate the heat of reaction, at constant pressure, between gaseous ammonia and hydrogen sulphide to form solid ammonium sulphide.

(London B.Sc. Special.)

41. A substance, *A*, has a molecular weight of 92; it melts at 57° and its latent heat of fusion is 3500 cal. per gm.-molecule. A solution of *A* in chlorobenzene (C_6H_5Cl) begins to deposit *A* at 33°. What is the solubility of *A* in chlorobenzene in gm. per 100 gm. of chlorobenzene at this temperature?

42. Using the equations:

$$Hg + \tfrac{1}{2}Cl_2 = \tfrac{1}{2}Hg_2Cl_2 ; \quad \Delta F_{298^\circ} = -25{,}140 \text{ cal.}$$

$$Ag + \tfrac{1}{2}Cl_2 = AgCl ; \quad \Delta F_{298^\circ} = -26{,}190 \text{ cal.}$$

calculate the *E.M.F.* of the cell:

$$Ag \left| AgCl_{(s)},\ \underset{\text{(solution)}}{KCl},\ Hg_2Cl_{2(s)} \right| Hg$$

and show that the cell reaction is:

$$Ag + \tfrac{1}{2}Hg_2Cl_2 = AgCl + Hg.$$

43. For the reaction $CO + \frac{1}{2}O_2 = CO_2$, $\Delta H = -68{,}300$ cal. Calculate the partial pressure of carbon monoxide in carbon dioxide at 1 atmosphere pressure at 1400°. (Conventional chemical constants: $CO = 3·5$; $O_2 = 2·8$; $CO_2 = 3·2$.)

44. The *E.M.F.* of the cell:

HgPb (3 per cent)	$PbSO_4$ (solid)	$Na_2SO_4 \cdot 10H_2O$	Hg_2SO_4 (solid)	Hg

is given by $E_t = 0{\cdot}96463 + 0{\cdot}000174(t-25) + 0{\cdot}00000038(t-25)^2$. The electrode HgPb is heterogeneous, the solid phase being Pb_2Hg and the removal of 1 gm. atom of lead from this electrode is accompanied by the evolution of 585 cal. The heat of formation of lead sulphate at 18° is 216,200 cal. and that of mercurous sulphate at the same temperature is 175,000 cal. Calculate (*a*) the heat of the reaction:

$$0{\cdot}5Pb_2Hg + Hg_2SO_4 = PbSO_4 + 2{\cdot}5Hg$$

at 18°, using the observed *E.M.F.*; (*b*) the heat of the reaction: $Pb + Hg_2SO_4 = PbSO_4 + 2Hg$ at 18°, using the observed *E.M.F.* and compare the value with that obtained from the given thermochemical data.

45. When air is heated to 2580° absolute the equilibrium mixture contains 2·05 per cent by volume of NO. Calculate the affinity of the change $N_2 + O_2 \rightarrow 2NO$ at this temperature. Assume that air is 21 per cent oxygen and 79 per cent nitrogen by volume. (London B.Sc. Special.)

46. Using the values for the standard electrode potentials given on p. 432, calculate the *E.M.F.* of the cell:

Cu	$M/50\ CuSO_4$	$M/100\ ZnSO_4$	Zn

assuming complete dissociation of the solutes. Calculate also the free energy change of the reaction taking place in the cell at 25°.

47. Starting from the expression:

$$l = T\left(\frac{dp}{dT}\right)_v,$$

where l = the latent heat of unit-volume expansion, p = pressure and T = absolute temperature, either show how the Clapeyron equation may be deduced or, alternatively, show the relation between l and p for a perfect gas. (Liverpool B.Sc. Hons.)

48. At a temperature of 1073°*A* and a total pressure of 2·57 atm. the percentage of CO_2 (by volume) in the gas mixture after establishment of the equilibrium $CO_2 + C$ (solid) $\rightleftharpoons 2CO$ is 26·45 per cent. The heat of the reaction $CO_2 + C \rightarrow 2CO$ at constant pressure and at a temperature of 1123°*A* is $-42,000$ cal. Calculate the percentage of CO_2 in the equilibrium gas mixture at 1173°*A* and a total pressure of 5 atm. (Liverpool B.Sc. Hons.)

49. In the following table $K_p = \frac{p_{SO_3}}{p_{SO_2} \times p_{O_2}^{\frac{1}{2}}}$. Calculate the mean value of ΔH in the reaction: $SO_2 + \frac{1}{2}O_2 = SO_3$.

$T°$ (C) - -	528	579	627	680	727	789	832
K_p - -	31·3	13·8	5·54	3·24	1·86	0·956	0·627

Assuming ΔH to remain constant, calculate the partial pressure of sulphur trioxide in the reaction mixture at 1 atmosphere pressure at 900°.

50. Derive the relationship between the initial concentration of the reactant molecules and the extent of the reaction after a lapse of time t for first and second order reactions. Calculate the energy of activation for the formation of hydrogen sulphide from hydrogen and sulphur from the following data:

Temperature - -	280°	290°	301°	322°	337°
Weight of H_2S formed gram per sec. $\times 10^{10}$ per c.c. of gaseous volume	2·77	5·49	11·47	44·23	150·2

In all experiments the closed reaction vessel contained the same initial weights of sulphur and hydrogen. (A.R.I.C.)

51. The analysis of a solution and of the moist solid in equilibrium with it at 40° gave the following results:

	$(NH_4)_2SO_4$ (mols)	Na_2SO_4 (mols)	H_2O (gm.)
Solution - - -	0·77	0·23	150
Moist solid - -	0·53	0·47	50

Find the value of x in the formula for the double salt.

(Manchester Hons. Chem.)

52. Use the following data to determine (a) ΔS_{1200} for the reaction: $N_2 + O_2 = 2NO$; (b) the partial pressure of nitric oxide in the equilibrium mixture obtained by allowing one gm.-molecule of nitrogen and one gm.-molecule of oxygen to react at 1200° A and at a total pressure of one atmosphere.

$$N_2 + O_2 = 2NO\ ; \quad \Delta H_{298} = 43{,}200 \text{ cal.}$$

$$N_2\ ; \quad C_p = 6{\cdot}50 + 0{\cdot}001T\ ; \quad S_{298} = 45{\cdot}8.$$

$$O_2\ ; \quad C_p = 6{\cdot}50 + 0{\cdot}001T\ ; \quad S_{298} = 49{\cdot}0.$$

$$NO\ ; \quad C_p = 6{\cdot}50 + 0{\cdot}001T\ ; \quad S_{298} = 43{\cdot}7.$$

53. Deduce the relationship between the equilibrium constant and the standard free energy increment:

$$-\Delta G^\circ = RT \log_e K.$$

Demonstrate the effect of reaction type on the extent of reaction at equilibrium by proceeding as follows: For each of the reactions $A + B = C$ and $A + B = 2C$, the standard free energy increment is +3,000 cal. at 327°. Start with an initially equimolar mixture of A and B, and calculate for each reaction the molar fraction of A (or B) converted into C at equilibrium. (A.R.I.C.)

54. Calculate the $E.M.F.$ at 18° of the cell:

	Pt		Pt	
H_2 (400 mm. press.)	$[H^+]$, $=0{\cdot}01$	KCl, solution	$[H^+]$ $=0{\cdot}001$	H_2 (760 mm. press.)

55. Deduce the Van't Hoff isotherm for a gaseous reaction and describe briefly other methods which are available for determining the free energy, ΔG, of a chemical reaction. When carbon dioxide and hydrogen were heated to 986° under a pressure of one atmosphere they yielded an equilibrium mixture containing 48·4 per cent CO_2, 22·8 per cent CO, 22·8 per cent H_2O and 6 per cent H_2. Calculate the free energy of the change:

$$CO_2 + H_2 = CO + H_2O$$

when the initial partial pressures of the reactants and the final partial pressures of the resultants are all at one atmosphere. (F.R.I.C.)

56. Calculate the $E.M.F.$ at 25° of the cell:

Pb		Ag
$PbCl_{2\,(s)}$,	$AgCl_{(s)}$,	

using the following data:

$$Pb + 2AgCl_{(s)} = PbCl_{2(s)} + 2Ag\,; \quad \Delta H_{298} = -21{,}580 \text{ cal.}$$

$$Pb\,; \quad S_{298} = 15{\cdot}53\,; \quad Ag\,; \quad S_{298} = 10{\cdot}3\,; \quad PbCl_2\,;$$

$$S_{298} = 33{\cdot}2\,; \quad AgCl\,; \quad S_{298} = 23{\cdot}4.$$

57. At 1480° A and at 1 atmosphere pressure, water vapour is dissociated to the degree of 0·0184 per cent. The heat of formation of water vapour at 25° is 57,820 cal. per gm.-molecule. Obtain an equation relating $\log_e K_p$ to the absolute temperature and use this equation to determine the percentage dissociation of water vapour at 2000° A.

H_2; $C_p = 6{\cdot}50 + 0{\cdot}0009T$.

O_2; $C_p = 6{\cdot}50 + 0{\cdot}001T$.

$H_2O_{(g)}$; $C_p = 8{\cdot}81 - 0{\cdot}0019T + 0{\cdot}00000222T^2$.

58. At 727° the equilibrium constant, K_p, of the reaction

$$CO + \tfrac{1}{2}O_2 = CO_2$$

is 2×10^{10} when partial pressures are expressed in atmospheres. Calculate the *E.M.F.* of a primary cell devised to harness this reaction at 727° for the production of electrical energy (*a*) when each of the three gases participates in the reaction at a partial pressure of 1 atm., (*b*) when the effective partial pressures at which the CO, O_2 and CO_2 participate are 19·75, 20·0 and 0·25 atm. respectively. (London B.Sc. Special.)

59. Nitrogen pentoxide decomposes according to the equation :

$$2N_2O_5 = 2N_2O_4 + O_2,$$

and yet the reaction is of the first order. Explain this and outline modern views on the mechanism of the reaction. The following table gives the velocity constant, *k*, for the decomposition :

Temperature	0°	25°	45°	65°
k min.$^{-1}$	0·0000472	0·00203	0·0299	0·292

Use these figures to derive an equation which expresses *k* as a function of the temperature and point out the significance of the various terms in the equation. Graphical methods may be used. [$R = 1{\cdot}986$ cal.] (London B.Sc. Special.)

60. At 283° at a concentration of 1 mole per litre the number of molecules of hydrogen iodide colliding per second is 6×10^{31} per c.c. The activation energy of the reaction is 44,500 cal. Calculate the number of molecules reacting per c.c. (A.R.I.C.)

APPENDIX

Significance of partial differentials

The use of partial differentials is probably most easily appreciated by reference to a simple example such as the variation of the volume of a rectangular solid with simultaneous changes in the lengths of the sides. Let the volume of such a solid be denoted by V when the three sides have lengths x, y and z respectively. If, now, y and z are allowed to remain constant while x increases to a new value x_1 (only slightly greater than x), the increase in volume, ΔV_x, is given by:

$$\Delta V_x = (\text{rate of increase of volume with } x) \times (x_1 - x)$$

$$= \left(\frac{\partial V}{\partial x}\right)_{y,\,z} \times \Delta x,$$

where the partial differential $\left(\frac{\partial V}{\partial x}\right)_{y,\,z}$ denotes the rate of increase of V with x, the subscripts indicating that y and z remain constant.

Similarly, and using the same notation:

$$\Delta V_y = \left(\frac{\partial V}{\partial y}\right)_{x,\,z}; \quad \Delta V_z = \left(\frac{\partial V}{\partial z}\right)_{x,\,y}.$$

If, now, the new values of x, y and z are denoted by x_1, y_1 and z_1 respectively, then the increase of volume, ΔV, is given by:

$$\Delta V = x_1 y_1 z_1 - xyz.$$

From a diagram it is easily seen that the difference between ΔV and the sum of the volumes, ΔV_x, ΔV_y and ΔV_z is given by the equation:

$$\Delta V - (\Delta V_x + \Delta V_y + \Delta V_z) = x\Delta y\Delta z + y\Delta x\Delta z + z\Delta x\Delta y.$$

For limiting values, that is, when Δx, Δy and Δz all approach zero, the right-hand side of the equation becomes vanishingly small.

$\therefore$ Increase in volume $= \Delta V = \Delta V_x + \Delta V_y + \Delta V_z$.

$\therefore$ With usual notation:

$$dV = \left(\frac{\partial V}{\partial x}\right)_{y,\,z} \cdot dx + \left(\frac{\partial V}{\partial y}\right)_{x,\,z} \cdot dy + \left(\frac{\partial V}{\partial z}\right)_{x,\,y} \cdot dz.$$

Also, from the equations given above:

$$\frac{dV}{dx} = \left(\frac{\partial V}{\partial x}\right)_{y,\,z}; \quad \frac{dV}{dy} = \left(\frac{\partial V}{\partial y}\right)_{x,\,z}; \quad \frac{dV}{dz} = \left(\frac{\partial V}{\partial z}\right)_{x,\,y}.$$

But: $\frac{dV}{dx} + \frac{dV}{dy} + \frac{dV}{dz} =$ rate of increase of volume with simultaneous variation of the lengths of the sides

$\therefore$ Total rate of increase of volume

$$= \left(\frac{\partial V}{\partial x}\right)_{y,\,z} + \left(\frac{\partial V}{\partial y}\right)_{x,\,z} + \left(\frac{\partial V}{\partial z}\right)_{y,\,x}.$$

Method of integration by parts

The process of integration by parts can be deduced from the equation for the differentiation of a product, namely:

$$\frac{d(uv)}{dx} = u\frac{dv}{dx} + v\frac{du}{dx},$$

where u and v are any functions of x.

Let $U = \int u\,dx$. Then if U is substituted for u:

$$\frac{d(Uv)}{dx} = U\frac{dv}{dx} + v\frac{dU}{dx} = U\frac{dv}{dx} + vu \quad \text{since} \quad \frac{dU}{dx} = u.$$

On integration:

$$Uv = \int U\frac{dv}{dx} + \int uv\,dx + C \quad \text{where } C = \text{the constant of integration.}$$

$$\therefore \int uv\,dx = Uv - \int U\frac{dv}{dx}\,.\,dx - C.$$

Method of solving a cubic equation.

One of the following methods can be employed to obtain an approximate solution to a cubic equation.

(*a*) **Graphical method**

Assume the equation is: $x^3 + 2{\cdot}65x^2 - 1{\cdot}4x - 5{\cdot}4 = 0$. Graphs of $y = x^3$ and $y = -2{\cdot}65x^2 + 1{\cdot}4x + 5{\cdot}4$ are plotted, the root then being obtained at the point of intersection.

(*b*) **By Taylor's theorem**

The theorem states:

$$f(a+h) = f(a) + hf'(a) + \frac{h^2}{\underline{|2}}f''(a) + \dots.$$

For the purposes of solving the cubic equation it is sufficient to write: $f(a+h) \doteq f(a) + hf'(a)$ where $f'(a)$ is the first differential of $f(a)$.

$$\therefore\ h = \frac{f(a+h) - f(a)}{f'(a)}.$$

We may now use this expression to find the approximate root of the equation:

$$x^3 + 2{\cdot}65x^2 - 1{\cdot}4x - 5{\cdot}4 = 0.$$

By trial it is found that the positive root lies between 1·0 and 1·5. If, now, the value 1·2 is assumed, the difference between this value and the real root is readily obtained by the approximate form of Taylor's theorem.

Let the value 1·2 correspond with a and let the accurate root be denoted by $(a+h)$.

Then: $h = \dfrac{f(a+h) - f(a)}{f'(a)} = \dfrac{f(1{\cdot}2)}{f'(1{\cdot}2)}$ since $f(a+h) = 0$.

Substitution gives $h = +0{\cdot}16$. $\therefore$ Root $= a + h = 1{\cdot}36$.

INTERNATIONAL ATOMIC WEIGHTS, 1941

	Symbol	Atomic Number	Atomic Weight		Symbol	Atomic Number	Atomic Weight
Aluminium	Al	13	26·97	Neodymium	Nd	60	144·27
Antimony	Sb	51	121·76	Neon	Ne	10	20·183
Argon	A	18	39·944	Nickel	Ni	28	58·69
Arsenic	As	33	74·91	Niobium	Nb	41	92·91
Barium	Ba	56	137·36	Nitrogen	N	7	14·008
Beryllium	Be	4	9·02	Osmium	Os	76	190·2
Bismuth	Bi	83	209·00	Oxygen	O	8	16·0000
Boron	B	5	10·82	Palladium	Pd	46	106·7
Bromine	Br	35	79·916	Phosphorus	P	15	30·98
Cadmium	Cd	48	112·41	Platinum	Pt	78	195·23
Caesium	Cs	55	132·91	Potassium	K	19	39·096
Calcium	Ca	20	40·08	Praseodymium	Pr	59	140·92
Carbon	C	6	12·010	Protoactinium	Pa	91	231
Cerium	Ce	58	140·13	Radium	Ra	88	226·05
Chlorine	Cl	17	35·457	Radon	Rn	86	222
Chromium	Cr	24	52·01	Rhenium	Re	75	186·31
Cobalt	Co	27	58·94	Rhodium	Rh	45	102·91
Copper	Cu	29	63·57	Rubidium	Rb	37	85·48
Dysprosium	Dy	66	162·46	Ruthenium	Ru	44	101·7
Erbium	Er	68	167·2	Samarium	Sm	62	150·43
Europium	Eu	63	152·0	Scandium	Sc	21	45·10
Fluorine	F	9	19·00	Selenium	Se	34	78·96
Gadolinium	Gd	64	156·9	Silicon	Si	14	28·06
Gallium	Ga	31	69·72	Silver	Ag	47	107·880
Germanium	Ge	32	72·60	Sodium	Na	11	22·997
Gold	Au	79	197·2	Strontium	Sr	38	87·63
Hafnium	Hf	72	178·6	Sulphur	S	16	32·06
Helium	He	2	4·003	Tantalum	Ta	73	180·88
Holmium	Ho	67	164·94	Tellurium	Te	52	127·61
Hydrogen	H	1	1·0080	Terbium	Tb	65	159·2
Indium	In	49	114·76	Thallium	Tl	81	204·39
Iodine	I	53	126·92	Thorium	Th	90	232·12
Iridium	Ir	77	193·1	Thulium	Tm	69	169·4
Iron	Fe	26	55·85	Tin	Sn	50	118·70
Krypton	Kr	36	83·7	Titanium	Ti	22	47·90
Lanthanum	La	57	138·92	Tungsten	W	74	183·92
Lead	Pb	82	207·21	Uranium	U	92	238·07
Lithium	Li	3	6·940	Vanadium	V	23	50·95
Lutecium	Lu	71	174·99	Xenon	Xe	54	131·3
Magnesium	Mg	12	24·32	Ytterbium	Yb	70	173·04
Manganese	Mn	25	54·93	Yttrium	Y	39	88·92
Mercury	Hg	80	200·61	Zinc	Zn	30	65·38
Molybdenum	Mo	42	95·95	Zirconium	Zr	40	91·22

Saturated aqueous vapour pressures

Temp.	V.P. mm.	Temp.	V.P. mm.	Temp.	V.P. mm.	Temp.	V.P. mm.
1	4·927	11	9·804	21	18·49	31	33·39
2	5·308	12	10·47	22	19·63	32	35·36
3	5·689	13	11·15	23	20·87	33	37·41
4	6·095	14	11·91	24	22·17	34	39·57
5	6·527	15	12·70	25	23·55	35	41·83
6	7·009	16	13·54	26	25·00	36	44·19
7	7·492	17	14·42	27	26·52	37	46·69
8	8·026	18	15·37	28	28·08	38	49·29
9	8·585	19	16·33	29	29·77	39	52·04
10	9·168	20	17·40	30	31·54	40	54·92

Freezing point and boiling point constants
(100 gm. of solvent)

Solvent	F.P. constant	B.P. constant	Solvent	F.P. constant	B.P. constant
Water	18·6	5·2	Phenol	75	—
Ethyl Alcohol	—	11·5	Aniline	—	32·2
Chloroform	—	36·6	Ether	—	21·1
Benzene	51·2	26·7	Acetic acid	39	25·3

Mobilities of ions

H^+	315	Br^-	67·7	Ag^+	54·0
OH^-	174	I^-	66·6	$\frac{1}{2}Cu^{++}$	46·0
Cl^-	65	NH_4^+	64·7	$\frac{1}{2}Ca^{++}$	52·0
NO_3^-	61·8	Na^+	43·4	$\frac{1}{2}Pb^{++}$	60·8
$\frac{1}{2}SO_4^{--}$	68·5	K^+	64·6	$\frac{1}{2}Zn$	47·0

Standard electrode potentials (volts)
$(H_{2(1\ atm.)}/H^+_{(u.\ a.)} = 0)$ at 25°

Li, Li^+	−2·959	Cd, Cd^+	−0·402
Rb, Rb^+	−2·926	Sn, Sn^{++}	−0·136
K, K^+	−2·924	Pb, Pb^{++}	−0·12
Na, Na^+	−2·715	Cu, Cu^{++}	+0·345
Zn, Zn^{++}	−0·762	Hg, Hg^{++}	+0·799
Fe, Fe^{++}	−0·44	Ag, Ag^+	+0·798

Saturated calomel electrode = +0·244
Normal ,, ,, = +0·2816
Decinormal ,, ,, = +0·3335

O_2, OH^- = +0·400 volt

Hydrogen overvoltages

Electrode		Electrode	
Platinised platinum	0·005	Copper	0·23
Gold	0·02	Cadmium	0·48
Iron	0·08	Tin	0·53
Smooth platinum	0·09	Lead	0·64
Silver	0·15	Zinc	0·70
Nickel	0·21	Mercury	0·78

Table of standard free energies

	ΔF° cal.		ΔF° cal.		ΔF° cal.
$H_2O_{(g)}$	-54,500	$KCl_{(s)}$	-96,000	$Br^-{}_{(u.\,a.)}$	-24,580
$H_2O_{(l)}$	-56,560	$NaCl_{(s)}$	-91,800	$I^-{}_{(u.\,a.)}$	-12,360
$H_2S_{(g)}$	-7,840	$AgCl_{(s)}$	-26,200	$NO_3^-{}_{(u.\,a.)}$	-26,500
$O_{3(g)}$	+32,400	$AgBr_{(s)}$	-23,700	$NO_2^-{}_{(u.\,a.)}$	-8,500
$HCl_{(g)}$	-22,700	$Ag_2O_{(s)}$	-2,400	$SO_4^{--}{}_{(u.\,a.)}$	-176,500
$HBr_{(g)}$	-12,500	$HgO_{(s)}$	-13,800	$CN^-{}_{(u.\,a.)}$	+39,400
$HI_{(g)}$	+315	$PbCl_{2(s)}$	-75,000	$SO_3^{--}{}_{(u.\,a.)}$	-116,700
$NO_{2(g)}$	+11,900	$PbO_{(s)}$	-45,000	$Ag^+{}_{(u.\,a.)}$	+18,450
$NO_{(g)}$	+20,900	$CH_{4(g)}$	-12,800	$Zn^{++}{}_{(u.\,a.)}$	-17,490
$NH_{3(g)}$	-3,900	$C_6H_{6(l)}$	+27,100	$Na^+{}_{(u.\,a.)}$	-62,600
$SO_{2(g)}$	-69,700	$HCOOH_{(l)}$	-84,000	$K^+{}_{(u.\,a.)}$	-67,400
$CO_{2(g)}$	-94,300	$CH_3COOH_{(l)}$	-96,600	$Cu^{++}{}_{(u.\,a.)}$	+15,900
$CO_{(g)}$	-32,510	$C_2H_5OH_{(l)}$	-44,000	$Hg_2^{++}{}_{(u.\,a.)}$	+36,900
$HCN_{(g)}$	+28,900	$H^+{}_{(u.\,a.)}$	0	$Pb^{++}{}_{(u.\,a.)}$	-5,630
$NOCl_{(g)}$	+8,600	$OH^-{}_{(u.\,a.)}$	-37,450	$Sn^{++}{}_{(u.\,a.)}$	-6,280
$SO_{3(g)}$	-85,900	$Cl^-{}_{(u.\,a.)}$	-31,370	$Fe^{++}{}_{(u.\,a.)}$	-20,350
$SO_2Cl_{2(g)}$	-71,600	$NH_4^+{}_{(u.\,a.)}$	-18,900	$Fe^{+++}{}_{(u.\,a.)}$	-3,100

Subscripts : (g) = gas ; (l) = liquid ; $(u.\ a.)$ = unit activity.

Table of standard molal entropies

	S°_{298}		S°_{298}		S°_{298}
$H_{2(g)}$	30·5	$Hg_{(l)}$	17·8	$NaCl_{(s)}$	17·2
$O_{2(g)}$	49·0	$Ni_{(s)}$	7·2	$KCl_{(s)}$	19·9
$N_{2(g)}$	45·8	$Pb_{(s)}$	15·5	$NH_4Cl_{(s)}$	23·3
$Cl_{2(g)}$	53·3	$Ca_{(s)}$	10·4	$NaF_{(s)}$	12·4
$Br_{2(l)}$	16·3	$Cd_{(s)}$	11·7	$KF_{(s)}$	15·8
$I_{2(s)}$	14·0	$H_2O_{(l)}$	15·9	$KBr_{(s)}$	22·5
$I_{2(g)}$	31·0	$H_2O_{(g)}$	45·2	$AgCl_{(s)}$	23·3
C (*graphite*)	1·4	$HCl_{(g)}$	44·6	$AgI_{(s)}$	26·6
C (*diamond*)	0·54	$HBr_{(g)}$	45·0	$Hg_2Cl_{2(s)}$	46·0
S (*rhombic*)	7·6	$HI_{(g)}$	48·0	$CuO_{(s)}$	9·8
S (*monoclinic*)	7·8	$NH_{3(g)}$	46·4	$HgO_{(s)}$	16·6
$Si_{(s)}$	4·5	$CO_{(g)}$	45·8	$CaO_{(s)}$	9·8
$Na_{(s)}$	12·2	$CO_{2(g)}$	51·1	$Al_2O_{3(s)}$	12·8
$Ag_{(s)}$	10·3	$NO_{(g)}$	43·8	$PbCl_{2(s)}$	33·7
$Zn_{(s)}$	9·8	$N_2O_{(g)}$	52·6	$MgO_{(s)}$	6·6
$Fe_{(s)}$	6·7	$SO_{2(g)}$	59·2	$ZnS_{(s)}$	14·5
$Co_{(s)}$	7·2	$CH_{4(g)}$	44·0	$PbS_{(s)}$	22·2
$Cu_{(s)}$	8·1	$C_2H_{6(g)}$	41·9	$CaCO_{3(s)}$	22·1
$Al_{(s)}$	6·7	$C_2H_5OH_{(l)}$	38·4	$KBr_{(s)}$	22·5

Conventional Chemical Constants

	C		*C*		*C*
H_2	1·6	HCl	3·0	N_2O	3·3
N_2	2·6	HI	3·4	H_2O	3·6
O_2	2·8	CO	3·5	CH_4	2·5
Cl_2	3·1	CO_2	3·5	NH_3	3·3
I_2	3·9	H_2S	3·0	CCl_4	3·1
Br_2	3·5	NO	3·5	C_6H_6	3·0

	0	1	2	3	4	5	6	7	8	9	1	2	3	4	5	6	7	8	9
10	0000	0043	0086	0128	0170						5	9	13	17	21	26	30	34	38
						0212	0253	0294	0334	0374	4	8	12	16	20	24	28	32	36
11	0414	0453	0492	0531	0569						4	8	12	16	20	23	27	31	35
						0607	0645	0682	0719	0755	4	7	11	15	18	22	26	29	33
12	0792	0828	0864	0899	0934						3	7	11	14	18	21	25	28	32
						0969	1004	1038	1072	1106	3	7	10	14	17	20	24	27	31
13	1139	1173	1206	1239	1271						3	6	10	13	16	19	23	26	29
						1303	1335	1367	1399	1430	3	7	10	13	16	19	22	25	29
14	1461	1492	1523	1553	1584						3	6	9	12	15	19	22	25	28
						1614	1644	1673	1703	1732	3	6	9	12	14	17	20	23	26
15	1761	1790	1818	1847	1875						3	6	9	11	14	17	20	23	26
						1903	1931	1959	1987	2014	3	6	8	11	14	17	19	22	25
16	2041	2068	2095	2122	2148						3	6	8	11	14	16	19	22	24
						2175	2201	2227	2253	2279	3	5	8	10	13	16	18	21	23
17	2304	2330	2355	2380	2405						3	5	8	10	13	15	18	20	23
						2430	2455	2480	2504	2529	3	5	8	10	12	15	17	20	22
18	2553	2577	2601	2625	2648						2	5	7	9	12	14	17	19	21
						2672	2695	2718	2742	2765	2	4	7	9	11	14	16	18	21
19	2788	2810	2833	2856	2878						2	4	7	9	11	13	16	18	20
						2900	2923	2945	2967	2989	2	4	6	8	11	13	15	17	19
20	3010	3032	3054	3075	3096	3118	3139	3160	3181	3201	2	4	6	8	11	13	15	17	19
21	3222	3243	3263	3284	3304	3324	3345	3365	3385	3404	2	4	6	8	10	12	14	16	18
22	3424	3444	3464	3483	3502	3522	3541	3560	3579	3598	2	4	6	8	10	12	14	15	17
23	3617	3636	3655	3674	3692	3711	3729	3747	3766	3784	2	4	6	7	9	11	13	15	17
24	3802	3820	3838	3856	3874	3892	3909	3927	3945	3962	2	4	5	7	9	11	12	14	16
25	3979	3997	4014	4031	4048	4065	4082	4099	4116	4133	2	3	5	7	9	10	12	14	15
26	4150	4166	4183	4200	4216	4232	4249	4265	4281	4298	2	3	5	7	8	10	11	13	15
27	4314	4330	4346	4362	4378	4393	4409	4425	4440	4456	2	3	5	6	8	9	11	13	14
28	4472	4487	4502	4518	4533	4548	4564	4579	4594	4609	2	3	5	6	8	9	11	12	14
29	4624	4639	4654	4669	4683	4698	4713	4728	4742	4757	1	3	4	6	7	9	10	12	13
30	4771	4786	4800	4814	4829	4843	4857	4871	4886	4900	1	3	4	6	7	9	10	11	13
31	4914	4928	4942	4955	4969	4983	4997	5011	5024	5038	1	3	4	6	7	8	10	11	12
32	5051	5065	5079	5092	5105	5119	5132	5145	5159	5172	1	3	4	5	7	8	9	11	12
33	5185	5198	5211	5224	5237	5250	5263	5276	5289	5302	1	3	4	5	6	8	9	10	12
34	5315	5328	5340	5353	5366	5378	5391	5403	5416	5428	1	3	4	5	6	8	9	10	11
35	5441	5453	5465	5478	5490	5502	5514	5527	5539	5551	1	2	4	5	6	7	9	10	11
36	5563	5575	5587	5599	5611	5623	5635	5647	5658	5670	1	2	4	5	6	7	8	10	11
37	5682	5694	5705	5717	5729	5740	5752	5763	5775	5786	1	2	3	5	6	7	8	9	10
38	5798	5809	5821	5832	5843	5855	5866	5877	5888	5899	1	2	3	5	6	7	8	9	10
39	5911	5922	5933	5944	5955	5966	5977	5988	5999	6010	1	2	3	4	5	7	8	9	10
40	6021	6031	6042	6053	6064	6075	6085	6096	6107	6117	1	2	3	4	5	6	8	9	10
41	6128	6138	6149	6160	6170	6180	6191	6201	6212	6222	1	2	3	4	5	6	7	8	9
42	6232	6243	6253	6263	6274	6284	6294	6304	6314	6325	1	2	3	4	5	6	7	8	9
43	6335	6345	6355	6365	6375	6385	6395	6405	6415	6425	1	2	3	4	5	6	7	8	9
44	6435	6444	6454	6464	6474	6484	6493	6503	6513	6522	1	2	3	4	5	6	7	8	9
45	6532	6542	6551	6561	6571	6580	6590	6599	6609	6618	1	2	3	4	5	6	7	8	9
46	6628	6637	6646	6656	6665	6675	6684	6693	6702	6712	1	2	3	4	5	6	7	7	8
47	6721	6730	6739	6749	6758	6767	6776	6785	6794	6803	1	2	3	4	5	5	6	7	8
48	6812	6821	6830	6839	6848	6857	6866	6875	6884	6893	1	2	3	4	4	5	6	7	8
49	6902	6911	6920	6928	6937	6946	6955	6964	6972	6981	1	2	3	4	4	5	6	7	8

	0	1	2	3	4	5	6	7	8	9	123	456	789
50	6990	6998	7007	7016	7024	7033	7042	7050	7059	7067	1 2 3	3 4 5	6 7 8
51	7076	7084	7093	7101	7110	7118	7126	7135	7143	7152	1 2 3	3 4 5	6 7 8
52	7160	7168	7177	7185	7193	7202	7210	7218	7226	7235	1 2 2	3 4 5	6 7 7
53	7243	7251	7259	7267	7275	7284	7292	7300	7308	7316	1 2 2	3 4 5	6 6 7
54	7324	7332	7340	7348	7356	7364	7372	7380	7388	7396	1 2 2	3 4 5	6 6 7
55	7404	7412	7419	7427	7435	7443	7451	7459	7466	7474	1 2 2	3 4 5	5 6 7
56	7482	7490	7497	7505	7513	7520	7528	7536	7543	7551	1 2 2	3 4 5	5 6 7
57	7559	7566	7574	7582	7589	7597	7604	7612	7619	7627	1 2 2	3 4 5	5 6 7
58	7634	7642	7649	7657	7664	7672	7679	7686	7694	7701	1 1 2	3 4 4	5 6 7
59	7709	7716	7723	7731	7738	7745	7752	7760	7767	7774	1 1 2	3 4 4	5 6 7
60	7782	7789	7796	7803	7810	7818	7825	7832	7839	7846	1 1 2	3 4 4	5 6 6
61	7853	7860	7868	7875	7882	7889	7896	7903	7910	7917	1 1 2	3 4 4	5 6 6
62	7924	7931	7938	7945	7952	7959	7966	7973	7980	7987	1 1 2	3 3 4	5 6 6
63	7993	8000	8007	8014	8021	8028	8035	8041	8048	8055	1 1 2	3 3 4	5 5 6
64	8062	8069	8075	8082	8089	8096	8102	8109	8116	8122	1 1 2	3 3 4	5 5 6
65	8129	8136	8142	8149	8156	8162	8169	8176	8182	8189	1 1 2	3 3 4	5 5 6
66	8195	8202	8209	8215	8222	8228	8235	8241	8248	8254	1 1 2	3 3 4	5 5 6
67	8261	8267	8274	8280	8287	8293	8299	8306	8312	8319	1 1 2	3 3 4	5 5 6
68	8325	8331	8338	8344	8351	8357	8363	8370	8376	8382	1 1 2	3 3 4	4 5 6
69	8388	8395	8401	8407	8414	8420	8426	8432	8439	8445	1 1 2	2 3 4	4 5 6
70	8451	8457	8463	8470	8476	8482	8488	8494	8500	8506	1 1 2	2 3 4	4 5 6
71	8513	8519	8525	8531	8537	8543	8549	8555	8561	8567	1 1 2	2 3 4	4 5 5
72	8573	8579	8585	8591	8597	8603	8609	8615	8621	8627	1 1 2	2 3 4	4 5 5
73	8633	8639	8645	8651	8657	8663	8669	8675	8681	8686	1 1 2	2 3 4	4 5 5
74	8692	8698	8704	8710	8716	8722	8727	8733	8739	8745	1 1 2	2 3 4	4 5 5
75	8751	8756	8762	8768	8774	8779	8785	8791	8797	8802	1 1 2	2 3 3	4 5 5
76	8808	8814	8820	8825	8831	8837	8842	8848	8854	8859	1 1 2	2 3 3	4 5 5
77	8865	8871	8876	8882	8887	8893	8899	8904	8910	8915	1 1 2	2 3 3	4 4 5
78	8921	8927	8932	8938	8943	8949	8954	8960	8965	8971	1 1 2	2 3 3	4 4 5
79	8976	8982	8987	8993	8998	9004	9009	9015	9020	9025	1 1 2	2 3 3	4 4 5
80	9031	9036	9042	9047	9053	9058	9063	9069	9074	9079	1 1 2	2 3 3	4 4 5
81	9085	9090	9096	9101	9106	9112	9117	9122	9128	9133	1 1 2	2 3 3	4 4 5
82	9138	9143	9149	9154	9159	9165	9170	9175	9180	9186	1 1 2	2 3 3	4 4 5
83	9191	9196	9201	9206	9212	9217	9222	9227	9232	9238	1 1 2	2 3 3	4 4 5
84	9243	9248	9253	9258	9263	9269	9274	9279	9284	9289	1 1 2	2 3 3	4 4 5
85	9294	9299	9304	9309	9315	9320	9325	9330	9335	9340	1 1 2	2 3 3	4 4 5
86	9345	9350	9355	9360	9365	9370	9375	9380	9385	9390	1 1 2	2 3 3	4 4 5
87	9395	9400	9405	9410	9415	9420	9425	9430	9435	9440	0 1 1	2 2 3	3 4 4
88	9445	9450	9455	9460	9465	9469	9474	9479	9484	9489	0 1 1	2 2 3	3 4 4
89	9494	9499	9504	9509	9513	9518	9523	9528	9533	9538	0 1 1	2 2 3	3 4 4
90	9542	9547	9552	9557	9562	9566	9571	9576	9581	9586	0 1 1	2 2 3	3 4 4
91	9590	9595	9600	9605	9609	9614	9619	9624	9628	9633	0 1 1	2 2 3	3 4 4
92	9638	9643	9647	9652	9657	9661	9666	9671	9675	9680	0 1 1	2 2 3	3 4 4
93	9685	9689	9694	9699	9703	9708	9713	9717	9722	9727	0 1 1	2 2 3	3 4 4
94	9731	9736	9741	9745	9750	9754	9759	9763	9768	9773	0 1 1	2 2 3	3 4 4
95	9777	9782	9786	9791	9795	9800	9805	9809	9814	9818	0 1 1	2 2 3	3 4 4
96	9823	9827	9832	9836	9841	9845	9850	9854	9859	9863	0 1 1	2 2 3	3 4 4
97	9868	9872	9877	9881	9886	9890	9894	9899	9903	9908	0 1 1	2 2 3	3 4 4
98	9912	9917	9921	9926	9930	9934	9939	9943	9948	9952	0 1 1	2 2 3	3 4 4
99	9956	9961	9965	9969	9974	9978	9983	9987	9991	9996	0 1 1	2 2 3	3 3 4

	0	1	2	3	4	5	6	7	8	9	123	456	789
·00	1000	1002	1005	1007	1009	1012	1014	1016	1019	1021	0 0 1	1 1 1	2 2 2
·01	1023	1026	1028	1030	1033	1035	1038	1040	1042	1045	0 0 1	1 1 1	2 2 2
·02	1047	1050	1052	1054	1057	1059	1062	1064	1067	1069	0 0 1	1 1 1	2 2 2
·03	1072	1074	1076	1079	1081	1084	1086	1089	1091	1094	0 0 1	1 1 1	2 2 2
·04	1096	1099	1102	1104	1107	1109	1112	1114	1117	1119	0 1 1	1 1 2	2 2 2
·05	1122	1125	1127	1130	1132	1135	1138	1140	1143	1146	0 1 1	1 1 2	2 2 2
·06	1148	1151	1153	1156	1159	1161	1164	1167	1169	1172	0 1 1	1 1 2	2 2 2
·07	1175	1178	1180	1183	1186	1189	1191	1194	1197	1199	0 1 1	1 1 2	2 2 2
·08	1202	1205	1208	1211	1213	1216	1219	1222	1225	1227	0 1 1	1 1 2	2 2 3
·09	1230	1233	1236	1239	1242	1245	1247	1250	1253	1256	0 1 1	1 1 2	2 2 3
·10	1259	1262	1265	1268	1271	1274	1276	1279	1282	1285	0 1 1	1 1 2	2 2 3
·11	1288	1291	1294	1297	1300	1303	1306	1309	1312	1315	0 1 1	1 2 2	2 2 3
·12	1318	1321	1324	1327	1330	1334	1337	1340	1343	1346	0 1 1	1 2 2	2 2 3
·13	1349	1352	1355	1358	1361	1365	1368	1371	1374	1377	0 1 1	1 2 2	2 3 3
·14	1380	1384	1387	1390	1393	1396	1400	1403	1406	1409	0 1 1	1 2 2	2 3 3
·15	1413	1416	1419	1422	1426	1429	1432	1435	1439	1442	0 1 1	1 2 2	2 3 3
·16	1445	1449	1452	1455	1459	1462	1466	1469	1472	1476	0 1 1	1 2 2	2 3 3
·17	1479	1483	1486	1489	1493	1496	1500	1503	1507	1510	0 1 1	1 2 2	2 3 3
·18	1514	1517	1521	1524	1528	1531	1535	1538	1542	1545	0 1 1	1 2 2	2 3 3
·19	1549	1552	1556	1560	1563	1567	1570	1574	1578	1581	0 1 1	1 2 2	3 3 3
·20	1585	1589	1592	1596	1600	1603	1607	1611	1614	1618	0 1 1	1 2 2	3 3 3
·21	1622	1626	1629	1633	1637	1641	1644	1648	1652	1656	0 1 1	2 2 2	3 3 3
·22	1660	1663	1667	1671	1675	1679	1683	1687	1690	1694	0 1 1	2 2 2	3 3 3
·23	1698	1702	1706	1710	1714	1718	1722	1726	1730	1734	0 1 1	2 2 2	3 3 4
·24	1738	1742	1746	1750	1754	1758	1762	1766	1770	1774	0 1 1	2 2 2	3 3 4
·25	1778	1782	1786	1791	1795	1799	1803	1807	1811	1816	0 1 1	2 2 2	3 3 4
·26	1820	1824	1828	1832	1837	1841	1845	1849	1854	1858	0 1 1	2 2 3	3 3 4
·27	1862	1866	1871	1875	1879	1884	1888	1892	1897	1901	0 1 1	2 2 3	3 3 4
·28	1905	1910	1914	1919	1923	1928	1932	1936	1941	1945	0 1 1	2 2 3	3 4 4
·29	1950	1954	1959	1963	1968	1972	1977	1982	1986	1991	0 1 1	2 2 3	3 4 4
·30	1995	2000	2004	2009	2014	2018	2023	2028	2032	2037	0 1 1	2 2 3	3 4 4
·31	2042	2046	2051	2056	2061	2065	2070	2075	2080	2084	0 1 1	2 2 3	3 4 4
·32	2089	2094	2099	2104	2109	2113	2118	2123	2128	2133	0 1 1	2 2 3	3 4 4
·33	2138	2143	2148	2153	2158	2163	2168	2173	2178	2183	0 1 1	2 2 3	3 4 4
·34	2188	2193	2198	2203	2208	2213	2218	2223	2228	2234	1 1 2	2 3 3	4 4 5
·35	2239	2244	2249	2254	2259	2265	2270	2275	2280	2286	1 1 2	2 3 3	4 4 5
·36	2291	2296	2301	2307	2312	2317	2323	2328	2333	2339	1 1 2	2 3 3	4 4 5
·37	2344	2350	2355	2360	2366	2371	2377	2382	2388	2393	1 1 2	2 3 3	4 4 5
·38	2399	2404	2410	2415	2421	2427	2432	2438	2443	2449	1 1 2	2 3 3	4 4 5
·39	2455	2460	2466	2472	2477	2483	2489	2495	2500	2506	1 1 2	2 3 3	4 5 5
·40	2512	2518	2523	2529	2535	2541	2547	2553	2559	2564	1 1 2	2 3 4	4 5 5
·41	2570	2576	2582	2588	2594	2600	2606	2612	2618	2624	1 1 2	2 3 4	4 5 5
·42	2630	2636	2642	2649	2655	2661	2667	2673	2679	2685	1 1 2	2 3 4	4 5 6
·43	2692	2698	2704	2710	2716	2723	2729	2735	2742	2748	1 1 2	3 3 4	4 5 6
·44	2754	2761	2767	2773	2780	2786	2793	2799	2805	2812	1 1 2	3 3 4	4 5 6
·45	2818	2825	2831	2838	2844	2851	2858	2864	2871	2877	1 1 2	3 3 4	5 5 6
·46	2884	2891	2897	2904	2911	2917	2924	2931	2938	2944	1 1 2	3 3 4	5 5 6
·47	2951	2958	2965	2972	2979	2985	2992	2999	3006	3013	1 1 2	3 3 4	5 5 6
·48	3020	3027	3034	3041	3048	3055	3062	3069	3076	3083	1 1 2	3 4 4	5 6 6
·49	3090	3097	3105	3112	3119	3126	3133	3141	3148	3155	1 1 2	3 4 4	5 6 6

ANTILOGARITHMS

	0	1	2	3	4	5	6	7	8	9	1	2	3	4	5	6	7	8	9
·50	3162	3170	3177	3184	3192	3199	3206	3214	3221	3228	1	1	2	3	4	4	5	6	7
·51	3236	3243	3251	3258	3266	3273	3281	3289	3296	3304	1	2	2	3	4	5	5	6	7
·52	3311	3319	3327	3334	3342	3350	3357	3365	3373	3381	1	2	2	3	4	5	5	6	7
·53	3388	3396	3404	3412	3420	3428	3436	3443	3451	3459	1	2	2	3	4	5	6	6	7
·54	3467	3475	3483	3491	3499	3508	3516	3524	3532	3540	1	2	2	3	4	5	6	6	7
·55	3548	3556	3565	3573	3581	3589	3597	3606	3614	3622	1	2	2	3	4	5	6	7	7
·56	3631	3639	3648	3656	3664	3673	3681	3690	3698	3707	1	2	3	3	4	5	6	7	8
·57	3715	3724	3733	3741	3750	3758	3767	3776	3784	3793	1	2	3	3	4	5	6	7	8
·58	3802	3811	3819	3828	3837	3846	3855	3864	3873	3882	1	2	3	4	4	5	6	7	8
·59	3890	3899	3908	3917	3926	3936	3945	3954	3963	3972	1	2	3	4	5	5	6	7	8
·60	3981	3990	3999	4009	4018	4027	4036	4046	4055	4064	1	2	3	4	5	6	6	7	8
·61	4074	4083	4093	4102	4111	4121	4130	4140	4150	4159	1	2	3	4	5	6	7	8	9
·62	4169	4178	4188	4198	4207	4217	4227	4236	4246	4256	1	2	3	4	5	6	7	8	9
·63	4266	4276	4285	4295	4305	4315	4325	4335	4345	4355	1	2	3	4	5	6	7	8	9
·64	4365	4375	4385	4395	4406	4416	4426	4436	4446	4457	1	2	3	4	5	6	7	8	9
·65	4467	4477	4487	4498	4508	4519	4529	4539	4550	4560	1	2	3	4	5	6	7	8	9
·66	4571	4581	4592	4603	4613	4624	4634	4645	4656	4667	1	2	3	4	5	6	7	9	10
·67	4677	4688	4699	4710	4721	4732	4742	4753	4764	4775	1	2	3	4	5	7	8	9	10
·68	4786	4797	4808	4819	4831	4842	4853	4864	4875	4887	1	2	3	4	6	7	8	9	10
·69	4898	4909	4920	4932	4943	4955	4966	4977	4989	5000	1	2	3	5	6	7	8	9	10
·70	5012	5023	5035	5047	5058	5070	5082	5093	5105	5117	1	2	4	5	6	7	8	9	11
·71	5129	5140	5152	5164	5176	5188	5200	5212	5224	5236	1	2	4	5	6	7	8	10	11
·72	5248	5260	5272	5284	5297	5309	5321	5333	5346	5358	1	2	4	5	6	7	9	10	11
·73	5370	5383	5395	5408	5420	5433	5445	5458	5470	5483	1	3	4	5	6	8	9	10	11
·74	5495	5508	5521	5534	5546	5559	5572	5585	5598	5610	1	3	4	5	6	8	9	10	12
·75	5623	5636	5649	5662	5675	5689	5702	5715	5728	5741	1	3	4	5	7	8	9	10	12
·76	5754	5768	5781	5794	5808	5821	5834	5848	5861	5875	1	3	4	5	7	8	9	11	12
·77	5888	5902	5916	5929	5943	5957	5970	5984	5998	6012	1	3	4	5	7	8	10	11	12
·78	6026	6039	6053	6067	6081	6095	6109	6124	6138	6152	1	3	4	6	7	8	10	11	13
·79	6166	6180	6194	6209	6223	6237	6252	6266	6281	6295	1	3	4	6	7	9	10	11	13
·80	6310	6324	6339	6353	6368	6383	6397	6412	6427	6442	1	3	4	6	7	9	10	12	13
·81	6457	6471	6486	6501	6516	6531	6546	6561	6577	6592	2	3	5	6	8	9	11	12	14
·82	6607	6622	6637	6653	6668	6683	6699	6714	6730	6745	2	3	5	6	8	9	11	12	14
·83	6761	6776	6792	6808	6823	6839	6855	6871	6887	6902	2	3	5	6	8	9	11	13	14
·84	6918	6934	6950	6966	6982	6998	7015	7031	7047	7063	2	3	5	6	8	10	11	13	15
·85	7079	7096	7112	7129	7145	7161	7178	7194	7211	7228	2	3	5	7	8	10	12	13	15
·86	7244	7261	7278	7295	7311	7328	7345	7362	7379	7396	2	3	5	7	8	10	12	13	15
·87	7413	7430	7447	7464	7482	7499	7516	7534	7551	7568	2	3	5	7	9	10	12	14	16
·88	7586	7603	7621	7638	7656	7674	7691	7709	7727	7745	2	4	5	7	9	11	12	14	16
·89	7762	7780	7798	7816	7834	7852	7870	7889	7907	7925	2	4	5	7	9	11	13	14	16
·90	7943	7962	7980	7998	8017	8035	8054	8072	8091	8110	2	4	6	7	9	11	13	15	17
·91	8128	8147	8166	8185	8204	8222	8241	8260	8279	8299	2	4	6	8	9	11	13	15	17
·92	8318	8337	8356	8375	8395	8414	8433	8453	8472	8492	2	4	6	8	10	12	14	15	17
·93	8511	8531	8551	8570	8590	8610	8630	8650	8670	8690	2	4	6	8	10	12	14	16	18
·94	8710	8730	8750	8770	8790	8810	8831	8851	8872	8892	2	4	6	8	10	12	14	16	18
·95	8913	8933	8954	8974	8995	9016	9036	9057	9078	9099	2	4	6	8	10	12	15	17	19
·96	9120	9141	9162	9183	9204	9226	9247	9268	9290	9311	2	4	6	8	11	13	15	17	19
·97	9333	9354	9376	9397	9419	9441	9462	9484	9506	9528	2	4	7	9	11	13	15	17	20
·98	9550	9572	9594	9616	9638	9661	9683	9705	9727	9750	2	4	7	9	11	13	16	18	20
·99	9772	9795	9817	9840	9863	9886	9908	9931	9954	9977	2	5	7	9	11	14	16	18	20

ANSWERS

Chapter I

1. 39·1. **2.** 32·8. **3.** 68·7. **4.** 32·0.
5. 1·001. **6.** 2·003. **7.** 121·3. **8.** 11·93.
9. 1·368. **10.** 103·5. **11.** 12·16. **12.** 306·2 c.c.
13. Percentage of nitrogen in the nitrate = 16·47; percentage of nitrogen in the nitrite = 20·30; percentage of oxygen in the nitrate = 56·45; percentage of oxygen in the nitrite = 46·36.
14. 38·94. **15.** 65·96. **16.** 32·83.
17. Equivalents are: potassium, 39·1; chlorine, 35·40; silver, 107·8.
18. 55·86. **19.** 39·6. **20.** 11·64. **21.** 20·06. **22.** 6·768.
23. Equivalent = 4·50; specific heat is too low for any definite conclusion about atomic weight.
24. 65·67. **25.** X_2O_7; 35·5.
26. Weight of water = 0·6958 gm.; weight of carbon dioxide = 3·398 gm.; volume of carbon dioxide = 1·730 litres.
27. 27·76. **28.** 68·5. **29.** 137·0.
30. Equivalents are 28·02 and 18·76; atomic weight (average) = 56·18; MCl_2 and MCl_3.
31. 12·00. **32.** 63·13. **33.** 53·16. **34.** 130·7.
35. Atomic weight = 186·3; formulae of the compounds are (*a*) X_2O_7; (*b*) XCl_4; (*c*) X_2S_7 and XS_2.
36. (*a*) 4·237 gm.; (*b*) 0·6595 litres. **37.** 203·7.
38. Atomic weight (average) = 209·3; X_2O_3; XO_2 or X_2O_4; X_2O_5; $X(OH)_3$.
39. 51·62 per cent. **40.** 52·02; 13·46 gm. **41.** 121·5. **42.** 103·6.
43. Atomic weight = 136·3; formula for the hydrated chloride $XCl_2 \cdot 2H_2O$.
44. 42·73. **45.** 45·0. **46.** 62·5. **47.** 32·56.
48. 50·9.
49. 184·2; $XO_2 + Cl_2 = XO_2Cl_2$; $XO_2Cl_2 + 2KOH = K_2XO_4 + 2HCl$;
$XO_2Cl_2 + C_2H_5OH + 2HCl = XCl_4 + CH_3CHO + 2H_2O$;
$XCl_4 + 2KOH = 4KCl + XO_2 + 2H_2O$.

Chapter II

1. $A = 31(30·5)$; $B = 46(45·7)$; $C = 81(80·7)$.
2. $D = 54·5$; $E = 35·9$; $F = 70·1$. **3.** 61·2.
4. Equivalents are 14·0 and 7·01; atomic weight = 14·0.
5. $C_4H_8O_2$. **6.** 12·0. **7.** $C_2H_2Cl_4$. **8.** 12·0.
9. 26·7. **10.** 61. **11.** 12·0. **12.** 31·1.
13. (*a*) 5·331 gm.; (*b*) 3·955 litres.
14. Percentage of carbon dioxide = 28·37;
percentage of carbon monoxide = 71·63.
15. 12·00.
16. Atomic weight = 200·6; molecular weight = 199·4; $C_p/C_v = 1·67$.
17. (*a*) 16; 30; 28; (*b*) 12·00. **18.** 8.
19. (*a*) 275·2 c.c.; 91·85 per cent (steam); 1·85 per cent of oxygen; (*b*) 45·72 c.c.; 82·71 per cent carbon dioxide; 17·29 per cent carbon monoxide.
20. 30·06.
21. Accurate atomic weight of $M = 208·8$; valency of $M = 3$; molecular weight of $G = 130$; G is a monatomic element in the gaseous state.
22. 50·4. **23.** 9·026.
24. Equivalent = 15·6; atomic weight = 31·2.
25. 24·0 (half the molecular weight calculated on 22·400 c.c. of ozone at *N.T.P.*)
26. Percentage of nitrogen = 45·45; percentage of hydrogen = 31·82; percentage of carbon monoxide = 22·73.

27. N_2O. **28.** 40 per cent. **29.** (*a*) 69·75 ; (*b*) M_2O_3.
30. 60 per cent. **31.** 27·1. **32.** (*a*) 9·068 ; (*b*) $XCl_2 . 4H_2O$.
33. C_3O_2.
34. 41·38 per cent H_2 ; 37·93 per cent CO ; 20·69 per cent N_2.
35. 70 c.c. N_2O ; 5 c.c. O_2 ; 19·7 c.c. NO_2 ; 5·15 c.c. N_2O_4. **36.** HCN.
37. Atomic weight = 27·00 ; $X_2(SO_4)_3 . 18H_2O$.
38. 22·22 per cent CO ; 33·33 per cent CO_2 ; 44·44 per cent O_2.
39. 20 per cent N_2 ; 40 per cent NH_3 ; 40 per cent O_2.
40. Atomic weight = 23·06 ; $A = X_2O_2$ (or XO) ; $X_2SO_4 . 10H_2O$.
41. (*a*) 39,000 cm. per sec. ; (*b*) 46,000 cm. per sec.
42. $4{\cdot}25 \times 10^4$ cm. per sec. **43.** 0·00749. **44.** 0·0078. **45.** 1·4276.
46. Compressibility coefficient = 0·0016 ; 12·1.
47. 34·22. **48.** 41·77.

Chapter III

1. 103. **2.** 6 mm. **3.** 52·9. **4.** 341. **5.** 181.
6. 34·2. **7.** 1·131 atmospheres. **8.** 9·824 atmospheres.
9. $A = 143{\cdot}6$; $B = 55{\cdot}2$; $C = 133{\cdot}5$; $D = 78{\cdot}6$.
10. 3·35°. **11.** 130. **12.** 342. **13.** 122·8. **14.** 147.
15. $A = 238{\cdot}6$ cm. ; $B = 151{\cdot}2$ cm. ; $C = 137{\cdot}7$ cm. ; $D = 452{\cdot}2$ cm.
16. 982·6 cm. **17.** 59·54. **18.** 284.
19. Molecular weight = 60·0 ; osmotic pressure = 9·614 atmospheres.
20. 5·4°. **21.** (*a*) 649 c.c. ; (*b*) 1300 c.c. ; (*c*) 2.
22. Mol fraction = 0·002625 ; vapour pressure = 758·005 mm.
23. 23·034 mm. **24.** 30·71 atmospheres ; 743·46 cm. **25.** 22·44 gm.
26. 23·575 mm. **27.** 60. **28.** 125. **29.** 70 : 1.
30. 42 atmospheres ; −3·31°. **31.** 1058°. **32.** 84.
33. 55·068 mm. ; 94·1 gm. **34.** 4·7 atmospheres. **36.** 20.
37. 31·71 mm. **38.** 82·5 per cent.
39. Boiling point = 69° ; vapour pressure of water at 69° = 235 mm. ; vapour pressure of benzene at 69° = 520 mm. ; percentage of benzene = 90·5.
40. 55·079 mm. **41.** 227 mm. ; 0·96.
42. Weight of distillate/weight of residue = 46·7/53·5. **43.** 13,730 mm.
44. (*a*) 62·0° ; 31·5 per cent chloroform ; (*b*) 6 ; (*c*) 62 per cent chloroform ; (*d*) 70 per cent chloroform. **45.** 55·68 c.c.

Chapter IV

1. 41·6. **2.** 36·72.
3. 1 c.c. of water dissolves 46·14 c.c. of SO_2 measured at *N.T.P.*
4. 1 c.c. of water dissolves 378 c.c. of NH_3 measured at *N.T.P.*
5. Total pressure = 228 ; partial pressures of oxygen and nitrogen are respectively 152 mm. and 76 mm.
6. Total pressure = 801·4 mm. ; partial pressures are respectively 229·6 mm. (N_2), 183·1 mm. (O_2) and 388·7 mm. (H_2).
7. Temperature of flask = 22·2° ; partial pressures are : 304·2 mm. (O_2) and 460·8 mm. (N_2).
8. Total pressure = 894·6 mm. ; partial pressures are : 389·2 mm. ($CHCl_3$) and 505·4 mm. (C_2H_5OH).
9. Total pressure = 1021 mm. ; partial pressures are : 10·3 mm. (NH_3), 252·7 mm. (N_2) and 758·0 mm. (H_2).
10. 34·55 per cent. **11.** 1·56 c.c. (N_2) ; 1·05 c.c. (O_2) ; 0·05 c.c. (A).
12. 2·4 gm. **13.** Cu_3Sb is formed. **14.** Mg_2Zn_3 is formed.
15. $H_2SO_4 . 4H_2O$, $H_2SO_4 . 2H_2O$ and $H_2SO_4 . H_2O$ are formed.
16. Below 24°, $Ba(CH_3COO)_2 . 3H_2O$; 24°–40°, $Ba(CH_3COO)_2 . H_2O$; above 40°, $Ba(CH_3COO)_2$.
17. Partition coefficient : $C_{(water)}/C_{(benzene)} = 5{\cdot}3$.
18. Benzoic acid consists entirely of double molecules, $(C_6H_5COOH)_2$, in benzene solution.

19. (*a*) 7·5 gm. ; (*b*) 8·4 gm. **20.** 120.
21. As in Q. 18. **22.** (*a*) 28·57 gm. ; (*b*) 35·704 gm.
23. 6·451 gm. per litre ; 18·45 c.c.
24. Alcohol forms hydrates of the formulae $C_2H_5OH \cdot 3H_2O$ and $C_2H_5OH \cdot 6H_2O$.
25. 0·0242. **26.** 1673 mm. **27.** 9.
28. Transition point at 58°. **29.** 35·9 mm.
30. Plot $\frac{p}{x/m}$ against p (straight line).

Chapter V

1. 0·179 gm.-molecule. **2.** 0·675 mm. **3.** 0·945.
4. 138·2.
5. 2·92 gm.-molecules of acetic acid to 1 gm.-molecule of ethyl alcohol.
6. 583 gm. **7.** 48·25 per cent.
8. 1·117 (partial pressures in atmospheres). **9.** $2{\cdot}997 \times 10^{-6}$.
11. 0·001607. **12.** 4·4 gm.-molecules.
13. Percentage dissociation $=87{\cdot}48$; 30·9 per cent.
14. 62·55 per cent dissociation ; K_p (atmospheres) $=2{\cdot}57$; 3·08 atmospheres.
15. (*a*) $\frac{2}{3}$; (*b*) 1·08 ; (*c*) 0·3714.
16. $[Ag^+]^2/[Hg^{++}]$ is constant and equation is $Hg_2^{++} + 2Ag \rightleftharpoons 2Hg + 2Ag^+$.
17. 13·6 mm. **18.** 1·20 per cent. **19.** 31 : 27. **20.** 7·73 gm.
21. $p_{HCl} = 0{\cdot}1686$ atmosphere ; $p_{O_2} = 0{\cdot}2337$ atmosphere ; $p_{CO_2} = 0{\cdot}2989$ atmosphere ; $p_{H_2O} = 0{\cdot}2989$ atmosphere ; $K_p = 4{\cdot}23$.
22. 25·5 per cent ; 13·7 per cent.
23. 27 per cent (graphical solution to cubic equation, see p. 429).
24. $1{\cdot}78 \times 10^{-4}$; 10·4 per cent. **25.** 5·64 gm.-molecules of HI.
26. $2{\cdot}1 \times 10^{-3}$. **27.** 144·5 minutes. **28.** 207·6 minutes.
29. 9·13 minutes. **30.** 80 minutes.
31. $0{\cdot}36 \times 10^{-10}$; $1{\cdot}37 \times 10^{-27}$; $1{\cdot}84 \times 10^{9}$. **32.** 0·66.
33. 31·18 c.c. **34.** $8{\cdot}85 \times 10^{-4}$.
35. $k = \frac{1}{2t}\left[\frac{x(2a-x)}{(a-x)^2 a^2}\right]$; $t_{\frac{1}{2}} = \frac{5}{8} \times \frac{1}{k} \times \frac{1}{a^2}$; $t_{\frac{1}{2}} \propto a^{-2}$.
36. Monomolecular ; $1{\cdot}51 \times 10^{-3}$.
38. Time for half conversion is 76 minutes in each experiment.
39. Bimolecular.

Chapter VI

1. 20·1 per cent NO_2 and 79·9 per cent N_2O_4. **2.** 38·45 per cent.
3. Apparent molecular weight $=69{\cdot}84$;
apparent degree of dissociation $=31{\cdot}74$ per cent.
4. 89·8 per cent. **5.** 63·5. **6.** 63·1 per cent.
7. 4·371 atmospheres. **8.** 96 per cent. **9.** $-1{\cdot}796°$.
10. Apparent degree of dissociation $=88{\cdot}4$ per cent. **11.** 2·54°.
12. 720 mm. **13.** (*a*) 14·18 atmospheres ; (*b*) 9·94 atmospheres.
14. 79·7 per cent. **15.** 3·088 atmospheres.
16. Assuming vapour density is normal, then atomic weight of mercury $=200$ and the chloride is not dissociated in water.
17. 80 per cent.
18. (*a*) apparent molecular weight $=39{\cdot}9$; (*b*) 86·7 per cent.
19. 1·768 gm. **20.** 72 per cent. **21.** 79 per cent.
22. 25 gm. per 100 gm. ; 3·11 gm. per 100 gm.
23. Mainly $(CH_3COOH)_2$.
24. 2·32 gm. urea per 100 c.c. ; 1·11 gm. NaCl per 100 c.c.
25. 84 per cent.
26. 17·67 ; 16·54 ; 16·00 ; 17·21 ; 19·47 ; 20·93 ; inversion temperature at which Q (in $2HI = H_2 + I_2 + Q$) changes sign.

27. $HgCl_2$ is not dissociated in aqueous solution.
28. 757·48 mm. **29.** Complete association as double molecules.
30. Apparent degree of dissociation of NaCl = 90·6 per cent; apparent degree of dissociation of KI = 90·6 per cent;

$$2KI + HgI_2 \rightleftharpoons K_2HgI_4 \rightleftharpoons 2K^+ + HgI_4^{--}.$$

31. 91·7 per cent dissociated.
32. Molecular surface energies are 341 dynes cm^2 (18·9°) and 293·0 dynes cm^2 (45·5°).
33. $\gamma\left(\frac{M}{d}\right)^{\frac{2}{3}}$ has values: 148·4; 130·8; 128·9; 126·9; 124·3; $\frac{d}{dT}\left(\gamma\left(\frac{M}{d}\right)^{\frac{2}{3}}\right) \doteq 20$; liquid oxygen is not associated.
34. 158°A.

Chapter VII

1. 22,100 cal. **2.** 70,000 cal. **3.** −26,100 cal.
4. 129,400 cal. **5.** 1,373,000 cal. **6.** 103,900 cal.
7. 31,600 cal. **8.** 2957 cal.; −41,500 cal.
9. 1,658,900 cal. **10.** 859,800 cal. **11.** 110,000 cal.
12. 117,400 cal. **13.** 1 : 2·28.
14. 5·965 therms per cubic foot. **15.** Water vapour/air = 1 : 3·33.
16. −38,000 cal. **17.** −30,300 cal. **18.** 28,200 cal.
19. 93,000 cal. **20.** 21,160 cal. **21.** 305,000 cal.
22. 210 cal. **23.** 62,000 cal. **24.** 284,600 cal.
25. 667 cal. **26.** 26,473 cal.
27. (*a*) $1·86 \times 10^9$ ergs; (*b*) 44·3 cal.
28. 33,900 cal.; work done = $9·6 \times 10^{10}$ ergs = 2292 cal.; heat of reaction at constant pressure = 36,192 cal.
29. 8264 cal. **30.** 70,714 cal. **31.** (*a*) $3·07 \times 10^9$ ergs; (*b*) 73·0 cal.
32. 1000 mm. **33.** $\left(\frac{\partial W}{\partial V}\right)_T = p.$ **34.** −50°.
35. 9915 cal. **36.** 7·89 atmospheres. **37.** 88·4 cal. per gm.
38. 22·8 cal. per gm. **39.** 0·39. **40.** +6060 cal.
41. $\Delta H_{1773} = 4700$ cal. **42.** No. **43.** $\Delta H_{773} = -216,560$ cal.

Chapter VIII

1. $2·56 \times 10^{-12}$. **2.** (*a*) 6×10^{-2}; (*b*) 1·00 gm.
3. 4·47 per cent. **4.** $6·35 \times 10^{-5}$.
5. $8·37 \times 10^{-4}$; 1·67 per cent. **6.** $4·80 \times 10^{-9}$ gm. per 100 c.c.
7. $K_a = 1·377 \times 10^{-3}$; degree of dissociation = $8·3 \times 10^{-2}$. **8.** $1·5 \times 10^{-2}$.
9. $1·1 \times 10^{-21}$. **10.** (*a*) 1; (*b*) 3·544. **11.** 2·068.
12. $1·995 \times 10^{-4}$. **13.** $7·194 \times 10^{-3}$. **14.** 11.
15. $K_a = 10^{-6}$; $[H^+] = 2 \times 10^{-4}$; percentage dissociation = 0·5.
16. pH = 12·4. **18.** $3·28 \times 10^{-7}$ gm.-ion per litre.
19. $1·29 \times 10^{-3}$ gm. **20.** pH = 3·2. **21.** $K_a = 1·20 \times 10^{-5}$.
22. Solubility product $[Ag^+][CH_3COO^-]$ is constant; values are $3·84 \times 10^{-3}$, $3·88 \times 10^{-3}$ and $3·87 \times 10^{-3}$.
23. pH = 4·64; $2·28 \times 10^{-5}$. **24.** 28·7 gm. per litre of acid.
25. 1·97 : 1. **26.** $7·38 \times 10^{-2}N$. **27.** $6·45 \times 10^{-5}$.
28. $6·0 \times 10^{-8}$; $5·5 \times 10^{-5}$. **29.** 8·67. **30.** 49·97 gm.
31. 198·8 c.c. **32.** 2·73. **33.** 10^{-2} molar.
34. $3·70 \times 10^{-4}$. **35.** $2·80 \times 10^{-13}$ gm.-ion per litre.
36. $\frac{5}{6}$. **37.** pH = 5·6. **38.** $2·74 \times 10^{-9}$. **39.** $9·2 \times 10^{-8}$.
40. 0·06084N. **41.** 0·55 per cent.

Chapter IX

1. $1{\cdot}053 \times 10^{-5}$; 1·060 gm. ; 3·599 gm. **2.** $7{\cdot}617 \times 10^{5}$ gm.
3. 33·61. **4.** (*a*) 7125 gm. ; (*b*) 5600 c.c. **5.** 4·322 gm.
6. 23·15 ohm^{-1}. **7.** (*a*) $5{\cdot}71 \times 10^{-4}$ ohm^{-1} ; (*b*) $1{\cdot}75 \times 10^{3}$ ohm.
8. 3·65 per cent. **9.** 4·32 per cent ; 9·6 per cent.
10. $1{\cdot}23 \times 10^{-2}$ ohm^{-1} ; 100·10°. **11.** −0·304°.
12. 0·521 atmospheres. **13.** 1·42 per cent.
14. 75·5 per cent ; −3·26°. **15.** $1{\cdot}11 \times 10^{-2}$ ohm^{-1}.
16. 8·8 per cent.
17. Transport numbers of Cu^{++} and SO_4^{--} are 0·547 and 0·453 respectively.
18. 65·8. **19.** $6{\cdot}92 \times 10^{-4}$ cm. per sec.
20. Mobilities of Ag^+ and NO_3^- are 54·2 and 61·8 respectively.
21. $6{\cdot}39 \times 10^{-4}$ cm. per sec. **22.** 64·35(l_{K^+}) ; 65·65 (l_{Cl^-}).
23. 373·45 ohm^{-1} c.c. **24.** 0·324(Cu^{++}) and 0·676(SO_4^{--}).
25. $5{\cdot}903 \times 10^{-4}$ ohm^{-1}. **26.** 5·53 ohm^{-1} c.c. **27.** 3·73 per cent.
28. $3{\cdot}406 \times 10^{-4}$ ohm^{-1}. **29.** 64·6(l_{K^+}) ; 65·2(l_{Cl^-}).
30. 3·62 per cent. **31.** 115·2. **32.** 0·975 ohm^{-1}.
33. $4{\cdot}82 \times 10^{-4}$. **34.** $6{\cdot}58 \times 10^{-4}$ $ohm.^{-1}$. **35.** 61·9 ohm^{-1} cm.
36. $[H^+] = 2{\cdot}42 \times 10^{-7}$; $[H^+] \times [OH^-] = 5{\cdot}84 \times 10^{-14}$.
37. 2·5(2·515). **38.** $1{\cdot}07 \times 10^{3}$ ohms.
39. Absolute mobility of the hydrogen ion $= 2{\cdot}54 \times 10^{-3}$ cm. per sec.; 327·8 (l_{H^+}) and 67·2 (l_{Cl^-}).
40. $8{\cdot}32 \times 10^{-6}$ gm. per 100 c.c. ; solubility product $= 1{\cdot}96 \times 10^{-13}$.
41. $3{\cdot}09 \times 10^{-4}$ ohm^{-1}. **42.** (*a*) $1{\cdot}95 \times 10^{-3}$; (*b*) $4{\cdot}16 \times 10^{-9}$.
43. 2·48. **44.** $1{\cdot}8 \times 10^{-4}$.
45. 0·650 ($n_{SO_4^{--}}$) ; 0·350 ($n_{Cu^{++}}$). **46.** 0·587 ($n_{SO_4^{--}}$) ; 0·413 ($n_{Cu^{++}}$).
47. 0·833 (n_{H^+}) ; 0·167 (n_{Cl^-}).
48. $V_{Na^+} = 4{\cdot}23 \times 10^{-4}$ cm. per sec. ; $V_{F^-} = 5{\cdot}17 \times 10^{-4}$ cm. per sec.
49. 237·4 ohm^{-1} ; 97·5.
50. $V_{K^+} = 6{\cdot}495 \times 10^{-4}$ cm. per sec. ; $\Lambda_{\infty(KCl)} = 124{\cdot}1$.
51. 0·426. **52.** 2·529 gm.
53 (*a*) $1{\cdot}302 \times 10^{-6}$ gm.-molecules per litre ; (*b*) 0·4643.

Chapter X

1. (*a*) 2·52 gm. ; (*b*) 1·89 gm. ; (*c*) 6·30 gm. ; (*d*) 3·38 gm.
2. (*a*) 0·0786*N* ; (*b*) 0·1295*N* ; (*c*) 0·0648*N* ; (*d*) 0·098*N*. **3**· 0·0311.
4. 5·116 gm. per litre ; 568·4 c.c. **5.** 6·61 gm. per litre.
6. 8·67 per cent. **7.** 9·31 gm. per litre.
8. (*a*) 5·003 gm. per litre ; (*b*) 2·486 gm. per litre.
9. 9·38 gm. per litre. **10.** 36·85 gm. per litre.
11. 3·198 gm. HCl per litre ; 6·974 gm. KCl per litre.
12. 11·92 gm. per litre. **13.** 56·2 per cent.
14. 68·6 per cent. **15.** 23·2 per cent. **16.** 90·0 per cent.
18. 0·188 per cent. **19.** 64·2 per cent ; 64·5 per cent.
20. 56·7 per cent. **21.** 7·39 c.c.
22. 24·19 per cent Na ; 13·81 per cent K ; 3·16 per cent N ; 0·90 per cent H ; 57·94 per cent Cl.
23. 7·311 gm. ; 249·5 c.c.
24. 0·318 gm. Na_2CO_3 ; 0·257 gm. $Ba(OH)_2$; 0·295 gm. $BaCO_3$.
25. 0·971 gm. HCl per litre ; 2·000 gm. H_3PO_4 per litre ; 4·608 gm. NaOH per litre.
26. 90·4 per cent. **27.** 0·6132 gm. $NaHCO_3$; 0·1208 gm. Na_2CO_3.

Chapter XI

1. (*a*) 2·695 gm. ; (*b*) 4·704 ; (*c*) 0·99 gm. ; (*d*) 15·25 gm. ; (*e*) 1·5875 gm. ; (*f*) 3·802 gm.
2. (*a*) 0·1266N ; (*b*) 0·03968N ; (*c*) 0·08849N ; (*d*) 0·2041N ; (*e*) 0·2062N ; (*f*) 0·07194N.
3. (*a*) 4·000 gm. per litre ; 28·00 gm. per litre. **4.** 0·686 ; 625 c.c.
5. Percentage of copper = 23·6 ; 27·65 c.c.
6. (*a*) 14·91 c.c. ; (*b*) 28·76 c.c.
7. 2·94 gm. H_2SO_4 per litre ; 4·41 gm. $H_2C_2O_4 . 2H_2O$ per litre.
8. 85·29 per cent. **9.** (*a*) 21·55 c.c. ; (*b*) 28·74 c.c.
10. (*a*) 49·44 gm. per litre ; (*b*) 16·29 volume solution. **11.** 0·1614 litres.
12. 33·78 gm. $CuSO_4$ per 100 gm. water. **13.** 208·3 c.c.
14. 52·3 per cent $FeSO_4$. **15.** (*a*) 236 c.c. ; (*b*) 256 c.c.
16. 100 c.c. ; 120 c.c. ; 0·49 gm. ; 0·588 gm. **17.** Valencies 2 and 3.
18. 561·5 c.c. ; 509·5 c.c. ; 450·3 c.c. **19.** 55·8. **20.** 408·2 c.c.
21. 13·45 gm. per litre. **22.** 33·5 c.c. **23.** 36·28 c.c. ; 24·19 c.c.
24. 50·48 gm. **25.** 19·56 c.c. **26.** 12·13 per cent.
27. Valencies 2, 3, 4 and 5. **28.** 34·8.
29. Hypochlorite chlorine = 28·4 per cent ; 0·575 per cent $Ca(ClO_3)_2$.
30. (*a*) 2·56 c.c. ; (*b*) 32·0 c.c.
31. Chemical equivalent = 56·0 ; weight of metallic chloride in 25 c.c. = 0·292 gm. ; weight of metallic iodide in 25 c.c. = 0·185 gm.

Chapter XII

1. $2Ag + Fe_2(SO_4)_3 = Ag_2SO_4 + 2FeSO_4 (Ag + Fe^{+++} = Ag^+ + Fe^{++})$.
2. $Na_2CO_3 . NaHCO_3 . 2H_2O$. **3.** $C_2O_4K_2 . 3C_2O_4H_2 . 4H_2O$.
4. (*a*) V_2O_4 ; (*b*) V_2O_3 ; (*c*) V_2O_4. **5.** CrO_2Cl_2.
6. $3ZnSO_4 + 2K_4Fe(CN)_6 = 3K_2SO_4 + K_2Zn_3[Fe(CN)_6]_2$.
7. $(NH_4)_2S_2O_8 + 2H_2O = H_2SO_4 + (NH_4)_2SO_4 + H_2O_2$.
8. $2KI + KIO_3 + 6HCl = 3KCl + 3H_2O + 3ICl$.
9. $Fe_2(SO_4)_3 + 2KI = 2FeSO_4 + I_2 + K_2SO_4$.
10. $2FeSO_4 + K_2S_2O_8 = Fe_2(SO_4)_3 + K_2SO_4$. **11.** $KIO_3 . HIO_3$.
12. (*a*) $5Na_2N_2O_2 + 8KMnO_4 + 16H_2SO_4$
$= 8KHSO_4 + 8MnSO_4 + 10NaNO_3 + 12H_2O$;
(*b*) $3Na_2N_2O_2 + 4KMnO_4 + 2H_2O = 6NaNO_2 + 4MnO_2 + 4KOH$.
13. $3Na_2S_2O_3 + 8KMnO_4 + H_2O = 3Na_2SO_4 + 3K_2SO_4 + 8MnO_2 + 2KOH$.
14. $K_2C_2O_6 + H_2SO_4 = K_2SO_4 + 2CO_2 + H_2O_2$.
15. $2NH_2OH + 2Fe_2(SO_4)_3 = 4FeSO_4 + 2H_2SO_4 + N_2O + H_2O$.
16. $3FeCl_2 + KNO_3 + 4HCl = 3FeCl_3 + KCl + 2H_2O + NO$.
17. $Na_2S_2O_3 + 4Cl_2 + 5H_2O = Na_2SO_4 + H_2SO_4 + 8HCl$.

MISCELLANEOUS QUESTIONS

Chapters I-XII

1. (*a*) 20·13 ; (*b*) $-1{\cdot}55°$; (*c*) 20·48. **2.** 121.
3. (*a*) 0·1441*N* ; (*b*) 0·03103*N* ; (*c*) 0·1632*N*. **4.** 0·986 gm. per litre.
5. 12·00. **6.** 59·7. **7.** (*a*) 25·51 c.c. ; (*b*) 208·4.
8. 30·36 gm. per litre. **9.** 35·86. **10.** 26·0 per cent.
11. 70·3. **12.** 11·7. **13.** 4·646 gm. per litre.
14. 37·38 c.c. **15.** 68·94. **16.** 0·3364 gm.
17. 24·35 c.c. **18.** C_2H_4. **19.** 45 per cent. **20.** 69.
21. 11·93 gm. $FeSO_4$; 8·36 gm. Na_2SO_4.
22. Compound Hg_5Tl_2 is formed.
23. (*a*) apparent degree of dissociation = 0·895 ; (*b*) apparent degrees of dissociation are 0·2010 and 0·8932.
24. 78·9 per cent and 78·8 per cent. **25.** 5·371.
26. 54·2 per cent of *A* ; 17·4 per cent of *B* ; 28·4 per cent of *C*.
27. 2·95. **28.** 6·75 c.c. **29.** (*a*) 29·7 (loss) ; (*b*) 5·75 (loss) ; 94·8 c.c.
30. SO_2Cl_2. **31.** 41·2. **32.** 90·5 per cent.
33. 7·5 gm. ; 8·75 gm. **34.** N_2H_4 (hydrazine). **35.** 48.
36. 16·15 atmospheres. **37.** 13·02 per cent.
38. 18 c.c. CO ; 16 c.c. CO_2 ; 16 c.c. H_2.
39. Apparent molecular weight = 39·9 ; apparent degree of dissociation = 86·7 per cent.
40. 20·0 per cent. **41.** (*a*) 3·366 gm. ; (*b*) 2·524 gm.
42. $2K_2S_2O_8 + 2H_2O = 2H_2SO_4 + 2K_2SO_4 + O_2$. **43.** 0·056 per cent.
44. 27·37 gm. **45.** 125. **46.** 61·6 per cent. **47.** $KIO_3 . HIO_3$.
48. Anhydride of nitric acid is N_2O_5 (empirical).
49. $2HIO_3 + 5SO_2 + 4H_2O = 5H_2SO_4 + I_2$. **50.** 2·925.
51. 31·81 per cent. **52.** $2{\cdot}58 \times 10^{-5}$. **53.** $1{\cdot}33 \times 10^{-5}$.
54. 44. **55.** 0·896 atmosphere ; 0·497 atmosphere.
56. (*a*) $HgO + 2KI + H_2O = HgI_2 + 2KOH$;
(*b*) $2Fe(CN)_6^{---} + H_2O = 2Fe(CN)^{----} + 2H^+$.
57. Compounds of the formulae P_4S_3, P_2S_3, P_2S_5 and PS_6.
58. Atomic weight = 126·0 ; complete dissociation $XCl_2 = X^{++} + 2Cl^-$.
59. $-1{\cdot}48°$; 749 mm. **60.** (*a*) 0·076 *N* ; (*b*) 0·148*N*.
61. 4·006 gm. Na_2CO_3 per litre ; 1·512 gm. $NaHCO_3$ per litre. **62.** 54.
63. (*a*) $pH = 3$; (*b*) $pH = 11$; $[H^+] = 3{\cdot}162 \times 10^{-3}$; $[H^+] = 5{\cdot}012 \times 10^{-5}$.
64. 55,120 cal. **65.** 60·0. **66.** 83·8 per cent.
67. *C* is 100 per cent associated in benzene solution.
68. $[H^+] = 6 \times 10^{-2}$; $pH = 1{\cdot}22$; $[OH^-] = 1{\cdot}67 \times 10^{-13}$.
69. 32·3 atmospheres ; 741·3 mm. ; boiling point = 100·71°.
70. $-145{,}000$ cal. **71.** $SO_2Cl_2 + 2H_2O = H_2SO_4 + 2HCl$.
72. 1. **73.** 35·5.
74. $C_2O_4K_2 . 3C_2O_4H_2 . 4H_2O$ or $C_2O_4H_2 . C_2O_4HK . 2H_2O$.
75. 83·75 c.c. **76.** Compound $C_{10}H_7NH_2 . C_6H_5OH$.
77. 7·43 per cent Na ; 2·14 per cent K. **78.** 39·94.
79. Atomic weight = 200. **80.** 1 c.c. of water dissolves 3·2 c.c. of H_2S.
81. 107·9 and 32·06. **82.** 6·75 per cent.
83. Mean atomic weight = 31·01 ; second chloride completely dissociated.
84. $X = MgNH_4PO_4 . 6H_2O$. **85.** 63·3 per cent zinc.
86. Complex ion $Cu(NH_3)_4^{--}$ in aqueous solution.
87. Percentage dissociation = 46 ; vapour density = 79·9.
88. $3{\cdot}63 \times 10^{-9}$ and $3{\cdot}63 \times 10^{-5}$. **89.** $XSO_4 . 4H_2O$.
90. 75 c.c. H_2 ; 30 c.c. CO ; 45 c.c. CH_4. **91.** 61·62 per cent NaCN.
92. (*a*) 4·5 per cent ; (*b*) $3{\cdot}8 \times 10^{-3}$ ohm^{-1}. **93.** 108·4. **94.** $pH = 2{\cdot}87$.

95. 8·4 per cent at 300°; 11·2 per cent at 500°; vapour density = 64 at both temperatures.
96. $HBrO_3$; $HBrO_3 + 3SO_2 + 3H_2O = 3H_2SO_4 + HBr$. **97.** 10·52.
98. (a) $8·75 \times 10^{-4}$; (b) $5·53 \times 10^{-4}$; (c) $pH = 3·26$.
99. $S_2O_5Cl_2$; $S_2O_5Cl_2 + 3H_2O = 2H_2SO_4 + 2HCl$. **100.** 29·05 mm.
101. $[(6 \times 10^{-7}) - (3·6 \times 10^{-10})]$ gm. molecules $= [(6 \times 10^{-7}) - (3·6 \times 10^{-10})] \times 188$ gm.
102. $Fe(COO)_2 . 1\frac{1}{2}H_2O$. **103.** $CH_3CH = CH_2$.
104. (a) 0·9375, $(\frac{15}{16})$; (b) 0·9655, $[(1 - \frac{2}{7})^{10}]$. **105.** $2·6 \times 10^3$ ohms.
106. General formula: $Na_2S_xO_{(3x+2)/2}$. Probably $Na_2S_2O_4$.
107. 32·45 per cent NH_4Cl; 31·35 per cent $(NH_4)_2SO_4$; 36·2 per cent NaCl.
108. Valencies probably 1, 2, 3 and 5, or 2, 3, 4 and 6; corresponding atomic weights are 50·9 and 42·9.
109. C_3O_2.
110. $[Fe^{+++}] = 1·74 \times 10^{-22}$ gm.-ion per litre; $[Mn^{++}] = 4·63 \times 10^{-5}$ gm.-ion per litre.
111. 41·5 per cent.
112. Gas is equal volumes of CH_4 and H_2; chemical equivalent = 41·2 $[Mn_3C + 6H_2O = 3Mn(OH)_2 + CH_4 + H_2]$.
113. *A* is N_3H; *B* is N_2H_4; compound formed is $N_2H_4 . N_3H$.
114. $[OH^-] = 9·49 \times 10^{-4}$ gm.-ion per litre; $pH = 10·98$.
115. $1·24 \times 10^{-3}$; $1·24 \times 10^{-3}$ gm.-ion per litre.
116. $(NH_4)_3PO_4 . 12XO_3$, where *X* is one atom of the element;
$$2(NH_4)_3PO_4 . 12XO_3 + 46NaOH = 2Na_2HPO_4 + 21Na_2XO_4 + 3(NH_4)_2XO_4 + 22H_2O.$$
117. 11·7 per cent. **118.** $6HCOH + 4NH_3 = N_4(CH_2)_6 + 6H_2O$.
119. (a) 74 per cent; (b) 9·8; (c) 0·44. **120.** 44·4 per cent CO.
121. $3·7 \times 10^{-5}$.
122. 17·0 per cent KCl; 17·8 per cent NaCl; 65·2 per cent K_2SO_4.
123. (a) 45·23 per cent; (b) 1·03; 2·18 litres. **124.** 62·07 minutes.
125. $7·5 \times 10^{-6}$. **26.** 3. **127.** 99·5 cal. per gm.
128. $3·45 \times 10^{-2}$ and $4·706 \times 10^{-2}$ (time in minutes); $[H^+] = 4·31 \times 10^{-4}$.
129. (a) $K_a = 1·4 \times 10^{-10}$; (b) 88 per cent; (c) 24 per cent; 2·4 per cent.
131. $4·1 \times 10^{-3}$ gm.-ion per litre. **132.** 12·8 atmospheres.
133. 36·51. **134.** $Q = -294$ cal.; $\Delta H_{773} = +294$ cal.
135. Monomolecular; 177 minutes. **136.** $2·49 \times 10^{-5}$. **137.** 181 c.c.
138. For reaction: $2H_2O = 2H_2 + O_2$, $K_p = 2·37 \times 10^{-13}$ and $K_c = 2·10 \times 10^{-15}$; for reaction: $2CO_2 = 2CO + O_2$, $K_p = 1·37 \times 10^{-12}$ and $K_c = 1·216 \times 10^{-14}$; for reaction: $CO_2 + H_2 = H_2O + CO$, $K_p = 2·4$; 1·2 per cent CO_2; 70·4 per cent H_2; 14·2 per cent H_2O; 14·2 per cent CO.
139. 94·7. **140.** 0·03827. **141.** 69·6 ohm^{-1}.
142. $Q = -2600$ cal. ($\Delta H_{373} = 2600$ cal.). **143.** 91·5°A.
144. 52·55 per cent.
145. $pH = 4·2$; $HCOOK/CH_3COOK = 3·49$; dilution has no effect on *p*H or distribution.
146. $\frac{dQ}{dT} = -0·5422$ cal. per degree.
147. $9·9 \times 10^{-7}$ gm.-molecules per litre.
148. Li^+, $3·88 \times 10^{-4}$ cm. per sec.; Cl^-, $6·89 \times 10^{-4}$ cm. per sec.
150. 8·2. **152.** 530 mm.
153. $[H^+] = 2·22 \times 10^{-9}$; no. **154.** 98·3. **155.** 0·4742.
156. (a) 0·660 atmospheres; (b) 0·182.
157. $K_p = 5·163$; $K_c = 381$; $p_{SO_3} = 0·24$ atmospheres.
158. $3·2 \times 10^{-6}$ (acetic acid) and $6·8 \times 10^{-6}$ (acetate ion); $0·74 \times 10^{-6}$.
160. (a) 6·39 atmospheres; (b) 147·8 gm.; (c) 28·06; (d) 31·08 minutes; (e) 10.

Chapter XIII

1. 37·5 per cent. **2.** 6·38 per cent. **3.** CH.
4. CH_2O. **5.** 40·7 per cent. **6.** 46·9 per cent.
7. C_5H_4. **8.** 25·6. **9.** C_7H_8.
10. 63·52 c.c. ; 0·7674 gm. **11.** 23·66. **12.** $C_6H_{14}O$.
13. CH_3Cl.
14. $C_4H_{10}O$; $CH_3 - O - C_3H_7$ (normal and iso) ; $(C_2H_5)_2O$; C_4H_9OH and isomeric alcohols.
15. C_3H_5ClO. **16.** $C_7H_{12}O_4$.
17. $C_6H_3N_3O_6$; $C_6H_3(NO_2)_3$, trinitrobenzene.
18. $C_7H_{10}NCl$. **19.** CH_4N_2O. **20.** C_2H_5NO. **21.** C_7H_6BrNO.
22. $C_3H_3Cl_3$. **23.** C_2H_8NCl. **24.** $C_2H_2Cl_2O_2$. **25.** $C_6H_5SClO_2$.

Chapter XIV

1. 62. **2.** 192. **3.** 93.
4. (*a*) 61·0 per cent ; (*b*) 35·6 per cent. **5.** 90·0.
6. 124. **7.** 59. **8.** 123.
9. 0·5244 gm. **10.** $C_2O_4H_2$. **11.** Diacid base. **12.** 2.
13. 3. **14.** 5. **15.** 69·0. **16.** 3. **17.** 4.
18. (*a*) 64·1 ; (*b*) 63·9 ; basicity = 3. **19.** 91·1. **20.** 353.
21. Probably $C_6H_4(COOH)_2$ (phthalic acid or isomers).
22. $CH_2OH . COOH$. **23.** $C_6H_5NH(CH_3)$.

Chapter XV

1. 5 c.c. C_2H_4 ; 10 c.c. CH_4. **2.** CH_4.
3. $3\frac{1}{2}$; $\frac{1}{2}$; $16\frac{2}{3}$ per cent C_2H_6 ; $83\frac{1}{3}$ per cent H_2.
4. C_2H_2. **5.** C_3H_8.
6. 5 c.c. C_2H_2 ; 12 c.c. C_2H_4 ; 2·5 c.c.
7. 4750 c.c. ; 320 c.c. C_3H_8 ; 80 c.c. C_3H_6.
8 (*a*) C_3H_8 ; (*b*) 4 c.c. CH_4 ; 4 c.c. CO ; 2 c.c. N_2.
9. C_3H_6. **10.** C_2H_6.
11. 37·7 per cent CH_4 ; 43·5 per cent CO ; 18·8 per cent N_2.
12. 25 per cent CH_4 ; 25 per cent C_2H_4 ; 50 per cent C_2H_2.
13. 24·2 per cent CH_4 ; 15·2 per cent CO ; 60·6 per cent O_2.
14. CH_2O.
15. (*a*) C_3H_4 ; (*b*) 50 per cent C_3H_4 ; 50 per cent CH_4.
16. C_2H_4 ; $CH_3 . O . CH_3$ (not C_2H_5OH since boiling point probably low).
17. CH_2O. **18.** CH_4O. **19.** C_2N_2.

Miscellaneous Questions

Chapters XIII-XV

1. C_3H_7OH. **2.** $(C_2H_5)_2O$. **3.** 43 per cent. **4.** C_2H_6.
5. $C_2H_4Br_2$.
6. $CH_3 . CH_2 . CH_2 . OH$; $(CH_3)_2 : CHOH$; $C_2H_5 . O . CH_3$.
7. (*a*) 1·294 gm. ; (*b*) 0·2647 gm. ; (*c*) 1·142 gm. ; (*d*) 59·7 c.c.
8. $C_2H_6SO_3$. **9.** CH_2O ; HCHO ; $CH_3 . COOH$.
10. C_3H_8O ; C_3H_7OH (normal and iso) ; $C_2H_5 . O . CH_3$.
11. C_2H_5COOH ; CH_3COOCH_3 ; $HCOOC_2H_5$.
12. $C_4H_{11}N$; isomers are $(C_2H_5)(CH_3) CH . NH_2$; $(CH_3)_3 : C . NH_2$; $(C_3H_7) . N(CH_3)H$ (normal) ; $C_3H_7 . CH_2 . NH_2$ (normal) ; $(CH_3)_2 : CH . CH_2NH_2$; $(CH_3)_2 : CH(NHCH_3)$; $(C_2H_5)N(CH_3)_2$.
13. $C_7H_{12}NCl$. **14.** C_3H_8.
15. $CH_3 . CH_2 . CH_2 . NH_2$; $(CH_3)_2 : CHNH_2$.

16. C_3H_9N; $CH_3 . CH_2 . CH_2 . NH_2$; $(CH_3)_2 : CH . NH_2$; $(C_2H_5)(CH_3)NH$; $(CH_3)_3N$.
17. 10 c.c. C_2H_2; 10 c.c. CH_4; 10 c.c. H_2.
18. 122; C_6H_5COOH. **19.** C_3H_9N; isomers as in Q. 16.
20. $ClCH_2 . CH_2Cl$; $CH_3 . CHCl_2$. **21.** C_3H_6.
22. $C_6H_8N_2$; $C_6H_4(NH_2)_2$ (*o*, *m* and *p*). **23.** $C_6H_5CONH_2$.
24. $CH_3 . O . C_2H_5$.
25. $\begin{matrix}COOC_2H_5\\ \cdot\\ COOC_2H_5\end{matrix}$; $\begin{matrix}COOC_2H_5\\ \cdot\\ COOC_2H_5\end{matrix} + 2NH_3 = \begin{matrix}CONH_2\\ \cdot\\ CONH_2\end{matrix} + 2C_2H_5OH$;

$\begin{matrix}CONH_2\\ \cdot\\ CONH_2\end{matrix} + 2NaOH = \begin{matrix}COONa\\ \cdot\\ COONa\end{matrix} + 2NH_3$;

$\begin{matrix}COONa\\ \cdot\\ COONa\end{matrix} + H_2SO_4 = Na_2SO_4 + CO + CO_2 + H_2O$.

26. $C_2H_5 . CHO$ (propionaldehyde).
27. $C_2H_5NO_2$ (nitroethane) and CH_2NH_2COOH (glycine).
28. $C_2H_5 . CHO$ (propionaldehyde); $C_2H_5CH : (OC_2H_5)_2$.
29. $C_3H_7NH_2$ and isomers. **30.** $CH_3 . O . C_2H_5$.
31. $CH_3 . CHCl_2$; $CH_3 . CHO$.
32. $C_3H_7OH + HBr = C_3H_7Br + H_2O$. **33.** C_2H_5CHO; C_2H_5COOH.
34. *A* is $CH_3 . CHO$; *B* is $CH_3 . CH(OH)(CN)$; *C* is $CH_3 . CH(OH)COOH$.
35. 88. **36.** *A* is $CH_3 . CH_2 . COOC_2H_5$; *B* is $CH_3 . CH_2 . CONH_2$.
37. $C_3H_7NH_2$ and isomers.
38. *A* is $CH_3 . CO . CH_3$; *B* is $CH_3 . C(NOH) . CH_3$.
39. $CH_3 . CO . C_2H_5$. **40.** $C_6H_5 . CH_2Cl$.
41. CH_3CHO; $CH_3CH(OH)(NH_2)$. **42.** $CH_2Cl . CH_2Cl$ and $CH_3 . CHCl_2$.
43. CH_2N_2 (diazomethane).
44. $CH_3 . CH_2 . CH_2OH$ and $CH_3 . CHOH . CH_3$;
$CH_3 . CH_2 . CH_2OH = CH_3 . CH : CH_2$;
$CH_3 . CH : CH_2 + HBr = CH_3 . CHBr . CH_3$;
$CH_3 . CHBr . CH_3 + H_2O = CH_3 . CHOH . CH_3 + HBr$.
45. $CH_3 . CH(NH)_2 . COOH$; $CH_3 . CH(OH) . COOH$.
46. *A* is C_3H_4; 40 per cent C_3H_4; 60 per cent C_3H_8.
47. $C_6H_4(CH_3)(NO_2) \rightarrow C_6H_4(CH_3)(NH_2) \rightarrow C_6H_4(CH_3)(CN)$
$\rightarrow C_6H_4(CH_3)(COOH)$.
48. $C_3H_6O_3$; $C_3H_5O_3Ag$; $CH_3 . CHOH . COOH$ and $CH_2OH . CH_2COOH$.
49. $HOCH_2 . CH_2OH$.
50. *A* is $C_6H_4(CH_3)(NH_2)$; *B* is $C_6H_4(CH_3)(OH)$; *C* is $C_6H_4(CH_3)(COOH)$.
51. $(CH_2OH)(CH_3) : N - OH \rightarrow (CH_2OH)(CH_3) : N . H \rightarrow (CH_2OH)(CH_3) : N . NO$.
52. $CCl_3 . CHO$; $CCl_3 . CHO + NaOH = HCCl_3 + HCOONa$.
53. C_2H_4; C_2H_6O; general formula: $C_2H_{(4+2x)}O_x$.
54. $CH_2 : CH . CH : CH_2 + Br_2 = CH_2Br . CH : CH . CH_2Br$.
55. $C_6H_4(NHCOCH_3)Cl$ (ortho or meta).
56. C_4H_9OH and isomeric alcohols.
57. $CO(NH_2)_2$; $2CO(NH_2)_2 = O : C(NH_2) . NH . C(NH_2) : O$ (biuret) $+ NH_3$;
$CO(NH_2)_2 + 2HNO_2 = CO_2 + 2H_2O + 2N_2$.
58. NH_2OH. **59.** $(CONH_2)_2$ (oxamide). **60.** C_2H_6O.
61. $(C_2H_5)(CH_3)NH$.
62. *A* is C_6H_5CHO; *B* is $C_6H_5CH : CH . COOH$; *C* is $C_6H_5CH : NOH$; *D* is $C_6H_5CHBr . CHBr . COOH$.
63. $CH_3 . CH(COOC_3H_7)_2$.
64. CH_3NC; hydrolysis: $CH_3NC + 2H_2O = CH_3NH_2 + HCOOH$.
65. $CH_3 . CO . COOH$. **66.** *A* is $(CH_3)_2NH$.
67. *A* is $CH_3 . CH_2 . CO . CH_3$; *B* is $CH_3 . CO . CO . CH_3$;
C is $CH_3 . C(NOH) . CO . CH_3$; *D* is $CH_3 . C(NOH) . C(NOH) . CH_3$.

68. Formic acid decomposes in two ways: $HCOOH = H_2O + CO$ (8·8 c.c.); $HCOOH = H_2 + CO_2$ (6·4 c.c. H_2; 6·4 c.c. CO_2).

69. $HOOC . CH : CH . COOH$. **70.** $HO . C(: NH)Cl$.

71. [benzene ring with Cl and Cl]; [benzene ring with Cl, COOH, Cl]; [benzene ring with Cl, Cl, COOH]; [benzene ring with Cl, HOOC, Cl]

$CH_3 . CH(NH_2) . COOH$; $CH_2NH_2 . CH_2 . COOH$.

72. $COOH . CH_2 . CH_2 . COOH$ or $CH(CH_3)(COOH)_2$.

73. $C_6H_4(CH_2Cl)(NO_2)$; $C_6H_4(CH_2OH)(NO_2)$; $C_6H_4(COOH)(NO_2)$; $C_6H(COOH)(NH_2)(Br_3)$.

74. $(CH_3)_2N . C_6H_4 . N : N . C_6H_4 . SO_2OH$.

75. *A* is $(C_2H_5)(CH_3)C(Br) . COOH$; *B* is $(C_2H_5)(CH_3)C(OH) . COOH$; *C* is $(CH_3)CH : C(CH_3) . COOH$.

76. *A* is $CH_2Cl . CO . CH_3$; *B* is $CH_3 . CO . CH_2CH_2 . CH_3$; *C* is

$$\begin{array}{c} HC - CH \\ (CH_3)C \quad C(CH_3) \\ \underset{H}{N} \end{array}$$

77. $C_6H_5NH . NHC_6H_4 . CH_3$.

78. $CH_2OH . CHOH . CHO$; $HOOC . CHOH . COOH$.

79. *A* is $CH_3 . C_6H_4 . CO . C_3H_7$; *B* is $CH_3C_6H_4C(: NOH) . C_3H_7$; *C* is $H . N . CH(CH_3)_2$; *D* is $C_6H_4(CH_3)(COOH)$;
$O : C . C_6H_4(CH_3)$

F is $C_6H_4\begin{matrix}CO\\CO\end{matrix}O$ (phthalic anhydride).

80. $C_6H_5 . CHO + H_2C(CH_2COOH)(COOH) = C_6H_5-C(H)=C(CH_2COOH)(COOH)$

$\rightarrow C_6H_5-\overset{H}{C}=\overset{H}{C}-CH_2COOH \rightarrow C_6H_5-CH_2 . CH_2 . CH_2COOH$

$\rightarrow C_6H_5-CH_2 . CH_2 . CH_2 . COCl \rightarrow$ [tetralone: ring fused with CH_2, CH_2, CH_2, $C=O$] $\rightarrow C_6H_4(COOH)(COOH)$.

81. $CO(CH_2CH_2CH_2CO_2H)_2 \rightarrow$ [ring: $O=C$, CH_2, CH_2, CH_2, $C=O$, $H-C$ with $HOOC . (CH_2)_2$]

$\xrightarrow{HNO_2} HOOC . (CH_2)_3 . CO . C(NOH) . (CH_2)_2 . COOH$

$\xrightarrow[\text{change}]{\text{Beckmann}} HOOC . (CH_2)_3 . COOH$ and $\begin{matrix}CH_2OH\\ CH_2OH.\end{matrix}$

Chapter XVI

1. 76·86 cal. **2.** 830 mm.
3. 6606 cal. ; Trouton coefficient = 23·26.
4. 9986 cal. per gm.-molecule. **5.** 105·9 mm. **6.** 7642 cal.
7. 8070 cal. **8.** 269·38°. **9.** 7830 cal. ; 9·04.
10. 9760 cal. **11.** 6420 cal. ; 0·00235 gm.-molecule per litre.
12. 6170 cal. **13.** 0·00545° per atmosphere. **14.** $\Delta F_{288} = -183$ cal.
15. 990 cal. **16.** 541 cal. per gm. **17.** 10,500 cal.
18. 72·2 cal. per gm. ; 78·7 cal. per gm. **19.** 8·60 cal. ; $3{\cdot}612 \times 10^8$ ergs.
20. 169 cal. per gm. ; 84·5°.
22. 0·4639 entropy units. **23.** 402 e.u. **24.** 2·085 e.u. **25.** 14·43 e.u.

Chapter XVII

1. 51·7. **2.** 12·753 mm. **3.** 215. **4.** 84. **5.** 100·43°.
6. 767 gm. per 100 gm. **7.** 213·7. **8.** 53 cal. per gm.
9. Complete association in benzene. **10.** 15·77 atmospheres.
11. 1 : 6·5, more soluble in water. **12.** 623 gm. per 100 gm.
13. 0·6536 ; 262·6 gm. naphthalene per 100 gm.
15. 47·11 gm. ; 72·12 gm. **16.** 17·2 mm. ; 1990 cm.
18. 3·37° ; 72·37 mm. **19.** 0·0484. **20.** 1020.
22. 0·174. **23.** (*a*) 1·51 ; (*b*) 1·55.

Chapter XVIII

1. (*a*) 67,250 cal. ; (*b*) 70,800 cal. **2.** $\Delta H = 104{,}000$ cal.
3. $\Delta H = 11{,}550$ cal. ; 33·7 per cent. **4.** $\Delta H = -24{,}600$ cal.
5. 2·53 ; 2·590 cal.
6. K_p at 1073°A = 5·257 ; K_p at 1173°A = 27·88 ; percentage CO_2 = 13·7.
8. $\Delta U = 40{,}550$ cal. **9.** $p = 2{\cdot}4 \times 10^{-66}$ atmospheres.
10. $\Delta F_{298} = -780$ cal.
11. $p_{NO} = 0{\cdot}4063$ atmospheres ; $p_{Cl_2} = 0{\cdot}2032$ atmospheres.
12. 65,800 cal. **13.** $\Delta F = -2270$ cal.
14. $4{\cdot}65 \times 10^{-8}$ atmospheres. **16.** 26,100 cal.
17. 47,000 cal. **18.** $1{\cdot}54 \times 10^{-9}$ atmospheres. **19.** 9·840 gm.
20. $\Delta F_{700} = 49{,}270$ cal. **21.** 0·730 atmospheres.

Chapter XIX

1. (*a*) $5{\cdot}17 \times 10^{-5}$; (*b*) 1·69 gm. per litre. **2.** 0·09145 volt.
3. 1·347 volt. **4.** $2{\cdot}65 \times 10^{-3}$ volt. **5.** 0·0459 volt.
6. $\dfrac{RT}{\phi} \log_e \dfrac{l_a + l_c}{l_a + l'_c}$. **7.** 0·0423 volt. **8.** 0·0164 volt.
9. +45,900 cal. **10.** +22,990 cal.
11. +1220 cal ; $\Delta F = -4580$ cal. ; heat is absorbed.
12. +31,870 cal. ; $\Delta F = -30{,}880$ cal. ; 990 cal. (evolved).
13. 0·0315 volt. **14.** +90,380 cal. **15.** $4{\cdot}72 \times 10^{-5}$ gm. per litre.
16. 0·2288 volt. **17.** 0·280. **18.** $1{\cdot}633 - [1{\cdot}693 \times 10^{-4}(t - 25)]$.
19. 0·0555 volt.

Chapter XX

1. −1·0975 volt. **2.** pH = 2·34 ; $[H^+] = 4{\cdot}59 \times 10^{-3}$. **3.** 1·135 volt.
4. −0·672 volt. **5.** $1{\cdot}10 \times 10^{-8}$ gm.-ion per litre. **6.** 0·396 volt.
7. 0·059 volt ; *A* is positive.
8. −16,925 cal. ; $4{\cdot}9 \times 10^{-12}$ gm.-molecules per litre.
9. Sb, Sb_2O_3, $(OH^-)_{(u.\,a.)}$ is −0·694 volt.
10. $[Fe^{3+}][Ce^{3+}]/[Fe^{2+}][Ce^{4+}] = 10^{11 \cdot 7}$; Fe^{++} is oxidised quantitatively by Ce^{4+}.

11. 0·776 volt. **12.** $6{\cdot}3 \times 10^{-23}$ atmospheres.
13. $K_a = 2{\cdot}32 \times 10^{-9}$; degree of hydrolysis $= 0{\cdot}66$ per cent.
14. 0·892 volt; $1{\cdot}82 \times 10^{-60}$ atmospheres. **15.** $-34{,}950$ cal.
16. 0·393 volt. **17.** 2·944.
18. (*a*) $7{\cdot}08 \times 10^{-7}$ gm.-molecules per litre; (*b*) $1{\cdot}2 \times 10^{-14}$; (*c*) $2{\cdot}8 \times 10^{-3}$ atmospheres.
19. Assuming hydrolysis to be: $AlCl_3 + 3H_2O = Al(OH)_3 + 3HCl$, degree of hydrolysis $= 1{\cdot}28 \times 10^{-2}$; 0·452 volt. Different values are obtained if hydrolysis is: $AlCl_3 + H_2O = AlCl_2(OH) + HCl$ (probable).
20. $1{\cdot}4 \times 10^{-14}$.
21. $\Delta F = -1570$ cal.; $\Delta H = +1255$ cal.; $\Delta S = 4{\cdot}211$ cal. per degree.
22. 155° **23.** 10^{-15}.
24. 3·61; reaction $AsO_3^{---} + I_2 + H_2O = 2I^- + 2H^+ + AsO_3^{---}$ is reversible.
25. $5{\cdot}9 \times 10^{-20}$ gm.-ion per litre. **26.** $2{\cdot}24 \times 10^{-13}$ gm.-ion per litre.
28. $-0{\cdot}143$ volt.

Chapter XXI

1. 15°. **2.** 0·596 volt. **4.** 4390 cal.
5. 3×10^{-4}. **6.** 35,900 cal. **7.** 0·109 atmosphere.
8. 56,450 cal. **9.** 66,200 cal. **10.** 283°. **11.** 960°.
12. 1·217 volt. **13.** $-43{,}500$ cal. **14.** $2{\cdot}9 \times 10^{-4}$ atmospheres.
15. 41·1 e.u. **16.** $\Delta F_{1273} = -40{,}200$ cal. **17.** $-22{,}600$ cal.
18. 0·17 atmosphere.
19. $\Delta H = 231{,}080 + 20{\cdot}04T + \frac{1}{2} \times 5{\cdot}17 \times 10^{-3}T^2 - \frac{1}{3} \times 7{\cdot}72 \times 10^{-5}T^3$;
$\Delta F = 231{,}080 - 20{\cdot}04T \log_e T - \frac{1}{2} \times 5{\cdot}17 \times 10^{-3}T^2 + \frac{1}{6} \times 7{\cdot}72 \times 10^{-5}T^3 - 67{\cdot}3T$; 0·72 atmosphere.

Miscellaneous Questions on Chapters XVI–XXI

1. 2·72°. **2.** 125·85°. **3.** 12,900 cal. **4.** 0·053 volt.
5. (*a*) $-22{,}260$ cal.; (*b*) 13,360 cal. **6.** 3720°; 8·4 atmospheres.
7. 0·488 volt. **8.** 16,140 cal. **9.** 900 mm.
10. 14·9 atmospheres; 53·2 gm. **11.** 90,000 cal. **12.** 0·19; 0·496.
13. 3·79 mm. **14.** pH = 7·0. **15.** 4×10^{-153} atmospheres.
16. $7{\cdot}7 \times 10^{-6}$ gm. **17.** 251. **18.** $4{\cdot}6 \times 10^{-2}$. **19.** 644 mm.
20. $6{\cdot}65 \times 10^4$. **21.** 207; mol fraction of naphthalene = 0·555.
22. 0·228 volt. **23.** $\Delta F = -36{,}475$ cal.; $3{\cdot}2 \times 10^{-2}$ per cent.
24. 3·41. **25.** 60·5 e.u. **26.** 0·0277 volt.
27. $\Delta H_{1063} = 21{,}450$ cal.; $\Delta H_{1667} = 22{,}200$ cal. **28.** $\Delta F_{1173} = 8100$ cal.
29. 82,000 cal.; $\Delta H_{673} = -82{,}000$ cal. **30.** 24,880 cal.
31. $\Delta F_{1073} = -18{,}200$ cal.; 2×10^{-3} atmosphere.
32. 50,200 cal. (graphical). **33.** $\Delta F = 5077$ cal.
34. $\Delta F = 10{,}120 - 1{\cdot}81T \log_e T + 0{\cdot}00445T^2 - 0{\cdot}00000068T^3 - 7{\cdot}5T$.
36. $K_p = 2{\cdot}05 \times 10^5$; $\Delta F = -19{,}400$ cal.
37. 210°. **38.** 10,210 cal. **39.** $[H^+] = 0{\cdot}00083$; 2·65 per cent.
40. 28,330 cal. **41.** 272·7. **42.** 0·0456 volt.
43. $1{\cdot}6 \times 10^{-10}$ atmospheres. **44.** (*a*) 42,120 cal.; (*b*) 41,555 cal.
45. $-30{,}520$ cal. (standard). **46.** 0·996 volt; 45,800 cal.
48. 13·7 per cent.
49. $\Delta H = -23{,}030$ cal.; $p_{SO_3} = 0{\cdot}112$ atmosphere. **50.** 48,300 cal.
51. 4. **52.** $\Delta S_{1200} = -7{\cdot}4$; $p_{NO} = 1{\cdot}98 \times 10^{-4}$ atmosphere.
53. k for each reaction $= 8{\cdot}241 \times 10^{-2}$; $3{\cdot}9 \times 10^{-2}$; $1{\cdot}25 \times 10^{-1}$.
54. 0·0112 volt. **55.** $\Delta G (= \Delta F) = -1480$ cal. **56.** 0·422 volt.
57. 0·43 per cent. **58.** 1·031 volt; 1·206 volt.
59. $\log_e k = 34{\cdot}2 - \dfrac{25{,}120}{RT}$. **60.** $6 \times 10^{31} \times e^{-44{,}500/2 \times 556} = 2{\cdot}5 \times 10^{14}$.

INDEX

PRINTED IN GREAT BRITAIN BY ROBERT MACLEHOSE AND CO. LTD.
THE UNIVERSITY PRESS, GLASGOW